# Ford Mondeo diesel
# Owners Workshop Manual

## R M Jex

**Models covered**

(3465 - 8AL2 - 320)

Saloon, Hatchback and Estate with 1.8 litre (1753cc) turbo-diesel engines, including special/limited editions

*For coverage of petrol models, see manual no. 1923*
*For coverage of revised range introduced October 2000, see manual no. 3990*

© Haynes Publishing 2008

ABCDE
FGHIJ
K

A book in the **Haynes Owners Workshop Manual Series**

ISBN **978 1 84425 262 6**

**British Library Cataloguing in Publication Data**
A catalogue record for this book is available from the British Library.

Printed in the USA

**Haynes Publishing**
Sparkford, Yeovil, Somerset BA22 7JJ, England

**Haynes North America, Inc**
861 Lawrence Drive, Newbury Park, California 91320, USA

**Haynes Publishing Nordiska AB**
Box 1504, 751 45 UPPSALA, Sverige

# Contents

## LIVING WITH YOUR FORD MONDEO

Safety first!     Page   0•5

Introduction     Page   0•6

## Roadside repairs

If your car won't start     Page   0•7

Jump starting     Page   0•8

Wheel changing     Page   0•9

Identifying leaks     Page   0•10

Towing     Page   0•10

## Weekly checks

Introduction     Page   0•11

Underbonnet check points     Page   0•11

Engine oil level     Page   0•12

Power steering fluid level     Page   0•12

Coolant level     Page   0•13

Brake (and clutch) fluid level     Page   0•13

Tyre condition and pressure     Page   0•14

Battery     Page   0•15

Electrical systems     Page   0•15

Washer fluid level     Page   0•16

Wiper blades     Page   0•16

## Lubricants and fluids     Page   0•17

## Tyre pressures     Page   0•17

## MAINTENANCE

### Routine maintenance and servicing

Servicing specifications     Page   1•2

Maintenance schedule     Page   1•2

Maintenance procedures     Page   1•6

# Contents

## REPAIRS AND OVERHAUL

### Engine and associated systems

Engine in-car repair procedures ......................................... Page **2A•1**

Engine removal and overhaul procedures ......................... Page **2B•1**

Cooling, heating and ventilation systems ......................... Page **3•1**

Fuel and exhaust systems ................................................. Page **4A•1**

Emission control systems ................................................. Page **4B•1**

Engine electrical systems ................................................. Page **5•1**

### Transmission

Clutch ................................................................................. Page **6•1**

Manual transmission ......................................................... Page **7•1**

Driveshafts ........................................................................ Page **8•1**

### Brakes and suspension

Braking system .................................................................. Page **9•1**

Suspension and steering ................................................... Page **10•1**

### Body equipment

Bodywork and fittings ....................................................... Page **11•1**

Body electrical systems .................................................... Page **12•1**

Wiring diagrams ................................................................ Page **12•32**

## REFERENCE

Dimensions and weights ................................................... Page **REF•1**

Conversion factors ............................................................ Page **REF•2**

Buying spare parts ............................................................ Page **REF•3**

Vehicle identification ......................................................... Page **REF•4**

General repair procedures ................................................ Page **REF•5**

Jacking and vehicle support ............................................. Page **REF•6**

Disconnecting the battery ................................................. Page **REF•7**

Tools and working facilities ............................................... Page **REF•8**

MOT test checks ............................................................... Page **REF•10**

Fault finding ...................................................................... Page **REF•14**

Glossary of technical terms .............................................. Page **REF•23**

### Index

........................................................................................... Page **REF•28**

# Advanced driving

Many people see the words 'advanced driving' and believe that it won't interest them or that it is a style of driving beyond their own abilities. Nothing could be further from the truth. Advanced driving is straightforward safe, sensible driving - the sort of driving we should all do every time we get behind the wheel.

An average of 10 people are killed every day on UK roads and 870 more are injured, some seriously. Lives are ruined daily, usually because somebody did something stupid. Something like 95% of all accidents are due to human error, mostly driver failure. Sometimes we make genuine mistakes - everyone does. Sometimes we have lapses of concentration. Sometimes we deliberately take risks.

For many people, the process of 'learning to drive' doesn't go much further than learning how to pass the driving test because of a common belief that good drivers are made by 'experience'.

Learning to drive by 'experience' teaches three driving skills:

☐ Quick reactions. (Whoops, that was close!)
☐ Good handling skills. (Horn, swerve, brake, horn).
☐ Reliance on vehicle technology. (Great stuff this ABS, stop in no distance even in the wet...)

Drivers whose skills are 'experience based' generally have a lot of near misses and the odd accident. The results can be seen every day in our courts and our hospital casualty departments.

Advanced drivers have learnt to control the risks by controlling the position and speed of their vehicle. They avoid accidents and near misses, even if the drivers around them make mistakes.

The key skills of advanced driving are **concentration,** effective all-round **observation, anticipation** and **planning.** When **good vehicle handling** is added to these skills, all driving situations can be approached and negotiated in a safe, methodical way, leaving nothing to chance.

**Concentration** means applying your mind to safe driving, completely excluding anything that's not relevant. Driving is usually the most dangerous activity that most of us undertake in our daily routines. It deserves our full attention.

**Observation** means not just looking, but seeing and seeking out the information found in the driving environment.

**Anticipation** means asking yourself what is happening, what you can reasonably expect to happen and what could happen unexpectedly. (One of the commonest words used in compiling accident reports is 'suddenly'.)

**Planning** is the link between seeing something and taking the appropriate action. For many drivers, planning is the missing link.

If you want to become a safer and more skilful driver and you want to enjoy your driving more, contact the Institute of Advanced Motorists at www.iam.org.uk, phone 0208 996 9600, or write to IAM House, 510 Chiswick High Road, London W4 5RG for an information pack.

Working on your car can be dangerous. This page shows just some of the potential risks and hazards, with the aim of creating a safety-conscious attitude.

# General hazards

## Scalding

• Don't remove the radiator or expansion tank cap while the engine is hot.
• Engine oil, automatic transmission fluid or power steering fluid may also be dangerously hot if the engine has recently been running.

## Burning

• Beware of burns from the exhaust system and from any part of the engine. Brake discs and drums can also be extremely hot immediately after use.

## Crushing

• When working under or near a raised vehicle, always supplement the jack with axle stands, or use drive-on ramps. *Never venture under a car which is only supported by a jack.*
• Take care if loosening or tightening high-torque nuts when the vehicle is on stands. Initial loosening and final tightening should be done with the wheels on the ground.

## Fire

• Fuel is highly flammable; fuel vapour is explosive.
• Don't let fuel spill onto a hot engine.
• Do not smoke or allow naked lights (including pilot lights) anywhere near a vehicle being worked on. Also beware of creating sparks (electrically or by use of tools).
• Fuel vapour is heavier than air, so don't work on the fuel system with the vehicle over an inspection pit.
• Another cause of fire is an electrical overload or short-circuit. Take care when repairing or modifying the vehicle wiring.
• Keep a fire extinguisher handy, of a type suitable for use on fuel and electrical fires.

## Electric shock

• Ignition HT voltage can be dangerous, especially to people with heart problems or a pacemaker. Don't work on or near the ignition system with the engine running or the ignition switched on.

• Mains voltage is also dangerous. Make sure that any mains-operated equipment is correctly earthed. Mains power points should be protected by a residual current device (RCD) circuit breaker.

## Fume or gas intoxication

• Exhaust fumes are poisonous; they often contain carbon monoxide, which is rapidly fatal if inhaled. Never run the engine in a confined space such as a garage with the doors shut.
• Fuel vapour is also poisonous, as are the vapours from some cleaning solvents and paint thinners.

## Poisonous or irritant substances

• Avoid skin contact with battery acid and with any fuel, fluid or lubricant, especially antifreeze, brake hydraulic fluid and Diesel fuel. Don't syphon them by mouth. If such a substance is swallowed or gets into the eyes, seek medical advice.
• Prolonged contact with used engine oil can cause skin cancer. Wear gloves or use a barrier cream if necessary. Change out of oil-soaked clothes and do not keep oily rags in your pocket.
• Air conditioning refrigerant forms a poisonous gas if exposed to a naked flame (including a cigarette). It can also cause skin burns on contact.

## Asbestos

• Asbestos dust can cause cancer if inhaled or swallowed. Asbestos may be found in gaskets and in brake and clutch linings. When dealing with such components it is safest to assume that they contain asbestos.

# Special hazards

## Hydrofluoric acid

• This extremely corrosive acid is formed when certain types of synthetic rubber, found in some O-rings, oil seals, fuel hoses etc, are exposed to temperatures above 400°C. The rubber changes into a charred or sticky substance containing the acid. *Once formed, the acid remains dangerous for years. If it gets onto the skin, it may be necessary to amputate the limb concerned.*
• When dealing with a vehicle which has suffered a fire, or with components salvaged from such a vehicle, wear protective gloves and discard them after use.

## The battery

• Batteries contain sulphuric acid, which attacks clothing, eyes and skin. Take care when topping-up or carrying the battery.
• The hydrogen gas given off by the battery is highly explosive. Never cause a spark or allow a naked light nearby. Be careful when connecting and disconnecting battery chargers or jump leads.

## Air bags

• Air bags can cause injury if they go off accidentally. Take care when removing the steering wheel and/or facia. Special storage instructions may apply.

## Diesel injection equipment

• Diesel injection pumps supply fuel at very high pressure. Take care when working on the fuel injectors and fuel pipes.

⚠ *Warning: Never expose the hands, face or any other part of the body to injector spray; the fuel can penetrate the skin with potentially fatal results.*

# Remember...

## DO

• Do use eye protection when using power tools, and when working under the vehicle.

• Do wear gloves or use barrier cream to protect your hands when necessary.

• Do get someone to check periodically that all is well when working alone on the vehicle.

• Do keep loose clothing and long hair well out of the way of moving mechanical parts.

• Do remove rings, wristwatch etc, before working on the vehicle – especially the electrical system.

• Do ensure that any lifting or jacking equipment has a safe working load rating adequate for the job.

## DON'T

• Don't attempt to lift a heavy component which may be beyond your capability – get assistance.

• Don't rush to finish a job, or take unverified short cuts.

• Don't use ill-fitting tools which may slip and cause injury.

• Don't leave tools or parts lying around where someone can trip over them. Mop up oil and fuel spills at once.

• Don't allow children or pets to play in or near a vehicle being worked on.

**Ford Mondeo Saloon (facelift model)**

Introduced in March 1993, the Ford Mondeo is available in four-door Saloon, five-door Hatchback and five-door Estate configurations. All feature a high standard of equipment, with driver/passenger safety a high design priority; all models are fitted with features such as side impact bars in all doors, 'anti-submarine' seats combined with 'seat belt grabbers' and pretensioners, and an airbag fitted to the steering wheel. Vehicle security is enhanced, with an in-built alarm system and engine immobiliser being fitted as standard, as well as double-locking doors with shielded locks, and security-coded audio equipment.

The range received a major facelift in October 1996, with heavily-modified front and rear styling reflecting the 'edge' design philosophy pioneered in the Ka. The already-acclaimed suspension and steering were further improved.

Two different generations of the 1.8 litre diesel engine have been fitted to the Mondeo, but most of the differences lie in the engine management system components. All are turbocharged and intercooled, with indirect injection. The transversely-mounted engine drives the front wheels through a five-speed manual transmission with a cable- or hydraulically-operated clutch.

The fully-independent suspension is by MacPherson strut on all four wheels, located by transverse lower arms at the front, and by transverse and trailing arms at the rear; anti-roll bars are fitted at front and rear. The Estate rear suspension is of a different design, to give maximum loadspace inside.

The steering is power-assisted, the pump being belt-driven from the engine, and the rack-and-pinion steering gear mounted behind the engine.

The vacuum servo-assisted brakes are disc at the front, with discs or drums at the rear; an electronically-controlled Anti-lock Braking System (ABS) is available on some models, with a Traction Control System (TCS) available as a further option where ABS is fitted.

Provided that regular servicing is carried out in accordance with the manufacturer's recommendations, the Mondeo should prove a reliable and economical car. The engine compartment is well-designed, and most of the items needing frequent attention are easily accessible.

## Your Ford Mondeo manual

The aim of this manual is to help you get the best value from your car. It can do so in several ways. It can help you decide what work must be done (even should you choose to get it done by a garage). It will also provide information on routine maintenance and servicing, and give a logical course of action and diagnosis when random faults occur. However, it is hoped that you will use the manual by tackling the work yourself. On simpler jobs it may even be quicker than booking the car into a garage and going there twice, to leave and collect it. Perhaps most important, a lot of money can be saved by avoiding the costs a garage must charge to cover its labour and overheads.

The manual has drawings and descriptions to show the function of the various components so that their layout can be understood. Tasks are described and photographed in a clear step-by-step sequence.

References to the 'left' and 'right' of the car are in the sense of a person in the driver's seat, facing forwards.

## Acknowledgements

Thanks are due to Draper tools Limited, who provided some of the workshop tools, and to all those people at Sparkford who helped in the production of this manual.

**Ford Mondeo Estate (pre-facelift model)**

The following pages are intended to help in dealing with common roadside emergencies and breakdowns. You will find more detailed fault finding information at the back of the manual, and repair information in the main chapters.

## If your car won't start and the starter motor doesn't turn

☐ Open the bonnet and make sure that the battery terminals are clean and tight.
☐ Switch on the headlights and try to start the engine. If the headlights go very dim when you're trying to start, the battery is probably flat. Get out of trouble by jump starting (see next page) using a friend's car.

## If your car won't start even though the starter motor turns as normal

☐ Is there fuel in the tank?
☐ Does the glow plug warning light come on and then go out when the ignition is switched on? If the light does not come on, check the wiring to the glow plugs. If there is moisture on the wiring, spray a water-repellent aerosol product (such as WD-40) or equivalent) on the wiring terminals shown in the photos.
☐ Is there air in the fuel system? If so, bleed the system as described in Chapter 4A.

**A** Check the security and condition of the battery connections.

**B** The stop solenoid wiring terminal may cause problems if not connected securely.

**C** Check the wiring to the glow plugs

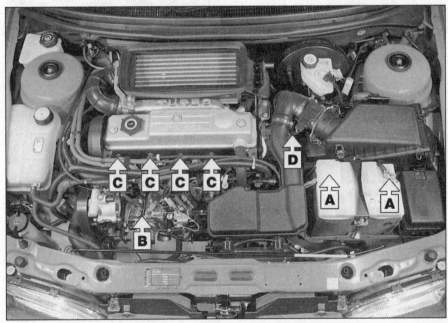

Check that electrical connections are secure (with the ignition switched off) and spray them with a water-dispersant spray like WD-40 if you suspect a problem due to damp

**D** If there is air in the fuel system, the system can be bled as described in Chapter 4A.

# Jump starting

When jump-starting a car using a booster battery, observe the following precautions:

✔ Before connecting the booster battery, make sure that the ignition is switched off.

✔ Ensure that all electrical equipment (lights, heater, wipers, etc) is switched off.

✔ Take note of any special precautions printed on the battery case.

✔ Make sure that the booster battery is the same voltage as the discharged one in the vehicle.

✔ If the battery is being jump-started from the battery in another vehicle, the two vehicles MUST NOT TOUCH each other.

✔ Make sure that the transmission is in neutral.

 **HAYNES HINT** *Jump starting will get you out of trouble, but you must correct whatever made the battery go flat in the first place. There are three possibilities:*

*1 The battery has been drained by repeated attempts to start, or by leaving the lights on.*

*2 The charging system is not working properly (alternator drivebelt slack or broken, alternator wiring fault or alternator itself faulty).*

*3 The battery itself is at fault (electrolyte low, or battery worn out).*

**1** Connect one end of the red jump lead to the positive (+) terminal of the flat battery

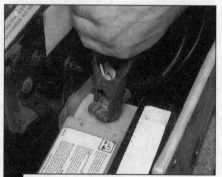

**2** Connect the other end of the red lead to the positive (+) terminal of the booster battery.

**3** Connect one end of the black jump lead to the negative (-) terminal of the booster battery

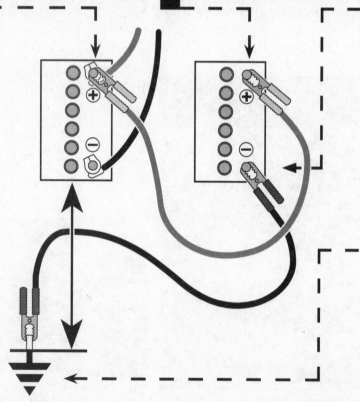

**4** Connect the other end of the black jump lead to a bolt or bracket on the engine block, well away from the battery, on the vehicle to be started.

**5** Make sure that the jump leads will not come into contact with the fan, drive-belts or other moving parts of the engine.

**6** Start the engine using the booster battery and run it at idle speed. Switch on the lights, rear window demister and heater blower motor, then disconnect the jump leads in the reverse order of connection. Turn off the lights etc.

# Wheel changing

 **Warning: Do not change a wheel in a situation where you risk being hit by other traffic. On busy roads, try to stop in a lay-by or a gateway. Be wary of passing traffic while changing the wheel – it is easy to become distracted by the job in hand.**

## Preparation

- [ ] When a puncture occurs, stop as soon as it is safe to do so.
- [ ] Park on firm level ground, if possible, and well out of the way of other traffic.
- [ ] Use hazard warning lights if necessary.

- [ ] If you have one, use a warning triangle to alert other drivers of your presence.
- [ ] Apply the handbrake and engage first or reverse gear.
- [ ] Chock the wheel diagonally opposite the

one being removed – a couple of large stones will do for this.
- [ ] Only jack the car up on firm, level ground. On gravel or soft ground, use a flat piece of wood under the jack to spread the load.

## Changing the wheel

**1** The spare wheel and tools are located in the boot – lift the carpet, then raise the spare wheel cover.

**2** Unscrew the central retainer and remove the spare wheel. The jack and wheel brace are secured by a bolt – also note the front towing eye (facelift models).

**3** Where applicable, remove the trim to expose the wheel nuts.

**4** Use the wheel brace to loosen the wheel nuts slightly. If locking wheel nuts are fitted, use the adapter (this may be in the glovebox).

**5** Locate the jack head in the correct jacking point (indicated by a triangular mark on the sill, or a notch in the sill edge) and raise the jack until the wheel is clear of the ground.

**6** Remove the wheel nuts and lift off the wheel.

**7** Fit the spare wheel, and tighten the nuts by hand. Lower the car to the ground, and tighten the nuts fully with the wheel brace.

## Finally . . .

- [ ] Remove the wheel chocks.
- [ ] Stow the damaged tyre or wheel, jack and tools in the correct locations in the car.
- [ ] Check the tyre pressure on the wheel just fitted. If it is low, or if you don't have a pressure gauge with you, drive slowly to the nearest garage and inflate the tyre to the correct pressure.
- [ ] Have the damaged tyre or wheel repaired as soon as possible.

# Identifying leaks

Puddles on the garage floor or drive, or obvious wetness under the bonnet or underneath the car, suggest a leak that needs investigating. It can sometimes be difficult to decide where the leak is coming from, especially if the engine bay is very dirty already. Leaking oil or fluid can also be blown rearwards by the passage of air under the car, giving a false impression of where the problem lies.

 *Warning: Most automotive oils and fluids are poisonous. Wash them off skin, and change out of contaminated clothing, without delay.*

 *The smell of a fluid leaking from the car may provide a clue to what's leaking. Some fluids are distinctively coloured. It may help to clean the car carefully and to park it over some clean paper overnight as an aid to locating the source of the leak.*
*Remember that some leaks may only occur while the engine is running.*

## Sump oil

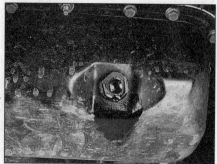

Engine oil may leak from the drain plug...

## Oil from filter

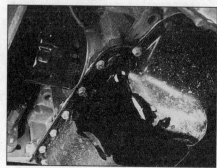

...or from the base of the oil filter.

## Gearbox oil

Gearbox oil can leak from the seals at the inboard ends of the driveshafts.

## Antifreeze

Leaking antifreeze often leaves a crystalline deposit like this.

## Brake fluid

A leak occurring at a wheel is almost certainly brake fluid.

## Power steering fluid

Power steering fluid may leak from the pipe connectors on the steering rack.

# Towing

When all else fails, you may find yourself having to get a tow home – or of course you may be helping somebody else. Long-distance recovery should only be done by a garage or breakdown service. For shorter distances, DIY towing using another car is easy enough, but observe the following points:

☐ Use a proper tow-rope – they are not expensive. The vehicle being towed must display an ON TOW sign in its rear window.
☐ Always turn the ignition key to the 'On' position when the vehicle is being towed, so that the steering lock is released, and the direction indicator and brake lights work.

☐ Towing eyes are provided at the front and rear of the car, on the right-hand side. Do not attach the tow-rope to anything else. On facelift models, the towing eye is in the boot, and screws into a hole in the bumper.
☐ Before being towed, release the handbrake and select neutral on the transmission.
☐ Note that greater-than-usual pedal pressure will be required to operate the brakes, since the vacuum servo unit is only operational with the engine running.
☐ The power steering will not work with the engine off, so much greater-than-usual steering effort will also be required.

☐ The driver of the car being towed must keep the tow-rope taut at all times to avoid snatching – this can be achieved by applying the brakes very gently, where this is appropriate.
☐ Make sure that both drivers know the route before setting off.
☐ Only drive at moderate speeds and keep the distance towed to a minimum. Drive smoothly and allow plenty of time for slowing down at junctions.

# Introduction

There are some very simple checks which need only take a few minutes to carry out, but which could save you a lot of inconvenience and expense.

These *Weekly checks* require no great skill or special tools, and the small amount of time they take to perform could prove to be very well spent, for example:

☐ Keeping an eye on tyre condition and pressures, will not only help to stop them wearing out prematurely, but could also save your life.

☐ Many breakdowns are caused by electrical problems. Battery-related faults are particularly common, and a quick check on a regular basis will often prevent the majority of these.

☐ If your car develops a brake fluid leak, the first time you might know about it is when your brakes don't work properly. Checking the level regularly will give advance warning of this kind of problem.

☐ If the oil or coolant levels run low, the cost of repairing any engine damage will be far greater than fixing the leak, for example.

# Underbonnet check points

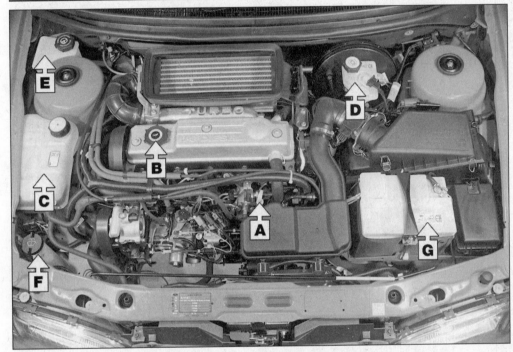

A *Engine oil level dipstick*

B *Engine oil filler cap*

C *Coolant expansion tank*

D *Brake (and clutch) fluid reservoir*

E *Power steering fluid reservoir*

F *Washer fluid reservoir*

G *Battery*

# Engine oil level

## Before you start
✔ Make sure that the car is on level ground.
✔ Check the oil level before the car is driven, or at least 5 minutes after the engine has been switched off.

 **HAYNES HINT** *If the oil is checked immediately after driving the vehicle, some of the oil will remain in the upper engine components, resulting in an inaccurate reading on the dipstick.*

## The correct oil
Modern engines place great demands on their oil. It is very important that the correct oil for your car is used (see *Lubricants and fluids*).

## Car care
● If you have to add oil frequently, you should check whether you have any oil leaks. Place some clean paper under the car overnight, and check for stains in the morning. If there are no leaks, then the engine may be burning oil (see *Fault finding*).
● Always maintain the level between the upper and lower dipstick marks (see photo 3). If the level is too low, severe engine damage may occur. Oil seal failure may result if the engine is overfilled by adding too much oil.

**1** The dipstick is located at the front of the engine. Withdraw the dipstick.

**2** Using a clean rag or paper towel, wipe all the oil from the dipstick. Insert the clean dipstick into the tube as far as it will go, then withdraw it again.

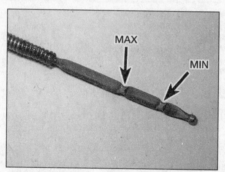

**3** Note the oil level on the end of the dipstick, which should be between the upper MAX mark and the lower MIN mark.

**4** Oil is added through the filler cap. A funnel may help to reduce spillage. Add oil slowly, checking the level on the dipstick often. Do not overfill.

# Power steering fluid level

## Before you start
✔ Park the car on level ground.
✔ Set the steering wheel straight-ahead.
✔ The engine should be turned off.

 **HAYNES HINT** *For the check to be accurate, the steering must not be turned once the engine has been stopped.*

## Safety first!
● The need for frequent topping-up indicates a leak, which should be investigated immediately.

**1** The power steering fluid reservoir is located on the right-hand rear corner of the engine compartment. MAX and MIN level marks are indicated on the side of the reservoir, and the fluid level should be maintained between these marks at all times.

**2** If topping-up is necessary, first wipe the area around the filler cap with a clean rag before removing the cap.

**3** When adding fluid, pour it carefully into the reservoir to avoid spillage. Be sure to use only the specified fluid. After filling the reservoir to the proper level, make sure that the cap is refitted securely to avoid leaks and the entry of foreign matter into the reservoir.

# Coolant level

⚠️ **Warning: DO NOT attempt to remove the radiator cap nor the expansion tank cap when the engine is hot, as there is a very great risk of scalding. Only check the level when the system is cold, after the car has been standing for several hours (preferably, after being left overnight). Do not leave open containers of coolant about, as it is poisonous.**

## Car care

● With a sealed-type cooling system, adding coolant should not be necessary on a regular basis. If frequent topping-up is required, it is likely there is a leak. Check the radiator, all hoses and joint faces for signs of staining or wetness, and rectify as necessary.

● It is important that antifreeze is used in the cooling system all year round, not just during the winter months. Don't top up with water alone, as the antifreeze will become too diluted.

**1** The coolant level varies with the temperature of the engine, and is visible through the expansion tank. When the engine is cold, the coolant level should be between the MAX mark on the side, and the MIN mark on the front of the reservoir. When the engine is hot, the level may rise slightly above the MAX mark.

**2** If topping-up is necessary, **wait until the engine is cold**. Slowly unscrew the expansion tank cap, to release any pressure present in the cooling system, and remove it.

**3** Add a mixture of water and antifreeze to the expansion tank until the coolant level is halfway between the level marks. Refit the cap and tighten it securely.

---

# Brake (and clutch*) fluid level

**\* Note:** *On models with a hydraulically-operated clutch, the brake fluid reservoir also supplies the clutch system.*

## Before you start

✔ Make sure that the car is on level ground.
✔ Cleanliness is of great importance when dealing with the braking system, so take care to clean around the reservoir cap before topping-up. Use only clean brake fluid.

## Safety first!

● If the reservoir requires repeated topping-up, this is an indication of a fluid leak somewhere in the brake (or clutch) system, which should be investigated immediately.

● If a leak is suspected, the car should not be driven until the braking system has been checked. Never take any risks where brakes are concerned.

⚠️ **Warning: Brake fluid can harm your eyes and damage painted surfaces, so use extreme caution when handling and pouring it. Do not use fluid which has been standing open for some time, as it absorbs moisture from the air, which can cause a dangerous loss of braking effectiveness.**

**1** The fluid reservoir is located on the left-hand side of the engine compartment. The MAX and MIN marks are indicated on the side of the reservoir. The fluid level must be kept between the marks at all times.

**2** If topping-up is necessary, first wipe clean the area around the filler cap to prevent dirt entering the hydraulic system, then unscrew and remove the reservoir cap. Inspect the reservoir; if the fluid is dirty, the hydraulic system should be drained and refilled (see Chapter 1).

**3** Carefully add fluid, taking care not to spill it onto the surrounding components. Use only the specified fluid; mixing different types can cause damage to the system. After topping-up to the correct level, securely refit the cap and wipe off any spilt fluid.

# Tyre condition and pressure

It is very important that tyres are in good condition, and at the correct pressure - having a tyre failure at any speed is highly dangerous. Tyre wear is influenced by driving style - harsh braking and acceleration, or fast cornering, will all produce more rapid tyre wear. As a general rule, the front tyres wear out faster than the rears. Interchanging the tyres from front to rear ("rotating" the tyres) may result in more even wear. However, if this is completely effective, you may have the expense of replacing all four tyres at once! Remove any nails or stones embedded in the tread before they penetrate the tyre to cause deflation. If removal of a nail does reveal that the tyre has been punctured, refit the nail so that its point of penetration is marked. Then immediately change the wheel, and have the tyre repaired by a tyre dealer.

Regularly check the tyres for damage in the form of cuts or bulges, especially in the sidewalls. Periodically remove the wheels, and clean any dirt or mud from the inside and outside surfaces. Examine the wheel rims for signs of rusting, corrosion or other damage. Light alloy wheels are easily damaged by "kerbing" whilst parking; steel wheels may also become dented or buckled. A new wheel is very often the only way to overcome severe damage.

New tyres should be balanced when they are fitted, but it may become necessary to re-balance them as they wear, or if the balance weights fitted to the wheel rim should fall off. Unbalanced tyres will wear more quickly, as will the steering and suspension components. Wheel imbalance is normally signified by vibration, particularly at a certain speed (typically around 50 mph). If this vibration is felt only through the steering, then it is likely that just the front wheels need balancing. If, however, the vibration is felt through the whole car, the rear wheels could be out of balance. Wheel balancing should be carried out by a tyre dealer or garage.

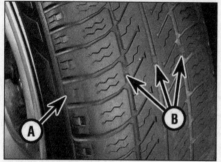

**1 Tread Depth - visual check**
The original tyres have tread wear safety bands (B), which will appear when the tread depth reaches approximately 1.6 mm. The band positions are indicated by a triangular mark on the tyre sidewall (A).

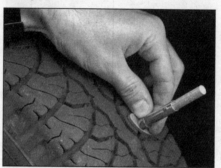

**2 Tread Depth - manual check**
Alternatively, tread wear can be monitored with a simple, inexpensive device known as a tread depth indicator gauge.

**3 Tyre Pressure Check**
Check the tyre pressures regularly with the tyres cold. Do not adjust the tyre pressures immediately after the vehicle has been used, or an inaccurate setting will result.

# Tyre tread wear patterns

### Shoulder Wear

**Underinflation (wear on both sides)**
Under-inflation will cause overheating of the tyre, because the tyre will flex too much, and the tread will not sit correctly on the road surface. This will cause a loss of grip and excessive wear, not to mention the danger of sudden tyre failure due to heat build-up.
*Check and adjust pressures*
**Incorrect wheel camber (wear on one side)**
*Repair or renew suspension parts*
**Hard cornering**
*Reduce speed!*

### Centre Wear

**Overinflation**
Over-inflation will cause rapid wear of the centre part of the tyre tread, coupled with reduced grip, harsher ride, and the danger of shock damage occurring in the tyre casing.
*Check and adjust pressures*

*If you sometimes have to inflate your car's tyres to the higher pressures specified for maximum load or sustained high speed, don't forget to reduce the pressures to normal afterwards.*

### Uneven Wear

Front tyres may wear unevenly as a result of wheel misalignment. Most tyre dealers and garages can check and adjust the wheel alignment (or "tracking") for a modest charge.
**Incorrect camber or castor**
*Repair or renew suspension parts*
**Malfunctioning suspension**
*Repair or renew suspension parts*
**Unbalanced wheel**
*Balance tyres*
**Incorrect toe setting**
*Adjust front wheel alignment*
**Note:** *The feathered edge of the tread which typifies toe wear is best checked by feel.*

# Battery

*Caution: Before carrying out any work on the vehicle battery, read the precautions given in 'Safety first!' at the start of this manual.*

✔ Make sure that the battery tray is in good condition, and that the clamp is tight. Corrosion on the tray, retaining clamp and the battery itself can be removed with a solution of water and baking soda. Thoroughly rinse all cleaned areas with water. Any metal parts damaged by corrosion should be covered with a zinc-based primer, then painted.

✔ Periodically (approximately every three months), check the charge condition of the battery as described in Chapter 5.

✔ If the battery is flat, and you need to jump start your vehicle, see *Roadside Repairs*.

**1** The battery is located on the left-hand side of the engine compartment. The exterior of the battery should be inspected periodically for damage such as a cracked case or cover.

**2** Check the tightness of the battery cable clamps to ensure good electrical connections. You should not be able to move them. Also check each cable for cracks and frayed conductors.

**HAYNES HINT**

*Battery corrosion can be kept to a minimum by applying a layer of petroleum jelly to the clamps and terminals after they are reconnected.*

**3** If corrosion (white fluffy deposits) is evident, remove the cables from the battery terminals, clean them with a small wire brush, then refit them. Automotive stores sell a useful tool for cleaning the battery post . . .

**4** . . . as well as the battery cable clamps.

# Electrical systems

✔ Check all external lights and the horn. Refer to the appropriate Sections of Chapter 12 for details if any of the circuits are found to be inoperative.

✔ Visually check all accessible wiring connectors, harnesses and retaining clips for security, and for signs of chafing or damage.

**HAYNES HINT**

*If you need to check your brake lights and indicators unaided, back up to a wall or garage door and operate the lights. The reflected light should show if they are working properly.*

**1** If a single indicator light, brake light or headlight has failed, it is likely that a bulb has blown and will need to be renewed. Refer to Chapter 12 for details. If both brake lights have failed, it is possible that the brake light switch operated by the brake pedal has failed. Refer to Chapter 9 for details.

**2** If more than one indicator light or headlight has failed, it is likely that either a fuse has blown or that there is a fault in the circuit (see Chapter 12). Most fuses are located behind the cover in the right-hand lower facia panel. Other fuses are located in the fusebox on the right-hand side of the engine compartment.

**3** To renew a blown fuse, simply pull it out. Fit a new fuse of the same rating. It is important that you find the reason for the fuse blowing.

# Washer fluid level

● Screenwash additives not only keep the windscreen clean during bad weather, they also prevent the washer system freezing in cold weather – which is when you are likely to need it most. Don't top-up using plain water, as the screenwash will become diluted, and will freeze in cold weather.

*Warning: On no account use engine coolant antifreeze in the screen washer system – this may damage the paintwork.*

**1** The washer fluid reservoir filler neck is located in the right-hand front corner of the engine compartment, behind the headlight.

**2** The washer level cannot easily be seen. Remove the filler cap, and look down the filler neck – if fluid is not visible, topping-up may be required. When topping-up the reservoir, add a screenwash additive in the quantities recommended on the additive bottle.

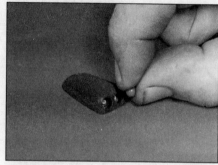

**3** Check the operation of the windscreen and (where applicable) rear window washers. Adjust the nozzle using a pin if necessary, aiming the spray slightly above the centre of the wipers' swept area.

# Wiper blades

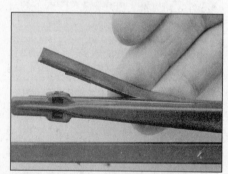

**1** Check the condition of the wiper blades; if they are cracked or show any signs of deterioration, or if the glass swept area is smeared, renew them. Wiper blades should be renewed annually, regardless of their apparent condition.

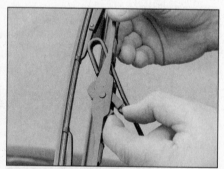

**2** To remove a windscreen wiper blade, pull the arm fully away from the screen until it locks. Swivel the blade through 90°, press the locking tab with your fingers and slide the blade out of the arm's hooked end.

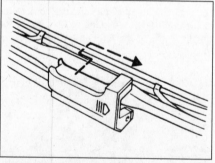

**3** Don't forget to check the tailgate wiper blade as well (where applicable). Remove the blade using a similar technique to the windscreen wiper blades.

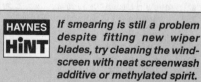

**HAYNES HiNT** *If smearing is still a problem despite fitting new wiper blades, try cleaning the windscreen with neat screenwash additive or methylated spirit.*

## Lubricants and fluids

| | |
|---|---|
| **Engine** . . . . . . . . . . . . . . . . . . . . . . . . . . . . . . . . . . . . | Multigrade engine oil, viscosity SAE 10W/40, to ACEA A3-96 or B3-96 |
| **Cooling system\*** . . . . . . . . . . . . . . . . . . . . . . . . . . . . . | Motorcraft Super Plus 4 antifreeze (blue-green) to Ford specification ESD-M97 B49-A or Motorcraft Super Plus 2000 antifreeze (orange) to Ford specification WSS-M97 B44-D |
| **Manual transmission** . . . . . . . . . . . . . . . . . . . . . . . . | SAE 75W/90 gear oil, to Ford specification WSD-M2C 200-C |
| **Brake hydraulic system** . . . . . . . . . . . . . . . . . . . . . . | Super DOT 4, paraffin-free hydraulic fluid to Ford specification ESD-M6C 57-A |
| **Power steering** . . . . . . . . . . . . . . . . . . . . . . . . . . . . . | Automatic transmission fluid to Ford specification ESP-M2C 166-H |

*\* Do not mix the two types of coolant listed with each other, nor top-up with any other type of coolant. Alternative types of coolant may only be used once the system has been drained and completely flushed, as described in Chapter 1.*

## Tyre pressures

| Tyre pressures (tyres cold) | Front | Rear |
|---|---|---|
| Normal loading with up to 3 people . . . . . . . . . . . . . . . . | 2.1 bar (30 psi) | 2.1 bar (30 psi) |
| Fully-laden with more than 3 people . . . . . . . . . . . . . . . | 2.4 bar (35 psi) | 2.8 bar (41 psi) |

**Note:** *Pressures apply only to original-equipment tyres, and may vary if any other make or type is fitted. Check with the tyre manufacturer or supplier for correct pressures if necessary.*

# Chapter 1
# Routine maintenance and servicing

## Contents

Section number

Air conditioning system check............................ 10
Air filter element renewal .................................. 25
Auxiliary drivebelts check and renewal .................. 5
Battery maintenance and charging ........................ 4
Brake fluid renewal........................................ 27
Braking system check ..................................... 19
Clutch adjustment check .................................. 13
Coolant renewal .......................................... 28
Door and bonnet check and lubrication.................. 20
Driveshaft rubber gaiter and CV joint check ............ 16
Electrical system check .................................... 7
Engine compartment wiring check........................ 9
Engine oil and filter renewal .............................. 3
Exhaust manifold/turbocharger fastener tightness check ........ 14
Exhaust system check...................................... 17

Section number

Expansion tank pressure cap check ...................... 29
Fuel filter renewal........................................ 24
Drain water from the fuel filter ........................... 6
Introduction .............................................. 1
Regular maintenance ..................................... 2
Road test ................................................ 22
Roadwheel nut tightness check........................... 21
Seat belt check........................................... 12
Steering, suspension and roadwheel check .............. 15
Timing belt and fuel injection pump drivebelt renewal........... 30
Transmission oil level check............................. 11
Underbody and fuel/brake line check .................... 18
Underbonnet check for fluid leaks and hose condition ........... 8
Valve clearance check .................................... 26
Ventilation system pollen filter renewal .................. 23

## Degrees of difficulty

| **Easy,** suitable for novice with little experience  | **Fairly easy,** suitable for beginner with some experience | **Fairly difficult,** suitable for competent DIY mechanic | **Difficult,** suitable for experienced DIY mechanic | **Very difficult,** suitable for expert DIY or professional 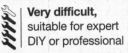 |
|---|---|---|---|---|

## Lubricants and fluids ............................... Refer to the end of *Weekly checks* on page 0•17

## Capacities
Engine oil:
  At oil and filter change ................................. 5.1 litres
  Difference between dipstick minimum and maximum marks....... 0.5 to 1 litre
Cooling system............................................. 9.3 to 9.5 litres
Fuel tank................................................. 61.5 litres
Transmission.............................................. 2.6 litres

## Cooling system
Coolant protection at standard 40% antifreeze/water mixture ratio:
  Slush point ............................................. -25°C
  Solidifying point ....................................... -30°C

## Auxiliary drivebelt deflection

| | New | Used |
|---|---|---|
| Alternator | 1 to 2 mm | 1 to 3 mm |
| Air conditioning compressor | 1 to 3 mm | 2 to 4 mm |
| Power steering pump | 1 to 2 mm | 1 to 3 mm |

## Fuel system
Injection order ........................................... 1-3-4-2
No 1 cylinder position..................................... Timing belt end of engine
Idle speed:
  Pre-facelift models (up to October 1996).................. 830 ± 20 rpm
  Facelift models (October 1996 on)........................ 850 ± 50 rpm
Anti-stall speed .......................................... 900 to 1000 rpm
Maximum no-load engine speed .............................. 5200 ± 50 rpm

## Braking system
**Note:** *No minimum lining thicknesses are given by Ford – the following is given as a general recommendation. If the pad wear warning light comes on before the front brake pad linings reach the minimum thickness, the pads should nevertheless be renewed immediately.*
Minimum front or rear brake pad lining thickness ................. 1.5 mm
Minimum rear brake shoe lining thickness....................... 1 mm

## Torque wrench settings

| | Nm | lbf ft |
|---|---|---|
| Air conditioning compressor drivebelt tensioner mounting bolts...... | 24 | 18 |
| Air conditioning compressor drivebelt tensioner pulley locking bolt ... | 24 | 18 |
| Alternator drivebelt tensioner mounting bolts .................. | 24 | 18 |
| Alternator drivebelt tensioner pulley locking bolt................. | 24 | 18 |
| Coolant drain plug ........................................ | 23 | 17 |
| Engine oil drain plug....................................... | 25 | 18 |
| Power steering pump drivebelt cover retaining bolts.............. | 10 | 7 |
| Power steering pump tensioner clamp and pump locking bolts ...... | 24 | 18 |
| Roadwheel nuts .......................................... | 85 | 63 |
| Seat belt mounting bolts .................................. | 38 | 28 |
| Transmission filler/level plug................................ | 35 | 26 |

# Maintenance schedule

The manufacturer's recommended maintenance schedule is as described below – note that the schedule starts from the car's date of registration. These are the minimum maintenance intervals recommended by the factory for Mondeos driven daily, but subjected only to 'normal' use. If you wish to keep your car in peak condition at all times, you may wish to perform some of these procedures even more often. Because frequent maintenance enhances the efficiency, performance and resale value of your car, we encourage you to do so. If your usage is not 'normal', shorter intervals are also recommended – the most important examples of these are noted in the schedule. These shorter intervals apply particularly if you drive in dusty areas, tow a caravan or trailer, sit with the engine idling or drive at low speeds for extended periods (ie, in heavy traffic), or drive for short distances (less than 4 miles) in below-freezing temperatures.

When the car is new, it should be serviced by a dealer service department (or other workshop recognised by the car manufacturer as providing the same standard of service) in order to preserve the warranty. The car manufacturer may reject warranty claims if you are unable to prove that servicing has been carried out as and when specified, using only original-equipment parts, or parts certified to be of equivalent quality.

## Every 250 miles or weekly

☐ Refer to *Weekly checks*

## Every 5000 miles or 6 months, whichever occurs first

☐ Change the engine oil and filter (Section 3)

**Note:** *Frequent oil and filter changes are good for the engine, so we recommend halving Ford's current interval, which is 10 000 miles or 12 months.*

## Every 10 000 miles or 12 months, whichever occurs first

☐ Check the battery (Section 4)
☐ Check the auxiliary drivebelts (Section 5)
☐ Drain any water from the fuel filter (Section 6)
☐ Check the electrical system (Section 7)
☐ Check under the bonnet for fluid leaks and hose condition (Section 8)
☐ Check the condition of all engine compartment wiring (Section 9)
☐ Check the condition of all air conditioning system components (Section 10)
☐ Check the transmission oil level (Section 11)
☐ Check the seat belts (Section 12)
☐ Check the adjustment of the clutch (Section 13)
☐ Check the security of all exhaust manifold/turbocharger fasteners (Section 14)
☐ Check the steering, suspension and roadwheels (Section 15)
☐ Check the driveshaft rubber gaiters and CV joints (Section 16)
☐ Check the exhaust system (Section 17)
☐ Check the underbody, and all fuel/brake lines (Section 18)
☐ Check the braking system (Section 19)
☐ Check the doors and bonnet, and lubricate their hinges and locks (Section 20)
☐ Check the security of all roadwheel nuts (Section 21)
☐ Road test (Section 22)

## Every 20 000 miles or 2 years, whichever occurs first

*In addition to the relevant items listed in the previous services, carry out the following:*

☐ Renew the ventilation system pollen filter (Section 23)
☐ Renew the fuel filter (Section 24)

## Every 30 000 miles or 3 years, whichever occurs first

*In addition to the relevant items listed in the previous services, carry out the following:*

☐ Renew the air filter element (Section 25). Note that this task must be carried out at more frequent intervals if the car is used in dusty or polluted conditions.
☐ Check the valve clearances (Section 26)

## Every 3 years (regardless of mileage)

☐ Renew the brake fluid (Section 27)
☐ Renew the coolant (Section 28)

**Note:** *This is Haynes' recommendation, to be applied if there is any doubt about the quality of antifreeze in the cooling system. If the car is known still to have the original coolant, Ford's own renewal intervals should be used, as given below. Seek the advice of a local Ford dealer if in doubt on this point.*

## Every 4 years (regardless of mileage)

☐ Check the condition of the expansion tank pressure cap seal (Section 29)

## Every 40 000 miles or 5 years, whichever occurs first

*In addition to the relevant items listed in the previous services, carry out the following:*

☐ Renew the timing belt and fuel injection pump drivebelt (Section 30)

**Note:** *It is strongly recommended that the timing belt renewal interval is reduced to 30 000 miles or 3 years on cars which are subjected to intensive use, ie. mainly short journeys or a lot of stop-start driving. The actual belt renewal interval is therefore very much up to the individual owner, but bear in mind that severe engine damage will result if the belt breaks.*

## Every 6 years (regardless of mileage)

☐ Renew the coolant (Section 28)

**Note:** *This is Ford's own renewal interval, to be used if the cooling system contains the original blue-green-coloured coolant. Seek the advice of a local Ford dealer if in doubt on this point.*

## Every 10 years (regardless of mileage)

☐ Renew the coolant (Section 28)

**Note:** *This is Ford's own renewal interval, to be used if the cooling system contains the original orange-coloured coolant. Seek the advice of a local Ford dealer if in doubt on this point.*

## Underbonnet view – pre-facelift model

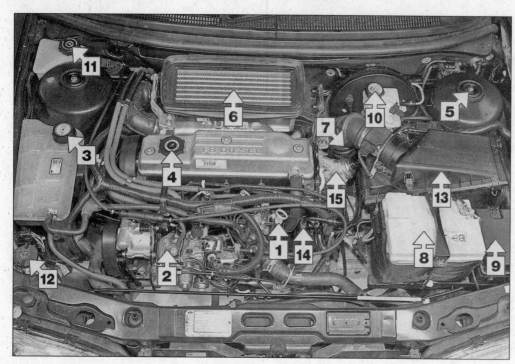

1 Engine oil level dipstick
2 Fuel injection pump
3 Coolant expansion tank
4 Engine oil filler cap
5 Suspension strut top mounting
6 Intercooler
7 Turbocharger inlet duct
8 Battery
9 Engine compartment relays and fuses
10 Brake and clutch fluid reservoir
11 Power steering fluid reservoir
12 Washer fluid reservoir cap
13 Air cleaner
14 Braking system vacuum pump
15 Fuel filter

## Underbonnet view – facelift model

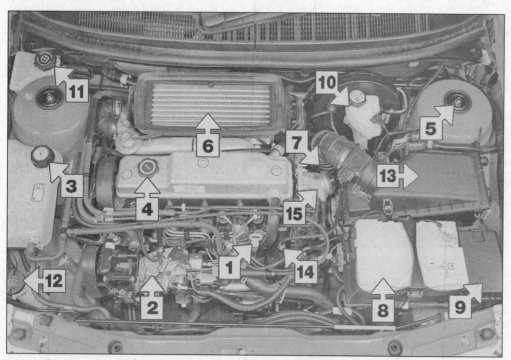

1 Engine oil level dipstick
2 Fuel injection pump
3 Coolant expansion tank
4 Engine oil filler cap
5 Suspension strut top mounting
6 Intercooler
7 Turbocharger inlet duct
8 Battery
9 Engine compartment relays and fuses
10 Brake and clutch fluid reservoir
11 Power steering fluid reservoir
12 Washer fluid reservoir cap
13 Air cleaner
14 Braking system vacuum pump
15 Fuel filter

## Front underbody view

1   Engine oil filter
2   Engine oil drain plug
3   Sump
4   Idle-up control unit
5   Engine/transmission front
    mounting
6   Starter motor
7   Gearbox
8   Engine/transmission rear
    mounting
9   Driveshaft
10  Front brake caliper
11  Front lower arm
12  Track rod
13  Exhaust downpipe

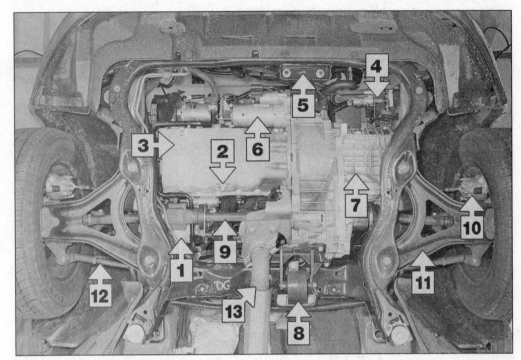

## Rear underbody view – Saloon/Hatchback

1   Fuel tank
2   Rear brakes
3   Exhaust system rubber
    mounting
4   Handbrake cables
5   Suspension struts
6   Anti-roll bar

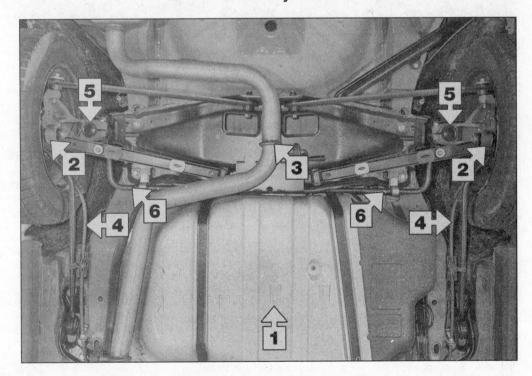

### Rear underbody view – Estate (petrol shown, diesel similar)

1 Silencers
2 Rear brakes
3 Exhaust system rubber mounting
4 Handbrake cables
5 Rear springs
6 Rear shock absorbers
7 Fuel tank filler neck
8 Charcoal canister (not fitted to diesel models)

# Maintenance procedures

## 1 Introduction

### General information

This Chapter is designed to help the home mechanic maintain his/her car for safety, economy, long life and peak performance.

The Chapter contains a master maintenance schedule, followed by Sections dealing specifically with each task in the schedule. Visual checks, adjustments, component renewal and other helpful items are included. Refer to the accompanying illustrations of the engine compartment and the underside of the car for the locations of the various components.

Servicing your car in accordance with the mileage/time maintenance schedule and the following Sections will provide a planned maintenance programme, which should result in a long and reliable service life. This is a comprehensive plan, so maintaining some items but not others at the specified service intervals will not produce the same results.

As you service your car, you will discover that many of the procedures can – and should – be grouped together, because of the particular procedure being performed, or because of the proximity of two otherwise unrelated components to one another. For example, if the car is raised for any reason, the exhaust can be inspected at the same time as the suspension and steering components.

The first step in this maintenance programme is to prepare yourself before the actual work begins. Read through all the Sections relevant to the work to be carried out, then make a list and gather all the parts and tools required. If a problem is encountered, seek advice from a parts specialist, or a dealer service department.

### Service interval display

The auxiliary warning system fitted to all models also includes a service interval reminder warning light, which is illuminated if the specified mileage (or time) since the last service has been reached.

The light should not necessarily be used as a definitive guide to the servicing needs of your Mondeo, but it is useful as a reminder, to ensure that servicing is not accidentally overlooked. Owners of older cars, or those covering a small annual mileage, may feel inclined to service their car more often, in which case the service interval reminder is perhaps less relevant.

The light should be reset whenever a service is carried out, as follows:

a) On models up to October 1996, a switch inside the glovebox must be depressed for a minimum of 4 seconds with the ignition switched on.

b) On October 1996 and later models, the switch is behind the arrow-shaped symbol in the display panel, and is depressed using a thin probe, again for 4 seconds with the ignition switched on **(see illustration)**.

## 2 Regular maintenance

If, from the time the car is new, the routine maintenance schedule is followed closely, and frequent checks are made of fluid levels and high-wear items, as suggested throughout this manual, the engine will be kept in relatively good running condition, and the need for additional work will be minimised.

It is possible that there will be times when the engine is running poorly due to the lack of regular maintenance. This is even more likely if a used car, which has not received regular and frequent maintenance checks, is purchased. In such cases, additional work may need to be carried out, outside of the regular maintenance intervals.

If engine wear is suspected, a compression

**1.8 On later models, use a thin wire to reset the service interval reminder switch**

test (refer to Chapter 2A) will provide valuable information regarding the overall performance of the main internal components. Such a test can be used as a basis to decide on the extent of the work to be carried out. If, for example, a compression test indicates serious internal engine wear, conventional maintenance as described in this Chapter will not greatly improve the performance of the engine, and may prove a waste of time and money, unless extensive overhaul work is carried out first.

The following series of operations are

those most often required to improve the performance of a generally poor-running engine:

### Primary operations

a) Clean, inspect and test the battery (See Weekly checks and Section 4, where applicable).
b) Check all the engine-related fluids (See Weekly checks).
c) Check the condition and tension of the auxiliary drivebelts (Section 5).
d) Check the condition of the air filter, and renew if necessary (Section 25).
e) Check the condition of the fuel filter, and renew if necessary (Section 24).
f) Check the condition of all hoses, and check for fluid leaks (Sections 8 and 18).

If the above operations do not prove fully effective, carry out the following secondary operations:

### Secondary operations

All items listed under *Primary operations*, plus the following:

a) Check the charging system (Chapter 5).
b) Check the glow plugs (Chapter 5).
c) Check the fuel system (see Chapter 4A).

# Every 5000 miles or 6 months

## 3 Engine oil and filter renewal

1 Make sure that you have all the necessary tools before you begin this procedure. You should also have plenty of rags or newspapers handy, for mopping-up any spills.

2 To avoid any possibility of scalding, and to protect yourself from possible skin irritants and other harmful contaminants in used engine oils, it is advisable to wear gloves when carrying out this work.

3 Access to the underside of the car is greatly improved if the car can be lifted on a hoist, driven onto ramps, or supported by axle stands.

⚠️ **Warning: Do not work under a car which is supported only by a hydraulic or scissors-type jack, or by bricks, blocks of wood, etc.**

4 If this is your first oil change, get under the car and familiarise yourself with the position of the engine oil drain plug, which is located at the rear of the sump. The engine and exhaust components will be warm during the actual work, so try to anticipate any potential problems while the engine and accessories are cool.

5 The oil should preferably be changed when the engine is still fully warmed-up to normal operating temperature, just after a run (the needle on the temperature gauge should be in the 'Normal' sector of the gauge); warm oil and sludge will flow out more easily.

6 Park the car on firm, level ground, and switch off the engine. Apply the handbrake firmly, then select 1st or reverse gear. Open the bonnet and remove the engine oil filler cap from the cylinder head cover, then remove the oil level dipstick from its tube.

7 Raise the front of the car and support it securely on axle stands.

8 Remove the front right-hand roadwheel to provide access to the oil filter, which is located on the right-hand rear face of the cylinder block.

9 Where necessary, remove the engine undershield, then remove the rear section of the wheel arch liner (two fasteners).

10 Being careful not to touch the hot exhaust components, place the drain pan under the drain plug, and unscrew the plug **(see illustration and Haynes hint)**.

**3.10 Use the correct-size spanner or socket to remove the oil drain plug and avoid rounding it off**

11 Allow the oil to drain into the drain pan, and check the condition of the plug's sealing washer; renew it if worn or damaged.

12 Allow some time for the old oil to drain, noting that it may be necessary to reposition the pan as the oil flow slows to a trickle; when the oil has completely drained, wipe clean the drain plug and its threads in the sump and refit the plug, tightening it to the specified torque wrench setting.

13 Move the drain pan into position below the oil filter.

14 Using a suitable filter removal tool if necessary, unscrew the oil filter from the

HAYNES
HINT

*Keep the plug pressed into the sump while unscrewing it by hand the last couple of turns. As the plug releases from the threads, move it away sharply, so the stream of oil issuing from the sump runs into the pan, not up your sleeve.*

**3.14 Using a chain-type wrench to remove the oil filter**

**3.16 Lubricate the filter's sealing ring with clean engine oil before installing the filter on the engine**

cylinder block; be prepared for some oil spillage **(see illustration)**. Check the old filter to make sure that the rubber sealing ring hasn't stuck to the engine; if it has, carefully remove it. Withdraw the filter, quickly turning it so that its open end is uppermost, in order to spill as little oil as possible.

**15** Using a clean, lint-free rag, wipe clean the cylinder block around the filter mounting.

Unless there are any specific instructions supplied with it, fit the new oil filter as follows.

**16** Apply a light coating of clean engine oil to the filter's sealing ring **(see illustration)**.

**17** Screw the filter into position on the engine until it seats, then tighten it through a further half- to three-quarters of a turn *only*. Tighten the filter by hand only – do not use any tools.

**18** Remove the old oil and all tools from

under the car. Refit any components removed for access, then lower the car to the ground. Tighten the right-hand roadwheel nuts to the specified torque.

**19** Refill the engine with the correct grade and type of oil, as specified at the end of the *Weekly checks* section. Pour in half the specified quantity of oil first, then wait a few minutes for the oil to run to the sump. Continue adding oil a small quantity at a time, until the level is up to the lower notch on the dipstick. Adding approximately 0.5 to 1.0 litre will raise the level to the dipstick's upper notch.

**20** Start the engine. The oil pressure warning light will take a few seconds to go out while the new filter fills with oil; do not race the engine while the light is on. Run the engine for a few minutes, while checking for leaks around the oil filter seal and the drain plug.

**21** Switch off the engine, and wait a few minutes for the oil to settle in the sump once more. With the new oil circulated and the filter now completely full, recheck the level on the dipstick, and add more oil as necessary.

**22** Dispose of the used engine oil safely, with reference to *General repair procedures*.

# Every 10 000 miles or 12 months

## 4 Battery maintenance and charging

⚠ *Warning: Certain precautions must be followed when checking and servicing the battery. Hydrogen gas, which is highly flammable, is always present in the battery cells, so keep lighted tobacco and all other open flames and sparks away from the battery. The electrolyte inside the battery is actually dilute sulphuric acid, which will cause injury if splashed on your skin or in your eyes. It will also ruin clothes and painted surfaces. When disconnecting the battery, always detach the negative (earth) lead first and connect it last.*

**Note:** *Before disconnecting the battery, see Disconnecting the battery in the reference section.*

### General

**1** A routine preventive maintenance pro-

gramme for the battery in your car is the only way to ensure quick and reliable starts. For general maintenance, refer to *Weekly checks* at the start of this manual. Also at the front of the manual is information on jump starting. For details of removing and installing the battery, refer to Chapter 5.

### Battery electrolyte level

**2** On models not equipped with a sealed or 'maintenance-free' battery, check the electrolyte level of all six battery cells.

**3** The level must be approximately 10 mm above the plates; this may be shown by maximum and minimum level lines marked on the battery's casing.

**4** If the level is low, use a coin or screwdriver to release the filler/vent cap, and add distilled water **(see illustrations)**. To improve access to the centre caps, it may be helpful to remove the battery hold-down clamp.

**5** Install and securely retighten the cap, then wipe up any spillage.

*Caution: Overfilling the cells may cause*

electrolyte to spill over during periods of heavy charging, causing corrosion or damage

### Charging

⚠ *Warning: When batteries are being charged, hydrogen gas, which is very explosive and flammable, is produced. Do not smoke, or allow open flames, near a charging or a recently-charged battery. Wear eye protection when near the battery during charging. Also, make sure the charger is unplugged before connecting or disconnecting the battery from the charger*

**6** Slow-rate charging is the best way to restore a battery that's discharged to the point where it will not start the engine. It's also a good way to maintain the battery charge in a car that's only driven a few miles between starts. Maintaining the battery charge is particularly important in winter, when the battery must work harder to start the engine, and electrical accessories that drain the battery are in greater use.

**7** Check the battery case for any instructions regarding charging the battery. Some maintenance-free batteries may require a particularly low charge rate or other special conditions, if they are not to be damaged.

**8** It's best to use a one- or two-amp battery charger (sometimes called a 'trickle' charger). They are the safest, and put the least strain on the battery. They are also the least expensive. For a faster charge, you can use a higher-amperage charger, but don't use one rated more than 1/10th the amp/hour rating of the battery (ie, no more than 5 amps, typically). Rapid boost charges that claim to restore the power of the battery in one to two hours

**4.4a Unscrew the filler/vent cap . . .**

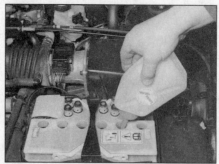

**4.4b . . . and top-up each cell with distilled water**

are hardest on the battery, and can damage batteries not in good condition. This type of charging should only be used in emergency situations.

**9** The average time necessary to charge a battery should be listed in the instructions that come with the charger. As a general rule, a trickle charger will charge a battery in 12 to 16 hours.

## 5 Auxiliary drivebelts check and renewal

### General

**1** The auxiliary drivebelts are of the flat, multi-ribbed (or 'polyvee') type, and are located on the right-hand end of the engine. The crankshaft outboard toothed pulley incorporates a flange for the crankshaft pulley which drives the alternator and air conditioning compressor, each via its own auxiliary drivebelt. The fuel injection pump toothed pulley incorporates mounting points for the pulley which drives the power steering pump, again via its own auxiliary drivebelt **(see illustration)**.

**2** The good condition and proper tension of the auxiliary drivebelts are critical to the operation of the engine.

**3** Because of their composition and the high stresses to which they are subjected, drivebelts stretch and deteriorate as they get older. They must, therefore, be regularly inspected.

### Check

**4** With the engine switched off, open and support the bonnet. For improved access to the right-hand end of the engine, first loosen the right-hand front wheel nuts, then jack up the front right-hand side of the car and support it securely on an axle stand. Remove the roadwheel, then remove the front section of

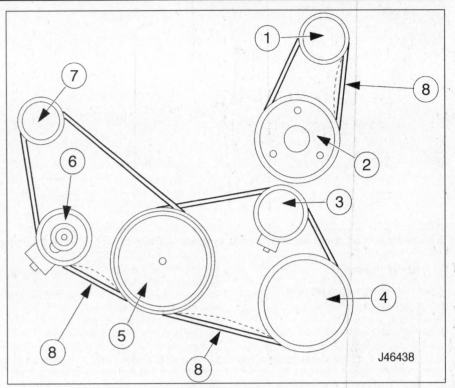

**5.1 Auxiliary drivebelt routing**

| | | |
|---|---|---|
| 1 Power steering pump | 4 Air conditioning | 6 Tensioner |
| 2 Fuel injection pump pulley | compressor | 7 Alternator |
| 3 Tensioner | 5 Crankshaft pulley | 8 Tension check points |

the wheel arch liner (two fasteners) from inside the wheel arch. If necessary, also remove the rear section of the liner, which is secured by two further bolts. To check the power steering pump drivebelt, unscrew the two bolts securing its cover to the right-hand end of the engine, then withdraw the cover **(see illustrations)**.

**5** Using an inspection light or a small electric torch, and rotating the engine when necessary with a spanner applied to the crankshaft pulley bolt, check the whole length of the

drivebelt for cracks, separation of the rubber, and torn or worn ribs. Also check for fraying and glazing, which gives the drivebelt a shiny appearance.

**6** Both sides of the drivebelt should be inspected, which means you will have to twist the drivebelt to check the underside. Use your fingers to feel the drivebelt where you can't see it.

**7** If you are in any doubt as to the condition of the drivebelt, renew it as described below.

**5.4a Remove the wheel arch cover sections (bolts arrowed)**

**5.4b Removing the power steering pump drivebelt cover**

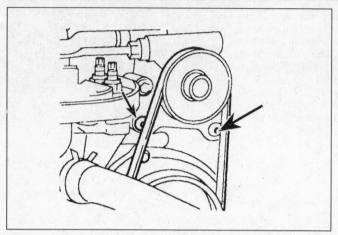

**5.8 Loosen the two power steering pump locking bolts (arrowed)**

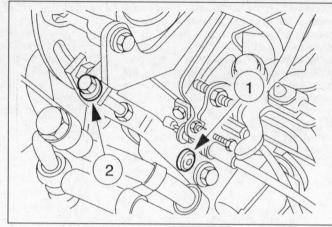

**5.9 Tensioner clamp bolt (1) and adjuster screw (2)**

### *Drivebelt renewal*

#### Power steering pump drivebelt

**8** Slacken the two pump locking bolts **(see illustration)**.

**9** Slacken the tensioner clamp bolt. Rotate the adjuster screw anti-clockwise to remove tension from the drivebelt **(see illustration)**. Remove the drivebelt – if the existing drivebelt is to be refitted, mark it, or note the maker's markings on its flat surface, so that it can be installed the same way round.

**10** On refitting, locate the drivebelt squarely in the centre of both pulleys, then tighten gently the tensioner clamp and pump locking bolts.

**11** Rotate the adjuster screw clockwise until the specified drivebelt deflection is obtained.

**12** When the setting is correct, tighten the tensioner clamp and pump locking bolts to the specified torque wrench setting.

**13** Refit the drivebelt cover; tighten the cover bolts to the specified torque wrench setting.

#### Alternator drivebelt

**14** Slacken the tensioner locking bolt. Rotate the adjuster screw clockwise to remove

tension from the drivebelt **(see illustration)**. Remove the drivebelt – if the existing drivebelt is to be refitted, mark it, or note the maker's markings on its flat surface, so that it can be installed the same way round.

**15** Check all the pulleys, ensuring that their grooves are clean, and removing all traces of oil and grease. Check that the tensioner works properly, and that its pulley rotates smoothly.

**16** If the original drivebelt is being refitted, use the marks or notes made on removal to ensure that it is installed to run in the same direction as it was previously. To fit the drivebelt, arrange it on the grooved pulleys so that it is centred in their grooves, not overlapping their raised sides, and routed correctly. Tighten gently the tensioner locking bolt.

**17** Rotate the adjuster screw anti-clockwise until the specified drivebelt deflection is obtained

**18** When the setting is correct, tighten the tensioner locking bolt to the specified torque wrench setting.

#### Air conditioning compressor drivebelt

**19** Slacken the tensioner locking bolt. Rotate the adjuster screw clockwise to remove

tension from the drivebelt **(see illustration)**. Remove the drivebelt – if the existing drivebelt is to be refitted, mark it, or note the maker's markings on its flat surface, so that it can be installed the same way round.

**20** Check all the pulleys, ensuring that their grooves are clean, and removing all traces of oil and grease. Check that the tensioner works properly, and that its pulley rotates smoothly.

**21** If the original drivebelt is being refitted, use the marks or notes made on removal to ensure that it is installed to run in the same direction as it was previously. To fit the drivebelt, arrange it on the grooved pulleys so that it is centred in their grooves, not overlapping their raised sides and routed correctly. Tighten gently the tensioner locking bolt.

**22** Rotate the adjuster screw anti-clockwise until the specified drivebelt deflection is obtained.

**23** When the setting is correct, tighten the tensioner locking bolt to the specified torque wrench setting.

#### All drivebelts

**24** Using a spanner applied to the crankshaft pulley bolt, rotate the crankshaft through at

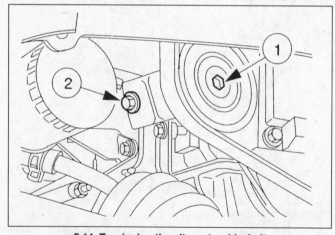

**5.14 Tensioning the alternator drivebelt**

*1 Tensioner pulley locking bolt    2 Tensioner adjuster screw*

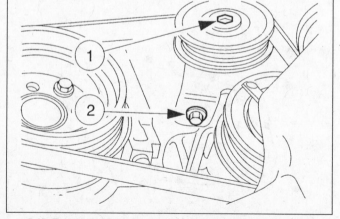

**5.19 Tensioning the air conditioning compressor drivebelt**

*1 Tensioner pulley locking bolt    2 Tensioner adjuster screw*

least two full turns clockwise to settle the drivebelt on the pulleys, then check that the drivebelt is properly installed.

**25** Refit the components removed for access, then (where applicable) lower the car to the ground. If the right-hand roadwheel was removed, tighten the wheel nuts to the specified torque.

## 6 Drain water from the fuel filter

*Caution: Before starting any work on the fuel filter, wipe clean the filter assembly and the area around it; it is essential that no dirt or other foreign matter is allowed into the system. Obtain a suitable container into which the filter can be drained and place rags or similar material under the filter assembly to catch any spillages. Do not allow diesel fuel to leak into the clutch bellhousing or it will contaminate the clutch disc friction material which will cause severe clutch slip which can be cured only by the renewal of the clutch disc and the degreasing of all fouled surfaces. Similarly, diesel fuel should never be allowed to contaminate components such as the alternator and starter motor, the coolant hoses and engine mountings, and any wiring.*

**1** In addition to taking the precautions noted above to catch any fuel spillages, place a small tray (such as a lid from a jar) under the drain spigot on the base of the fuel filter – ideally, attach a tube to the drain spigot, and direct the fuel into a container.

**2** Open the drain cock by unscrewing the knurled wheel, or by unscrewing the bolt **(see illustration)**.

**3** Allow the filter to drain until clean fuel, free of dirt or water, emerges from the tube (approximately 100 cc is usually sufficient). Close the drain cock and remove the tube, containers and rag, moppin-up any spilt fuel.

**4** If no fuel emerges on opening the drain cock, depress the black button on top of the filter several times.

**5** If this does not work, remove the filter cartridge and check it carefully until the

reason for the lack of flow can be identified and is cured. It is unwise simply to probe the drain cock with a piece of wire in an attempt to clear the obstruction; the small seals in the drain cock may be damaged or dislodged.

**6** On completion, dispose safely of the drained. Check carefully all disturbed components to ensure that there are no leaks (of air or fuel) when the engine is restarted.

## 7 Electrical system check

**1** Check the operation of all external lights and indicators (front and rear).

**2** Check for satisfactory operation of the instrument panel, its illumination and warning lights, the switches and their function lights.

**3** Check the horn(s) for satisfactory operation.

**4** Check all other electrical equipment for satisfactory operation.

## 8 Underbonnet check for fluid leaks and hose condition

*Caution: Renewal of air conditioning hoses must be left to a dealer service department or air conditioning specialist who has the equipment to depressurise the system safely. Never remove air conditioning components or hoses until the system has been depressurised*

### General

**1** High temperatures in the engine compartment can cause the deterioration of the rubber and plastic hoses used for engine, accessory and emission systems operation. Periodic inspection should be made for cracks, loose clamps, material hardening and leaks.

**2** Carefully check the large top and bottom radiator hoses, along with the other smaller-diameter cooling system hoses and metal pipes; do not forget the heater hoses/pipes which run from the engine to the bulkhead, and those to the engine oil cooler (where fitted). Inspect each hose along its entire length, renewing any that is cracked, swollen or shows signs of deterioration. Cracks

**6.2 Draining water from fuel filter using a container (arrowed) to prevent spillage**

may become more apparent if the hose is squeezed, and may often be apparent at the hose ends **(see illustration)**.

**3** Make sure that all hose connections are tight. If the large-diameter air hoses from the air cleaner are loose, they will leak air, and upset the engine idle quality **(see illustration)**. if the spring clamps that are used to secure many of the hoses appear to be slackening, they should be updated with worm-drive clips to prevent the possibility of leaks.

**4** Some other hoses are secured to their fittings with clamps. Where clamps are used, check to be sure they haven't lost their tension, allowing the hose to leak. If clamps aren't used, make sure the hose has not expanded and/or hardened where it slips over the fitting, allowing it to leak **(see Haynes Hint)**.

**5** Check all fluid reservoirs, filler caps, drain plugs and fittings, etc, looking for any signs of leakage of oil, transmission and/or brake hydraulic fluid, coolant and power steering fluid.

**6** If the car is regularly parked in the same place, close inspection of the ground underneath it will soon show any leaks; ignore the puddle of water which will be left if the air conditioning system is in use. Place a clean piece of cardboard below the engine, and examine it for signs of contamination after the car has been parked over it overnight – be aware, however, of the fire risk inherent in placing combustible material below the catalytic converter.

*A leak in the cooling system will usually show up as white- or antifreeze-coloured deposits on the area adjoining the leak.*

**8.2 Check the condition of all coolant hoses**

**8.3 The clips securing the air hoses should be checked regularly**

**7** Remember that some leaks will only occur with the engine running, or when the engine is hot or cold. With the handbrake firmly applied, start the engine from cold, and let the engine idle while you examine the underside of the engine compartment for signs of leakage.

**8** If an unusual smell is noticed inside or around the car, especially when the engine is thoroughly hot, this may point to the presence of a leak.

**9** As soon as a leak is detected, its source must be traced and rectified. Where oil has been leaking for some time, it is usually necessary to use a steam cleaner, pressure washer or similar, to clean away the accumulated dirt, so that the exact source of the leak can be identified.

### Vacuum hoses

**10** It's quite common for vacuum hoses, especially those in the emissions system, to be colour-coded, or to be identified by coloured stripes moulded into them. Various systems require hoses with different wall thicknesses, collapse resistance and temperature resistance. When renewing hoses, be sure the new ones are made of the same material.

**11** Often the only effective way to check a hose is to remove it completely from the car. If more than one hose is removed, be sure to label the hoses and fittings to ensure correct installation.

**12** When checking vacuum hoses, be sure to include any plastic T-fittings in the check. Inspect the fittings for cracks, and check the hose where it fits over the fitting for distortion, which could cause leakage **(see illustration)**.

**13** A small piece of vacuum hose (quarter-inch inside diameter) can be used as a stethoscope to detect vacuum leaks. Hold one end of the hose to your ear, and probe around vacuum hoses and fittings, listening for the 'hissing' sound characteristic of a vacuum leak.

⚠ *Warning: When probing with the vacuum hose stethoscope, be very careful not to come into contact with moving engine components such as the auxiliary drivebelts, radiator electric cooling fan, etc.*

### Fuel hoses

⚠ *Warning: There are certain precautions which must be taken when inspecting or servicing fuel system components. Work in a well-ventilated area, and do not allow open flames (cigarettes, appliance pilot lights, etc) or bare light bulbs near the work area. Mop-up any spills immediately, and do not store fuel-soaked rags where they could ignite.*

**14** Check all fuel hoses for deterioration and chafing. Check especially for cracks in areas where the hose bends, and also just before fittings, such as where a hose attaches to the fuel filter.

**15** High-quality fuel line should be used for fuel line renewal. Never, under any circumstances, use unreinforced vacuum

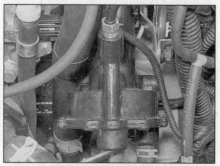

**8.12 Inspect the vacuum pump hoses for leakage and security**

line, clear plastic tubing or water hose as a substitute for fuel lines.

**16** Spring-type clamps are commonly used on fuel lines. These clamps often lose their tension over a period of time, and can be 'sprung' during removal. Replace all spring-type clamps with screw clamps whenever a hose is renewed.

### Metal lines

**17** Sections of metal piping are often used for fuel line between the fuel filter and the engine. Check carefully to be sure the piping has not been bent or crimped, and that cracks have not started in the line.

**18** If a section of metal fuel line must be renewed, only seamless steel piping should be used, since copper and aluminium piping don't have the strength necessary to withstand normal engine vibration.

**19** Check the metal lines where they enter the brake master cylinder, ABS hydraulic unit or clutch master/slave cylinders (as applicable) for cracks in the lines or loose fittings. Any sign of brake fluid leakage calls for an immediate and thorough inspection.

### 9 Engine compartment wiring check

**1** With the car parked on level ground, apply the handbrake firmly and open the bonnet. Using an inspection light or a small electric torch, check all visible wiring within and beneath the engine compartment.

**9.5 Check the condition of all visible electrical connectors and their wiring**

**2** What you are looking for is wiring that is obviously damaged by chafing against sharp edges, or against moving suspension/transmission components and/or the auxiliary drivebelts, by being trapped or crushed between carelessly-refitted components, or melted by being forced into contact with the hot engine castings, coolant pipes, etc. In almost all cases, damage of this sort is caused in the first instance by incorrect routing on reassembly after previous work has been carried out.

**3** Depending on the extent of the problem, damaged wiring may be repaired by rejoining the break or splicing-in a new length of wire, using solder to ensure a good connection, and remaking the insulation with adhesive insulating tape or heat-shrink tubing, as appropriate. If the damage is extensive, given the implications for the car's future reliability, the best long-term answer may well be to renew that entire section of the loom, however expensive this may appear.

**4** When the actual damage has been repaired, ensure that the wiring loom is re-routed correctly, so that it is clear of other components, and not stretched or kinked, and is secured out of harm's way using the plastic clips, guides and ties provided.

**5** Check all electrical connectors, ensuring that they are clean, securely fastened, and that each is locked by its plastic tabs or wire clip, as appropriate **(see illustration)**. If any connector shows external signs of corrosion (accumulations of white or green deposits, or streaks of 'rust'), or if any is thought to be dirty, it must be unplugged and cleaned using electrical contact cleaner. If the connector pins are severely corroded, the connector must be renewed; note that this may mean the renewal of that entire section of the loom – see your local Ford dealer for details.

**6** If the cleaner completely removes the corrosion to leave the connector in a satisfactory condition, it would be wise to pack the connector with a suitable material which will exclude dirt and moisture, preventing the corrosion from occurring again; a Ford dealer may be able to recommend a suitable product.

**7** Check the condition of the battery connections – remake the connections or renew the leads if a fault is found (see Chapter 5). Use the same techniques to ensure that all earth points in the engine compartment provide good electrical contact through clean, metal-to-metal joints, and that all are securely fastened.

### 10 Air conditioning system check

⚠ *Warning: The air conditioning system is under high pressure. Do not loosen any fittings or remove any components until after the system has been discharged. Air conditioning refrigerant must be properly discharged into an approved type of container, at a*

*dealer service department or an automotive air conditioning repair facility capable of handling R134a refrigerant. Always wear eye protection when disconnecting air conditioning system fittings.*

1 The following maintenance checks should be performed on a regular basis, to ensure that the air conditioner continues to operate at peak efficiency:

a) *Check the auxiliary drivebelt. If it's worn or deteriorated, renew it (see Section 5).*

b) *Check the system hoses. Look for cracks, bubbles, hard spots and deterioration. Inspect the hoses and all fittings for oil bubbles and seepage. If there's any evidence of wear, damage or leaks, renew the hose(s).*

c) *Inspect the condenser fins for leaves, insects and other debris. Use a 'fin comb' or compressed air to clean the condenser.*

d) *Check that the drain tube from the front of the evaporator is clear – note that it is normal to have clear fluid (water) dripping from this while the system is in operation, to the extent that quite a large puddle can be left under the car when it is parked.*

 *Warning: Wear eye protection when using compressed air.*

2 It's a good idea to operate the system for about 30 minutes at least once a month, particularly during the winter. Long term non-use can cause hardening, and subsequent failure, of the seals.

3 Because of the complexity of the air conditioning system and the special equipment necessary to service it, in-depth fault diagnosis and repairs are not included in this manual.

4 The most common cause of poor cooling is simply a low system refrigerant charge. If a noticeable drop in cool air output occurs, the following quick check will help you determine if the refrigerant level is low.

5 Warm the engine up to normal operating temperature.

6 Place the air conditioning temperature selector at the coldest setting, and put the blower at the highest setting. Open the doors – to make sure the air conditioning system doesn't cycle off as soon as it cools the passenger compartment.

7 With the compressor engaged – the clutch will make an audible click, and the centre of the clutch will rotate – feel the inlet and outlet pipes at the compressor. One side should be cold, and one hot. If there's no perceptible difference between the two pipes, there's something wrong with the compressor or the system. It might be a low charge – it might be something else. Take the car to a dealer service department or an automotive air conditioning specialist **(see Tool tip)**.

## 11 Transmission oil level check

1 The transmission does not have a dipstick. To check the oil level, raise the car and support it securely on axle stands, making sure that the car is level.

2 Remove the engine undershields as necessary for access to the front of the transmission.

3 On the lower front side of the transmission housing, you will see the filler/level plug. Using a suitable Allen key or socket, unscrew and remove it – take care, as it will probably be very tight **(see illustrations)**.

4 If the lubricant level is correct, the oil should be up to the lower edge of the hole.

5 If the transmission needs more lubricant (if the oil level is not up to the hole), use a syringe, or a plastic bottle and tube, to add more **(see illustration)**.

6 Stop filling the transmission when the lubricant begins to run out of the hole, then wait until the flow of oil ceases.

7 Refit the filler/level plug, and tighten it to the specified torque wrench setting. Drive the car a short distance, then check for leaks.

8 A need for regular topping-up can only be due to a leak, which should be found and rectified without delay.

## 12 Seat belt check

Check the seat belts for satisfactory operation and condition. Inspect the webbing for fraying and cuts. Check that they retract smoothly and without binding into their reels.

**TOOL TiP**

*Many car accessory shops sell one-shot air conditioning recharge aerosols. These generally contain refrigerant, compressor oil, leak sealer and system conditioner. Some also have a dye to help pinpoint leaks.*

⚠ *Warning: These products must only be used as directed by the manufacturer, and do not remove the need for regular maintenance.*

Check that the seat belt mounting bolts are tight, and if necessary tighten them to the specified torque wrench setting.

## 13 Clutch adjustment check

Refer to Chapter 6.

## 14 Exhaust manifold/ turbocharger fastener tightness check

Remove the intercooler (see Chapter 4A) – unbolt and remove completely the intercooler mounting brackets and the intercooler/inlet manifold ducting. Pack the turbocharger opening with clean rag to prevent dirt or other objects falling in.

Check that all exhaust manifold, turbocharger and exhaust system mounting nuts and bolts are securely fastened – use a torque wrench if necessary to ensure their security.

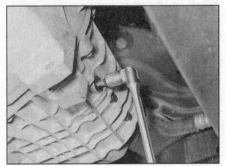
**11.3a Using a suitable Allen key or socket, unscrew . . .**

**11.3b . . . and remove the transmission oil filler/level plug**

**11.5 Topping-up the transmission oil**

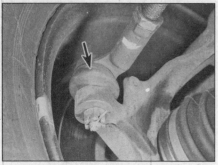

**15.2a Check the condition of the track rod balljoint dust cover (arrowed)**

**15.2b Check the condition of the lower arm balljoint dust cover (arrowed)**

**15.2c Check the condition of the steering rack gaiters**

## 15 Steering, suspension and roadwheel check

### Front suspension and steering

1 Apply the handbrake, then raise the front of the car and support it on axle stands.

2 Visually inspect the balljoint dust covers and the steering gear gaiters for splits, chafing or deterioration (see illustrations). Any wear of these components will cause loss of lubricant, together with dirt and water entry, resulting in rapid deterioration of the balljoints or steering gear.

3 Check the power-assisted steering fluid hoses for chafing or deterioration, and the pipe and hose unions for fluid leaks. Also check for signs of fluid leakage under pressure from the steering gear rubber gaiters, which would indicate failed fluid seals within the steering gear.

4 Grasp the roadwheel at the 12 o'clock and 6 o'clock positions, and try to rock it (see illustration). Very slight free play may be felt, but if the movement is appreciable, further investigation is necessary to determine the source. Continue rocking the wheel while an assistant depresses the footbrake. If the movement is now eliminated or significantly reduced, it is likely that the hub bearings are at fault. If the free play is still evident with the footbrake depressed, then there is wear in the suspension joints or mountings.

5 Now grasp the wheel at the 9 o'clock and 3 o'clock positions, and try to rock it as before. Any movement felt now may again be caused

by wear in the hub bearings or the steering track rod balljoints. If the outer track rod balljoint is worn, the visual movement will be obvious. If the inner joint is suspect, it can be felt by placing a hand over the rack-and-pinion rubber gaiter, and gripping the track rod. If the wheel is now rocked, movement will be felt at the inner joint if wear has taken place.

6 Using a large screwdriver or flat bar, check for wear in the suspension mounting and subframe bushes by levering between the relevant suspension component and its attachment point. Some movement is to be expected as the mountings are made of rubber, but excessive wear should be obvious. Also check the condition of any visible rubber bushes, looking for splits, cracks or contamination of the rubber.

7 With the car standing on its wheels, have an assistant turn the steering wheel back-and-forth, about an eighth of a turn each way. There should be very little, if any, lost movement between the steering wheel and roadwheels. If this is not the case, closely observe the joints and mountings previously described, but in addition, check the steering column joints for wear, and also check the rack-and-pinion steering gear itself.

### Rear suspension

8 Chock the front wheels, then raise the rear of the car and support it on axle stands.

9 Check the rear hub bearings for wear, using the method described for the front hub bearings (paragraph 4).

10 Using a large screwdriver or flat bar, check for wear in the suspension mounting bushes by levering between the relevant suspension component and its attachment point. Some movement is to be expected as the mountings are made of rubber, but excessive wear should be obvious.

### Roadwheel check and balancing

11 Periodically remove the roadwheels, and clean any dirt or mud from the inside and outside surfaces. Examine the wheel rims for signs of rusting, corrosion or other damage. Light alloy wheels are easily damaged by 'kerbing' whilst parking, and similarly, steel wheels may become dented or buckled. Renewal of the wheel is very often the only course of remedial action possible.

12 The balance of each wheel and tyre assembly should be maintained, not only to avoid excessive tyre wear, but also to avoid wear in the steering and suspension components. Wheel imbalance is normally signified by vibration through the car's bodyshell, although in many cases it is particularly noticeable through the steering wheel. Conversely, it should be noted that wear or damage in suspension or steering components may cause excessive tyre wear. Out-of-round or out-of-true tyres, damaged wheels and wheel bearing wear/maladjustment also fall into this category. Balancing will not usually cure vibration caused by such wear.

13 Wheel balancing may be carried out with the wheel either on or off the car. If balanced on the car, ensure that the wheel-to-hub relationship is marked in some way prior to subsequent wheel removal, so that it may be refitted in its original position.

## 16 Driveshaft rubber gaiter and CV joint check

1 The driveshaft rubber gaiters are very important, because they prevent dirt, water and foreign material from entering and damaging the constant velocity (CV) joints. External contamination can cause the gaiter material to deteriorate prematurely, so it's a good idea to wash the gaiters with soap and water occasionally.

2 With the car raised and securely supported on axle stands, turn the steering onto

**15.4 Checking for wear in the front suspension and hub bearings**

**16.2 Check the driveshaft gaiters by hand for cracks and/or leaking grease**

full-lock, then slowly rotate each front wheel in turn. Inspect the condition of the outer constant velocity (CV) joint rubber gaiters, squeezing the gaiters to open out the folds **(see illustration)**. Check for signs of cracking, splits, or deterioration of the rubber, which may allow the escape of grease, and lead to the ingress of water and grit into the joint. Also check the security and condition of the retaining clips. Repeat these checks on the inner CV joints. If any damage or deterioration is found, the gaiters should be renewed as described in Chapter 8.

**3** At the same time, check the general condition of the outer CV joints themselves, by first holding the driveshaft and attempting to rotate the wheels. Repeat this check on the inner joints, by holding the inner joint yoke and attempting to rotate the driveshaft.

**4** Any appreciable movement in the CV joint indicates wear in the joint, wear in the driveshaft splines, or a loose driveshaft retaining nut.

## 17 Exhaust system check

**1** With the engine cold (at least three hours after the car has been driven), check the complete exhaust system, from its starting point at the engine to the end of the tailpipe. Ideally, this should be done on a hoist, where unrestricted access is available; if a hoist is not available, raise and support the car on axle stands. Remove any engine undershields as necessary for full access to the exhaust system.

**2** Make sure that all brackets and rubber mountings are in good condition, and tight; if any of the mountings are to be renewed, ensure that the new ones are of the correct type **(see illustration)**. If any of the exhaust system rubber mountings are to be renewed, ensure that the new ones are of the correct type – their colour is a good guide. Those nearest to the catalytic converter are more heat-resistant than the others.

**3** Check the pipes and connections for evidence of leaks, severe corrosion, or damage **(see illustration)**. Leakage at any of the joints or in other parts of the system will usually show up as a black sooty stain in the vicinity of the leak. **Note:** *Exhaust sealants should not be used on any part of the exhaust system upstream of the catalytic converter – even if the sealant does not contain additives harmful to the converter, pieces of it may break off and foul the element, causing local overheating.*

**4** At the same time, inspect the underside of the body for holes, corrosion, open seams, etc, which may allow exhaust gases to enter the passenger compartment. Seal all body openings with silicone or body putty.

**5** Rattles and other noises can often be traced to the exhaust system, especially the rubber

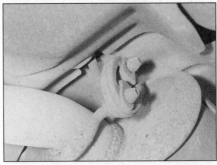

**17.2 Check the condition of the exhaust system rubber mountings**

mountings. Try to move the system, silencer(s) and catalytic converter. If any components can touch the body or suspension parts, secure the exhaust system with new mountings.

**6** Check the running condition of the engine by inspecting inside the end of the tailpipe; the exhaust deposits here are an indication of the engine's state of tune. The inside of the tailpipe should be dry, and should vary in colour from dark grey to light grey/brown; if it is black and sooty, or coated with white deposits, the engine is in need of a thorough fuel system inspection.

## 18 Underbody and fuel/brake line check

**1** With the car raised and supported on axle stands or over an inspection pit, thoroughly inspect the underbody and wheel arches for signs of damage and corrosion. In particular, examine the bottom of the side sills, and any concealed areas where mud can collect.

**2** Where corrosion and rust is evident, press and tap firmly on the panel with a screwdriver, and check for any serious corrosion which would necessitate repairs.

**3** If the panel is not seriously corroded, clean away the rust, and apply a new coating of underseal. Refer to Chapter 11 for more details of body repairs.

**4** At the same time, inspect the PVC-coated lower body panels for stone damage and general condition.

**5** Inspect all of the fuel and brake lines on the underbody for damage, rust, corrosion and leakage. Also make sure that they are correctly supported in their clips. Where applicable, check the PVC coating on the lines for damage.

## 19 Braking system check

**1** The work described in this Section should be carried out at the specified intervals, or whenever a defect is suspected in the braking system. Any of the following symptoms could indicate a potential brake system defect:

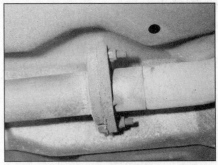

**17.3 Look for signs of leakage at the exhaust joints**

a) *The car pulls to one side when the brake pedal is depressed.*
b) *The brakes make squealing, scraping or dragging noises when applied.*
c) *Brake pedal travel is excessive, or pedal feel is poor.*
d) *The brake fluid requires repeated topping-up. Note that, on models with a hydraulic clutch (see Chapter 6), this problem could be due to a leak in the clutch system.*

### Front disc brakes

**2** Apply the handbrake, then loosen the front wheel nuts. Jack up the front of the car, and support it on axle stands (see *Jacking and vehicle support*).

**3** For better access to the brake calipers, remove the wheels.

**4** Look through the inspection window in the caliper, and check that the thickness of the friction lining material on each of the pads is not less than the recommended minimum thickness given in the Specifications **(see illustration)**. **Note:** *Bear in mind that the lining material is normally bonded to a metal backing plate.*

**5** If it is difficult to determine the exact thickness of the pad linings, or if you are at all concerned about the condition of the pads, then remove them from the calipers for further inspection (refer to Chapter 9).

**6** Check the other caliper in the same way.

**7** If any one of the brake pads has worn down to, or below, the specified limit, *all four* pads at that end of the car must be renewed as a set.

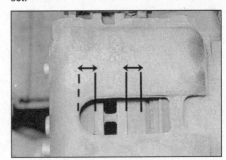

**19.4 Check the thickness of the pad friction material through the caliper inspection window**

**19.8 Check the disc thickness with a micrometer, if available**

**19.9 Checking the condition of a flexible brake hose**

**8** Measure the thickness of the discs with a micrometer, if available, to make sure that they still have service life remaining **(see illustration)**. If any disc is thinner than the specified minimum thickness, renew it (refer to Chapter 9). In any case, check the general condition of the discs. Look for excessive scoring and discolouration caused by overheating. If these conditions exist, remove the relevant disc and have it resurfaced or renewed (refer to Chapter 9).

**9** Before refitting the wheels, check all brake lines and hoses (refer to Chapter 9). In particular, check the flexible hoses in the vicinity of the calipers, where they are subjected to most movement. Bend them between the fingers (but do not actually bend them double, or the casing may be damaged) and check that this does not reveal previously-hidden cracks, cuts or splits **(see illustration)**.

**10** On completion, refit the wheels and lower the car to the ground. Tighten the wheel nuts to the specified torque.

### Rear disc brakes

**11** Loosen the rear wheel nuts, then chock the front wheels. Jack up the rear of the car, and support it on axle stands (see *Jacking and vehicle support*). Remove the rear wheels.

**12** The procedure for checking the rear brakes is much the same as described in paragraphs 2 to 10 above.

### Rear drum brakes

**13** Loosen the rear wheel nuts, then chock the front wheels. Jack up the rear of the car, and support on axle stands (see *Jacking and vehicle support*). Remove the rear wheels.

**14** To check the brake shoe lining thickness without removing the brake drums, prise the rubber plugs from the backplates, and use an electric torch to inspect the linings of the leading brake shoes. Check that the thickness of the lining material on the brake shoes is not less than the recommendation given in the Specifications **(see illustrations)**.

**15** If it is difficult to determine the exact thickness of the brake shoe linings, or if you are at all concerned about the condition of the shoes, then remove the rear drums for a more comprehensive inspection (refer to Chapter 9).

**16** With the drum removed, check the shoe return and hold-down springs for correct installation, and check the wheel cylinders for leakage of brake fluid. Check the friction surface of the brake drums for scoring and discoloration. If excessive, the drum should be resurfaced or renewed.

**17** Before refitting the wheels, check all brake lines and hoses (refer to Chapter 9). On completion, apply the handbrake and check that the rear wheels are locked. The handbrake is self-adjusting, and no manual adjustment is possible.

**18** On completion, refit the wheels and lower the car to the ground. Tighten the wheel nuts to the specified torque.

## 20 Door and bonnet check and lubrication

Check that the doors, bonnet and tailgate/boot lid close securely. Check that the bonnet safety catch operates correctly. Check the operation of the door check straps.

Lubricate the hinges, door check straps, the striker plates and the bonnet catch sparingly with a little oil or grease.

## 21 Roadwheel nut tightness check

**1** Apply the handbrake, chock the wheels, and engage 1st gear.

**2** Remove the wheel cover (or wheel centre cover), using the flat end of the wheel brace supplied in the tool kit.

**3** Loosen the first wheel nut, using the wheel brace if possible. If the nut proves stubborn, use a close-fitting socket and a long extension bar.

**4** Once the nut has been loosened, remove it and check that the wheel stud threads are clean. Use a small wire brush to clean any rust or dirt from the threads, if necessary.

**5** Refit the nut, with the tapered side facing inwards. Tighten it fully, using the wheel brace alone – no other tools. This will ensure that the wheel nuts can be loosened using the wheel brace if a puncture occurs. However, it is preferable if a torque wrench is available, to tighten the nuts to the specified torque wrench setting.

**6** Repeat the procedure for the remaining three nuts in turn, then refit the wheel cover or centre cover, as applicable.

**7** Work around the car, checking and re-tightening the nuts for all four wheels.

## 22 Road test

**Braking system**

**1** Make sure that the car does not pull to one side when braking, and that the wheels do not lock prematurely when braking hard.

**2** Check that there is no vibration through the steering when braking. On models equipped with ABS brakes, if vibration or pulsing is felt through the pedal under heavy braking, this is a normal characteristic of the system operation, and is not a cause for concern.

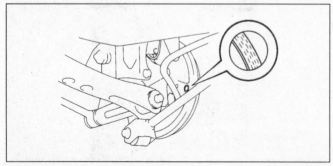

**19.14a Prise the rubber plugs from the backplates to inspect the leading brake shoe linings**

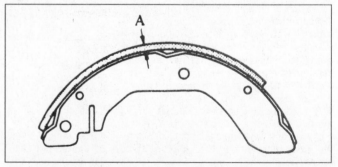

**19.14b On bonded linings, measure the thickness as shown. On riveted linings, measure to the rivet heads**

**3** Check that the handbrake operates correctly, without excessive movement of the lever, and that it holds the car stationary on a slope, in both directions (facing up or down a slope).

**4** With the engine switched off, test the operation of the brake servo unit as follows. Depress the footbrake four or five times to exhaust the vacuum, then start the engine. As the engine starts, there should be a noticeable 'give' in the brake pedal as vacuum builds-up. Allow the engine to run for at least two minutes, and then switch it off. If the brake pedal is now depressed again, it should be possible to detect a hiss from the servo as the pedal is depressed. After about four or five applications, no further hissing should be heard, and the pedal should feel considerably harder.

### Steering and suspension

**5** Check for any abnormalities in the steering, suspension, handling or road 'feel'.
**6** Drive the car, and check that there are no unusual vibrations or noises.
**7** Check that the steering feels positive, with no excessive sloppiness or roughness, and check for any suspension noises when cornering and driving over bumps.

### Drivetrain

**8** Check the performance of the engine, transmission and driveshafts.
**9** Check that the engine starts correctly, both when cold and when hot.
**10** Listen for any unusual noises from the engine and transmission.
**11** Make sure that the engine runs smoothly when idling, and that there is no hesitation when accelerating.
**12** Check that all gears can be engaged smoothly without noise, and that the gear lever action is smooth and not abnormally vague or 'notchy'.
**13** Listen for a metallic clicking sound from the front of the car as it is driven slowly in a circle with the steering on full-lock. Carry out this check in both directions. If a clicking noise is heard, this indicates wear in a driveshaft joint, in which case renew the joint if necessary.

### Clutch

**14** Check that the clutch pedal moves smoothly and easily through its full travel, and that the clutch itself functions correctly, with no trace of slip or drag.
**15** On models with a cable-operated clutch, if the movement is uneven or stiff in places, check that the cable is routed correctly, with no sharp turns. Inspect both ends of the clutch inner cable, both at the gearbox end and inside the car, for signs of wear and fraying.
**16** On models with a hydraulically-operated clutch, if the clutch is slow to release, it is possible that the system requires bleeding (see Chapter 6). Also check the fluid pipes under the bonnet for signs of leakage.
**17** Check the clutch adjustment as described in Chapter 6.

### Instruments and electrical equipment

**18** Check the operation of all instruments and electrical equipment.
**19** Make sure that all instruments read correctly, and switch on all electrical equipment in turn, to check that it functions properly.

# Every 20 000 miles or 2 years

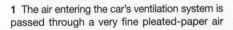

### 23 Ventilation system pollen filter renewal

**1** The air entering the car's ventilation system is passed through a very fine pleated-paper air filter element, which removes particles of pollen, dust and other airborne foreign matter. To ensure its continued effectiveness, this filter's element must be renewed at regular intervals. Failure to renew the element will also result in greatly-reduced airflow into the passenger compartment, reducing demisting and ventilation.

**2** Where necessary, remove the left-hand side windscreen wiper arm (see Chapter 12).
**3** Prise off their trim caps, then unscrew the two screws securing the windscreen edge of the cowl grille panel; remove the clips beneath the screws. Open the bonnet and remove the remaining Torx screws (see illustrations).

23.3a Remove cowl grille panel screws (arrowed) – on some models, only two lower (Torx) screws are fitted . . .

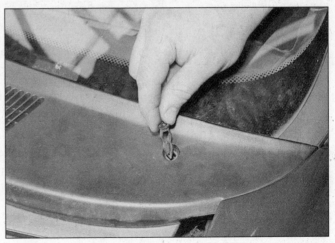

23.3b . . . and remove the clips beneath the upper screws

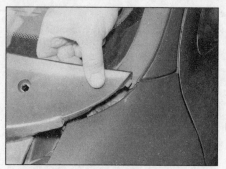

**23.4a Unclip the end of the grille panel from the wing . . .**

**23.4b . . . and remove the grille panel**

**4** Peel back the rubber seal and withdraw the cowl grille panel, unclipping it where it joins the top of the wing (see illustrations).

**5** Releasing the clip at each end, lift out the pollen filter housing, and withdraw the element (see illustrations).

**6** Wipe out the ventilation system intake and the filter housing, removing any leaves, dead insects, etc.

**7** If carrying out a routine service, the element must be renewed regardless of its apparent condition. If you are checking the element for any other reason, inspect its front surface; if it is very dirty, renew the element. If it is only moderately dusty, it can be re-used by blowing

it clean from the rear to the front surface with compressed air. Because it is a pleated-paper type filter, it cannot be washed or re-oiled. If it cannot be cleaned satisfactorily with compressed air, discard and renew it.

 **Warning: Wear eye protection when using compressed air.**

**8** Refitting is the reverse of the removal procedure; ensure that the element and housing are securely seated, so that unfiltered air cannot enter the passenger compartment.

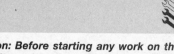

**24 Fuel filter renewal**

**Caution: Before starting any work on the fuel filter, wipe clean the filter assembly and the area around it; it is essential that no dirt or other foreign matter is allowed into the system. Obtain a suitable container into which the filter can be drained, and place rags or similar material under the filter assembly to catch any spillages. Do not allow diesel fuel to leak into the clutch bellhousing, or it will contaminate the clutch disc friction material which will cause severe clutch slip – curable only**

by the renewal of the clutch disc and the degreasing of all fouled surfaces. Similarly, diesel fuel should never be allowed to contaminate components such as the alternator and starter motor, the coolant hoses and engine mountings, and any wiring.

**Note:** *On later models, a cartridge type fuel filter may be fitted, which simply unscrews from the filter head.*

**1** The fuel filter is located on a bracket on the left-hand end of the cylinder head (see illustration). To improve access, remove the air filter components as described later in this Chapter, or in Chapter 4A.

**2** Drain the fuel filter completely, using the information in Section 6.

**3** Loosen the clamp bolt retaining the filter to the mounting bracket, or unscrew it from the filter head.

**4** Remove the filter from the retaining bracket and withdraw from the engine compartment. Recover the sealing ring, where applicable – a new one should be used when refitting (this should be supplied with the new filter).

**5** If possible, fill the new filter with clean fuel prior to fitting – this will greatly simplify restarting the engine.

**6** Ensure that the mating faces of the filter and housing are clean, then offer the filter into position (with new sealing ring, where applicable). Tighten the clamp bolt securely, or screw the filter on firmly by hand, according to type. Refit any components removed for access.

**7** If the filter was filled with fuel prior to fitting, the engine should start after only a few attempts. If the filter was not pre-filled, bleed the system using the information in Chapter 4A before trying to start the engine, and only operate the starter in short bursts.

**8** Once the engine has started, run it at a fast idle until there are no air bubbles visible in the clear fuel hose from the filter. At the same time, check for signs of leakage from the new filter.

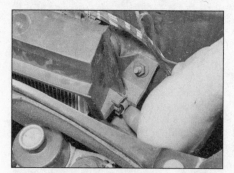

**23.5a Release the clips to lift out pollen filter housing . . .**

**23.5b . . . then withdraw the pollen filter element from its housing**

**24.1 The fuel filter is located on a bracket at the left-hand end of the cylinder head – clamp bolt arrowed**

# Every 30 000 miles or 3 years

## 25 Air filter element renewal

**Caution: Never drive the car with the air cleaner filter element removed. Excessive engine wear could result, and backfiring could even cause a fire under the bonnet.**

**1** The air filter element is located in the air cleaner assembly on the left-hand side of the engine compartment. Release the over-centre wire clips around the cover and at the air mass meter, disconnect the breather hose, and lift up the air cleaner cover **(see illustrations)**.

**2** Lift out the element, noting its direction of fitting, and wipe out the housing **(see illustration)**. Check that no foreign matter is visible, either in the air intake or in the air mass meter.

**3** If carrying out a routine service, the element must be renewed regardless of its apparent condition.

**4** If you are checking the element for any other reason, inspect its lower surface; if it is oily or very dirty, renew the element. If it is only moderately dusty, it can be re-used by blowing it clean from the upper to the lower surface with compressed air. Because it is a pleated-paper type filter, it cannot be washed or re-oiled. If it cannot be cleaned satisfactorily with compressed air, discard and renew it.

 **Warning: Wear eye protection when using compressed air.**

**5** Refitting is the reverse of the removal procedure, noting the following points:
a) Make sure that the filter is fitted the correct way up (observe any direction-of-fitting markings).
b) Ensure that the element and cover are securely seated, so that unfiltered air cannot enter the engine.
c) Secure the cover with all the over-centre wire clips. If the cover was removed, reconnect the cover or hose to the air mass meter.

## 26 Valve clearance check

**Note:** For DIY purposes, note that while checking the valve clearances is an easy operation, changing the shims requires the use of Ford special tools – owners may prefer to have this work carried out by a Ford dealer.

Refer to Chapter 2A.

**25.1a Release the two retaining clips (arrowed) and detach the air mass meter from the air cleaner cover**

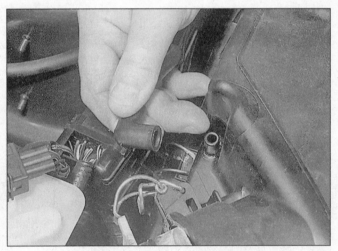

**25.1b Unplug the breather hose from the cover**

**25.1c Release the air cleaner cover retaining clips, and lift the cover to access the air cleaner element**

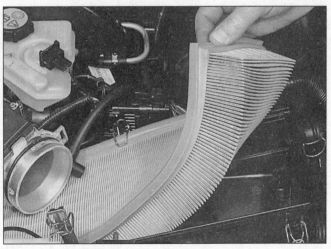

**25.2 Removing the air cleaner element**

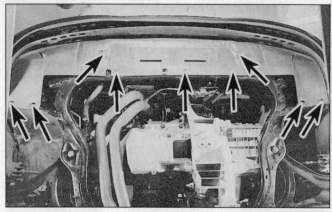

28.3a Remove the screws (arrowed) and withdraw the radiator undershield . . .

28.3b . . . then unscrew the radiator drain plug (arrowed) and empty the cooling system

# Every 3 years (regardless of mileage)

## 27 Brake fluid renewal

The procedure is similar to that for the bleeding of the hydraulic system as described in Chapter 9, except that the brake fluid reservoir should be emptied by syphoning, and allowance should be made for the old fluid to be removed from the circuit when bleeding a section of the circuit.

## 28 Coolant renewal

**Note:** *If the antifreeze used is Ford's own, or of similar quality, Ford state that the coolant need only be renewed every 6 or 10 years, depending on the type of the antifreeze used at the factory. If the car's history is unknown, if antifreeze of lesser quality is known to be in the system, or simply if you prefer to follow conventional servicing intervals, the coolant should be changed periodically (typically, every 3 years) as described here.*

⚠ **Warning: Do not allow antifreeze to come in contact with your skin, or painted surfaces of the car.**

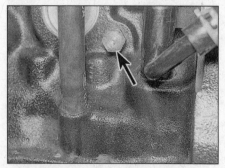

28.4 The engine block coolant drain plug (arrowed) next to dipstick tube

*Flush contaminated areas immediately with plenty of water. Antifreeze is poisonous – do not leave it anywhere it's accessible to children or pets, as they're attracted by its sweet smell. Wipe up spills immediately, and keep antifreeze containers covered. Repair cooling system leaks as soon as they're noticed.*

⚠ *Warning: Never remove the expansion tank filler cap when the engine is running, or has just been switched off, as the cooling system will be hot, and the consequent escaping steam and scalding coolant could cause serious injury.*

### Coolant draining

⚠ *Warning: Wait until the engine is cold before starting this procedure.*

**1** To drain the system, first remove the expansion tank filler cap.

**2** If the additional working clearance is required, raise the front of the car and support it securely on axle stands (see *Jacking and vehicle support*).

**3** Remove the radiator undershield (eight or nine screws), then place a large drain tray underneath, and unscrew the radiator drain plug; direct as much of the escaping coolant as possible into the tray **(see illustrations)**.

**4** To drain the engine completely, unscrew and remove the cylinder block drain plug, located next to the base of the dipstick tube **(see illustration)**. When the engine has finished draining, refit and tighten the block drain plug securely.

### System flushing

**5** With time, the cooling system may gradually lose its efficiency, as the radiator core becomes choked with rust, scale deposits from the water, and other sediment. To minimise this, as well as using only good-quality antifreeze and clean soft water, the system should be flushed as follows whenever any part of it is disturbed, and/or when the coolant is renewed.

**6** With the coolant drained, refit the drain plug and refill the system with fresh water. Refit the expansion tank filler cap, start the engine and warm it up to normal operating temperature, then stop it and (after allowing it to cool down completely) drain the system again. Repeat as necessary until only clean water can be seen to emerge, then refill finally with the specified coolant mixture.

**7** If only clean, soft water and good-quality antifreeze (even if not to Ford's specification) has been used, and the coolant has been renewed at the suggested intervals, the above procedure will be sufficient to keep clean the system for a considerable length of time. If, however, the system has been neglected, a more thorough operation will be required, as follows.

**8** First drain the coolant, then disconnect the radiator top and bottom hoses. Insert a garden hose into the radiator top hose connection, and allow water to circulate through the radiator until it runs clean from the bottom outlet.

**9** To flush the engine, insert the garden hose into the bottom hose, wrap a piece of rag around the garden hose to seal the connection, and allow water to circulate until it runs clear. Try the effect of repeating this procedure in the top hose, although this may not be effective, since the thermostat will probably close and prevent the flow of water.

**10** In severe cases of contamination, reverse-flushing of the radiator may be necessary. This may be achieved by inserting the garden hose into the bottom outlet, wrapping a piece of rag around the hose to seal the connection, then flushing the radiator until clear water emerges from the top hose outlet.

**11** If the radiator is suspected of being severely choked, remove the radiator (Chapter 3), turn it upside-down, and repeat the procedure described in paragraph 10.

**12** Flushing the heater matrix can be achieved using a similar procedure to that described in paragraph 10, once the heater inlet and outlet hoses have been identified. These two hoses will be of the same diameter, and pass through the engine compartment bulkhead (refer to the heater matrix removal procedure in Chapter 3 for more details).

**13** If, after a reasonable period, the water still does not run clear, the radiator should be flushed with a good proprietary cleaning agent. However, the use of chemical cleaners is not recommended, and should be necessary only as a last resort. Normally, regular renewal of the coolant will prevent excessive contamination of the system.

### Coolant filling

**HAYNES HiNT** *It is rare to ever drain the cooling system completely – a small quantity will remain. If the system has been extensively flushed with clean water, this remaining quantity will in fact be plain water. For this reason, some people will first fill the system with the required quantity of neat antifreeze (half the total system capacity, for a 50% mixture), and then complete the filling process with plain water. This ensures that the resulting coolant (once it has mixed inside the engine) is not 'diluted' by old coolant or water remaining in the system.*

**14** With the cooling system drained and flushed, ensure that all disturbed hose unions are correctly secured, and that the radiator drain plug is securely tightened. Refit the radiator undershield, noting that it is located by three clips at its front edge; tighten the retaining screws securely **(see illustration)**. If it was raised, lower the car to the ground.

**15** Prepare a sufficient quantity of the specified coolant mixture (see below); allow for a surplus, so as to have a reserve supply for topping-up.

**16** Slowly fill the system through the expansion tank. Since the tank is the highest point in the system, all the air in the system should be displaced into the tank by the rising liquid. Slow pouring reduces the possibility of air being trapped and forming airlocks.

**17** Continue filling until the coolant level reaches the expansion tank MAX level line, then cover the filler opening to prevent coolant splashing out.

**18** Start the engine and run it at idle speed, until it has warmed-up to normal operating temperature and the radiator electric cooling fan has cut in; watch the temperature gauge to check for signs of overheating. If the level in the expansion tank drops significantly, top-up to the MAX level line, to minimise the amount of air circulating in the system.

**19** Stop the engine, allow it to cool down *completely* (overnight, if possible), then uncover the expansion tank filler opening and top-up the tank to the MAX level line. Refit the

filler cap, tightening it securely, and wash off any spilt coolant from the engine compartment and bodywork.

**20** After refilling, always check carefully all components of the system (but especially any unions disturbed during draining and flushing) for signs of coolant leaks. Fresh antifreeze has a searching action, which will rapidly expose any weak points in the system.

**21** If, after draining and refilling the system, symptoms of overheating are found which did not occur previously, then the fault is almost certainly due to trapped air at some point in the system, causing an airlock and restricting the flow of coolant; usually, the air is trapped because the system was refilled too quickly. In some cases, airlocks can be released by tapping or squeezing the various hoses. If the problem persists, stop the engine and allow it to cool down completely, before unscrewing the expansion tank filler cap or disconnecting hoses to bleed out the trapped air.

### Antifreeze type and mixture

**22** Ford state that, if the only antifreeze used is the type with which the system was first filled at the factory, it need only be renewed every 6 or 10 years depending on type. The antifreeze used at the factory is to Ford specification ESDM-97B49-A (Motorcraft Super Plus 4, which is blue-green in colour), or on cars built since August 1998 (1999 and later models), specification WSS-M97B44-D (the orange-coloured Motorcraft Super Plus 2000). This is subject to it being used in the recommended concentration, unmixed with any other type of antifreeze or additive, and topped-up when necessary using only that antifreeze mixed 50/50 with clean water. If any other type of antifreeze is added, Ford's renewal interval no longer applies; to restore full protection, the system must be drained and thoroughly reverse-flushed before fresh coolant mixture is poured in.

**23** If the car's history (and therefore the quality of the antifreeze in it) is unknown, owners who wish to follow Ford's recommendations are advised to drain and thoroughly reverse-flush the system, before refilling with fresh coolant mixture. If the appropriate quality of antifreeze is used, the coolant can then be left until Ford's renewal interval.

**24** If any antifreeze other than Ford's is to be used, the coolant must be renewed at regular intervals to provide an equivalent degree of protection; the conventional recommendation is to renew the coolant every three years.

**25** If the antifreeze used is to Ford's specification, the levels of protection it affords are indicated in the Specifications Section of this Chapter. To give the recommended *standard* mixture ratio for this antifreeze, 40% (by volume) of antifreeze must be mixed with 60% of clean, soft water; if you are using any other type of antifreeze, follow its manufacturer's instructions to achieve the correct ratio.

**26** It is best to make up slightly more than

**28.14 Ensure the radiator undershield is located securely in three clips at front edge (arrowed) when refitting**

the system's specified capacity, so that a supply is available for subsequent topping-up. However, note that you are unlikely to fully drain the system at any one time (unless the engine is being completely stripped), and the capacities quoted are therefore slightly academic for routine coolant renewal.

**27** Before adding antifreeze, the cooling system should be completely drained, preferably flushed, and all hoses checked for condition and security. As noted earlier, fresh antifreeze will rapidly find any weaknesses in the system.

**28** After filling with antifreeze, a label should be attached to the expansion tank, stating the type and concentration of antifreeze used, and the date installed. Any subsequent topping-up should be made with the same type and concentration of antifreeze. If topping-up using antifreeze to Ford's specification, note that a 50/50 mixture is permissible, purely for convenience.

*Caution: Do not use engine antifreeze in the windscreen/tailgate washer system, as it will damage the car's paintwork. A screenwash additive should be added to the washer system in its maker's recommended quantities.*

### General cooling system checks

**29** The engine should be cold for the cooling system checks, so perform the following procedure before driving the car, or after it has been shut off for at least three hours.

**30** Remove the expansion tank filler cap (also see Section 29), and clean it thoroughly inside and out with a rag. Also clean the filler neck on the expansion tank. The presence of rust or corrosion in the filler neck indicates that the coolant should be changed. The coolant inside the expansion tank should be relatively clean and transparent. If it is rust-coloured, drain and flush the system, and refill with a fresh coolant mixture.

**31** Carefully check the radiator hoses and heater hoses along their entire length; renew any hose which is cracked, swollen or deteriorated (see Section 8).

**32** Inspect all other cooling system components (joint faces, etc) for leaks. A leak in the cooling system will usually show up as white- or antifreeze-coloured deposits on the area adjoining the leak. Where any problems of this nature are found on system components, renew the component or gasket with reference to Chapter 3.

**33** Clean the front of the radiator with a soft brush to remove all insects, leaves, etc, embedded in the radiator fins. Be careful not to damage the radiator fins, or cut your fingers on them. To do a more thorough job, remove the radiator grille as described in Chapter 11.

### Airlocks

**34** If, after draining and refilling the system, symptoms of overheating are found which did not occur previously, then the fault is almost certainly due to trapped air at some point in the system, causing an airlock and restricting the flow of coolant; usually, the air is trapped because the system was refilled too quickly.

**35** If an airlock is suspected, first try gently squeezing all visible coolant hoses. A coolant hose which is full of air feels quite different to one full of coolant, when squeezed. After refilling the system, most airlocks will clear once the system has cooled, and been topped-up.

**36** While the engine is running at operating temperature, switch on the heater and heater fan, and check for heat output. Provided there is sufficient coolant in the system, any lack of heat output could be due to an airlock in the system.

**37** Airlocks can have more serious effects than simply reducing heater output – a severe airlock could reduce coolant flow around the engine. Check that the radiator top hose is hot when the engine is at operating temperature – a top hose which stays cold could be the result of an airlock (or a non-opening thermostat).

**38** If the problem persists, stop the engine and allow it to cool down **completely**, before unscrewing the radiator and expansion tank caps or loosening the hose clips and squeezing the hoses to bleed out the trapped air. In the worst case, the system will have to be at least partially drained (this time, the coolant can be saved for re-use) and flushed to clear the problem.

# Every 4 years (regardless of mileage)

## 29 Expansion tank pressure cap check

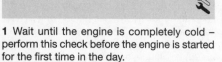

**1** Wait until the engine is completely cold – perform this check before the engine is started for the first time in the day.

**2** Place a wad of cloth over the expansion tank cap, then unscrew it slowly and remove it.

**3** Examine the condition of the rubber seal on the underside of the cap. If the rubber appears to have hardened, or cracks are visible in the seal edges, a new cap should be fitted.

**4** If the car is several years old, or has covered a large mileage, consider renewing the cap regardless of its apparent condition – they are not expensive. If the pressure relief valve built into the cap fails, excess pressure in the system will lead to puzzling failures of hoses and other cooling system components.

# Every 40 000 miles or 5 years

## 30 Timing belt and fuel injection pump drivebelt renewal

Refer to Chapter 2A.

# Chapter 2 Part A:
## Engine in-car repair procedures

## Contents

Section number

| | |
|---|---|
| Auxiliary drivebelt check and renewal . . . . . . . . . . . . . . See Chapter 1 | |
| Auxiliary shaft oil seal – renewal. . . . . . . . . . . . . . . . . . . . . . . . . . . 12 | |
| Braking system vacuum pump – removal and refitting . . See Chapter 9 | |
| Camshaft and tappets – removal, inspection and refitting. . . . . . . . 14 | |
| Camshaft oil seal – renewal . . . . . . . . . . . . . . . . . . . . . . . . . . . . . . 13 | |
| Compression and leakdown tests – description and interpretation. . 3 | |
| Crankshaft oil seals – renewal . . . . . . . . . . . . . . . . . . . . . . . . . . . 21 | |
| Crankshaft pulley – removal and refitting. . . . . . . . . . . . . . . . . . . . . 8 | |
| Cylinder head – dismantling and overhaul . . . . . . . . . . See Chapter 2B | |
| Cylinder head – removal and refitting. . . . . . . . . . . . . . . . . . . . . . . 16 | |
| Cylinder head cover – removal and refitting. . . . . . . . . . . . . . . . . . . 5 | |
| Engine oil and filter change . . . . . . . . . . . . . . . . . . . . .See Chapter 1 | |
| Engine oil level check. . . . . . . . . . . . . . . . . . . . . . . .See Weekly checks | |
| Engine/transmission mountings – inspection and renewal . . . . . . . 23 | |
| Exhaust manifold – removal, inspection and refitting. . . . . . . . . . . . 7 | |

Section number

Flywheel – removal, inspection and refitting . . . . . . . . . . . . . . . . . . 22
General information . . . . . . . . . . . . . . . . . . . . . . . . . . . . . . . . . . . . . 1
Inlet manifold – removal and refitting . . . . . . . . . . . . . . . . . . . . . . . . 6
Oil cooler – removal and refitting . . . . . . . . . . . . . . . . . . . . . . . . . . 19
Oil pressure warning light switch – removal and refitting. . . . . . . . . 20
Oil pump – removal, inspection and refitting . . . . . . . . . . . . . . . . . . 18
Repair operations possible with the engine in the car . . . . . . . . . . . 2
Sump – removal and refitting . . . . . . . . . . . . . . . . . . . . . . . . . . . . . . 17
Timing belt and injection pump drivebelt – removal, refitting and
  adjustment . . . . . . . . . . . . . . . . . . . . . . . . . . . . . . . . . . . . . . . . . 10
Timing belt covers – removal and refitting . . . . . . . . . . . . . . . . . . . . 9
Timing belt/drivebelt tensioners and toothed pulleys – removal and
  refitting . . . . . . . . . . . . . . . . . . . . . . . . . . . . . . . . . . . . . . . . . . . . 11
Top Dead Centre (TDC) for No 1 piston – locating. . . . . . . . . . . . . . 4
Valve clearances – checking and adjustment . . . . . . . . . . . . . . . . . 15

## Degrees of difficulty

| Easy, suitable for novice with little experience | Fairly easy, suitable for beginner with some experience | Fairly difficult, suitable for competent DIY mechanic | Difficult, suitable for experienced DIY mechanic | Very difficult, suitable for expert DIY or professional |
|---|---|---|---|---|

## Specifications

### General

Engine code (type)*
  Pre-facelift models (1993 to October 1996), 1.8 TCI, 65 kW:

| | |
|---|---|
| Without catalytic converter. . . . . . . . . . . . . . . . . . . . . . . . . . . . . . | RFM |
| With catalytic converter . . . . . . . . . . . . . . . . . . . . . . . . . . . . . . . | RFN |
| Facelift models (October 1996 on), Endura-DE (TCI), 66 kW. . . . . . | RFN |
| Capacity . . . . . . . . . . . . . . . . . . . . . . . . . . . . . . . . . . . . . . . . . . . | 1753 cc |
| Bore . . . . . . . . . . . . . . . . . . . . . . . . . . . . . . . . . . . . . . . . . . . . . . | 82.5 mm |
| Stroke. . . . . . . . . . . . . . . . . . . . . . . . . . . . . . . . . . . . . . . . . . . . . | 82 mm |
| Compression ratio . . . . . . . . . . . . . . . . . . . . . . . . . . . . . . . . . . . . | 21.5:1 |
| Compression pressure (at starter motor cranking speed) . . . . . . . . . . | 28 to 34 bar |
| Firing order. . . . . . . . . . . . . . . . . . . . . . . . . . . . . . . . . . . . . . . . . . | 1-3-4-2 (No 1 cylinder at timing belt end) |
| Direction of crankshaft rotation . . . . . . . . . . . . . . . . . . . . . . . . . . . | Clockwise (seen from right-hand side of car) |

* Stamped in box 8 of VIN plate and on left-hand end of cylinder head or block – see Vehicle Identification

### Camshaft

| | |
|---|---|
| Endfloat . . . . . . . . . . . . . . . . . . . . . . . . . . . . . . . . . . . . . . . . . . . . | 0.1 to 0.24 mm |
| Bearing journal diameter: | |
| Pre-facelift models (1993 to October 1996) . . . . . . . . . . . . . . . . . | 27.96 to 27.98 mm |
| Facelift models (October 1996 on) . . . . . . . . . . . . . . . . . . . . . . . | 27.995 to 28.055 mm |
| Bearing running clearance . . . . . . . . . . . . . . . . . . . . . . . . . . . . . . . | 0.016 to 0.075 mm |

### Valve timing

| | |
|---|---|
| Inlet opens . . . . . . . . . . . . . . . . . . . . . . . . . . . . . . . . . . . . . . . . . . | 6° BTDC |
| Inlet closes . . . . . . . . . . . . . . . . . . . . . . . . . . . . . . . . . . . . . . . . . . | 32° ABDC |
| Exhaust opens . . . . . . . . . . . . . . . . . . . . . . . . . . . . . . . . . . . . . . . | 57° BBDC |
| Exhaust closes . . . . . . . . . . . . . . . . . . . . . . . . . . . . . . . . . . . . . . . | 7° ATDC |

### Valve clearances (cold)

| | |
|---|---|
| Inlet. . . . . . . . . . . . . . . . . . . . . . . . . . . . . . . . . . . . . . . . . . . . . . . . | 0.35 ± 0.05 mm |
| Exhaust. . . . . . . . . . . . . . . . . . . . . . . . . . . . . . . . . . . . . . . . . . . . . | 0.50 ± 0.05 mm |
| Tappet shim thicknesses available. . . . . . . . . . . . . . . . . . . . . . . . . . | 3.00 to 4.75 mm, in increments of 0.05 mm |

## Cylinder head gasket thickness

According to piston protrusion of:
| | |
|---|---|
| 0.50 to 0.68 mm | 1.36 mm – 2 tooth marks (standard bore) or holes (oversize) |
| 0.681 to 0.74 mm | 1.42 mm – 3 tooth marks (standard bore) or holes (oversize) |
| 0.741 to 0.84 mm | 1.52 mm – 4 tooth marks (standard bore) or holes (oversize) |

## Cylinder head

Valve tappet bore diameter:
| | |
|---|---|
| Standard | 35.00 to 35.03 mm |
| Oversize | 35.5 to 35.53 mm |

Camshaft bearing bore diameter:
| | |
|---|---|
| Standard | 30.5 to 30.525 mm |
| Oversize | 30.575 to 30.6 mm |

## Lubrication system

| | | |
|---|---|---|
| Oil pressure relief valve setting | 2 to 4 bars | |
| Oil pump inner-to-outer rotor maximum clearance | 0.174 mm | |
| Oil pressure – at oil temperature of 80 °C: | **@ idle speed** | **@ 2000 rpm** |
| Oil pressure switch with black cover – engines up to 7/1998 | 0.75 bar | 1.5 bar |
| Oil pressure switch with green cover – engines from 8/1998 | 0.5 bar | 1.3 bar |

## Torque wrench settings

| | Nm | lbf ft |
|---|---|---|
| Alternator mounting bracket-to-cylinder block bolts | 42 | 31 |
| Auxiliary shaft oil seal housing | 23 | 17 |
| Auxiliary shaft thrustplate bolts | 9 | 7 |
| Auxiliary shaft toothed pulley bolt | 45 | 33 |
| Big-end bearing cap bolts: | | |
| Stage 1 | 25 | 18 |
| Stage 2 (tighten bolt through angle of) | 60° | 60° |
| Stage 3 (further tighten bolt through angle of) | 20° | 20° |
| Camshaft bearing cap nuts | 20 to 23 | 15 to 17 |
| Camshaft toothed pulley fasteners – pre-facelift models: | | |
| Pulley-to-hub bolts | 9 | 7 |
| Pulley hub-to-camshaft centre bolt | 30 | 22 |
| Camshaft toothed pulley-to-camshaft bolt – facelift models: | | |
| 8 mm bolt – engines up to 7/1998 | 35 | 26 |
| 10 mm bolt – engines 7/1998 onwards | 48 | 35 |
| Coolant pipe bracket nut | 27 | 20 |
| Coolant pipe-to-sump bolts | 25 | 18 |
| Crankshaft left-hand oil seal carrier bolts | 20 | 15 |
| Crankshaft pulley-to-toothed pulley flange bolts | 35 | 26 |
| Crankshaft speed/position sensor bracket bolt | 21 | 15 |
| Crankshaft toothed pulley centre bolt: | | |
| Stage 1 | 150 | 111 |
| Stage 2 (slacken bolt through angle of) | 90° | 90° |
| Stage 3 (tighten bolt to) | 120 | 88 |
| Stage 4 (further tighten bolt through angle of) | 60° | 60° |
| Cylinder block oilway blanking plugs | 22 | 16 |
| Cylinder head bolts: | | |
| Stage 1 | 10 | 7 |
| Stage 2 | 100 | 74 |
| Stage 3 (after waiting 3 minutes): | | |
| a) Slacken No 1 bolt through angle of | 180° | 180° |
| b) Tighten No 1 bolt to | 70 | 52 |
| c) Further tighten No 1 bolt through angle of | 120° | 120° |
| Repeat Stage 3 with each of the remaining bolts in sequence | | |
| Cylinder head cover bolts | 5 | 4 |
| Driveshaft support bracket-to-cylinder block bolts | 48 | 35 |
| Earth lead-to-cylinder block retaining bolt | 40 | 30 |
| Engine lifting eye-to-engine mounting/power steering pump bracket bolts | 23 | 17 |
| Engine mounting/power steering pump bracket-to-cylinder block bolts | 47 | 34 |
| Engine oil drain plug | 25 | 18 |
| Engine/transmission front mounting: | | |
| Mounting bracket to transmission | 84 | 62 |
| Mounting-to-subframe bolts/nuts: | | |
| Stage 1 | 10 | 7 |
| Stage 2 | 48 | 35 |
| Mounting through-bolt | 120 | 89 |

## Torque wrench settings (continued)

| | Nm | lbf ft |
|---|---|---|
| Engine/transmission left-hand mounting: | | |
| Bracket-to-transmission nuts | 83 | 61 |
| Mounting through-bolt | Not available | |
| Mounting-to-body bolts | Not available | |
| Engine/transmission rear mounting: | | |
| Mounting bracket-to-transmission: | | |
| 12 mm fasteners | 84 | 62 |
| 10 mm fasteners | 48 | 35 |
| Mounting-to-subframe bolts and nut: | | |
| Stage 1 | 10 | 7 |
| Stage 2 | 48 | 35 |
| Mounting through-bolt | 120 | 89 |
| Engine/transmission right-hand mounting: | | |
| Bracket-to-engine and mounting nuts | 83 to 90 | 61 to 66 |
| Mounting-to-body bolts | 84 | 62 |
| Exhaust downpipe/catalytic converter-to-turbocharger nuts | 40 | 29.5 |
| Exhaust Gas Recirculation (EGR) pipe bolts | 15 | 11 |
| Exhaust manifold nuts and bolts | 24 | 18 |
| Exhaust manifold studs-to-cylinder head | 10 maximum | 7 maximum |
| Flywheel: | | |
| Stage 1 | 18 | 13 |
| Stage 2 (tighten bolt through angle of) | 45° | 45° |
| Stage 3 (further tighten bolt through angle of) | 45° | 45° |
| Front suspension subframe bolts | 130 | 96 |
| Fuel injection pump drivebelt tensioner centre bolt | 45 | 33 |
| Fuel injection pump toothed pulley hub-to-pump shaft nut | Not available | |
| Fuel injection pump toothed pulley-to-hub bolts | 23 | 17 |
| Inlet manifold nuts and bolts | 24 | 18 |
| Inlet manifold studs-to-cylinder head | 10 maximum | 7 maximum |
| Main bearing cap bolts: | | |
| Stage 1 | 27 | 20 |
| Stage 2 (tighten bolt through angle of) | 75° | 75° |
| Oil baffle plate mounting nuts | 20 | 15 |
| Oil cooler mounting bolt | 70 | 52 |
| Oil cooler mounting bracket bolts | 23 to 25 | 17 to 18 |
| Oil dipstick tube bracket mounting bolt | 10 | 7 |
| Oil pressure warning light switch | 20 | 15 |
| Oil pump mounting bolts | 23 | 17 |
| Oil pump pick-up pipe bracket bolts | 22 | 16 |
| Power steering drivebelt tensioner-to-timing belt/drivebelt housing bolt | 23 | 17 |
| Power steering line-to-body bracket bolts | 10 | 7 |
| Power steering line-to-subframe bolts | 24 | 18 |
| Power steering pump pulley-to-injection pump toothed pulley bolts | 25 | 18 |
| Retaining plate for fuel filter and fuel heater | 20 | 15 |
| Sump bolts | 11 | 8 |
| Timing belt cover bolts | 8 | 6 |
| Timing belt/drivebelt housing fasteners | 24 | 18 |
| Timing belt idler pulley bolt: | | |
| Pre-facelift models (1993 to October 1996) | 45 | 33 |
| Facelift models (October 1996 on) – eccentric idler pulley bolt | 45 | 33 |
| Timing belt inner shield bolt | 24 | 18 |
| Timing belt tensioner backplate bolts | 9 | 7 |
| Timing belt tensioner centre bolt | 50 | 37 |
| Timing pin blanking plug | 24 | 18 |
| Transmission-to-engine mounting bolts | 40 | 30 |
| Turbocharger: | | |
| Oil feed line banjo union bolts | 18 | 13 |
| Oil feed line mounting bracket bolt | 23 | 17 |
| Oil return hose clamp | 5 | 4 |
| Turbocharger mounting bracket-to-cylinder block bolt | 47 | 35 |
| Turbocharger mounting bracket-to-turbocharger bolts | 23 | 17 |
| Turbocharger-to-exhaust manifold mounting nuts – early models | 38 | 28 |
| Wiring loom bracket-to-lifting eye bolt | 23 | 17 |

## 1 General information

### How to use this Chapter

This Part of Chapter 2 is devoted to repair procedures possible while the engine is still in the car, and includes only the specifications relevant to those procedures. Since these procedures are based on the assumption that the engine is installed in the car, if the engine has been removed from the car and mounted on a stand, some of the preliminary dismantling steps outlined will not apply.

Information concerning engine/transmission removal and refitting and engine overhaul, can be found in Part B of this Chapter, which also includes the Specifications relevant to those procedures.

### General description

#### Engine

While two different generations of diesel engines have been fitted to the Mondeo, most differences lie essentially in the specification of the engine management system components, updated to keep pace with the introduction of ever-stricter anti-pollution legislation. The engines fitted to early models were known by Ford's internal code name of 1.8 TCI (TurboCharged Intercooled), which changed to Endura-DE (TCI) – this change of designation does not indicate any significant mechanical changes, apart from modified timing belt tensioner components. The Endura-DE (TCI) units, introduced with the facelift in October 1996, can be identified by their manifolds – the exhaust manifold incorporates the (previously separate) turbocharger, while the intake manifold incorporates the (previously separate) Exhaust Gas Recirculation (EGR) valve.

The engine is of four-cylinder, in-line type, mounted transversely at the front of the car, with the clutch and transmission on its left-hand end. It is a four-stroke compression-ignition (diesel) unit, with conventional indirect injection using pintle-type injectors spraying fuel into separate swirl chambers fitted into the cylinder head, its power output being boosted by the fitment of a turbocharger and an intercooler. Both the cylinder block and the cylinder head are of cast iron, while the sump is of cast aluminium alloy.

Two toothed drivebelts are fitted, the inboard one to drive the fuel injection pump (and the power steering pump) and the outboard one (the timing belt) to drive the single overhead camshaft, the (oil pump) auxiliary shaft and the water pump. The valves are operated by bucket tappets. Valve clearance adjustment is by means of a shim located in a recess in the top of each tappet. The cam lobes bear directly on the shims and tappets, which in turn bear directly on the

valves. The inlet and exhaust valves are each closed by coil springs; they operate in guides which are shrink-fitted into the cylinder head, as are the valve seat inserts. The camshaft runs in five renewable shell bearings and drives the braking system vacuum pump via a pushrod operated by an eccentric on the camshaft's left-hand end.

The crankshaft runs in five main bearings, the centre main bearing's upper half incorporating thrustwashers to control crankshaft endfloat. The connecting rods rotate on horizontally-split bearing shells at their big-ends. The pistons are attached to the connecting rods by gudgeon pins which are fully-floating in the connecting rod small-end eyes and are retained by circlips. The aluminium alloy pistons are fitted with three piston rings: two compression rings and an oil control ring. Pistons, gudgeon pins and connecting rods are carefully selected to be of matching weight. The connecting rods are also graded by length. After manufacture, the cylinder bores and piston skirts are measured and classified into four grades, which must be carefully matched together to ensure the correct piston/cylinder clearance; two oversizes are available to permit reboring.

The water pump is bolted to the right-hand end of the cylinder block, inboard of the timing belt, and is driven with the (oil pump) auxiliary shaft and camshaft by the timing belt.

The crankshaft toothed pulley incorporates a flange for the crankshaft pulley which drives the alternator and air conditioning compressor, each via its own auxiliary drivebelt. The fuel injection pump toothed pulley incorporates mounting points for the pulley which drives the power steering pump, again via its own auxiliary drivebelt. All three auxiliary drivebelts are of the flat 'polyvee' type.

When working on this engine, note that Torx-type (both male and female heads) and hexagon socket (Allen head) fasteners are widely used; a good selection of bits, with the necessary adapters, will be required, so that these can be unscrewed without damage and, on reassembly, tightened to the torque wrench settings specified.

#### Lubrication system

The oil pump is mounted externally, at the rear of the engine, and is driven by the auxiliary shaft. The pump is an eccentric-rotor trochoidal type which draws oil through a strainer located in the sump and forces it through an externally-mounted full-flow cartridge-type filter – an oil cooler is fitted to the oil filter mounting, so that clean oil entering the engine's galleries is cooled by the main engine cooling system. From the filter, the oil is pumped into a main gallery in the cylinder block/crankcase, from where it is distributed to the crankshaft (main bearings) and cylinder head. A separate supply serves the turbocharger through an external line.

The big-end bearings are supplied with oil via internal drillings in the crankshaft.

Each piston crown is cooled by a spray of oil directed at its underside by a jet. These jets are fed by passages off the crankshaft oil supply galleries.

While the crankshaft and camshaft bearings and the tappets receive a pressurised supply, the camshaft lobes and valves are lubricated by splash, as are all other engine components.

### Valve clearances

It is necessary for a clearance to exist between the tip of each valve stem and the valve operating mechanism, to allow for the expansion of the various components as the engine reaches normal operating temperature. These engines are fitted with conventional tappets and shims. These require that the clearances be checked at regular intervals (see Chapter 1) and may need the shims to be changed to compensate for wear, as described in Section 15 of this Chapter.

## 2 Repair operations possible with the engine in the car

The following major repair operations can be accomplished without removing the engine from the car. However, owners should note that any operation involving the removal of the sump requires careful forethought, depending on the level of skill and the tools and facilities available – refer to the relevant text for details.

a) Compression pressure – testing.
b) Cylinder head cover – removal and refitting.
c) Timing belt covers – removal and refitting.
d) Timing belt and injection pump drivebelt – renewal.
e) Timing belt/drivebelt tensioners and toothed pulleys – removal and refitting.
f) Camshaft oil seal – renewal.
g) Camshaft and tappets – removal and refitting.
h) Auxiliary shaft oil seal – renewal.
i) Cylinder head – removal, overhaul and refitting.
j) Cylinder head and pistons – decarbonising.
k) Sump – removal and refitting.
l) Crankshaft oil seals – renewal.
m) Oil pump – removal and refitting.
n) Piston/connecting rod assemblies – removal and refitting (but see note below).
o) Flywheel – removal and refitting.
p) Engine/transmission mountings – removal and refitting.

Clean the engine compartment and the exterior of the engine with some type of degreaser before any work is done. It will make the job easier, and will help to keep dirt out of the internal areas of the engine.

Depending on the components involved, it may be helpful to remove the bonnet, to improve access to the engine as repairs are performed (refer to Chapter 11 if necessary).

Cover the wings to prevent damage to the paint; special covers are available, but an old bedspread or blanket will also work.

If vacuum, exhaust, oil or coolant leaks develop, indicating a need for component/ gasket or seal renewal, the repairs can generally be made with the engine in the car. The intake and exhaust manifold gaskets, sump gasket, crankshaft oil seals and cylinder head gasket are all accessible with the engine in place.

Exterior components such as the intake and exhaust manifolds, the sump, the oil pump, the water pump, the starter motor, the alternator and the fuel system components can be removed for repair with the engine in place.

Since the cylinder head can be removed without lifting out the engine, camshaft and valve component servicing can also be accomplished with the engine in the car, as can renewal of the timing belt and toothed pulleys.

In extreme cases caused by a lack of necessary equipment, repair or renewal of piston rings, pistons, connecting rods and big-end bearings is possible with the engine in the car. However, this practice is not recommended, because of the cleaning and preparation work that must be done to the components involved and because of the amount of preliminary dismantling work required – these operations are therefore covered in Part B of this Chapter.

### 3  Compression and leakdown tests – description and interpretation

## Compression test

**Note:** *A compression tester specifically designed for diesel engines must be used for this test.*

1 When engine performance is down, or if misfiring occurs which cannot be attributed to a fault in the fuel system, a compression test can provide diagnostic clues as to the engine's condition. If the test is performed regularly it can give warning of trouble before any other symptoms become apparent.

2 A compression tester specifically intended for diesel engines must be used, because of the higher pressures involved. The tester is connected to an adapter which screws into the glow plug or injector hole. It is unlikely to be worthwhile buying such a tester for occasional use, but it may be possible to borrow or hire one – if not, have the test performed by a garage.

3 Unless specific instructions to the contrary are supplied with the tester, observe the following points:

a) *The battery must be in a good state of charge, the air filter must be clean and the engine should be at normal operating temperature.*

b) *All the injectors, or all the glow plugs, should be removed before starting the test. If removing the injectors, also remove the fire seal washers (which must be renewed when the injectors are refitted – see Chapter 4A), otherwise they may be blown out.*

c) *It is advisable to disconnect the stop solenoid on the pump, to reduce the amount of fuel discharged as the engine is cranked.*

4 There is no need to hold the accelerator pedal down during the test because a diesel engine's air inlet is not throttled.

5 The actual compression pressures measured are not as important as the balance between cylinders. All cylinders should produce very similar pressures; any difference greater than 10% indicates the existence of a fault.

6 The cause of poor compression is less easy to establish on a diesel engine than on a petrol one. The effect of introducing oil into the cylinders ('wet' testing) is not conclusive, because there is a risk that the oil will sit in the swirl chamber or in the recess on the piston crown instead of passing to the rings. However, the following can be used as a rough guide to diagnosis:

7 The compression should build-up quickly in a healthy engine; low compression on the first stroke, followed by gradually increasing pressure on successive strokes, indicates worn piston rings. A low compression reading on the first stroke, which does not build-up during successive strokes, indicates leaking valves or a blown head gasket (a cracked head could also be the cause). Deposits on the undersides of the valve heads can also cause low compression.

8 A low reading from two adjacent cylinders is almost certainly due to the head gasket having blown between them; the presence of coolant in the engine oil will confirm this.

9 If one cylinder is about 20 percent lower than the others and the engine has a slightly rough idle, a worn camshaft lobe could be the cause.

10 If the compression is unusually high, the combustion chambers are probably coated with carbon deposits. If this is the case, the cylinder head should be removed and decarbonised.

## Leakdown test

11 A leakdown test measures the rate at which compressed air is lost that has been fed into the cylinder. It is an alternative to a compression test and in many ways it is better, since the escaping air provides easy identification of where pressure loss is occurring (piston rings, valves or head gasket).

12 The equipment needed for leakdown testing is unlikely to be available to the home mechanic. If poor compression is suspected, have the test performed by a suitably-equipped garage.

### 4  Top Dead Centre (TDC) for No 1 piston – locating

## General

1 Top Dead Centre (TDC) is the highest point in its travel up-and-down its cylinder bore that each piston reaches as the crankshaft rotates. While each piston reaches TDC both at the top of the compression stroke and again at the top of the exhaust stroke, for the purpose of timing the engine, TDC refers to the No 1 piston position at the top of its compression stroke.

2 No 1 piston and cylinder are at the right-hand (timing belt) end of the engine (right- and left-hand are always quoted as seen from the driver's seat). Note that the crankshaft rotates clockwise when viewed from the right-hand side of the car. Proceed as follows:

3 It is useful for several servicing procedures to be able to position the engine at TDC.

## Locating TDC

**Note:** *A timing pin and, on engines with a timing belt automatic tensioner, a camshaft aligning tool are required for this procedure (see text).*

4 Disconnect the battery negative (earth) lead (refer to Chapter 5) unless the starter motor is to be used to turn the engine.

5 Apply the handbrake, then jack up the front of the car and support it on axle stands (see *Jacking and vehicle support*). If the engine is to be turned using the right-hand front roadwheel with top gear engaged, it is only necessary to raise the right-hand front roadwheel off the ground.

6 Where necessary, remove the engine undershield, then remove the wheel arch liner for access to the crankshaft pulley and bolt.

7 Remove the glow plugs as described in Chapter 5. This will enable the engine to be turned easily. It is best to rotate the crankshaft using a spanner applied to the crankshaft pulley bolt; however, it is possible also to use the starter motor (switched on either by an assistant using the ignition key, or by using a remote starter switch) to bring the engine close to TDC, then finish with a spanner. If the starter is used, be sure to disconnect the battery leads immediately it is no longer required.

## Pre-facelift models

**Note:** *Engines fitted to early models (1993 to October 1996) can be identified by removing the timing belt outer cover (see Section 9). The camshaft toothed pulley is secured to its hub by four small bolts; the hub being secured to the camshaft itself by a large centre bolt – as shown in illustration 4.15. The timing belt mechanical tensioner itself is fitted with an external coil spring.*

8 Remove the timing belt outer cover as described in Section 9.

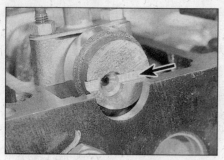

**4.12 Offset slot (arrowed) in camshaft left-hand end – note larger segment uppermost**

**4.13a Remove the blanking plug from the cylinder block . . .**

**4.13b . . . and screw in . . .**

**4.13c . . . a crankshaft timing pin (arrowed)**

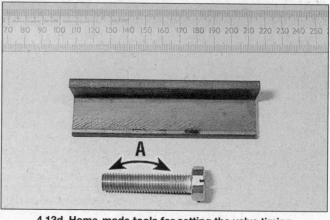

**4.13d Home-made tools for setting the valve timing**

*A Head of bolt and area indicated will need grinding to allow the timing pin to be inserted*

**9** The piston of No 1 cylinder must now be positioned just before top dead centre (TDC). To do this, have an assistant turn the crankshaft until the timing hole in the camshaft toothed pulley is aligned with the corresponding hole in the cylinder head and the slot in the injection pump toothed pulley is in the 11 o'clock position. Turn the crankshaft slightly anti-clockwise from this position (viewed from the right-hand end of the engine).

### Facelift models

**Note:** *In addition to the points noted in Section 1 of this Chapter, the engines fitted to later models (1997 on) can be identified*

**4.15 Timing 'pin' inserted through the camshaft toothed pulley**

*by removing the timing belt outer cover (see Section 9). The camshaft toothed pulley has five spokes, and is secured to the camshaft by a single bolt – as shown in illustration 10.44. The timing belt automatic tensioner no longer has an external coil spring.*

**10** Disconnect the crankcase breather hoses. Plug the rear hose's opening with clean rag to prevent dirt or other objects falling into the turbocharger.

**11** Unbolt the cylinder head cover and remove the gasket.

**12** The piston of No 1 cylinder must now be positioned just before top dead centre (TDC). To do this, have an assistant turn the crankshaft until the slot in the left-hand end of the camshaft is parallel with the upper surface of the cylinder head. Note that the slot is slightly offset so make sure that the larger semi-circular segment is uppermost. Turn the crankshaft slightly anti-clockwise from this position (viewed from the right-hand end of the engine) **(see illustration)**.

### All engines

**13** Unscrew the blanking plug from the right-hand side front of the engine cylinder block. A timing pin (Ford service tool 21-104 – now 303-193), obtainable from Ford dealers or a tool supplier) must now be inserted and tightened into the hole. If necessary,

a home-made pin can be made from an M10 bolt cut to a length of 47.5 mm from beneath its head to the tip; however it will be necessary to grind and slot the head to allow it to be inserted. If difficulty is experienced in using this modified bolt as a timing pin when inserted, it will be necessary to grind the first 36 mm of the threaded length down to a diameter of 6 mm **(see illustrations)**.

**14** With the timing pin in position, turn the crankshaft slowly clockwise until the specially machined surface on the crank web just touches the timing pin. No 1 piston is now at TDC on its compression stroke.

**15** On pre-facelift engines – with a timing belt mechanical tensioner – it should now be possible to insert a timing pin (Ford service tool 23-019 – now 310-018) through the camshaft toothed pulley timing hole and into the cylinder head hole. If the Ford special tool is not available, a drill bit 6 mm in diameter will serve as an adequate substitute **(see illustration)**. **Note:** *The camshaft aligning tool described below is equally applicable to these earlier engines, but will of course require the removal of the cylinder head cover to establish TDC.*

**16** On facelift engines – with a timing belt automatic tensioner – obtain Ford service tool 21-162B (now 303-376), or fabricate a substitute from a strip of metal 5 mm thick

4.16 Home-made camshaft aligning tool inserted in the offset slot

4.17 Timing 'pin' inserted through the injection pump toothed pulley

(while the strip's thickness is critical, its length and width are not, but should be approximately 180 to 230 mm by 20 to 30 mm). The tool should slip snugly into the slot while resting on the cylinder head mating surface (see illustration).

17 On all engines, remove the timing belt covers (see Section 9) and insert Ford timing pin 23-019/310-018 (or 6 mm drill bit) through the injection pump toothed pulley timing hole, down the slot in the pulley hub and into the hole in the pump body (see illustration).

18 If any of the timing pins cannot be fitted, reset the valve timing as described in Section 10.

19 Once work is complete, remove the timing pins and (where applicable) the camshaft aligning tool, then refit the blanking plug, tightening it to its specified torque wrench setting (see illustration). Refit all removed components referring to the relevant Chapters.

Caution: NEVER use a timing pin (or the camshaft aligning tool) as a means of locking the crankshaft (or camshaft) – they are not strong enough for this, and will shear off. Always ensure that all timing pins are removed before the crankshaft pulley bolt (or similar fasteners) is slackened or tightened.

## 5 Cylinder head cover – removal and refitting

### Removal

1 To improve access, remove the air cleaner cover as described in Chapter 1.

2 Disconnect the two crankcase breather hoses from the left-hand end of the cylinder head cover (see illustration). Plug the rear hose's opening with clean rag to prevent dirt or other objects falling into the turbocharger.

3 Unscrew the mounting bolts and withdraw the cylinder head cover (see illustration). Check the gasket and renew it if necessary.

4 Check that the sealing faces are undamaged and that the rubber seal at each retaining bolt is serviceable; renew any worn or damaged seals.

### Refitting

5 On refitting, clean the cover and cylinder head gasket faces carefully, then fit the gasket to the cover, ensuring that it locates correctly in the cover grooves (see illustration).

6 Refit the cover to the cylinder head, then insert the rubber seal at each bolt location – apply a thin smear of engine oil to each seal and to the gasket to help it seat. Start all bolts

4.19 Refit the blanking plug to the timing pin hole in the block

finger-tight, ensuring that the gasket remains seated in its groove.

7 Tighten the cover bolts evenly to the specified torque wrench setting.

8 Reconnect the crankcase breather hoses, then refit any other components removed for access.

## 6 Inlet manifold – removal and refitting

### Removal

1 Remove the intercooler (see Chapter 4A) –

5.2 Removing a crankcase breather hose from the cylinder head cover

5.3 Removing the cylinder head cover

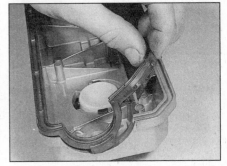

5.5 Check that the gasket locates in the cover grooves

**7.1 Removing the air mass meter and air inlet duct**

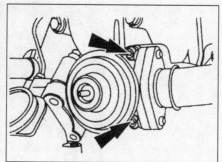

**7.4 If necessary, unbolt the EGR valve and pipe**

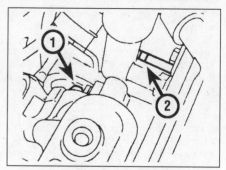

**7.6 Disconnect the turbocharger oil feed line (1) and vacuum pipe (2)**

unbolt and remove completely the intercooler mounting brackets and the intercooler/inlet manifold ducting. Pack the turbocharger opening with clean rag to prevent dirt or other objects falling in.

2 Disconnect the Exhaust Gas Recirculation (EGR) pipe to separate the inlet manifold from the exhaust manifold. On early models, either unscrew the two bolts securing the pipe to the valve and withdraw the pipe with the inlet manifold, or unscrew the three bolts to separate the pipe from the inlet manifold. On later models, unscrew the two bolts securing the pipe to the exhaust manifold and withdraw the pipe with the inlet manifold; disconnect the vacuum hose from the EGR valve.

3 Unscrew the bolts and nuts securing the manifold to the cylinder head and withdraw it. Take care not to damage vulnerable components such as the EGR pipe and valve as the manifold assembly is manoeuvred out of the engine compartment.

### Refitting

4 Refitting is the reverse of the removal procedure, noting the following points:

a) When using a scraper and solvent to remove all traces of old gasket material and sealant from the manifold and cylinder head, be careful to ensure that you do not scratch or damage the material of either; while the cylinder head is of cast iron, the manifold is of aluminium alloy and requires care.

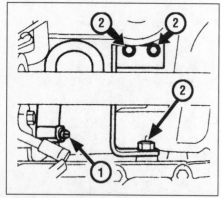

**7.7 Turbocharger oil return hose (1) and mounting bracket bolts (2)**

b) If the gasket was leaking, have the mating surfaces checked for warpage at an automotive machine shop. While it may be possible to have the cylinder head gasket surface skimmed if necessary, to remove any distortion, the manifold must be renewed if it is found to be warped, cracked – check with special care around the mounting points for components such as the EGR pipe – or otherwise faulty.

c) Provided the relevant mating surfaces are clean and flat, a new gasket will be sufficient to ensure the joint is gas-tight. **Do not** use any kind of silicone-based sealant on any part of the fuel system or inlet manifold.

d) Fit a new gasket, then locate the manifold on the head and install the nuts and bolts.

e) Tighten the nuts/bolts in three or four equal steps to the torque listed in this Chapter's Specifications. Work from the centre outwards, to avoid warping the manifold.

### 7 Exhaust manifold – removal, inspection and refitting

⚠️ **Warning: The engine must be completely cool before beginning this procedure.**

**Note:** For all engines, this procedure incorporates the removal and refitting of the turbocharger. On pre-facelift models (1993 to October 1996), the turbocharger can be separated from the manifold once the assembly has been removed from the engine. On facelift models (October 1996 and later), the turbocharger is an integral part of the manifold.

**Note:** In addition to the new gaskets and any other parts, tools or facilities needed to carry out this operation, a new plastic guide sleeve will be required on reassembly.

### Pre-facelift models – separate turbocharger

#### Removal

1 Remove the intercooler (see Chapter 4A) – unbolt and remove completely the intercooler mounting brackets and the intercooler/inlet

manifold ducting. To improve access, remove the air cleaner, air inlet duct and air mass meter as described in Chapter 4A **(see illustration)**. Pack the turbocharger opening with clean rag to prevent dirt or other objects falling in.

2 Disconnect the crankcase breather hose from the rear left-hand end of the cylinder head cover. Plug the hose opening with clean rag to prevent dirt or other objects falling into the turbocharger.

3 Disconnect the vacuum hose from the exhaust gas recirculation (EGR) valve.

4 Disconnect the EGR pipe to separate the exhaust manifold from the inlet manifold. Either unscrew the three bolts securing the pipe to the inlet manifold and withdraw the pipe (and valve) with the exhaust manifold, or unbolt the pipe and valve as an assembly from both manifolds **(see illustration)**.

5 Disconnect the turbocharger wastegate vacuum pipe.

6 Unscrew the banjo bolt securing the oil feed line to the turbocharger. Collect the copper washer on each side of the union – these must be renewed as a matter of course whenever they are disturbed **(see illustration)**.

7 Slacken the hose clip securing the oil return hose and disconnect the hose from the return pipe on the turbocharger **(see illustration)**.

8 Unscrew the bolt(s) securing the turbocharger mounting bracket to the turbocharger or to the cylinder block/crankcase.

9 Unscrew the nuts to disconnect the exhaust system front downpipe from the turbocharger (see the relevant Part of Chapter 4).

10 Unscrew the bolts and nuts securing the exhaust manifold to the cylinder head and withdraw it. Take care not to damage vulnerable components such as the EGR pipe and valve as the manifold/turbocharger assembly is manoeuvred out of the engine compartment **(see illustration)**.

11 Unscrew the three nuts to separate the turbocharger from the exhaust manifold. Discard the gasket – this must be renewed on reassembly.

### Inspection

**Note:** Due to the Positive Crankcase Ventilation system being routed through the turbocharger, it is quite normal to see small deposits of oil in the compressor. The turbocharger oil seals will normally only fail if its bearings are badly worn.

**12** Use a scraper to remove all traces of old gasket material and carbon deposits from the manifold and cylinder head mating surfaces. If the gasket was leaking, have the manifold checked for warpage at an automotive machine shop and have it resurfaced if necessary.

*Caution: When scraping, be very careful not to gouge or scratch the delicate aluminium alloy manifold casting.*

**13** Provided both mating surfaces are clean and flat, a new gasket will be sufficient to ensure the joint is gas-tight. Do not use any kind of exhaust sealant upstream of the catalytic converter.

**14** On early models, note that the downpipe is secured to the manifold by two bolts, with a coil spring, spring seat and self-locking nut on each. On refitting, tighten the nuts until they stop on the bolt shoulders; the pressure of the springs will then suffice to make a leakproof joint.

**15** Do not overtighten the nuts to cure a leak – the bolts will shear; renew the gasket and the springs if a leak is found. The bolts themselves are secured by spring clips to the manifold and can be renewed easily if damaged.

### Refitting

**16** Refitting is the reverse of the removal procedure, noting the following points:

a) Fit a new gasket to the exhaust manifold and refit the turbocharger, tightening its mounting nuts to the specified torque wrench setting.

b) Position a new gasket over the cylinder head studs and fit a new plastic guide sleeve to the stud nearest to the timing belt, so that the manifold will be correctly located. **Do not** refit the manifold without this sleeve.

c) Refit the manifold and finger-tighten the mounting bolts and nuts.

d) Working from the centre out and in three or four equal steps, tighten the bolts and nuts to the specified torque wrench setting.

e) Refit the remaining parts in the reverse order of removal. Tighten all fasteners to the specified torque wrench settings.

f) Fit new copper washers to the turbocharger oil feed line banjo union and tighten the bolt to the specified torque wrench setting.

g) Run the engine and check for exhaust leaks.

### *Facelift models – integral turbocharger*

#### Removal

**17** Remove the intercooler (see Chapter 4A) – unbolt and remove completely the intercooler mounting brackets and the intercooler/inlet manifold ducting. To improve access, remove the air cleaner, air inlet duct and air mass meter as described in Chapter 4A. Pack

the turbocharger opening with clean rag to prevent dirt or other objects falling in.

**18** Disconnect the crankcase breather hose from the rear left-hand end of the cylinder head cover. Plug the hose opening with clean rag to prevent dirt or other objects falling into the turbocharger.

**19** Disconnect the vacuum hose from the Exhaust Gas Recirculation (EGR) valve.

**20** Unbolt the EGR pipe from the exhaust manifold and from the inlet manifold.

**21** Disconnect the turbocharger wastegate vacuum pipe.

**22** Unscrew the banjo bolt securing the oil feed line to the turbocharger. Collect the

copper washer on each side of the union – these must be renewed as a matter of course whenever they are disturbed.

**23** Slacken the hose clip securing the oil return hose and disconnect the hose from the return pipe on the turbocharger.

**24** Unscrew the nuts to disconnect the catalytic converter from the turbocharger (see Chapter 4B).

**25** Unscrew the bolts and nuts securing the exhaust manifold to the cylinder head and withdraw it. Take care not to damage vulnerable components as the manifold/ turbocharger assembly is manoeuvred out of the engine compartment.

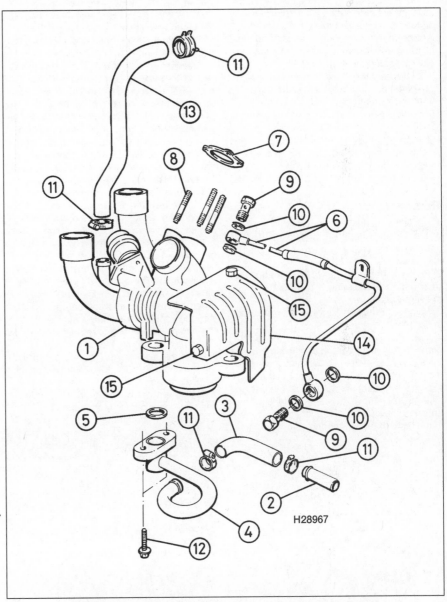

**7.10 Turbocharger and associated components – early models**

| | | | |
|---|---|---|---|
| 1 Turbocharger | 5 O-ring | 9 Banjo bolt | 13 Crankcase |
| 2 Oil return stub | 6 Oil feed line | 10 Copper washer | breather hose |
| 3 Oil return hose | 7 Gasket | 11 Clip | 14 Heat shield |
| 4 Oil return pipe | 8 Stud | 12 Bolt | 15 Screw |

### Inspection

**26** Refer to paragraphs 12 to 13 (and Note) above.

### Refitting

**27** Refitting is the reverse of the removal procedure, noting the following points:

a) Position a new gasket over the cylinder head studs and fit a new plastic guide sleeve to the stud nearest to the timing belt, so that the manifold will be correctly located. **Do not refit the manifold without this sleeve.**

b) Refit the manifold and finger-tighten the mounting bolts and nuts.

c) Working from the centre out and in three or four equal steps, tighten the bolts and nuts to the specified torque wrench setting.

d) Refit the remaining parts in the reverse order of removal. Tighten all fasteners to the specified torque wrench settings.

e) Fit new copper washers to the turbocharger oil feed line banjo union and tighten the bolt to the specified torque wrench setting.

f) Run the engine and check for exhaust leaks.

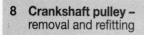

## 8 Crankshaft pulley – removal and refitting

### Removal

**1** Apply the handbrake, then jack up the front of the car and support it on axle stands (see *Jacking and vehicle support*). Remove the engine undershield if fitted.

**2** Remove the right-hand front roadwheel, then undo the retaining screws and remove the wheel arch liner.

**3** Remove the auxiliary drivebelts as described in Chapter 1.

**4** Unscrew the bolts and remove the crankshaft pulley from the crankshaft toothed pulley. To hold the crankshaft stationary while loosening the bolts, have an assistant engage top gear and depress the footbrake pedal, or alternatively remove the starter motor and have an assistant insert a wide-bladed screwdriver in the teeth of the starter ring gear.

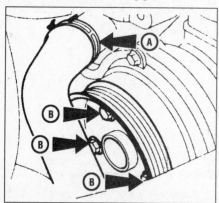

**9.4 If necessary, remove the bottom hose (A) to access the pulley bolts (B)**

### Refitting

**5** Refitting is a reversal of removal, but tighten the mounting bolts to the specified torque.

## 9 Timing belt covers – removal and refitting

### Removal

**1** Apply the handbrake, then jack up the front of the car and support it on axle stands (see *Jacking and vehicle support*). Remove the engine undershield if fitted.

**2** Remove the right-hand front roadwheel, then undo the retaining screws and remove the wheel arch liner.

**3** Unscrew the three bolts retaining the timing belt lower cover.

**4** Referring to Chapter 1 if required, unbolt the power steering pump drivebelt cover and remove the drivebelt, then unbolt the power steering pump drive pulley from the fuel injection pump toothed pulley. Note that it may be necessary to remove the radiator bottom hose for access to the pulley bolts, and to remove the cover – if this is the case, drain the cooling system as described in Chapter 1 **(see illustration)**.

**5** The engine right-hand mounting bracket must now be removed for access to the timing belt covers. First support the weight of the engine using a trolley jack and block of wood beneath the sump. Alternatively, use a support bar across the top of the engine resting in the front wing water drain channels. Note that if a support bar is located over the engine, it must be positioned to allow sufficient room to remove the camshaft toothed pulley. Make sure the engine is adequately supported. With the engine supported, unscrew the four (or five) nuts and remove the bracket.

**6** Unscrew the single retaining bolt and release the three clips, then remove the timing belt outer cover.

**7** With the outer cover removed, the timing belt side cover can be unbolted.

**8** The timing belt inner shield cannot be unbolted from the cylinder head until the timing belt and injection pump drivebelt have been removed and their associated tensioner components, idler pulleys, etc, have been unbolted – see Sections 10 and 11.

### Refitting

**9** Refitting is a reversal of removal, but tighten all fasteners to their specified torque wrench settings.

## 10 Timing belt and injection pump drivebelt – removal, refitting and adjustment

 *Warning: Never re-use or retension a timing belt/injection pump drivebelt. This could lead to*

*the belt becoming over-tensioned, leading to its failure and resulting in serious engine damage.*

### Removal

**1** Disconnect the battery negative (earth) lead (see Chapter 5).

**2** Apply the handbrake, then jack up the front of the car and support it on axle stands (see *Jacking and vehicle support*). Where fitted, remove the engine undershield and radiator lower cover. Remove the right-hand front roadwheel, then undo the retaining screws and remove the wheel arch liner.

**3** Drain the coolant as described in Chapter 1. Refit the coolant drain plug(s) and tighten securely.

**4** Remove the crankshaft pulley as described in Section 8. This includes the removal of the auxiliary drivebelts as described in Chapter 1.

**5** Remove the timing belt outer and side covers as described in Section 9. This includes the removal of the engine right-hand mounting bracket.

**6** Disconnect the radiator bottom hose from the water pump union.

**7** Set piston No 1 to TDC on its compression stroke as described in Section 4. This includes, on later models, the removal of the cylinder head cover to enable the use of the camshaft aligning tool.

**8** Remove the intercooler (see Chapter 4A) – unbolt and remove completely the intercooler mounting brackets and the intercooler/inlet manifold ducting. Pack the turbocharger opening with clean rag to prevent dirt or other objects falling in.

**9** To improve access, unclip the coolant expansion tank hoses and the fuel return pipe from their brackets, then unbolt the coolant expansion tank so that it can be secured to one side, out of the way.

**10** Unbolt the engine right-hand mounting.

### Pre-facelift models – mechanical timing belt tensioner

**11** With piston No 1 at TDC on its compression stroke (crankshaft web firmly in contact with the timing pin), insert a timing pin (see Section 4) through the camshaft toothed pulley and into the special hole in the cylinder head.

**12** Loosen the bolts securing the camshaft toothed pulley to its hub.

**13** Loosen the tensioner centre bolt, then use a pair of water pump pliers or similar to compress the tensioner spring and retighten the tensioner bolt to release the tension from the belt and to hold the tensioner away from the belt.

**14** Remove the timing belt from the crankshaft and camshaft toothed pulleys and from the tensioner and idler pulley.

### Facelift models – automatic timing belt tensioner

**15** With piston No 1 at TDC on its compression stroke (crankshaft web firmly in contact with the timing pin), slacken the eccentric idler pulley's bolt, then turn the eccentric's teardrop anti-clockwise to the 6 o'clock position – ie, the narrow end of the plate should be facing vertically downwards – to release the belt tension.

**16** If necessary, turn the camshaft using water pump pliers until the camshaft aligning tool will fit exactly.

**17** Hold the camshaft toothed pulley stationary using a tool which engages the pulley holes, then loosen the retaining bolt two or three turns.

**18** Insert a screwdriver between the timing belt inner shield and the camshaft toothed pulley, and apply light pressure to the pulley. Insert a soft metal drift through the hole in the inner shield and tap lightly on the pulley to release it from the camshaft taper. Unscrew the pulley bolt.

**19** Remove the timing belt (with the camshaft toothed pulley) from the crankshaft toothed pulley, from the tensioner and from the idler pulley.

### All engines

**20** To remove the injection pump drivebelt, loosen the tensioner bolt, then use a pair of water pump pliers or similar to compress the tensioner spring and retighten the tensioner bolt to release the tension from the belt and to hold the tensioner away from the belt. Remove the belt from the crankshaft and injection pump toothed pulleys and from the tensioner.

### Inspection

**Note:** *On early models, do not interchange the timing belt and injection pump drivebelt tensioner springs. Note their installed direction before removing either spring, and ensure that each is refitted the same way round.*

**21** Clean the toothed pulleys, idler pulley and tensioner pulleys and wipe them dry. **Do not** apply excessive amounts of solvent to the idler pulley and tensioner pulleys otherwise the bearing lubricant may be contaminated. Also clean the timing belt covers and inner shield, the timing belt/drivebelt housing, and the surfaces of the cylinder head and block. If signs of oil or coolant contamination are found, trace the source of the leak and rectify it, then wash down the engine timing belt area and related components, to remove all traces of oil or coolant.

**22** Examine carefully the timing belt/drivebelt for any signs of oil or coolant – the presence of either would indicate a leak, which must be cured before fitting the new belts. A new timing belt and injection pump drivebelt **must** be fitted once the old ones have been removed – **never** refit a used drivebelt of this type. Similarly, check each tensioner spring (where fitted), renewing it if there is any doubt about its condition. Check also the toothed pulleys for signs of wear or damage and ensure that the tensioner and idler pulleys rotate smoothly on their bearings; renew any worn or damaged components. **Note:** *It is considered good practice by many professional mechanics to*

renew tensioner and idler pulley assemblies as a matter of course, whenever the timing belt/ drivebelt is renewed.

### Refitting

***Caution: The engine must be cold, having been switched off for at least 4 hours.***

**23** With piston No 1 at TDC on its compression stroke (crankshaft web firmly in contact with the timing pin), locate the new injection pump drivebelt on the crankshaft and injection pump toothed pulleys so that it is taut between the two pulleys with all slack on the tensioner side, and the directional arrows correct for normal crankshaft rotation. Ensure that the drivebelt is squarely in the centre of the pulleys.

**24** Slacken through half a turn the injection pump toothed pulley bolts and the tensioner bolt – allow the tensioner pulley to snap against the belt. Retighten all the slackened bolts and make sure that the injection pump toothed pulley bolts are centralised in their elongated holes.

### Pre-facelift models – mechanical timing belt tensioner

**25** With piston No 1 at TDC on its compression stroke (crankshaft web firmly in contact with the timing pin), locate the new timing belt on the pulleys so that it is taut between the pulleys with all slack on the tensioner side and the directional arrows correct for normal crankshaft rotation. Fit it first on the crankshaft toothed pulley, then over the auxiliary shaft

toothed pulley and water pump pulley, over the camshaft toothed pulley and idler pulley, then on the tensioner. Ensure that the timing belt is squarely in the centre of all pulleys.

**26** The bolts securing the camshaft toothed pulley to its hub should still be slack, with each in the middle of its elongated hole. Slacken through half a turn the tensioner centre bolt – allow the tensioner to snap against the belt.

**27** Retighten all slackened bolts, and make sure that the toothed pulley bolts are centralised in the elongated holes. Remove all the timing pins and turn the crankshaft through six revolutions in the normal direction of rotation until the slot in the injection pump toothed pulley is again at the 11 o'clock position.

**28** Screw in the crankshaft timing pin as described in Section 4, then slowly turn the crankshaft clockwise until the crankshaft web contacts the timing pin.

**29** Insert the timing pins in the camshaft and the injection pump toothed pulleys.

**30** Slacken the bolts (through half a turn) that secure the camshaft and injection pump toothed pulleys.

**31** Slacken the bolts (through one-quarter of a turn) that secure the belt tensioners.

**32** If all timing pins fit perfectly and the pulley-to-hub bolts are centralised in their elongated holes, retighten all slackened bolts to their specified torque wrench settings. The valve timing is now set correctly **(see illustration)**.

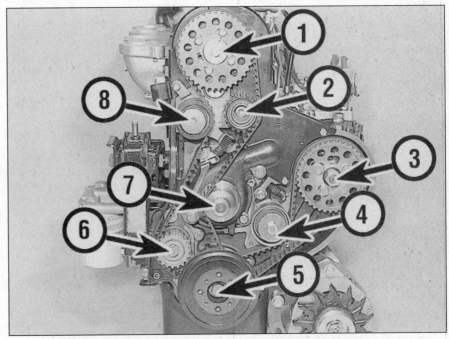

**10.32 Timing belt and injection pump drivebelt components – pre-facelift models**

| | |
|---|---|
| 1  Camshaft toothed pulley | 5  Crankshaft pulley |
| 2  Idler pulley | 6  Auxiliary shaft toothed pulley |
| 3  Injection pump toothed pulley | 7  Coolant pump pulley |
| 4  Injection pump drivebelt tensioner | 8  Timing belt tensioner |

### Facelift models – automatic timing belt tensioner

**33** Make sure that the crankshaft is positioned at TDC with the crankshaft web in contact with the timing pin and the camshaft aligning tool fitted into the camshaft slot.

**34** Apply engine oil to the head contact face of the camshaft toothed pulley bolt. Refit the pulley, screw in the bolt finger-tight then undo it a quarter-turn. Make sure that the pulley is free to turn on the camshaft.

**35** Locate the new timing belt on the pulleys so that it is taut between the pulleys with all slack on the eccentric idler pulley's side, and the directional arrows correct for normal crankshaft rotation. Fit it first on the crankshaft toothed pulley, then over the auxiliary shaft toothed pulley and water pump pulley, over the tensioner pulley and camshaft toothed pulley, then on the idler. Ensure that the timing belt is squarely in the centre of all pulleys.

**36** Unscrew the eccentric idler pulley's bolt and apply engine oil to the head contact face. Screw in the bolt finger-tight, then turn the eccentric idler's teardrop clockwise to the 9 o'clock position to tension the timing belt and tighten the bolt to lock the idler pulley.

**37** Hold the camshaft toothed pulley stationary using a tool which engages the pulley holes, then tighten the retaining bolt.

**38** Remove all timing pins and the camshaft aligning tool and turn the crankshaft through six revolutions in the normal direction of rotation until the slot in the injection pump toothed pulley is again in the 11 o'clock position.

**39** Screw in the timing pin as far as it will go.

**40** Slowly turn the crankshaft clockwise until the crankshaft web contacts the timing pin.

**41** Slacken (through half a turn) the eccentric idler pulley's bolt, then if necessary, turn the camshaft using water pump pliers until the camshaft aligning tool will fit exactly into the camshaft slot.

**42** Hold the camshaft toothed pulley stationary using a tool which engages the pulley holes, then loosen the retaining bolt through three turns.

**43** Insert a screwdriver between the timing belt inner shield and the camshaft toothed pulley and apply light pressure to the pulley. Insert a soft metal drift through the hole in the inner shield and tap lightly on the pulley to release it from the camshaft taper. Tighten the pulley retaining bolt finger-tight then undo it half a turn. Make sure that the pulley is free to turn on the camshaft.

**44** Using an Allen key engaged in the socket on the eccentric's teardrop, turn the teardrop in a clockwise direction to tension the timing belt until the arrow on the tensioner aligns with the right-hand edge of the setting window, then tighten the eccentric idler pulley's bolt to the specified torque wrench setting **(see illustration)**. **Note:** *Turn the eccentric smoothly and make sure that it is finally set between the 6 o'clock (MIN) and 12 o'clock (MAX) positions.*

**45** If the tensioner setting is correct – the arrow on the tensioner aligns with the fixed arrow (at least within the limits of the adjustment range A) – proceed with the next step **(see illustration)**. If the tensioner setting is not correct, repeat the procedure given in paragraph 44.

**46** Hold the camshaft toothed pulley stationary using a tool which engages the pulley holes, then tighten the retaining bolt to its specified torque wrench setting.

**47** Recheck the tensioner setting. If it is correct, proceed with the next step. If the tensioner setting is not correct, repeat the procedure from paragraph 42 onwards.

**48** Remove all timing pins and the camshaft aligning tool and turn the crankshaft through six revolutions in the normal direction of rotation until the slot in the injection pump toothed pulley is again in the 11 o'clock position.

**49** Screw in the timing pin as far as it will go.

**50** Slowly turn the crankshaft clockwise until the crankshaft web contacts the timing pin.

**51** Recheck the tensioner setting. If it is correct, proceed with the next step. If the tensioner setting is not correct, repeat the procedure from paragraph 42 onwards.

**52** Check that the camshaft aligning tool will fit exactly into the camshaft slot. If it is not possible to fit the aligning tool, repeat the procedure from paragraph 42 onwards.

**53** Make a final check of the tensioner setting. If it is correct, proceed with the next step. If the tensioner setting is not correct, repeat the procedure from paragraph 42 onwards.

**54** Remove the timing pin and camshaft aligning tool, then refit the cylinder head cover with a new gasket and tighten the bolts.

**55** Reconnect the crankcase breather hoses.

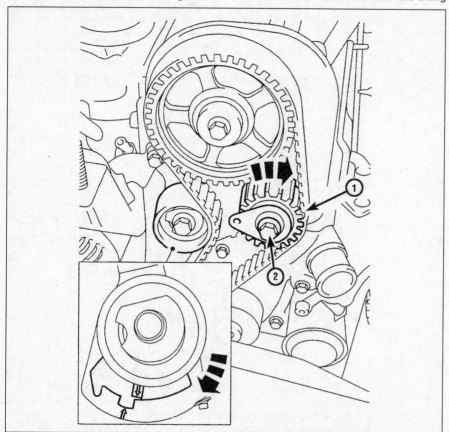

**10.44 Turn the eccentric idler pulley's teardrop (1) until the arrow on the tensioner (inset) is aligned with the right-hand edge of the adjustment range, then tighten the pulley's bolt (2)**

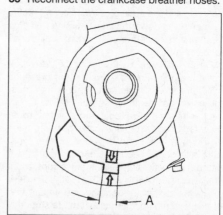

**10.45 The timing belt tension is correct when the arrows align – or in the range A**

**11.3 Removing the crankshaft outboard (timing belt) toothed pulley**

**11.4a Removing the crankshaft inboard (injection pump drivebelt) toothed pulley**

**11.4b Crankshaft inboard toothed pulley, showing O-ring seal (arrowed)**

## All engines

**56** Refit and tighten the timing pin blanking plug.

**57** Refit the timing belt covers with reference to Section 9. Refit and tension the auxiliary drivebelts as described in Chapter 1.

**58** Reconnect the radiator bottom hose to the water pump union.

**59** Refit the engine right-hand mounting bracket.

**60** Refit the coolant expansion tank, then clip the coolant expansion tank hoses and the fuel return pipe into their brackets. Refill the cooling system (see Chapter 1).

**61** Refit the undershield (where applicable), then refit the roadwheel and lower the car to the ground.

**62** Reconnect the battery negative (earth) lead (see Chapter 5).

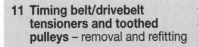

## 11 Timing belt/drivebelt tensioners and toothed pulleys – removal and refitting

**Note:** *A new timing belt and injection pump drivebelt must always be fitted whenever either of them is disturbed.*

### Crankshaft toothed pulleys

**Note:** *On early engines – up to October 1995 – the inboard toothed pulley is located on the crankshaft by a roll-pin fitted in the crankshaft end, while a V-shaped lug on the outboard toothed pulley engages with a notch on the inboard pulley, to positively lock the two pulleys together. On later engines, the roll-pin is fitted to the inboard toothed pulley which engages in holes in both the crankshaft end and in the outboard toothed pulley. Ford state that this revised assembly relies entirely for security and for correct location on the clamping pressure of the crankshaft toothed pulleys' centre bolt.*

### Removal

**1** Remove the timing belt and injection pump drivebelt as described in Section 10. This procedure includes removal of the crankshaft pulley.

**2** Hold the crankshaft stationary using a length of metal bar bolted to the outboard toothed pulley flange, then unscrew the centre bolt.

**Note:** *The bolt is very tight. Discard the bolt – a new one must be obtained for refitting.*

**Caution: NEVER use a timing pin (or the camshaft aligning tool) as a means of locking the crankshaft (or camshaft) – they are not strong enough for this and will shear off. Always ensure that all timing pins are removed before the crankshaft pulleys' bolt (or similar fasteners) is slackened or tightened**

**3** Remove the outboard toothed pulley, using a suitable puller if necessary **(see illustration)**.

**4** Remove the inboard toothed pulley and recover the O-ring from the pulley **(see illustrations)**. To remove the pulley, use the Ford special tool (No 21-200 – now 303-497) which uses an expanding collet to engage the inside diameter of the pulley or a similar tool (if no such tool is available, the timing belt/drivebelt housing must be removed completely so that an ordinary legged puller can be used). Check that the roll-pin is a tight fit in the crankshaft or inboard toothed pulley (as applicable) – if necessary to avoid its loss, remove the roll-pin and store it with the toothed pulleys. Discard the inboard toothed pulley's O-ring – this must be renewed as a matter of course.

### Inspection

**5** Examine the pulleys for wear and damage and renew them if necessary. Wipe clean the inboard toothed pulley oil seal surface and check for grooves or raised areas which might damage the seal lips and cause oil leakage.

**11.12 Unscrewing the camshaft toothed pulley-to-hub retaining bolts – pre-facelift models**

**6** If there is any sign of oil leakage from the crankshaft right-hand oil seal, renew it with reference to Section 21. Note that the support ring on the new oil seal must remain in position until just before the inboard toothed pulley is fitted.

### Refitting

**7** On early engines, make sure that the roll-pin is fitted into the crankshaft. Check that the crankshaft spigot and the bore of the inboard toothed pulley are completely clean and free from traces of oil.

**8** Fit a new O-ring to the inboard toothed pulley groove and lubricate the O-ring with a thin smear of clean engine oil. Remove the oil seal support ring, then slide on the toothed pulley – on early engines ensure that the roll-pin passes through the hole; on later engines ensure that the roll-pin engages the hole in the crankshaft. Press the toothed pulley fully onto the crankshaft.

**9** Fit the outboard toothed pulley onto the inboard toothed pulley making sure that the vee in the outboard pulley engages with the cut-out in the inboard pulley (early engines only) and that the outboard pulley engages correctly with the roll-pin. Lubricate the head of a new bolt with oil (but keep the threads dry), then insert it and tighten it while holding the toothed pulley stationary. Observe the four stages specified and use an angle gauge where required.

**10** Fit the new timing belt and injection pump drivebelt as described in Section 10.

### Camshaft toothed pulley

### Removal

**11** Remove the timing belt as described in Section 10 – there is no need to remove the injection pump drivebelt.

**12** On pre-facelift models – with a mechanical timing belt tensioner – hold the toothed pulley stationary using a tool engaged with the holes in the pulley, then loosen the hub centre bolt and the four pulley-to-hub retaining bolts **(see illustration)**. Remove the toothed pulley from the hub, then extract the hub from the end of the camshaft using a suitable puller. Remove the Woodruff key from the groove in the camshaft.

**13** On facelift models – with an automatic

**11.19 Removing the auxiliary shaft toothed pulley**

timing belt tensioner – hold the toothed pulley stationary using a tool engaged with the holes in the pulley, then loosen through two or three turns the retaining bolt. Insert a screwdriver between the timing belt inner shield and the camshaft toothed pulley and apply light pressure to the pulley. Insert a soft metal drift through the hole in the inner shield and tap lightly on the pulley to release it from the camshaft taper. Fully unscrew the bolt and remove the pulley.

## Inspection

**14** Inspect the toothed pulley for wear and damage and renew it if necessary.

## Refitting

**15** Refit the toothed pulley to the camshaft using a reversal of the removal procedure. On facelift models – with an automatic timing belt tensioner – leave the bolt finger-tight. On pre-facelift models – with a mechanical timing belt tensioner – fully tighten the hub centre bolt, but leave the pulley-to-hub retaining bolts finger-tight and centralised in their elongated holes.

**16** Fit the new timing belt with reference to Section 10.

### Auxiliary shaft toothed pulley

## Removal

**17** Remove the timing belt as described in Section 10 – there is no need to remove the injection pump drivebelt.

**18** Unscrew the timing belt side cover retaining bolt immediately above the auxiliary shaft toothed pulley. The pulley must now be

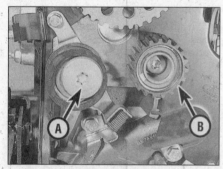

**11.29 Timing belt mechanical tensioner (A) and idler pulley (B)**

held stationary while the bolt is loosened. To do this, wrap the old timing belt around the pulley and clamp it with a pair of water pump pliers, self-locking pliers or similar.

**19** Unscrew the bolt and remove the toothed pulley – note the presence of the locating dowel pin in the end of the auxiliary shaft; if necessary to avoid its loss, remove the dowel pin and store it with the toothed pulley **(see illustration)**.

## Inspection

**20** Inspect the toothed pulley for wear and damage and renew it if necessary.

## Refitting

**21** Refitting is a reversal of removal, but tighten all nuts and bolts to the specified torque – do not forget the timing belt side cover retaining bolt. Fit the new timing belt as described in Section 10.

### Injection pump toothed pulley

## Removal

**22** Remove the timing belt and injection pump drivebelt as described in Section 10.

**23** Hold the toothed pulley stationary using a suitable tool engaged with the pulley holes.

**24** Unscrew the three pulley-to-hub bolts and remove the toothed pulley from its hub.

## Inspection

**25** Inspect the toothed pulley for wear and damage and renew it if necessary.

## Refitting

**26** Locate the toothed pulley on its hub ensuring that each of the pulley-to-hub bolts is in the centre of its slotted hole in the pulley. Leave the pulley-to-hub retaining bolts finger-tight.

**27** Fit the new timing belt/injection pump drivebelt as described in Section 10.

### Mechanical tensioner (timing belt and injection pump drivebelt)

**Note:** *Do not interchange the timing belt and injection pump drivebelt tensioner springs. Note their installed direction before removing either spring, and ensure that each is refitted the same way round.*

## Removal

**28** Remove the timing belt/injection pump drivebelt as described in Section 10.

**29** Unscrew the bolts and remove the tensioner and tension spring **(see illustration)**.

## Inspection

**Note:** *It is considered good practice by many professional mechanics to renew tensioner assemblies as a matter of course, whenever the timing belt/injection pump drivebelt is renewed.*

**30** Spin the tensioner pulley by hand and check for roughness and resistance. If evident, renew the tensioner. Similarly, check the tensioner spring, renewing it if there is any doubt about its condition. Check the tensioner components for wear and damage and renew

as necessary if there is the slightest doubt about their condition.

## Refitting

**31** Clean the tensioner pulley and wipe it dry. **Do not** apply excessive amounts of solvent to the pulley otherwise the bearing lubricant may be contaminated. Also clean the timing belt covers and inner shield, the timing belt/drivebelt housing, and the surfaces of the cylinder head and block.

**32** Refit the tensioner and spring and tighten the mounting bolt to the specified torque.

**33** Fit the new timing belt/injection pump drivebelt as described in Section 10.

### Automatic tensioner (timing belt)

## Removal

**34** Remove the timing belt as described in Section 10 – there is no need to remove the injection pump drivebelt.

**35** Unscrew the tensioner centre bolt to release the tensioner.

**36** Unscrew the backplate bolt and remove the tensioner assembly.

## Inspection

**Note:** *It is considered good practice by many professional mechanics to renew tensioner assemblies as a matter of course, whenever the timing belt/injection pump drivebelt is renewed.*

**37** Spin the tensioner pulley by hand and check for noisy bearings, roughness and resistance. Check the tensioner components for wear and damage and renew as necessary if there is the slightest doubt about their condition.

## Refitting

**38** Clean the tensioner pulley and wipe it dry. **Do not** apply excessive amounts of solvent to the pulley otherwise the bearing lubricant may be contaminated. Also clean the timing belt covers and inner shield, the timing belt/drivebelt housing, and the surfaces of the cylinder head and block.

**39** Refit the tensioner and tighten the bolts to the specified torque wrench settings.

**40** Fit the new timing belt as described in Section 10.

### Idler pulley

## Removal

**41** Remove the timing belt as described in Section 10 – there is no need to remove the injection pump drivebelt.

**42** Unbolt and remove the idler.

## Inspection

**Note:** *It is considered good practice by many professional mechanics to renew idler pulley assemblies as a matter of course, whenever the timing belt/injection pump drivebelt is renewed.*

**43** Spin the idler pulley by hand and check for noise, roughness and resistance in the bearings. Check also the pulley teeth for signs

**12.3 Auxiliary shaft oil seal housing on the timing belt/drivebelt housing**

**12.6a Auxiliary shaft oil seal retainer with plastic fitting ring**

**12.6b Tightening the auxiliary shaft oil seal housing bolts**

of wear or damage such as cracks or chips; if a plastic idler is fitted, place a straight-edge across its teeth and check that there is no more than 0.5 mm gap (ie, wear) between the straight-edge and the teeth at any point. If any wear at all is evident, renew the pulley.

**Refitting**

**44** Refit the idler pulley and tighten the mounting bolt to the specified torque. On facelift models – with an automatic timing belt tensioner – turn the eccentric's teardrop anti-clockwise to the 6 o'clock position – ie, the narrow end of the plate should be facing vertically downwards – to minimise the belt tension.

**45** Fit the new timing belt as described in Section 10.

## 12 Auxiliary shaft oil seal – renewal

**1** Remove the auxiliary shaft toothed pulley as described in Section 11.
**2** Unbolt and remove the timing belt side cover.
**3** Unscrew the bolts and remove the oil seal housing **(see illustration)**. The oil seal is integral with the housing.
**4** Clean the timing belt/drivebelt housing, the cylinder block and the auxiliary shaft end.
**5** Smear fresh engine oil on the auxiliary shaft and on the sealing lips of the new oil seal. Before fitting the new seal, locate the special fitting ring inside the sealing lips.
**6** Locate the new oil seal over the end of the

auxiliary shaft, then insert the bolts and tighten **(see illustrations)**.
**7** Carefully remove the special ring and make sure that the seal lips are located on the shaft correctly.
**8** Refit the timing belt side cover and tighten the bolts.
**9** Refit the auxiliary shaft toothed pulley as described in Section 11.

## 13 Camshaft oil seal – renewal

**1** Remove the camshaft toothed pulley as described in Section 11.
**2** Note the fitted depth of the oil seal before removing it, as a guide to fitting the new one.
**3** Using a screwdriver or suitable hooked instrument, pull the oil seal from the cylinder head. If the seal is tight, drill two or three small holes in its outer face, then screw in self-tapping screws. Pull on the screws with a pair of pliers to remove the oil seal.
**4** Wipe clean the seating and end of the camshaft.
**5** Dip the new seal in oil, then locate it over the camshaft and initially press it in by hand making sure that it enters the cylinder head squarely.
**6** Using a piece of metal tubing or a socket, carefully drive the oil seal into the cylinder head to the previously noted depth.
**7** Wipe any excess oil from the oil seal and surrounding area.
**8** Refit the camshaft toothed pulley and fit a new timing belt with reference to Section 11.

## 14 Camshaft and tappets – removal, inspection and refitting

### *Removal*

**1** Remove the camshaft toothed pulley (and hub, on early engines) as described in Section 11.
**2** If not already done, remove the cylinder head cover as described in Section 5.
**3** The oil baffle plate attached to bearing caps Nos 2 and 4 must be removed **(see illustration)**. Progressively loosen (by half a turn at a time, from one side to the other) the bearing cap/oil baffle plate nuts.
**4** Remove bearing caps Nos 2 and 4 and their shells. Keep the shells with their caps if they are to be re-used. Note that the caps are numbered and carry an arrow pointing to the pulley end of the engine **(see illustration)**.
**5** Slacken the nuts of bearing caps Nos 1, 3 and 5 one turn at a time, working from end to end so that the camshaft is released gradually. Remove the bearing caps and shells, again keeping the shells with their caps if necessary.
**6** Lift out the camshaft with its oil seal.
**7** Recover the lower half bearing shells, keeping them with their caps if they are to be refitted.
**8** If purchasing new bearing shells, note that either standard or undersize shells may have been fitted in production. Undersize shells are identified by a green mark.
**9** Obtain eight small, clean containers, and number them 1 to 8 from the timing end.

**14.3 Oil baffle plate securing nuts (arrowed)**

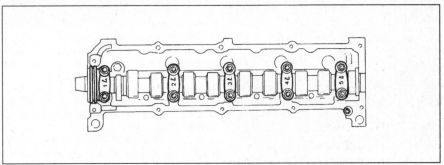

**14.4 Camshaft bearing caps – note numbers and arrows**

14.9 Removing a tappet

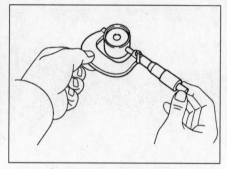

14.11 Check the tappet diameter with a micrometer

14.12 Check the cam lobes for scoring, wear or pitting – this camshaft is excessively worn

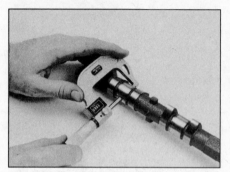

14.14 Check the bearing journal diameters with a micrometer

14.15a Lay a piece of Plastigauge on each bearing journal

14.15b Compare the width of crushed Plastigauge against the card

Lift the tappets one by one from the cylinder head, keeping the shims with their respective tappets **(see illustration)**.

### Inspection

**10** With the camshaft and tappets removed, check for signs of obvious wear (scoring, pitting, etc) and for ovality, and renew if necessary.

**11** If possible, use a micrometer to measure the outside diameter of each tappet – take measurements at the top and bottom of each tappet, then a second set at right-angles to the first; if any measurement is significantly different from the others, the tappet is tapered or oval (as applicable) and must be renewed **(see illustration)**. If the tappets or the cylinder head bores are excessively worn, new tappets and/or a new cylinder head will be required.

**12** Visually examine the camshaft lobes for score marks, pitting, and evidence of overheating (blue, discoloured areas). Look for flaking away of the hardened surface layer of each lobe. If any such signs are evident, renew the component concerned **(see illustration)**.

**13** Examine the camshaft bearing journals and the bearing shells for signs of obvious wear or pitting. If any such signs are evident, renew the camshaft and/or obtain a set of bearing shells.

**14** Check the diameter of each of the camshaft bearing journals at several points, using a micrometer **(see illustration)**. A new camshaft will be needed if excessive wear is evident.

**15** To check the camshaft bearing running clearances, first ensure that the cylinder head, bearing cap and camshaft bearing surfaces are completely clean and dry. Lay the camshaft in position in the cylinder head. Lay a length of Plastigauge on top of each of the camshaft bearing journals. Lubricate each bearing cap with a little silicone release agent, then place them in position over the camshaft and tighten the retaining nuts down to the specified torque. Carefully remove the bearing caps again, lifting them vertically away from the camshaft to avoid disturbing the Plastigauge. The Plastigauge should remain on the camshaft bearing surface, squashed into a uniform sausage shape. If it disintegrates as the bearing caps are removed, re-clean the components and repeat the exercise, using a little more release agent on the bearing cap. Hold the scale card supplied with the kit against each bearing journal, and match the width of the crushed Plastigauge

with the graduated markings on the card; use this to determine the running clearances **(see illustrations)**.

**16** If the clearance is excessive, repeat the check with new bearing shells; renew the camshaft if the clearance is still excessive.

**17** To check camshaft endfloat, remove the tappets, clean the bearing surfaces carefully, and refit the camshaft and bearing caps with shells. Tighten the bearing cap nuts to the specified torque wrench setting, then measure the endfloat using a dial gauge mounted on the cylinder head so that its tip bears on the camshaft end.

**18** Tap the camshaft fully towards the gauge, zero the gauge, then tap the camshaft fully away from the gauge, and note the gauge reading. If the endfloat measured is found to be more than the value given in the Specifications, fit a new camshaft and repeat the check; if the clearance is still excessive, the cylinder head must be renewed.

### Refitting

**19** Commence reassembly by lubricating the cylinder head tappet bores and the tappets with clean engine oil. Carefully refit the tappets (together with their respective shims – lettering facing downwards) to the cylinder head, ensuring that each tappet is refitted to its original bore **(see illustration)**. Some care will be required to enter the tappets squarely into their bores.

**20** Place the lower half bearing shells (the ones with the oil holes) in position **(see illustration)**. Lubricate the shells.

14.19 Refit the tappet shims with their size markings face down

14.20 Fitting a camshaft lower bearing shell

14.21a Lubricate the cam lobes and bearings with oil or grease . . .

14.21b . . . then lay the camshaft in place

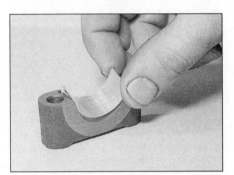

14.22a Fitting a camshaft upper bearing shell to its cap

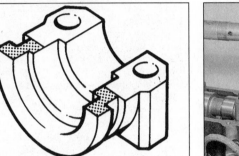

14.22b Camshaft No 1 bearing cap – coat shaded area with sealant

14.24 Tightening the camshaft bearing cap nuts

**21** Make sure that all tappets, shims and the vacuum pump pushrod are in place. Remove the old oil seal, if not already done. Lubricate the camshaft lobes and bearings with oil, assembly paste, or molybdenum grease, and place the camshaft on the lower half bearings **(see illustrations)**. Position the camshaft so that the slot in its left-hand end is parallel with the cylinder head mating surface and the larger semi-circular segment is uppermost (see Section 4).

**22** Clean any old sealant from No 1 bearing cap. Fit the upper bearing shells to their caps and lubricate them. Coat the mating surfaces of No 1 cap with sealant (to Ford specification SPM-4G-9112-F/G) in the areas shown **(see illustrations)**.

**23** Fit bearing caps and shells Nos 1, 3 and 5, making sure that they are the right way round (the arrows point to the timing belt end).

**24** Tighten the cap nuts, half a turn at a time, in the sequence 1-3-5. Carry on until the caps are seated, then tighten the nuts to the specified torque **(see illustration)**.

**25** Insert the camshaft aligning tool into the slot in the camshaft left-hand end – check that it is a snug fit.

**26** Fit caps and shells Nos 2 and 4, tapping them down with a mallet if necessary to seat them. Fit their nuts.

**27** Refit the oil baffle plate and the mounting nuts. Working in a diagonal sequence, tighten the nuts half a turn at a time until the caps are seated and square to the head. Tighten the nuts to the specified torque.

**28** Fit a new oil seal to the camshaft

right-hand end as described in Section 13. Apply a thin smear of sealant to the joint between No 1 bearing cap and the cylinder head.

**29** Refit the camshaft toothed pulley (and hub) as described in Section 11. Remember the timing belt has to be renewed.

**30** Refit the cylinder head cover as described in Section 5.

## 15 Valve clearances – checking and adjustment

**Note:** *For DIY purposes, note that while checking the valve clearances is a relatively easy operation, changing the shims requires the use of Ford special tools – owners may prefer to have this work carried out by a Ford dealer.*

### Checking

**1** Remove the cylinder head cover as described in Section 5.

**2** The oil baffle plate attached to bearing caps Nos 2 and 4 must be removed. Progressively loosen (by half a turn at a time, from one side to the other) the bearing cap/oil baffle plate nuts. Lift off the baffle plate without disturbing the bearing caps.

**3** Temporarily refit the bearing cap nuts (with suitable washers underneath, to make up for the missing baffle plate). Tighten the nuts half a turn at a time in a diagonal sequence until the caps are seated and square to the head. Tighten the nuts to the specified torque.

**4** During the following procedure, the crankshaft must be turned to position the camshaft lobes away from the valves. To do this, either turn the crankshaft on the pulley bolt or alternatively raise the front right-hand corner of the car, engage top gear and turn the front roadwheel. Access to the pulley bolt is gained by jacking up the front of the car and supporting on axle stands, then removing the pulley lower cover.

**5** If desired, to enable the crankshaft to be turned more easily, remove the glow plugs (Chapter 5) or the fuel injectors (Chapter 4A).

**6** Draw the valve positions on a piece of paper, numbering them 1 to 8 from the timing end of the engine. Identify them as inlet or exhaust (ie, 1I, 2E, 3I, 4E, 5I, 6E, 7I, 8E).

**7** Turn the crankshaft until the valves of No 4 cylinder (flywheel end) are 'rocking'. The exhaust valve will be closing and the inlet valve will be opening. The piston of No 1 cylinder will be at the top of its compression stroke, with both valves fully closed. The clearances for both valves of No 1 cylinder may be checked at the same time.

**8** Insert a feeler blade of the correct thickness (see Specifications) between the cam lobe and the shim on the top of the tappet bucket, and check that it is a firm sliding fit **(see illustration)**. If it is not, use the feeler blades to ascertain the exact clearance, and record this for use when calculating the new shim thickness required. Note that the inlet and exhaust valve clearances are different, so it is important that you know which valve clearance you are checking.

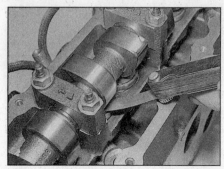

**15.8 Measuring a valve clearance with a feeler blade**

**9** With No 1 cylinder valve clearances checked, turn the engine through half a turn so that No 2 valves are 'rocking', then check the valve clearances of No 3 cylinder in the same way. Similarly check the valve clearances of No 4 cylinder with No 1 valves 'rocking' and No 2 cylinder with No 3 valves 'rocking'.

### Adjustment

**10** If adjustment is required, turn the engine in the normal direction of rotation through approximately 90°, to bring the pistons to mid-stroke. If this is not done, the pistons at TDC will prevent the tappets being depressed, and damage may result. Depress the tappets and then either shim can be withdrawn if the peak of the cam does not prevent access. The Ford service tools for this operation are tappet depressor No 21-106 (now 303-195), and shim pliers No 21-107 (now 303-196), but with care and patience a C-spanner or screwdriver can be used to depress the tappet and the shim can be flicked out with a small screwdriver **(see illustrations)**.

**11** If the valve clearance was too small, a thinner shim must be fitted. If the clearance was too large, a thicker shim must be fitted. The thickness of the shim (in mm) is engraved on the side facing away from the camshaft **(see illustration)**. If the marking is missing or illegible, a micrometer will be needed to establish shim thickness.

**12** When the shim thickness and the valve clearance are known, the required thickness of the new shim can be calculated as follows:

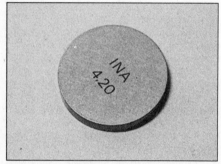

**15.11 Shim thickness marking**

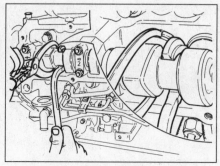

**15.10a Maker's tools for tappet depression and shim extraction**

**Sample calculation – clearance too small**

| | |
|---|---|
| *Desired clearance (A)* | = 0.50 mm |
| *Measured clearance (B)* | = 0.35 mm |
| *Shim thickness found (C)* | = 3.95 mm |
| *Shim thickness required (D)* | = C + B – A |
| | = 3.80 mm |

**Sample calculation – clearance too large**

| | |
|---|---|
| *Desired clearance (A)* | = 0.35 mm |
| *Measured clearance (B)* | = 0.40 mm |
| *Shim thickness found (C)* | = 4.05 mm |
| *Shim thickness required (D)* | = C + B – A |
| | = 4.10 mm |

**13** With the correct shim fitted, release the tappet depressing tool. Turn the engine back so that the cam lobes are again pointing upwards and check that the clearance is now correct.

**14** Repeat the process for the remaining valves, turning the engine each time to bring a pair of cam lobes upwards.

**15** It will be helpful for future adjustment if a record is kept of the thickness of shim fitted at each position. The shims required can be purchased in advance once the clearances and the existing shim thicknesses are known.

**16** It is permissible to interchange shims between tappets to achieve the correct clearances but **do not** turn the camshaft with any of the shims removed, since there is a risk that the cam lobe will jam in the empty tappet.

**17** When all the clearances are correct, refit the fuel injectors or glow plugs (Chapter 4A or 5).

**18** Unscrew the temporarily-refitted Nos 2 and 4 bearing cap nuts, and remove the washers. Lay the baffle plate back in position, and hand-tighten the nuts. Tighten the nuts half a turn at a time in a diagonal sequence until the caps are seated and square to the head. Tighten the nuts to the specified torque.

**19** Refit the cylinder head cover as described in Section 5.

## 16 Cylinder head – removal and refitting

### Removal

**1** Disconnect the battery negative (earth) lead (see Chapter 5).

**2** Apply the handbrake, then jack up the front

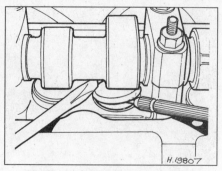

**15.10b Depressing a tappet with a screwdriver and removing a shim**

of the car and support it on axle stands (see *Jacking and vehicle support*). Where fitted, remove the engine undershield and radiator lower cover. Remove the right-hand front roadwheel, then undo the retaining screws and remove the wheel arch liner.

**3** Drain the cooling system as described in Chapter 1. Refit the coolant drain plug(s) and tighten securely.

**4** Unplugging the electrical connector and disconnecting the vacuum hose (where fitted), remove the air cleaner assembly with the air mass meter and the resonator (where fitted) as described in Chapter 4A.

**5** Remove the intercooler (see Chapter 4A) – unbolt and remove completely the intercooler mounting brackets and the intercooler/inlet manifold ducting. Pack the turbocharger opening with clean rag to prevent dirt or other objects falling in.

**6** Remove the timing belt as described in Section 10. There is no need to remove the injection pump drivebelt, but since the timing belt must be renewed once it has been removed, it is good practice to renew the other drivebelt at the same time.

**7** If a support bar was used to take the weight of the engine, locate a trolley jack and block of wood beneath the sump then remove the support bar.

**8** Remove the camshaft toothed pulley (early engines) and timing belt tensioner with reference to Section 11.

**9** On early engines only, disconnect the crankcase breather hoses from the left-hand of the cylinder head cover. Plug the rear hose's opening with clean rag to prevent dirt or other objects falling into the turbocharger.

**10** Unplugging their electrical connectors, disconnect the coolant temperature gauge sender unit, the engine coolant temperature sensor, radiator fan switch, and the needle lift sensor (later engines only) **(see illustrations)**.

**11** Disconnect the hose from the coolant expansion tank.

**12** Disconnect the fuel return pipe from the fuel injection pump union **(see illustration)**.

**13** Unscrew the nut to disconnect the glow plug wiring. Disconnect the wiring from the oil pressure switch, and from the fuel heater **(see illustration)**.

**14** Unplugging the two electrical connectors

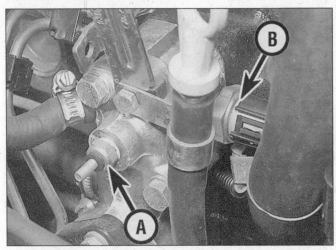

**16.10a Disconnect the gauge sender unit (A) and coolant temperature sensor (B) . . .**

**16.10b . . . and the radiator fan switch on the base of the thermostat housing**

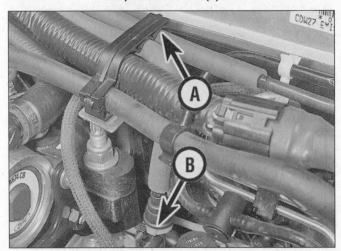

**16.12 Unclip the hoses and wiring harness from the head (A), then disconnect the fuel return pipe (B)**

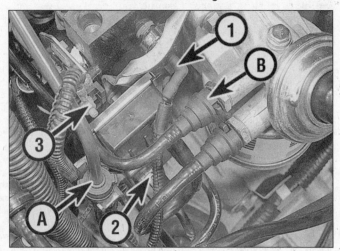

**16.13 Disconnect the following:**

1 Oil pressure switch     A Fuel pipes
2 Fuel heater     B Fuel pipes
3 Glow plug wiring nut

located next to the fuel filter, disconnect the engine wiring loom.

15 Disconnect the fuel pipes from the top of the filter **(see illustration 16.13)**.

16 Unscrew the union nut and disconnect the vacuum line from the top of the vacuum pump (see Chapter 9). Release the retaining clip and disconnect the oil return hose from the base of the pump **(see illustration)**.

17 Unbolt the glow plug wiring bracket, then unbolt the oil dipstick tube. Discard the seal (where applicable).

18 Disconnect the fuel leak-off pipes from the injectors.

19 Unscrew the union nuts and remove the injection pipes from the injectors and injection pump. Be prepared for some loss of fuel and cover the pump, injection pipe and injector openings (see Chapter 4A) to prevent the entry of dirt.

20 Unbolt the fuel filter assembly and withdraw it from the cylinder head.

21 Unclip the coolant hoses from the cylinder head and secure them out of the way. Disconnect the vacuum hose from the Exhaust Gas Recirculation (EGR) valve.

22 Unbolt the thermostat housing and withdraw it from the cylinder head. Discard the gasket.

23 Unscrew the nuts securing the exhaust system front downpipe/catalytic converter to the turbocharger.

24 Slacken the hose clip securing the oil return hose and disconnect the hose from the return pipe on the turbocharger.

25 Remove the injectors and fire seal washers as described in the relevant Part of Chapter 4.

26 Unscrew the cylinder head bolts **in the reverse** of the sequence shown in illustration 16.37b. As new bolts will be required when refitting the cylinder head, note that the bolts have an M12 thread and a Torx TX70 head.

27 With the help of an assistant, lift the

cylinder head, with the manifolds and the timing belt inner shield, from the block.

28 Remove the cylinder head gasket, but retain it for comparison with the new gasket. Three possible thicknesses of gasket are available according to the piston protrusion,

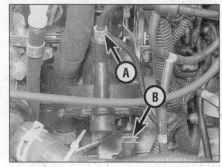

**16.16 Disconnect the vacuum pipe (A) and oil return hose (B) from the vacuum pump**

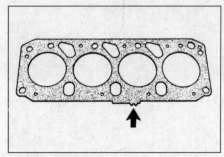

**16.28  Cylinder head gasket thickness is indicated by the number of teeth or holes at point arrowed**

**16.36a  Fit the new gasket over the dowels located at bolt holes 8 and 10 . . .**

**16.36b  . . . with the OBEN/TOP marking uppermost**

the details of which are given in the Specifications at the start of this Chapter **(see illustration)**.

### Inspection

**29** The mating faces of the cylinder head and block must be perfectly clean before refitting the head. Use a scraper to remove all traces of gasket and carbon, and also clean the tops of the pistons. Take particular care with the aluminium cylinder head, as the soft metal is damaged easily. Also, make sure that debris is not allowed to enter the oil and water channels – this is particularly important for the oil circuit, as carbon could block the oil supply to the camshaft or crankshaft bearings. Using adhesive tape and paper, seal the water, oil and bolt holes in the cylinder block. Clean the piston crowns in the same way.

**30** Check the block and head for nicks, deep scratches and other damage. If slight, they may be removed carefully with a file. More serious damage may be repaired by machining, but this is a specialist job.

**31** If warpage of the cylinder head is suspected, use a straight-edge to check it for distortion. Refer to Chapter 2B if necessary.

**32** Clean out the bolt holes in the block using a pipe cleaner, or a rag and screwdriver. Make sure that all oil is removed, otherwise there is a possibility of the block being cracked

by hydraulic pressure when the bolts are tightened.

**33** Examine the bolt threads and the threads in the cylinder block for damage. If necessary, use the correct-size tap to chase out the threads in the block.

**34** If necessary, the valve clearances may be checked and adjusted with the cylinder head on the bench. Refer to Section 15.

### Refitting

**35** Before fitting the cylinder head, ensure that the slot in the camshaft left-hand end is parallel with the cylinder head mating surface, with the larger semi-circular segment uppermost, and that the crankshaft is at TDC (see Section 4).

**36** Fit the new selected gasket and use new cylinder head bolts. Make sure that the centralising dowel sleeves are located at bolt holes 8 and 10, and the word TOP/OBEN is visible **(see illustrations)**.

**37** Fit the cylinder head, ensuring the at the timing belt inner shield locates correctly and is not damaged, screw in new bolts (**do not** oil the threads), and tighten in the stages indicated in the Specifications and in the sequence shown **(see illustrations)**.

**38** Refit the injectors and fire seal washers as described in Chapter 4A.

**39** Fit and tension a new timing belt (and

injection pump drivebelt) with reference to Section 10. It is not recommended to renew only one belt, even though only the timing belt strictly has to be renewed.

**40** With the valve clearances checked and correct (see Section 15), refit the oil baffle plate and tighten the nuts to the specified torque wrench setting. Refit the cylinder head cover with a new gasket and tighten the bolts to the specified torque wrench setting.

**41** Reconnect the crankcase breather hoses to the cylinder head cover.

**42** Refit the timing belt covers with reference to Section 9. Refit and tension the auxiliary drivebelts as described in Chapter 1.

**43** Connect the oil return hose to the turbocharger return pipe and tighten the securing hose clip.

**44** Reconnect the radiator bottom hose to the water pump union.

**45** Refit the engine right-hand mounting and bracket. Remove the trolley jack and block of wood from beneath the sump.

**46** Refit the coolant expansion tank, then clip the coolant expansion tank hoses to the cylinder head and the fuel return pipe into its brackets. Reconnect the vacuum hose to the EGR valve.

**47** Refit the exhaust system front downpipe/catalytic converter to the turbocharger (using a new gasket if required), then tighten the

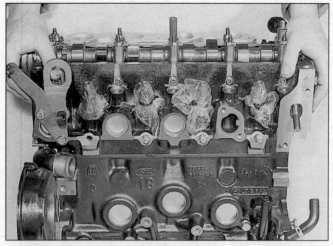

**16.37a  Refitting the cylinder head – note the covers fitted to the injectors**

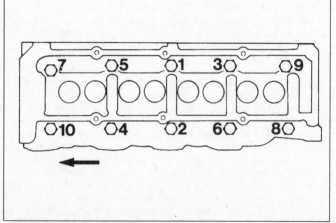

**16.37b  Cylinder head bolt tightening sequence – arrow points to timing belt end of engine**

**16.50 Always use a new gasket when refitting the thermostat housing**

**16.51a Refit the dipstick tube into the block . . .**

**16.51b . . . then tighten its upper mounting bracket bolt**

retaining nuts to the specified torque wrench setting.

**48** Refit the fuel filter assembly.

**49** Refit the injection pipes and tighten the union nuts. Reconnect the leak-off pipes.

**50** Refit the thermostat housing, using a new gasket **(see illustration)**.

**51** Refit the glow plug wiring bracket and the oil dipstick tube, using a new seal (where applicable) **(see illustrations)**.

**52** Reconnect the vacuum line and the oil return hose to the vacuum pump (see Chapter 9).

**53** Reconnect the fuel pipes to the filter, then reconnect the wiring to the oil pressure switch and to the fuel heater and reconnect the engine wiring loom connectors.

**54** Reconnect the hose to the coolant expansion tank and the fuel return pipe to the fuel injection pump.

**55** Reconnect the wiring to the coolant temperature gauge sender, the engine coolant temperature sensor, radiator fan switch, the needle lift sensor (later engines only), and the glow plugs.

**56** Refit the intercooler and the air cleaner assembly with the air mass meter and the resonator (where fitted) – see Chapter 4A.

**57** Refill the cooling system as described in Chapter 1.

**58** Refit the engine undershield, then lower the car to the ground.

**59** Reconnect the battery earth lead (see Chapter 5).

**60** The fuel system should now be bled, with reference to Chapter 4A.

**61** Start the engine and run it to normal

operating temperature. Check for leaks of oil and coolant.

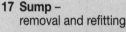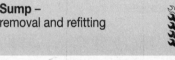

**17 Sump –**
removal and refitting

**Note 1:** *The crankshaft left-hand oil seal carrier is bolted directly onto the sump and cylinder block, making it necessary to remove the flywheel (and therefore the clutch and transmission) and the housing before the sump can be unbolted.*

**Note 2:** *The full procedure outlined below must be followed so that the mating surfaces can be cleaned and prepared to achieve an oil-tight joint on reassembly and so that the sump can be aligned correctly; depending on your skill and experience and the tools and facilities available, it may be that this task can be carried out only with the engine removed from the car.*

**Removal**

**1** Apply the handbrake, then jack up the front of the car and support it on axle stands (see *Jacking and vehicle support*).

**2** Drain the engine oil, then check the sealing washer and renew if necessary. Clean and refit the engine oil drain plug together with the washer, and tighten it to the specified torque wrench setting. Although not strictly necessary as part of the dismantling procedure, owners are advised to remove and discard the oil filter, so that it can be renewed with the oil (see Chapter 1).

**3** Remove the transmission as described in

Chapter 7. Make sure the engine is adequately and safely supported.

**4** Remove the flywheel as described in Section 22.

**5** Unbolt the crankshaft left-hand oil seal carrier and withdraw it from the crankshaft (refer to Section 21).

**6** If necessary, remove the crankshaft position sensor and unbolt its bracket from the sump. Unbolt the coolant pipe bracket from the sump and unscrew the nut securing the coolant pipe's remaining bracket **(see illustration)**. Secure the coolant pipe clear of the sump.

**7** Progressively unscrew the sump retaining bolts, then lower the sump from the crankcase and withdraw it from under the car.

**8** Recover and discard the sump gasket **(see illustration)**.

**9** While the sump is removed, take the opportunity to remove the oil pump pick-up/strainer pipe and clean it with reference to Section 18.

**Refitting**

**Note:** *The sump gasket must be renewed whenever it is disturbed.*

**10** Thoroughly clean the contact surfaces of the sump and crankcase. If necessary, use a cloth rag to clean the interior of the sump and crankcase. If the oil pump pick-up/strainer pipe was removed, fit a new O-ring and refit the pipe with reference to Section 18.

**11** Apply suitable sealant (Ford recommend SPM-4G-9112-F/G) to the joint (on each side) between the timing belt/drivebelt housing and cylinder block/crankcase **(see illustration)**.

**12** Locate the gasket on the engine, noting

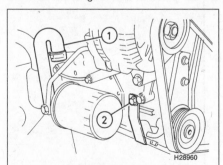

**17.6 Unscrew the coolant pipe bracket bolt (2) – note the oil cooler hose (1)**

**17.8 Removing the sump gasket from the crankcase**

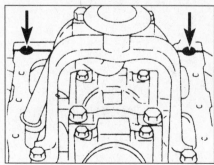

**17.11 Apply suitable sealant to the joints arrowed**

**17.12 Fit the sump gasket, locating the tab (arrowed) into the crankcase**

that there is a locating tab which must engage in the recess on the crankcase, at the timing end **(see illustration)**. Offer the sump onto the cylinder block/crankcase, and insert the retaining bolts finger-tight.

**13** Before tightening the bolts, the sump must be accurately aligned with the end face of the cylinder block using a straight-edge.

**14** Refit the crankshaft left-hand oil seal carrier and tighten the bolts to the specified torque (refer to Section 21).

**15** Once the sump is correctly aligned and the oil seal carrier is installed, progressively tighten the sump-to-crankcase bolts to the specified torque wrench setting.

**16** If removed, refit the crankshaft position sensor and bracket. Refit the coolant pipe to the sump and tighten the mounting bolt and nut to their specified torque wrench settings.

**17** Refit the flywheel with reference to Section 22.

**18** Refit the transmission as described in Chapter 7.

**19** Lower the car to the ground, then fit a new oil filter (if necessary) and refill the engine with oil with reference to Chapter 1.

**20** Finally start the engine and check for signs of oil or coolant leaks.

## 18 Oil pump – removal, inspection and refitting

**Note:** *The following procedure includes removal of the oil filter, and it is recommended that the filter be renewed rather than refitting the old one. The engine oil should also be changed at the same time.*

### Removal

**1** Drain the engine oil and unscrew the oil filter with reference to Chapter 1.

**2** Unbolt the coolant pipe bracket from the sump and unscrew the nut securing the coolant pipe's remaining bracket. Secure the coolant pipe clear of the sump.

**3** Unscrew the driveshaft support bracket bolts from the back of the engine.

**4** Unscrew the nuts to disconnect the exhaust system front downpipe from the turbocharger (see Chapter 4A). If the additional working clearance is required, unbolt the downpipe/catalytic converter completely.

**5** Unscrew the oil cooler's retaining bolt and separate the cooler from its adapter. Collect and discard the gasket – a new one must be used when refitting.

**6** Unscrew the two bolts and single nut securing the oil cooler mounting bracket to the cylinder block/crankcase.

**7** Unscrew the banjo bolt securing the turbocharger oil feed line to the oil pump. Collect the copper washer on each side of the union – these must be renewed as a matter of course whenever they are disturbed. Unbolt the oil feed line bracket from the cylinder block/crankcase.

**8** Unscrew the mounting bolts and move the oil pump so that the oil cooler mounting bracket can be withdrawn, then withdraw the pump itself. Recover and discard the gasket **(see illustrations)**.

### Inspection

**9** Unscrew the special bolt and separate the oil cooler/oil filter adapter from the oil pump, then undo the crosshead screws and remove the cover plate from the pump.

**10** Clean all parts and inspect them for wear or damage. Using a feeler gauge, measure the inner-to-outer rotor clearance. If the clearance exceeds that specified then the pump must be renewed as pump components are not available individually. It is wise to renew the pump on a precautionary basis at time of major overhaul, especially if there is evidence of oil starvation elsewhere.

**11** If there are any signs of metallic debris inside the oil pump, it is recommended that the sump be removed and the pick-up pipe and strainer cleaned thoroughly. Renew the pick-up tube O-ring and the sump gasket on refitting, and tighten the bolts to the specified torque **(see illustrations)**.

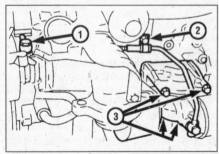

**18.8a Turbo oil feed banjo bolt (1), oil feed pipe bracket bolt (2) and pump mounting bolts (3)**

**18.8b Unscrew the mounting bolts . . .**

**18.8c . . . remove the oil pump from the cylinder block . . .**

**18.8d . . . and recover the gasket**

**18.11a Removing the oil pump pick-up tube from the crankcase – note the O-ring which must be renewed**

**18.11b Tightening the oil pump pick-up tube mounting bolts**

## Refitting

**12** Before refitting the oil pump, pour approximately 10 cc of engine oil into the pump to prime it and oil the pump drive gear and driven gear. Refit the cover plate using a new gasket and tighten the crosshead screws securely and evenly.

**13** Clean the mating faces of the pump and cylinder block, then refit the oil pump (with the oil cooler mounting bracket) using a new gasket. Tighten by hand the oil pump mounting bolts; tighten the mounting bracket's bolts to the specified torque wrench setting.

**14** Tighten the oil pump mounting bolts to the specified torque wrench setting.

**15** Fit new copper washers to the turbocharger oil feed line banjo union and tighten the bolt to the specified torque wrench setting. Bolt the oil feed line bracket on to the cylinder block/crankcase.

**16** Refit the oil cooler to its adapter, using a new gasket, and tighten the cooler's retaining bolt to the specified torque wrench setting.

**17** Refit the coolant pipe to the sump and tighten the mounting bolt and nut to their specified torque wrench settings.

**18** Refit the driveshaft support bracket to the back of the engine, and tighten the bolts to the specified torque.

**19** Refit the exhaust system front downpipe/ catalytic converter and the intercooler.

**20** Fit a new oil filter, and fill the engine with fresh oil as described in Chapter 1.

**21** Lower the car to the ground.

## 19 Oil cooler – removal and refitting

**Note:** *While the following procedure does not necessitate the removal of the oil filter, it is strongly recommended that the filter be renewed and that the engine oil should be changed whenever the oil cooler is disturbed.*

### Removal

**1** Drain the engine oil and unscrew the oil filter, then drain the coolant with reference to Chapter 1.

**2** Disconnect the coolant hose from the oil cooler **(see illustration 17.6)**.

**3** Unscrew the retaining bolt and withdraw the oil cooler **(see illustration)**. Note how its unions are aligned, and be prepared for oil loss from the cooler. Note also the arrangement of washers, sealing rings and O-rings underneath the bolt and the gasket sealing the oil cooler/adapter joint – all seals must be renewed as a matter of course whenever they are disturbed.

### Refitting

**4** Refitting is the reverse of the removal procedure, noting the following points:
   a) *Renew all O-rings and seals disturbed on removal.*
   b) *Align the cooler's unions as noted on*

removal and tighten securely the retaining bolt.
   c) *Refill the cooling system (see Chapter 1).*
   d) *Refit the oil filter, then check the engine oil level and top-up as necessary (see Weekly checks).*
   e) *Check for signs of oil or coolant leaks once the engine has been restarted and warmed-up to normal operating temperature.*

## 20 Oil pressure warning light switch – removal and refitting

**Note:** *Two different types of switch have been fitted – engines built up to July 1998 were fitted with a switch with a black cover, while engines built from August 1998 onwards were fitted with a switch with a green cover – the correct switch must be obtained.*

### Removal

**1** The switch is screwed into the left-hand end of the cylinder head, next to the fuel filter.

**2** With the car parked on firm level ground, open the bonnet and disconnect the battery negative (earth) lead – see Chapter 5, Section 1.

**3** Unplug the wiring from the switch and unscrew it; be prepared for some oil loss.

### Refitting

**4** Refitting is the reverse of the removal procedure; apply a thin smear of suitable sealant to the switch threads and tighten it to the specified torque wrench setting. Check the engine oil level and top-up as necessary (see *Weekly checks*). Check for signs of oil leaks once the engine has been restarted and warmed-up to normal operating temperature.

## 21 Crankshaft oil seals – renewal

### Right-hand (timing belt end) seal

**1** Remove the crankshaft toothed pulleys as described in Section 11.

**2** Note the fitted depth of the oil seal in the timing belt/drivebelt housing.

**3** Using a screwdriver or other suitable instrument, prise the oil seal from the timing belt/drivebelt housing. An alternative method is to drill two small holes in the oil seal, then screw in self-tapping screws and use grips to pull out the oil seal. If this method is used, make sure that all swarf is removed.

**4** Inspect the seal rubbing surface on the crankshaft inboard toothed pulley and if necessary renew the pulley.

**5** Wipe clean the oil seal seating in the timing belt/drivebelt housing.

**6** Note that the new oil seal is supplied with a support ring which must remain in position until just before the crankshaft inboard toothed pulley is fitted. The oil seal must be fitted dry.

**19.3 Oil cooler location**

**7** Using a length of metal tube or a socket, drive the new oil seal into the timing belt/ drivebelt housing to the previously noted depth. Leave the support ring in place at this stage.

**8** Refit the crankshaft toothed pulleys and timing belt with reference to Section 11.

### Left-hand (flywheel end) seal

**9** Remove the flywheel as described in Section 22.

**10** Unbolt the left-hand oil seal carrier from the sump and cylinder block and withdraw it over the end of the crankshaft. Note that the carrier incorporates an integral oil seal and a vulcanised gasket.

**11** Wipe clean the mating faces of the sump and cylinder block. Also wipe all oil from the crankshaft end. Note that the oil seal must be fitted dry.

**12** Make sure that the support ring is located inside the oil seal, then locate the carrier over the crankshaft. Screw in the retaining bolts finger-tight.

**13** Make sure that the oil seal is centred on the end of the crankshaft, then progressively tighten the carrier mounting bolts to the specified torque **(see illustration)**.

**14** Carefully remove the support ring so that the lips of the oil seal rest on the crankshaft. If the ring is tight, it is likely that the left-hand faces of the sump and cylinder block/ crankcase are not accurately aligned with each other. To rectify this situation, loosen all the sump bolts, reposition the sump and retighten the bolts to the specified torque.

**15** With the carrier bolts tightened, refit the flywheel and transmission.

**21.13 Tightening the left-hand oil seal carrier mounting bolts**

**22.11 Note method used to lock flywheel while (new) bolts are tightened**

## 22 Flywheel –
removal, inspection and refitting

### Removal

**1** Remove the transmission (see Chapter 7). Now is a good time to check components such as oil seals and renew them if necessary.
**2** Remove the clutch (Chapter 6). Now is a good time to check or renew the clutch components and pilot bearing.
**3** Use a centre-punch or paint to make alignment marks on the flywheel and crankshaft, to ensure correct alignment during refitting.
**4** Prevent the flywheel from turning by locking the ring gear teeth, or by bolting a strap between the flywheel and the cylinder block/crankcase. Slacken the bolts evenly until all are free.
**5** Remove each bolt in turn and ensure that new ones are obtained for reassembly; these bolts are subjected to severe stresses and so must be renewed, regardless of their apparent condition, whenever they are disturbed.
**6** Withdraw the flywheel; do not drop it – it is very heavy.

### Inspection

**7** Clean the flywheel to remove grease and oil. Inspect the surface for cracks, rivet grooves, burned areas and score marks. Light scoring can be removed with emery cloth. Check for cracked and broken ring gear teeth. Lay the flywheel on a flat surface and use a straight-edge to check for warpage.
**8** Clean and inspect the mating surfaces of the flywheel and the crankshaft. If the crankshaft left-hand seal is leaking, renew it (see Section 21) before refitting the flywheel.
**9** While the flywheel is removed, clean carefully its inboard (right-hand) face, particularly the recesses which serve as the reference points for the crankshaft speed/position sensor. Clean the sensor's tip and check that the sensor is securely fastened. Thoroughly clean the threaded bolt holes in the crankshaft and also clean the threads of the bolts – this is important, since if old sealer remains in the threads, the bolts will settle over a period and will not retain their correct torque wrench settings.

### Refitting

**10** On refitting, ensure that the engine/transmission adapter plate is in place (where necessary), then fit the flywheel to the crankshaft so that all bolt holes align – it will fit only one way – check this using the marks made on removal. Apply suitable sealer to the threads of the bolts then insert them.
**11** Lock the flywheel by the method used on dismantling. Working in a diagonal sequence to tighten them evenly and increasing to the final amount in three stages, tighten the new bolts to the specified torque wrench setting **(see illustration)**.
**12** The remainder of reassembly is the reverse of the removal procedure, referring to the relevant text for details where required.

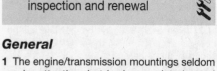

## 23 Engine/transmission mountings –
inspection and renewal

### General

**1** The engine/transmission mountings seldom require attention, but broken or deteriorated mountings should be renewed immediately, or the added strain placed on the driveline components may cause damage or wear.
**2** While separate mountings may be removed and refitted individually, if more than one is disturbed at a time – such as if the engine/transmission unit is removed from its mountings – they must be reassembled and their fasteners tightened in a strict sequence.
**3** On reassembly, the weight of the engine/transmission unit must not be taken by the mountings until all are correctly aligned. Fitting the Ford service tool in place of the front mounting, tighten the engine/transmission mounting fasteners to their specified torque wrench settings.

### Inspection

**4** During the check, the engine/transmission unit must be raised slightly, to remove its weight from the mountings.
**5** Raise the front of the vehicle and support it securely on axle stands. Position a jack under the sump, with a large block of wood between the jack head and the sump, then carefully raise the engine/transmission just enough to take the weight off the mountings.

⚠ **Warning: DO NOT place any part of your body under the engine when it is supported only by a jack.**

**6** Check the mountings to see if the rubber is cracked, hardened or separated from the metal components. Sometimes the rubber will split right down the centre.
**7** Check for relative movement between each mounting's brackets and the engine/transmission or body (use a large screwdriver or lever to attempt to move the mountings). If movement is noted, lower the engine and check-tighten the mounting fasteners.

### Renewal

**Note:** *The following paragraphs assume the engine is supported beneath the sump as described earlier.*

#### Front mounting

**8** On early models, unbolt and remove the resonator fitted to the engine compartment front crossmember (see Chapter 4A). Remove the bolts/nuts securing the mounting to the subframe, unscrew the through-bolt and withdraw the mounting; note the location of the wiring connector bracket. The mounting's bracket can be unbolted from the transmission if required **(see illustration)**.
**9** On refitting, ensure that the mounting-to-transmission bolts are securely tightened, then refit the mounting and wiring connector

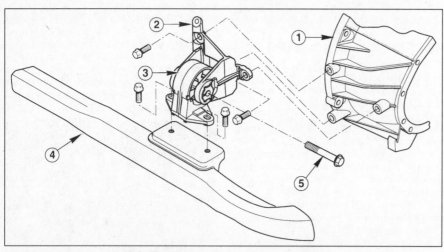

**23.8 Engine/transmission front mounting**

| | |
|---|---|
| 1 *Transmission* | 4 *Front suspension subframe* |
| 2 *Mounting bracket* | 5 *Mounting through-bolt* |
| 3 *Mounting* | |

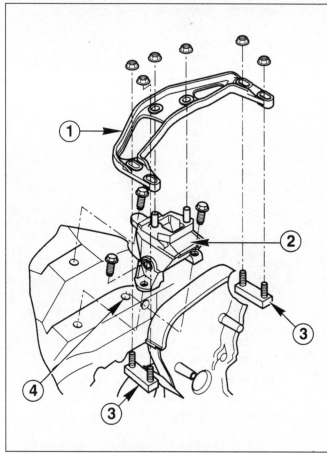

**23.10  Engine/transmission standard type right-hand mounting –
models up to 4/1998**

1  *Bracket*
2  *Mounting*
3  *Brackets bolted to cylinder
  block/crankcase*
4  *Vehicle body*

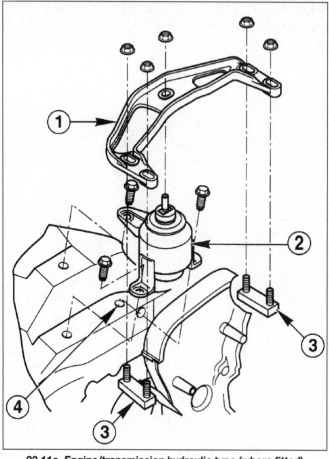

**23.11a  Engine/transmission hydraulic type (where fitted)
right-hand mounting – models up to 4/1998**

1  *Bracket*
2  *Hydraulic mounting*
3  *Brackets bolted to cylinder
  block/crankcase*
4  *Vehicle body*

bracket. Tighten first the mounting-to-subframe bolts/nuts, noting that these are to be tightened in two stages to the final specified torque wrench setting. Finally tighten the mounting's through-bolt, again to the specified torque wrench setting.

### Right-hand mounting

**10**  Unscrew the nuts and withdraw the bracket (models up to 4/1998 only); note that these nuts are self-locking and must therefore be renewed whenever they are disturbed. Unbolt the mounting from the body **(see illustration)**.
**11**  Where hydraulic-type mountings are fitted to early models – there are only five nuts securing the bracket and the mounting is clearly identifiable from its shape – take care never to tilt these more than 5° from the vertical. On models from 5/1998-on, the bracket is no longer fitted, but note that one of the body mounting bolts secures a hose support bracket **(see illustrations)**.
**12**  On refitting, renew the self-locking nuts and tighten all fasteners to the torque wrench settings specified. When tightening

the bracket nuts on early models, tighten first the four bracket-to-engine nuts, then release the hoist or jack to allow the engine/transmission's weight to rest on the mounting. Do not allow the mounting to twist as the last two (or one, with hydraulic mountings) of the nuts are tightened **(see illustration)**.

**23.11b  Engine/transmission right-hand
mounting – models from 5/1998-on**

*Note that one of the mounting-to-body
bolts secures a hose support bracket*

### Left-hand mounting

**13**  Remove the complete air cleaner assembly with the air mass meter and the resonator (where applicable) – see Chapter 4A.
**14**  Unscrew the three nuts to release the mounting from the transmission, then unbolt

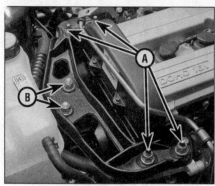

**23.12  Tighten nuts A first, release the
lifting equipment, then tighten nuts B
(petrol engine shown)**

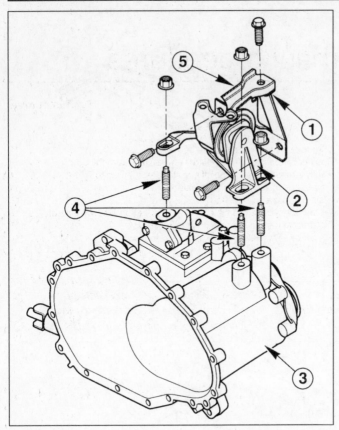

**23.14 Engine/transmission left-hand mounting**

1 *Mounting bracket*
2 *Mounting*
3 *Transmission*
4 *Studs*
5 *Fastening plate – where fitted*

**23.15 Engine/transmission left-hand mounting self-locking nuts (A) to transmission, and bolts (B) to body**

it from the body **(see illustration)**. Note that the nuts are self-locking and must therefore be renewed whenever they are disturbed. Unscrew the through-bolt to dismantle the mounting, if necessary to renew components.

**15** On refitting, renew the self-locking nuts and do not allow the mounting to twist as the nuts are tightened **(see illustration)**. Tighten all fasteners to the specified torque wrench settings.

### Rear mounting

**16** Unbolt the mounting from the subframe, then unscrew the mounting's through-bolt. If required, unbolt the mounting's bracket from the transmission **(see illustration)**.

**17** On refitting, ensure that the mounting-to-transmission bolts are securely tightened, then refit the mounting. Tighten first the mounting-to-subframe bolts, noting that these are to be tightened in two stages to the final specified torque wrench setting. Finally tighten the mounting's through-bolt, again to the specified torque wrench setting.

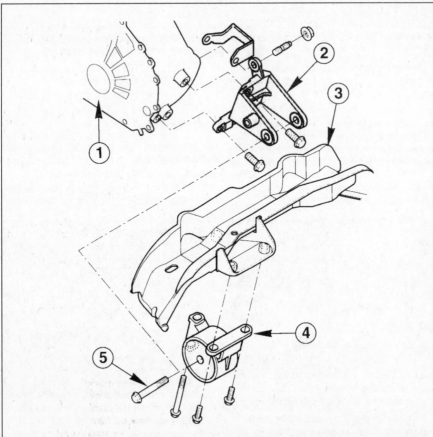

**23.16 Engine/transmission rear mounting**

| | |
|---|---|
| 1 *Transmission* | 4 *Mounting* |
| 2 *Mounting bracket* | 5 *Mounting* |
| 3 *Front suspension* | *through-bolt* |
| *subframe* | |

# Chapter 2 Part B:
## Engine removal and overhaul procedures

## Contents

| | Section number |
|---|---|
| Auxiliary shaft – removal, inspection and refitting | 9 |
| Compression test – description and interpretation | See Chapter 2A |
| Crankshaft – inspection | 14 |
| Crankshaft – refitting | 17 |
| Crankshaft – removal | 11 |
| Cylinder block/crankcase – cleaning and inspection | 12 |
| Cylinder head – dismantling | 6 |
| Cylinder head – reassembly | 8 |
| Cylinder head and valve components – cleaning and inspection | 7 |
| Engine – initial start-up after overhaul | 19 |

| | Section number |
|---|---|
| Engine overhaul – dismantling sequence | 5 |
| Engine overhaul – general information | 2 |
| Engine overhaul – reassembly sequence | 16 |
| Engine/transmission – removal, separation and refitting | 4 |
| Engine/transmission removal – methods and precautions | 3 |
| General information and precautions | 1 |
| Main and big-end bearings – inspection | 15 |
| Piston/connecting rod assemblies – inspection and reassembly | 13 |
| Piston/connecting rod assemblies – refitting | 18 |
| Piston/connecting rod assemblies – removal | 10 |

## Degrees of difficulty

| **Easy,** suitable for novice with little experience | **Fairly easy,** suitable for beginner with some experience | **Fairly difficult,** suitable for competent DIY mechanic | **Difficult,** suitable for experienced DIY mechanic | **Very difficult,** suitable for expert DIY or professional |
|---|---|---|---|---|

## Specifications

### Cylinder head

| | |
|---|---|
| Maximum distortion limit | 0.08 mm overall* |
| Swirl chamber projection | 0.0 to 0.061 mm |
| Valve guide bore diameter: | |
| Standard | 8.0 to 8.025 mm |
| First oversize | 8.263 to 8.288 mm |
| Second oversize | 8.463 to 8.488 mm |

**\* Note:** *Cylinder head gasket surface may NOT be skimmed.*

### Cylinder bore diameter*

| | |
|---|---|
| Class A | 82.5 to 82.515 mm |
| Class B | 82.515 to 82.53 mm |
| Class C | 82.66 to 82.675 mm |
| Class D | 82.675 to 82.69 mm |
| Class E (first rebore) | 83.0 to 83.015 mm |
| Class F (second rebore) | 83.5 to 83.515 mm |

**\* Note:** *Cylinder bore diameter classification stamped into machined surface at front left-hand end of cylinder block.*

### Pistons

| Diameter (measured at 90° to gudgeon pin axis): | Pre-facelift models | Facelift models |
|---|---|---|
| Class A | 82.461 to 82.479 mm | 82.463 to 82.477 mm |
| Class B | 82.476 to 82.494 mm | 82.478 to 82.492 mm |
| Class C | 82.621 to 82.639 mm | 82.622 to 82.639 mm |
| Class D | 82.636 to 82.654 mm | 82.636 to 82.654 mm |
| Class E (first rebore) | 82.961 to 82.979 mm | 82.963 to 82.977 mm |
| Class F (second rebore) | 83.461 to 83.479 mm | 83.463 to 83.477 mm |
| Clearance in bore (new) | 0.021 to 0.054 mm | |
| Piston protrusion at TDC | 0.5 to 0.84 mm | |

### Piston rings

| Clearance in groove: | | |
|---|---|---|
| Top compression | 0.09 to 0.122 mm | |
| Second compression | 0.07 to 0.102 mm | |
| Oil control | 0.05 to 0.082 mm | |
| End gap (fitted)*: | **Pre-facelift models** | **Facelift models** |
| Top compression | 0.35 to 0.5 mm | 0.31 to 0.5 mm |
| Second compression | 0.35 to 0.5 mm | 0.31 to 0.5 mm |
| Oil control | 0.25 to 0.58 mm | 0.25 to 0.58 mm |

**\* Note:** *Values quoted apply to a gauge ring used in production – when measured in the cylinder bore, these values may be exceeded by 0.15 mm.*

## Gudgeon pin

| | |
|---|---|
| Gudgeon pin diameter | 25.996 to 26.0 mm |
| Small-end bore diameter (with bush) | 26.012 to 26.02 mm |

## Crankshaft and bearings

| | |
|---|---|
| Main bearing bore diameter | 57.683 to 57.696 mm |
| Main bearing journal diameter: | |
| Standard | 53.97 to 53.99 mm |
| Undersize (0.25 mm) | 53.72 to 53.74 mm |
| Undersize (0.5 mm) | 53.47 to 53.49 mm |
| Main bearing running clearance: | |
| Pre-facelift models | 0.016 to 0.074 mm |
| Facelift models | 0.015 to 0.062 mm |
| Big-end bearing journal diameter: | |
| Standard | 48.97 to 48.99 mm |
| Undersize (0.25 mm) | 48.72 to 48.74 mm |
| Undersize (0.5 mm) | 48.47 to 48.49 mm |
| Big-end bearing running clearance | 0.016 to 0.074 mm |
| Crankshaft endfloat | 0.11 to 0.37 mm |
| Connecting rod big-end bearing-to-crank web axial clearance | 0.125 to 0.325 mm |
| Torque to rotate fitted crankshaft (without connecting rods or pistons) | 10 Nm (7 lbf ft) max |

## Connecting rods

| | | |
|---|---|---|
| Big-end bore diameter | 52.0 to 52.02 mm | |
| Length – distance between centres of small- and big-end bearings: | **Pre-facelift models** | **Facelift models** |
| Class A | 129.88 to 129.94 mm | 129.872 to 129.948 mm |
| Class B | 129.941 to 130.0 mm | 129.932 to 130.008 mm |
| Class C | 130.001 to 130.06 mm | 129.992 to 130.068 mm |
| Class D | 130.062 to 130.12 mm | 130.052 to 130.128 mm |

## Torque wrench settings

Refer to Chapter 2A Specifications

## 1 General information and precautions

### How to use this Chapter

This Part of Chapter 2 is devoted to engine/transmission removal and refitting, to those repair procedures requiring the removal of the engine/transmission from the car, and to the overhaul of engine components. It includes only the Specifications relevant to those procedures. Refer to Part A for additional Specifications, and for all torque wrench settings.

### General information

The information ranges from advice concerning preparation for an overhaul and the purchase of replacement parts, to detailed step-by-step procedures covering removal and installation of internal engine components and the inspection of parts.

The following Sections have been written based on the assumption that the engine has been removed from the car. For information concerning in-car engine repair, as well as removal and installation of the external components necessary for the overhaul, see Part A of this Chapter.

When overhauling the engine, it is essential to establish first exactly what parts are available. At the time of writing, very few under- or oversized components are available for engine reconditioning. In many cases, it would appear that the easiest and most economically-sensible course of action is to replace a worn or damaged engine with an exchange unit.

## 2 Engine overhaul – general information

It's not always easy to determine when, or if, an engine should be completely overhauled, as a number of factors must be considered.

High mileage is not necessarily an indication that an overhaul is needed, while low mileage doesn't preclude the need for an overhaul. Frequency of servicing is probably the most important consideration. An engine that's had regular and frequent oil and filter changes, as well as other required maintenance, will most likely give many thousands of miles of reliable service. Conversely, a neglected engine may require an overhaul very early in its life.

Excessive oil consumption is an indication that piston rings, valve seals and/or valve guides are in need of attention. Make sure that oil leaks aren't responsible before deciding that the rings and/or guides are worn. Perform a cylinder compression check (Part A of this Chapter) to determine the extent of the work required.

Loss of power, rough running, knocking or metallic engine noises, excessive valve train noise and high fuel consumption rates may also point to the need for an overhaul, especially if they're all present at the same time. If a full service doesn't remedy the situation, major mechanical work is the only solution.

An engine overhaul involves restoring all internal parts to the specification of a new engine. **Note:** *Always check first what parts are available before planning any overhaul operation; refer to Section 1 of this Part. Ford dealers, or a good engine reconditioning specialist/automotive parts supplier may be able to suggest alternatives which will enable you to overcome the lack of new parts.*

During an overhaul, it is usual to renew the piston rings, and to rebore and/or hone the cylinder bores; where the rebore is done by an automotive machine shop, new oversize pistons and rings will also be installed – all these operations, of course, assume the availability of suitable new parts. The main and big-end bearings are generally renewed and, if necessary, the crankshaft may be reground to restore the journals.

Generally, the valves are serviced as well during an overhaul, since they're usually in less-than-perfect condition at this point. While the engine is being overhauled, other components, such as the starter and alternator, can be renewed as well, or rebuilt, if the necessary parts can be found. The end result should be an as-new engine that will give many trouble-free miles. **Note:** *Critical cooling system components such as the hoses, drivebelt, thermostat and water pump MUST be renewed when an engine is overhauled. The radiator should be checked carefully, to ensure that it isn't clogged or* leaking (see Chapter 3). Also, as a general rule, the oil pump should be renewed when an engine is rebuilt.

Before beginning the engine overhaul, read through the entire procedure to familiarise yourself with the scope and requirements of the job. Overhauling an engine isn't difficult, but it is time-consuming. Plan on the car being off the road for a minimum of two weeks, especially if parts must be taken to an automotive machine shop for repair or reconditioning. Check on availability of parts, and make sure that any necessary special tools and equipment are obtained in advance. Most work can be done with typical hand tools, although a number of precision measuring tools are required, for inspecting parts to determine if they must be renewed. Often, an automotive machine shop will handle the inspection of parts, and will offer advice concerning reconditioning and renewal.

**Note:** *Always wait until the engine has been completely dismantled, and all components, especially the cylinder block/crankcase, have been inspected, before deciding what service and repair operations must be performed by an automotive machine shop. Since the block's condition will be the major factor to consider when determining whether to overhaul the original engine or buy a rebuilt one, never purchase parts or have machine work done on other components until the cylinder block/ crankcase has been thoroughly inspected. As a general rule, time is the primary cost of an overhaul, so it doesn't pay to install worn or sub-standard parts.*

As a final note, to ensure maximum life and minimum trouble from a rebuilt engine, everything must be assembled with care, in a spotlessly-clean environment.

## 3  Engine/transmission removal – methods and precautions

If you've decided that an engine must be removed for overhaul or major repair work, several preliminary steps should be taken.

Locating a suitable place to work is extremely important. Adequate work space, along with storage space for the car, will be needed. If a workshop or garage isn't available, at the very least, a flat, level, clean work surface made of concrete or asphalt is required.

Cleaning the engine compartment and engine/transmission before beginning the removal procedure will help keep tools clean and organised.

The engine can only be withdrawn by removing it complete with the transmission. On pre-facelift models, the body must be raised and supported securely, sufficiently high that the engine/transmission can be unbolted as a single unit and lowered to the ground; the engine/transmission unit can then be withdrawn from under the car and

separated. On facelift models, the engine and transmission are lifted out of the car.

In both cases, an engine hoist or A-frame will therefore be necessary (and engine support beam may be used on early models, but a hoist is easier to use). Make sure the equipment is rated in excess of the combined weight of the engine and transmission. Safety is of primary importance, considering the potential hazards involved in removing the engine/transmission from the car.

If this is the first time you have removed an engine, a helper should ideally be available. Advice and aid from someone more experienced would also be helpful. There are many instances when one person cannot simultaneously perform all of the operations required when removing the engine/ transmission from the car.

Plan the operation ahead of time. Arrange for, or obtain, all of the tools and equipment you'll need prior to beginning the job. Some of the equipment necessary to perform engine/transmission removal and installation safely and with relative ease, and which may have to be hired or borrowed, includes (in addition to the engine hoist) a heavy-duty trolley jack, a strong pair of axle stands, some wooden blocks, and an engine dolly (a low, wheeled platform capable of taking the weight of the engine/transmission, so that it can be moved easily when on the ground). A complete set of spanners and sockets (as described in the front of this manual) will obviously be needed, together with plenty of rags and cleaning solvent for mopping-up spilled oil, coolant and fuel. If the hoist is to be hired, make sure that you arrange for it in advance, and perform all of the operations possible without it beforehand. This will save you money and time.

Plan for the car to be out of use for quite a while. A machine shop will be required to perform some of the work which the do-it-yourselfer can't accomplish without special equipment. These establishments often have a busy schedule, so it would be a good idea to consult them before removing the engine, to accurately estimate the amount of time required to rebuild or repair components that may need work.

Always be extremely careful when removing and installing the engine/transmission. Serious injury can result from careless actions. By planning ahead and taking your time, the job (although a major task) can be accomplished successfully.

## 4  Engine/transmission – removal, separation and refitting

**Caution: Before starting any work on the fuel filter, wipe clean the filter assembly and the area around it; it is essential that no dirt or other foreign matter is allowed into the system. Obtain a suitable container**

into which the filter can be drained, and place rags or similar material under the filter assembly to catch any spillages. Do not allow diesel fuel to leak into the clutch bellhousing, or it will contaminate the clutch disc friction material which will cause severe clutch slip – curable only by the renewal of the clutch disc and the degreasing of all fouled surfaces. Similarly, diesel fuel should never be allowed to contaminate components such as the alternator and starter motor, the coolant hoses and engine mountings, and any wiring.

### Pre-facelift models (1993 to October 1996)

**Note:** *Read through the entire Section, as well as reading the advice in the preceding Section, before beginning this procedure. The engine and transmission are removed as a unit, lowered to the ground and removed from underneath, then separated outside the car.*

### Removal

**1** Park the car on firm, level ground, apply the handbrake and chock the rear wheels. Loosen the front wheel nuts.

**2** Disconnect the battery negative lead, and position the lead away from the battery (also see *Disconnecting the battery*). For the best access, remove the battery as described in Chapter 5.

**3** Fit protective covers to both wings and the front crossmember (old pieces of carpet will suffice, as long as they are clean).

**4** Remove the bonnet as described in Chapter 11.

**5** Before disconnecting any of the coolant and vacuum hoses, fuel lines, wiring and earth connections, take careful note of how they are routed for refitting – if possible, take a few digital photos to serve as a reminder.

**6** Remove the air cleaner assembly (including resonator, where applicable) and intercooler as described in Chapter 4A. Block the turbocharger openings with clean rag to prevent the entry of dirt.

**7** Disconnect the accelerator cable (and where applicable, the cruise control cable) from the injection pump, referring to Chapters 4A and 12 if necessary. Move the cable(s) to one side.

**8** Unclip the hoses and wiring harnesses from the cylinder head, then remove the mounting bracket from the engine lifting eye at the front of the head. Move the hoses and wiring clear. Disconnect the fuel return hose from the injection pump.

**9** Jack up the front of the car, and support it on axle stands (see *Jacking and vehicle support*). Remove the engine undershield, and the cover below the radiator. Drain the cooling system as described in Chapter 1, then disconnect the radiator hoses. Also drain the transmission oil as described in Chapter 7. If the engine is being overhauled, drain the engine oil and fit a new oil filter as described in Chapter 1.

**4.15a Disconnect the electronic control unit wiring connector**

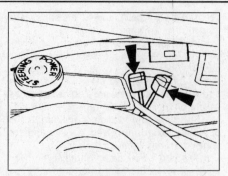

**4.15b Unclip the diagnostic plugs from the bulkhead**

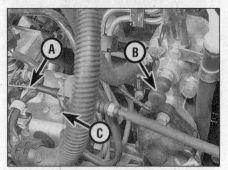

**4.15c Accelerator cable (A), engine temperature sensor (B) and cable support bracket bolt (C)**

**4.15d Disconnect the vehicle speed sensor**

**10** Disconnect the crankshaft position sensor from the sump, then release the wiring harness (and where necessary, the speedometer cable) from the transmission.

**11** Lower the car, and disconnect the remaining coolant hoses from the expansion tank and thermostat housing. Disconnect the heater hoses – one from the oil cooler, one from the cylinder head. Tie all the hoses clear, so they will not be damaged during engine removal.

**12** Disconnect the fuel supply pipe at the quick-release fitting in front of the fuel heater.

**13** Disconnect the EGR valve vacuum hose.

**14** Unscrew and disconnect the vacuum line from the top of the brake vacuum pump.

**15** Disconnect the following wiring harness connections from the engine, and move the harness clear as necessary:

a) Unscrew the nut in front of the fuel heater, and disconnect the glow plug wiring.
b) Electronic control unit wiring plug **(see illustration)**.
c) Alternator wiring.
d) Unclip the diagnostic plugs from the bulkhead **(see illustration)**.
e) Injection pump wiring.
f) Unscrew the nut and disconnect the stop solenoid wire, then unbolt the accelerator cable support bracket **(see illustration)**.
g) Temperature gauge sensor, coolant temperature sensor, radiator fan switch, oil pressure switch, fuel heater and injection pump needle lift sensor (later models only).
h) Starter motor wiring, and where applicable, vehicle speed sensor wiring from the back of the transmission **(see illustration)**.

i) Disconnect the reversing light switch, then release the wiring harness from its support bracket on top of the transmission.
j) On the left of the engine compartment (left as seen from the driver's seat), disconnect the two large wiring plugs next to the suspension strut mounting – note the metal clips on some connectors. Also disconnect the vacuum control valve **(see illustration)**.
k) As necessary, release any cable-ties securing the harness to the engine.

**16** Disconnect the clutch cable (early models) or the clutch hydraulic pipe from the transmission, referring to Chapter 6 as necessary. Move the cable or pipe clear of the transmission.

**17** Remove the power steering pump drive-belt as described in Chapter 1. Working as described in Chapter 10, unbolt the power steering pump from the engine, and tie it to one side without disconnecting the fluid hoses.

**18** Disconnect the harness plug on top of the radiator, then disconnect the individual plugs from the fan resistor and diode, as applicable **(see illustrations)**.

**19** Attach a hoist (or engine support beam) to the engine and transmission. Raise and support the car securely on axle stands, sufficiently high to allow the engine to be withdrawn from under the car. Remove the front wheels.

**20** Where applicable, unbolt the air conditioning receiver/dryer from the subframe, and tie it clear of the engine without disconnecting or straining the hoses.

**21** Support the radiator, then unscrew the air conditioning condenser lower mounting bolts and move the condenser aside without disconnecting the hoses. When removing the radiator mounting rubbers, note that they are handed.

**22** Remove the radiator and fan assembly, referring to Chapter 3 if necessary.

**23** Remove the exhaust downpipe/front section as described in Chapter 4A.

**24** Note the fitted positions of the gear-change rods. Either unbolt the rods from the transmission (early models), or remove the exhaust heat shield and unbolt the selector mechanism from the floor (later models – see

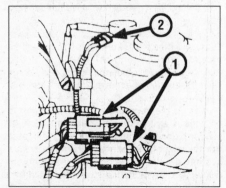

**4.15e Release and disconnect the large connectors (1) and the vacuum control valve (2)**

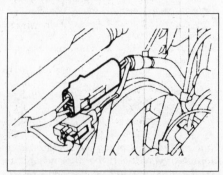

**4.18a Disconnect the harness plug on top of the radiator . . .**

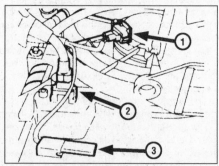

**4.18b . . . and the radiator fan plug (1), resistor (2) and diode (3)**

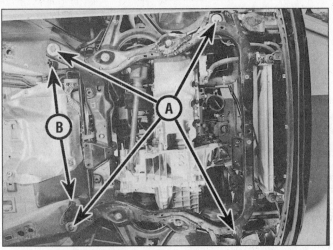

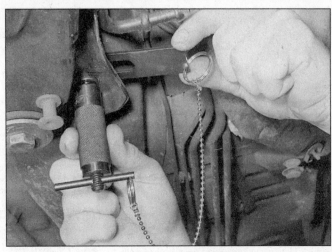

**4.44a  Subframe bolts (A) should only be tightened once the subframe is aligned – here using Ford tools (B) . . .**

**4.44b  . . . which are used as shown . . .**

Chapter 7 for more details). Unbolt the transmission rear support bar, and tie it to one side.

**25** Disconnect the two anti-roll bar link rods from the suspension arms, noting that the brake hoses (and where applicable, the ABS wiring) are attached. Disconnect the track rod ends from the wheel hubs, Unscrew and remove the through-bolt securing the outer end of each lower arm, and separate the lower arm balljoints – once the balljoints have been separated, refit them loosely for now, using the through-bolts.

**26** Ensure that the engine and transmission are adequately supported. Unbolt the rear mounting from the subframe, then remove the rear mounting through-bolt, and separate the mounting from the engine/transmission.

**27** Unbolt the steering rack from the subframe.

**28** Unbolt and remove the rear mounting from the transmission.

**29** Remove the through-bolt from the front mounting, and detach the mounting from the subframe. Mark the exact position of the front mounting, for easier refitting.

**30** Unbolt the power steering fluid cooler from the subframe.

**31** Mark the exact fitted position of the subframe, relative to the underside, using white paint, for instance (don't scribe its position, as this may encourage rust). In most cases, it will be possible to see the subframe's fitted position, thanks to the dirty/clean areas, but this should not be relied on.

**32** Unscrew the four subframe bolts, noting that they are of different lengths (the front bolts are gold in colour, while the rear ones are silver). If the lower arms were loosely refitted as described earlier, the subframe can be rested on them – when the lower arms are released once more, the subframe can be lowered out.

**33** Remove the driveshafts from the transmission as described below, and referring to Chapter 8 for more details if necessary:

a) *Unbolt the right-hand driveshaft support from the engine, and recover the heat shield.*

b) *Prise out the driveshafts from the transmission – provided the transmission was drained, there should be no significant oil loss. Keep the driveshafts as straight as possible  – bending the joints by more than 18° may cause damage.*

c) *Tie the driveshafts clear of the transmission, remembering that the engine/transmission are being lowered out.*

**34** On models with air conditioning, remove the compressor drivebelt as described in Chapter 1. Disconnect the compressor wiring plug, then remove the three mounting bolts and move it clear of the engine – tie it up without disconnecting the hoses.

**35** The engine should now be resting only on its left- and right-hand mountings, and everything else should have been disconnected from it. Check around the engine and transmission from above and below, to make sure there is nothing still attached or in the way which will prevent it from being lowered out. Also make sure there is enough room under the front of the car for the engine/transmission to be lowered out and withdrawn.

> **HAYNES HINT** *Lowering the engine/transmission onto a large board, some strong card, or even an old piece of carpet, will not only protect it from damage, but will make it easier to drag out from under the car.*

**36** Raise the engine hoist (or adjust the beam) to take the weight off the mountings, then remove the four nuts from the right-hand mounting, and three from the left-hand one.

**37** With the help of an assistant, begin by lowering the engine a little so that it clears its left- and right-hand mountings. Stop at this point, and check once more that nothing remains connected, and that nothing is in danger of getting caught up as the engine is lowered.

**38** Carefully lower the engine out, while your assistant guides the engine past any obstructions. When clear of the car, lower it to the ground. Be prepared to steady the engine when it touches down, to stop it toppling over. Withdraw the assembly from under the car, and remove it to wherever it will be worked on.

**Separation**

**39** Refer to Chapter 7 when separating the transmission from the engine.

**40** With the engine removed, take time to really inspect the items which are either hidden or taken for granted when the engine is installed – items such as the engine mountings, fuel lines, coolant and vacuum hoses. Similarly, it makes sense to inspect and renew the clutch components as described in Chapter 6 – given the amount of work required to access them, not to do so is a false economy. Also inspect the transmission oil seals, which are easily renewed while the unit is removed.

**Refitting**

**41** When the engine and transmission are ready to be lifted into place, once again have an assistant on hand to guide the assembly up to the left- and right-hand mountings. Use new mounting nuts, but do not fully tighten them until all the mountings have been refitted.

**42** Refit the driveshafts as described in Chapter 8 – take care not to bend the joints excessively.

**43** Where applicable, refit the air conditioning compressor and its drivebelt, referring to Chapter 1 if necessary.

**44** With the help of an assistant, offer up the subframe under the car, and align the marks made on removal. It is essential that the subframe is aligned correctly, or the car's handling will be affected. The subframe mounting holes should sit centrally over the threaded holes in the car – this can be done 'by eye', using an electric torch to see with, or there is a cone-shaped special tool which Ford dealers use **(see illustrations)**. When the

**4.44c ... although ordinary tools, used carefully, will achieve acceptable alignment**

alignment is correct, refit the subframe bolts, and tighten to the specified torque.

**45** Refit the engine front and rear mountings, tightening the bolts by hand only at this stage. There is a Ford special tool which fits in place of the front mounting, to align the engine exactly on the other three, but in the absence of this, it is acceptable just to let the engine settle on its mountings. Tighten the mounting nuts and bolts to the specified torque, moving the engine as little as possible, as this may place strain on the other mountings **(see illustrations)**.

**46** Refit the steering rack and the power steering fluid cooler to the subframe – refer to Chapter 10 if necessary.

**47** Further refitting is a reversal of removal, noting the following additional points:
  a) Tighten all nuts and bolts to the specified torque setting.
  b) Check and if necessary adjust the gearchange linkage as described in Chapter 7.
  c) Replenish the transmission oil, and check the level with reference to Chapter 1.
  d) Adjust the clutch cable, or top-up and bleed the clutch hydraulic system, as described in Chapter 6.
  e) Refill the cooling system as described in Chapter 1. If the engine oil was drained, refill it also as described in Chapter 1.

**4.45a Left-hand mounting nuts**

  f) Since the suspension and subframe have been disturbed, have the front wheel alignment checked as soon as possible.

## Facelift models (October 1996 on)

**Note:** *Read through the entire Section, as well as reading the advice in the preceding Section, before beginning this procedure. The engine and transmission are lifted out as a unit, then separated outside the car.*

### Removal

**48** Park the car on firm, level ground, apply the handbrake and chock the rear wheels. Loosen the front wheel nuts.

**49** Disconnect the battery negative lead, and position the lead away from the battery (also see *Disconnecting the battery*). For the best access, remove the battery as described in Chapter 5.

**50** Fit protective covers to both wings and the front crossmember (old pieces of carpet will suffice, as long as they are clean).

**51** Remove the bonnet as described in Chapter 11.

**52** Before disconnecting any of the coolant and vacuum hoses, fuel lines, wiring and earth connections, take careful note of how they are routed for refitting – if possible, take a few digital photos to serve as a reminder.

**53** Remove the air cleaner assembly and intercooler as described in Chapter 4A. Block the turbocharger openings with clean rag to prevent the entry of dirt.

**54** Unbolt and remove the auxiliary fusebox from the battery tray. Unbolt the earth lead, then remove the mounting bolts and take out the battery tray.

**55** Holding the strut piston still using an Allen key, loosen the upper nut on each front suspension strut by 5 turns – do not remove the nut.

**56** Inside the car, lock the gear lever in neutral using the Ford tool 16-088 (now tool number 308-273). If this tool is not available, the gearchange cables will have to be reset manually on completion, which should not be a problem.

**57** Jack up the front of the car, and support it on axle stands (see *Jacking and vehicle support*). Remove the front wheels.

**58** Remove the engine undershield, the cover below the radiator, and the wheel arch liners as described in Chapter 11.

**59** Drain the cooling system as described in Chapter 1, then disconnect the radiator hoses. Also drain the transmission oil as described in Chapter 7. If the engine is being overhauled, drain the engine oil and fit a new oil filter as described in Chapter 1.

**60** Disconnect the expansion tank hoses, then remove the expansion tank from the inner wing.

**61** Disconnect the radiator bottom hose from the water pump, and the top hose from the thermostat housing.

**62** Disconnect the fuel return hose from the injection pump.

**63** Unscrew and disconnect the vacuum line from the top of the brake vacuum pump.

**64** Disconnect the accelerator cable (and where applicable, the cruise control cable) from the injection pump, referring to Chapters 4A and 12 if necessary. Move the cable(s) to one side.

**65** Disconnect the EGR valve vacuum hose.

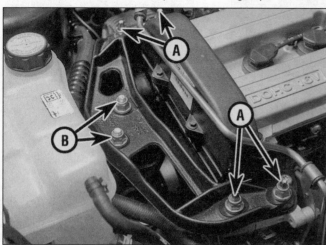

**4.45b Tighten the four right-hand mounting nuts (A) – mounting-to-bracket nuts (B) also shown (petrol engine shown)**

**4.45c Align the front mounting, then tighten the bracket nuts and through-bolt**

**66** Unscrew the nut in front of the fuel heater, and disconnect the glow plug wiring.

**67** On the left of the engine compartment (left as seen from the driver's seat), disconnect the two large wiring plugs next to the suspension strut mounting – note the metal clips on some connectors..

**68** Disconnect the vehicle speed sensor wiring plug from the back of the transmission. Also disconnect the reversing light switch, then release the wiring harness from its support bracket on top of the transmission.

**69** Release the wiring harness from the engine, and move it clear to avoid damage during engine removal.

**70** Unbolt the earth strap from the transmission.

**71** Remove the power steering pump drivebelt as described in Chapter 1. Working as described in Chapter 10, unbolt the power steering pump from the engine, and tie it to one side without disconnecting the fluid hoses. Unbolt the steering fluid hose bracket from the alternator.

**72** Disconnect the heater hoses – one from the oil cooler, one from the cylinder head. Tie the hoses clear, so they will not be damaged during engine removal.

**73** Remove the exhaust downpipe/front section as described in Chapter 4A.

**74** Disconnect the starter motor wiring.

**75** On models with air conditioning, remove the compressor drivebelt as described in Chapter 1. Disconnect the compressor wiring plug, then remove the three mounting bolts and move it clear of the engine – tie it up without disconnecting the hoses.

**76** Remove the crankshaft pulley as described in Chapter 2A.

**77** Where applicable, unbolt the air conditioning compressor mounting bracket from the engine.

**78** On the right-hand side of the car, note which way round the front suspension lower arm balljoint clamp bolt is fitted, then unscrew and remove it from the knuckle assembly. Lever the balljoint down from the knuckle; if it is tight, prise the joint open carefully using a large flat-bladed tool. Take care not to damage the balljoint seal or the ABS sensor during the separation procedure

**79** On the left-hand side of the car, disconnect the lower arm as described in paragraph 78. In addition, unscrew the nut securing the anti-roll bar drop link to the arm (noting that the brake hose and ABS wiring are attached), and disconnect the track rod end from the hub (see Chapter 10 if necessary).

**80** Remove the bolts securing the coolant pipe to the sump.

**81** Remove the driveshafts from the transmission as described below, and referring to Chapter 8 for more details if necessary:
a) *Unbolt the right-hand driveshaft support from the engine, and recover the heat shield.*
b) *Prise out the driveshafts from the transmission – provided the transmission*

*was drained, there should be no significant oil loss. Keep the driveshafts as straight as possible – bending the joints by more than 18° may cause damage.*
c) *Tie the driveshafts clear of the transmission, remembering that the engine/transmission are being lowered out.*

**82** Refit the coolant pipe to the sump, but only tighten the bolts by hand for now.

**83** Disconnect the gearchange cables from the transmission as described in Chapter 7.

**84** Disconnect the clutch hydraulic pipe from its connection on the transmission, as described in Chapter 6. Move the pipe clear of the transmission.

**85** Remove the through-bolt from the front mounting, and detach the mounting from the subframe. Note the exact position of the mounting, for easier refitting.

**86** Remove the through-bolt from the rear mounting on the subframe. Note the position of the mounting, for refitting, then remove the mounting bracket from the engine/transmission.

**87** Attach a hoist to the engine and transmission.

**88** The engine should now be resting only on its left- and right-hand mountings, and everything else should have been disconnected from it. Check around the engine and transmission from above and below, to make sure there is nothing still attached or in the way which will prevent it from being lifted out.

**89** Raise the engine hoist to take the weight off the mountings, then remove the five nuts from the right-hand mounting, and three from the left-hand one.

**90** With the help of an assistant, begin by lowering the engine a little so that it clears its left- and right-hand mountings. Stop at this point, and check once more that nothing remains connected, and that nothing is in danger of getting caught up as the engine is raised.

> **HAYNES HINT** *Lowering the engine/transmission onto a large board, some strong card, or even an old piece of carpet, will not only protect it from damage, but will make it easier to move, once it has been removed from the car.*

**91** Carefully lift the engine, while your assistant guides it past any obstructions. When clear of the car, swing the hoist to one side and lower it to the ground. Be prepared to steady the engine when it touches down, to stop it toppling over. Remove the assembly to wherever it will be worked on.

### Separation

**92** Refer to Chapter 7 when separating the transmission from the engine.

**93** With the engine removed, take time to really inspect the items which are either hidden or

taken for granted when the engine is installed – items such as the engine mountings, fuel lines, coolant and vacuum hoses. Similarly, it makes sense to inspect and renew the clutch components as described in Chapter 6 – given the amount of work required to access them, not to do so is a false economy. Also inspect the transmission oil seals, which are easily renewed while the unit is removed.

### Refitting

**94** When the engine and transmission are ready to be lifted and lowered into place, once again have an assistant on hand to guide the assembly onto the left- and right-hand mountings. Do not fully tighten the mounting nuts until all the mountings have been refitted.

**95** Refit and reconnect the clutch hydraulic pipe to the transmission (see Chapter 6).

**96** Reconnect the gearchange cables to the transmission as described in Chapter 7.

**97** Refit the engine front and rear mountings, aligning them as noted on removal, and tightening the bolts by hand only at first. Let the engine settle on its mountings, then tighten the mounting nuts and bolts to the specified torque, moving the engine as little as possible, as this may place strain on the other mountings.

**98** Refit the driveshafts – take care not to bend the joints excessively.

**99** Where applicable, refit the air conditioning compressor and its drivebelt, referring to Chapter 1 if necessary.

**100** Further refitting is a reversal of removal, noting the following additional points:
a) *Tighten all nuts and bolts to the specified torque setting.*
b) *Check and if necessary adjust the gearchange cables as described in Chapter 7.*
c) *Replenish the transmission oil, and check the level with reference to Chapter 1.*
d) *Top-up and bleed the clutch hydraulic system, as described in Chapter 6.*
e) *Refill the cooling system as described in Chapter 1.*
f) *Since the suspension has been disturbed, have the front wheel alignment checked as soon as possible.*

### 5 Engine overhaul – dismantling sequence

**1** It is much easier to dismantle and work on the engine if it is mounted on a portable engine stand. These stands can often be hired from a tool hire shop. Before the engine is mounted on a stand, the flywheel should be removed (Part A of this Chapter) so that the stand bolts can be tightened into the end of the cylinder block/crankcase.

**2** If a stand is not available, it is possible to dismantle the engine with it mounted on blocks, on a sturdy workbench or on the floor. Be extra careful not to tip or drop the engine when working without a stand.

**6.2a Removing the oil pressure switch . . .**

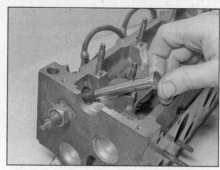

**6.2b . . . and the vacuum pump pushrod**

**6.3a Standard valve spring compressor modified for the diesel engine as shown**

**3** If you are going to obtain a reconditioned engine, all external components must be removed first, to be transferred to the new engine (just as they will if you are doing a complete engine overhaul yourself). **Note:** *When removing the external components from the engine, pay close attention to details that may be helpful or important during refitting. Note the fitted position of gaskets, seals, spacers, pins, washers, bolts and other small items.* These external components include the following:

a) Alternator and brackets (Chapter 5).
b) Glow plugs (Chapter 5).
c) Thermostat and housing (Chapter 3).
d) Dipstick tube.
e) Fuel system components (Chapter 4A).
f) All electrical switches and sensors.
g) Inlet and exhaust manifolds (Part A of this Chapter).
h) Oil filter (Chapter 1).

**6.3b Removing a valve spring and seat**

i) Engine/transmission mounting brackets (Part A of this Chapter).
j) Flywheel (Part A of this Chapter).

**4** If you are obtaining a 'short' engine (which consists of the engine cylinder block/crankcase, crankshaft, pistons and connecting rods all assembled), then the cylinder head, sump, oil pump and timing belt will have to be removed also.

**5** If you are planning a complete overhaul, the engine can be dismantled and the internal components removed in the following order.

a) Inlet and exhaust manifolds (Part A of this Chapter)
b) Timing belt and toothed pulleys (Part A of this Chapter)
c) Cylinder head (Part A of this Chapter)
d) Flywheel (Part A of this Chapter)
e) Sump (Part A of this Chapter)
f) Oil pump (Part A of this Chapter)
g) Auxiliary shaft (Section 9)

h) Piston/connecting rod assemblies (Section 10)
i) Crankshaft (Section 11)

**Note:** *The timing belt/drivebelt housing must be removed from the right-hand end of the cylinder block/crankcase to permit thorough cleaning and examination of the major engine castings. This can be done by removing the retaining screws and bolts once the timing belt/ injection pump drivebelt, their tensioners and all associated pulleys have been removed (see the relevant Sections of Part A of this Chapter) – collect and discard the housing gasket and the two rubber oilway seals from behind the housing – these must be renewed as a matter of course whenever they are disturbed.*

**6** Before beginning the dismantling and overhaul procedures, make sure that you have all of the correct tools necessary.

## 6 Cylinder head – dismantling

**Note:** *New and reconditioned cylinder heads are available from the manufacturers, and from engine overhaul specialists. Due to the fact that some specialist tools are required for the dismantling and inspection procedures, and new components may not be readily available (refer to Section 1), it may be more practical and economical for the home mechanic to purchase a reconditioned head, rather than to dismantle, inspect and recondition the original head.*

**1** Remove the camshaft and tappets (Part A of this Chapter).

**2** Remove the cylinder head (Part A of this Chapter) **(see illustrations)**.

**3** Using a valve spring compressor, compress each valve spring in turn until the split collets can be removed. A special valve spring compressor will be required, to reach into the deep wells in the cylinder head; such compressors are now widely available from most good motor accessory shops. Release the compressor, and lift off the spring upper seat and spring **(see illustrations)**.

**4** If, when the valve spring compressor is screwed down, the spring upper seat refuses to free and expose the split collets, gently tap the top of the tool, directly over the upper seat, with a light hammer. This will free the seat.

**5** Withdraw the valve through the combustion chamber. If it binds in the guide (won't pull through), push it back in, and de-burr the area around the collet groove with a fine file or whetstone; take care not to mark the tappet bores.

**6** It is essential that the valves are kept together with their collets, spring seats and springs, and in their correct sequence (unless they are so badly worn that they are to be renewed). If they are going to be kept and used again, place them in a labelled polythene bag or similar small container **(see illustrations)**. Note that No 1 valve is nearest to the timing belt end of the engine.

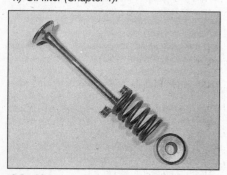

**6.6a Valve, spring, spring seat and collets**

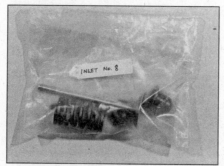

**6.6b Use a clearly-labelled bag to store and identify the valve components**

7 If the oil supply jet is to be removed (to flush out the cylinder head oil galleries thoroughly), seek the advice of a Ford dealer as to how it can be extracted; it may be that the only course of action involves destroying the jet as follows. Screw a self-tapping screw into its hole, and use the screw to provide purchase with which the jet can be drawn out; a new jet must be purchased and pressed into place on reassembly **(see illustration)**.

8 If the swirl chambers are badly burnt or cracked, they can be tapped out with a soft metal drift, through the injector holes. If the swirl chambers are likely to be refitted, mark them for position.

**6.7 Cylinder head oil supply jet – arrowed**

## 7 Cylinder head and valve components – cleaning and inspection

1 Thorough cleaning of the cylinder head and valve components, followed by a detailed inspection, will enable you to decide how much valve service work must be carried out during the engine overhaul. **Note:** *If the engine has been severely overheated, it is best to assume that the cylinder head is warped, and to check carefully for signs of this.*

### Cleaning

2 Scrape away all traces of old gasket material and sealing compound from the cylinder head.

3 Scrape away the carbon from the combustion chambers and ports, then wash the cylinder head thoroughly with paraffin or a suitable solvent.

4 Scrape off any heavy carbon deposits that may have formed on the valves, then use a power-operated wire brush to remove deposits from the valve heads and stems.

5 The swirl chambers may be removed from their locations using a soft metal drift inserted through the injector holes (if this is done, mark the swirl chambers so that they can be refitted in their original locations). Before removing the swirl chambers use feeler blades and a straight-edge to measure their projection, and compare with the information given in the Specifications **(see illustration)**. Alternatively, use a dial test indicator to make the check. Zero the dial test indicator on the gasket surface of the cylinder head, then measure the protrusion of the swirl chamber.

6 If the head is extremely dirty, it should be steam-cleaned. On completion, make sure that all oil holes and oil galleries are cleaned.

### Inspection

**Note:** *Be sure to perform all the following inspection procedures before concluding that the services of a machine shop or engine overhaul specialist are required. Make a list of all items that require attention.*

#### Cylinder head

7 Inspect the head very carefully for cracks, evidence of coolant leakage, and other damage. If cracks are found, a new cylinder head should be obtained.

8 Use a straight-edge and feeler blade to check that the cylinder head surface is not distorted. Do not position the straight-edge over the swirl chambers, as these may be proud of the cylinder head face. If the specified distortion limit is exceeded, machining of the gasket face is not recommended by the manufacturers, so the only course of action is to renew the cylinder head.

9 Examine the valve seats in each of the combustion chambers. If they are severely pitted, cracked or burned, then they will need to be renewed or re-cut by an engine overhaul specialist. If they are only slightly pitted, this can be removed by grinding-in the valve heads and seats with fine valve-grinding compound, as described below.

10 If the valve guides are worn, indicated by a side-to-side motion of the valve in the guide, new guides must be fitted. If necessary, insert a new valve in the guides to determine if the wear is on the guide or valve. If new guides

are to be fitted, the valves must be renewed as a matter of course. Valve guides may be renewed using a press and a suitable mandrel, however, the work is best carried out by an engine overhaul specialist, since if it is not done skilfully, there is a risk of damaging the cylinder head.

11 The renewal of valve guides is best carried out by an engine overhaul specialist.

12 If the valve seats are to be re-cut, this must be done only after the guides have been renewed.

13 Inspect the swirl chambers for burning or cracks, and renew the chambers if necessary.

#### Valves

14 Examine the head of each valve for pitting, burning, cracks and general wear, and check the valve stem for scoring and wear ridges. Rotate the valve, and check for any obvious indication that it is bent. Look for pits and excessive wear on the end of each valve stem. If the valve appears satisfactory at this stage, measure the valve stem diameter at several points using a micrometer **(see illustration)**. Any significant difference in the readings obtained indicates wear of the valve stem. Should any of these conditions be apparent, the valve(s) must be renewed.

15 If the valves are in satisfactory condition, they should be ground (lapped) into their respective seats, to ensure a smooth gas-tight seal. If the seat is only lightly pitted, or if it has been re-cut, fine grinding compound only should be used to produce the required finish. Coarse valve-grinding compound should not be used unless a seat is badly burned or deeply pitted; if this is the case, the cylinder head and valves should be inspected by an expert, to decide whether seat re-cutting, or even the renewal of the valve or seat insert, is required.

16 Valve grinding is carried out as follows. Place the cylinder head upside-down on a bench, with a block of wood at each end to give clearance for the valve stems.

17 Smear a trace of (the appropriate grade of) valve-grinding compound on the seat face, and press a suction grinding tool onto the valve head. With a semi-rotary action, grind the valve head to its seat, lifting the valve occasionally to redistribute the grinding compound **(see illustration)**. A light spring

**7.5 Measuring swirl chamber projection**

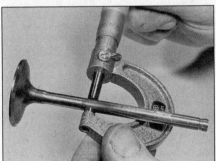

**7.14 Measuring the diameter of a valve stem**

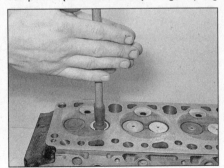

**7.17 Grinding-in a valve**

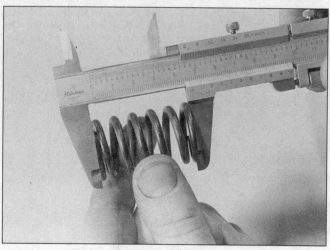

**7.20 Checking the valve spring free length**

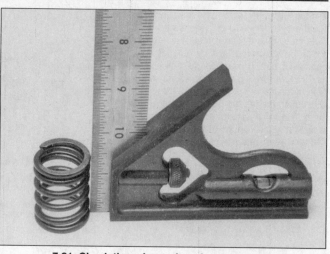

**7.21 Check the valve springs for squareness**

placed under the valve head will greatly ease this operation.

**18** If coarse grinding compound is being used, work only until a dull, matt even surface is produced on both the valve seat and the valve, then wipe off the used compound, and repeat the process with fine compound. When a smooth unbroken ring of light grey matt finish is produced on both the valve and seat, the grinding operation is complete. Do not grind in the valves any further than absolutely necessary, or the seat will be prematurely sunk into the cylinder head.

**19** When all the valves have been ground-in, carefully wash off all traces of grinding compound, using paraffin or a suitable solvent, before reassembly of the cylinder head.

### Valve components

**20** Examine the valve springs for signs of damage and discolouration, and also measure their free length (or compare each of the existing springs with a new component) **(see illustration)**.

**21** Stand each spring on a flat surface, and check it for squareness **(see illustration)**. If any of the springs are damaged, distorted, or have lost their tension, obtain a complete set of new springs.

**22** Check the spring seats and collets for obvious wear and cracks. Any questionable

**8.4 Fitting a valve stem oil seal. The end of the stem is covered with plastic film**

parts should be renewed, as extensive damage will occur if they fail during engine operation. Any damaged or excessively-worn parts must be renewed; the valve stem oil seals must be renewed as a matter of course whenever they are disturbed.

**23** Check the tappets as described in Part A of this Chapter.

### 8 Cylinder head – reassembly

**1** Regardless of whether or not the head was sent away for repair work of any sort, make sure that it is clean before beginning reassembly. Be sure to remove any metal particles and abrasive grit that may still be present from operations such as valve grinding. Use compressed air, if available, to blow out all the oil holes and passages.

**2** If the swirl chambers have been removed, refit them to their original locations. Check the protrusion of the swirl chambers as described in Section 7.

**3** Beginning at one end of the head, lubricate and install the first valve. Apply molybdenum disulphide-based grease or clean engine oil to the valve stem, and refit the valve. Where the original valves are being re-used, ensure that each is refitted in its original guide. If new valves are being fitted, insert them into the locations to which they have been ground.

**4** Fit the plastic protector supplied with new valve stem oil seals to the end of the valve stem – if no sleeves are provided, cover the collet grooves at the top of each valve by wrapping round a little adhesive tape. Lubricate the oil seal with clean engine oil, and put the seal squarely on top of the valve stem **(see illustration)**. Fit the seals by pushing into position using a suitable deep socket. Ensure that the seals are fully engaged with the valve guide. Note that new inlet and exhaust seals are usually different colours – green for the inlet valves, red for the exhaust valves.

**5** Refit the valve spring and spring seat, keeping the components in their original fitted positions, as applicable.

**6** Compress the spring with a valve spring compressor, and carefully install the collets in the stem grooves. Apply a small dab of grease to each collet to hold it in place if necessary **(see illustration)**. Slowly release the compressor, and make sure the collets seat properly.

**7** When the valve is installed, place the cylinder head flat on the bench and, using a hammer and interposed block of wood, tap the end of the valve stem gently, to settle the components.

**8** Repeat the procedure for the remaining valves.

**9** Refit the tappets as described in Part A of this Chapter.

### 9 Auxiliary shaft – removal, inspection and refitting

**Note:** *A new auxiliary shaft oil seal/housing and oil pump gasket will be required on refitting.*

#### *Removal*

**1** Remove the auxiliary shaft toothed pulley and the oil pump as described in Chapter 2A.

**8.6 Apply a little grease to the collets before installation, to hold them in place**

**2** Unbolt the timing belt inner shield.

**3** Unscrew the bolts and remove the oil seal housing from the cylinder block. The oil seal is integral with the housing.

**4** Unscrew the bolts securing the thrustplate to the cylinder block, then carefully withdraw the auxiliary shaft, taking care not to allow the oil pump gear to snag on the shaft bearing.

**5** Remove the thrustplate from the shaft, noting that the oilways are facing outwards **(see illustrations)**.

### Inspection

**6** Examine the auxiliary shaft and oil pump drivegear for pitting, scoring or wear ridges on the bearing journals, and for chipping or wear of the gear teeth. Renew as necessary. Check the auxiliary shaft bearings in the cylinder block for wear and, if worn, have these renewed by your Ford dealer or suitably-equipped engineering works. Wipe them clean if they are still serviceable.

**7** Temporarily fit the thrustplate to its position on the auxiliary shaft, and check for excessive wear. If possible, compare the shaft and thrustplate with new components to indicate the amount of wear, and renew them if necessary.

### Refitting

**8** Lubricate the bearing journals of the auxiliary shaft and the bearings in the cylinder block with fresh engine oil.

**9** Lubricate the thrustplate, then locate it on the shaft with the oilways facing outwards (ie, towards the toothed pulley). Insert the shaft and thrustplate into the cylinder block, then refit the bolts and tighten to the specified torque.

**10** Clean the timing belt/drivebelt housing, the cylinder block and the auxiliary shaft end.

**11** Smear fresh engine oil on the auxiliary shaft, and on the sealing lips of the new oil seal. Before fitting the new seal, locate the special fitting ring inside the sealing lips.

**12** Locate the new oil seal housing over the end of the auxiliary shaft, then insert the bolts and tighten.

**13** Carefully remove the special ring and make sure that the seal lips are located on the shaft correctly.

**14** Refit the timing belt side cover and tighten the bolts.

**15** Refit the auxiliary shaft toothed pulley and the oil pump as described in Chapter 2A.

### 10 Piston/connecting rod assemblies – removal

**1** Remove the cylinder head, sump, oil pump pick-up tube and baffle plate with reference to Chapter 2A.

**2** Rotate the crankshaft so that No 1 big-end cap (timing end of the engine) is at the lowest point of its travel. If the big-end cap and rod are not already numbered, mark them with a

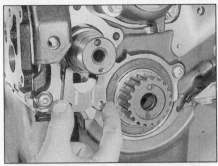

**9.5a Withdraw the auxiliary shaft a little, then remove the thrust plate**

marker pen **(see illustration)**. Mark both cap and rod to identify the cylinder they operate in.

**3** Unscrew and remove the big-end bearing cap bolts, and withdraw the cap complete with shell bearing from the connecting rod. Make sure that the shell remains in the cap, and if necessary identify it for position.

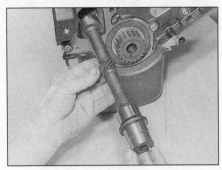

**9.5b Removing the auxiliary shaft**

**4** If only the bearing shells are being attended to, push the connecting rod up and off the crankpin, and remove the upper bearing shell. Keep the bearing shells and cap together in their correct sequence if they are to be refitted.

**5** If the piston is being removed, push the connecting rod up and remove the piston and

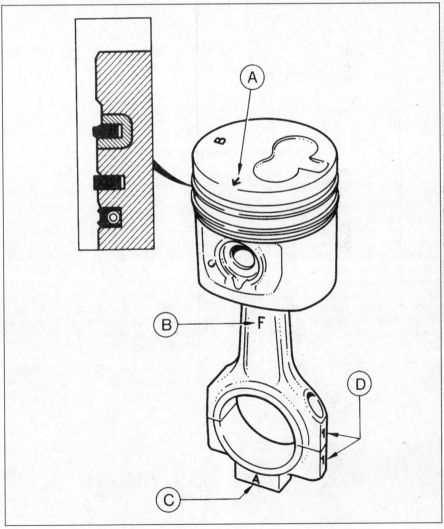

**10.2 Piston and connecting rod. Inset shows ring profiles**

*A Arrow*          *B Front mark*          *C Length class mark*          *D Cylinder number*

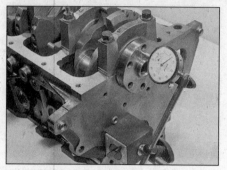

**11.2 Checking crankshaft endfloat with a dial gauge**

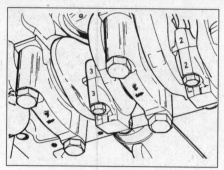

**11.5 Big-end and main bearing cap markings**

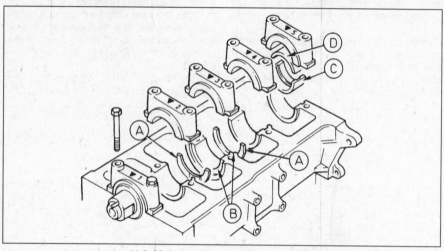

**11.6 Main bearing cap removal details**

A   Thrustwashers
B   Thrustwasher grooves – No 3 bearing
C   Upper shell – with groove
D   Lower shell – plain

rod from the top of the bore. Note that if there is a pronounced wear ridge at the top of the bore, there is a risk of damaging the piston as the rings foul the ridge. However, it is reasonable to assume that a rebore and new pistons will be required in any case if the ridge is so pronounced.

**6** Repeat the procedure for the remaining piston/connecting rod assemblies. Ensure that the caps and rods are marked before removal, as described previously, and keep all components in order.

## 11 Crankshaft – removal

**1** Remove the timing belts, crankshaft sprocket, timing belt inner shield, sump, oil pick-up tube, flywheel and left-hand/flywheel end oil seal housing. The pistons/connecting rods must be free of the crankshaft journals, however it is not essential to remove them completely from the cylinder block.

**2** Before the crankshaft is removed, check the endfloat. Mount a dial gauge with the probe in line with the crankshaft and just touching the crankshaft (see illustration).
**3** Push the crankshaft fully away from the gauge, and zero it. Next, lever the crankshaft towards the gauge as far as possible, and check the reading obtained. The distance that the crankshaft moved is its endfloat; if it is greater than specified, new thrustwashers will be required.
**4** If no dial gauge is available, feeler blades can be used. Gently lever or push the crankshaft in one direction, then insert feeler blades between the crankshaft web and the main bearing to determine the clearance.
**5** Check that the main bearing caps have marks to indicate their respective fitted positions in the block. They also have arrow marks pointing towards the timing end of the engine to indicate correct orientation (see illustration).
**6** Unscrew the retaining bolts, and remove the main bearing caps (see illustration). If the caps are reluctant to separate from the block face, lightly tap them free using a plastic- or copper-faced hammer. If the bearing shells are likely to be used again, keep them with their bearing caps for safekeeping. However, unless the engine is known to be of low mileage, it is recommended that they be renewed.
**7** Lift the crankshaft out from the crankcase, then extract the upper bearing shells and side thrustwashers (see illustration). Keep them with their respective caps for correct repositioning if they are to be used again.

## 12 Cylinder block/crankcase – cleaning and inspection

### Cleaning

**1** For complete cleaning, the core plugs should be removed. Drill a small hole in them, then insert a self-tapping screw and pull out the plugs using a pair of grips or a slide-hammer (see illustration). Also remove all external components and senders (if not already done), noting their locations. Remove the oil jets from the bottom of each bore.
**2** Scrape all traces of gasket or sealant from the cylinder block, taking care not to damage the head and sump mating faces.
**3** If the block is extremely dirty, it should be steam-cleaned.
**4** After the block has been steam-cleaned, clean all oil holes and oil galleries one more time. Flush all internal passages with warm water until the water runs clear, dry the block thoroughly and wipe all machined surfaces with a light rust-preventative oil. If you have access to compressed air, use it to speed up the drying process and to blow out all the oil holes and galleries.

 **Warning: Wear eye protection when using compressed air.**

**11.7 Felt marker pens can be used as shown to identify bearing shells without damaging them**

**12.1 The core plugs should be removed with a puller – if they're driven into the block, they may be impossible to retrieve**

**12.6  All bolt holes in the block – particularly the main bearing cap and head bolt holes – should be cleaned and restored with a tap**

5  If the block is not very dirty, you can do an adequate cleaning job with hot soapy water and a stiff brush. Take plenty of time, and do a thorough job. Regardless of the cleaning method used, be sure to clean all oil holes and galleries very thoroughly, dry the block completely and coat all machined surfaces with light oil.

6  The threaded holes in the block must be clean to ensure accurate torque wrench readings during reassembly. Run the proper-size tap into each of the holes to remove rust, corrosion, thread sealant or sludge, and to restore damaged threads **(see illustration)**. If possible, use compressed air to clear the holes of debris produced by this operation. Now is a good time to clean the threads on the head bolts and the main bearing cap bolts as well.

7  Where applicable, refit the main bearing caps, and tighten the bolts finger-tight.

8  After coating the mating surfaces of the new core plugs with suitable sealant, refit them in the cylinder block. Make sure that they are driven in straight and seated properly, or leakage could result. Special tools are available for this purpose, but a large socket, with an outside diameter that will just slip into the core plug, will work just as well **(see illustration)**.

9  Make sure that the oil jets are cleaned thoroughly. After cleaning the cylinder block, refit the jets **(see illustration)**.

10  If the engine is not going to be reassembled right away, cover it with a large plastic bag to keep it clean and prevent it rusting.

### Inspection

11  Visually check the block for cracks, rust and corrosion. Look for stripped threads in the threaded holes. If there has been any history of internal water leakage, it may be worthwhile having an engine overhaul specialist check the block with special equipment. If defects are found, have the block repaired, if possible, or renewed.

12  Check the cylinder bores for scuffing and scoring. Normally, bore wear will be evident in the form of a wear ridge at the top of the bore. This ridge marks the limit of piston travel.

13  Measure the diameter of each cylinder at the top (just under the ridge area), centre

**12.8  A large socket on an extension can be used to drive the new core plugs into their bores**

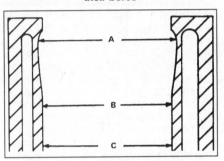

**12.13  Measure the diameter of each cylinder just under the wear ridge (A), at the centre (B) and at the bottom (C)**

and bottom of the cylinder bore, parallel to the crankshaft axis **(see illustration)**.

14  Next measure each cylinder's diameter at the same three locations across the crankshaft axis. If the difference between any of the measurements is greater than 0.20 mm, indicating that the cylinder is excessively out-of-round or tapered, then remedial action must be considered.

15  Repeat this procedure for the remaining cylinders, then measure the diameter of each piston at right-angles to the gudgeon pin axis, and compare the result with the information given in the Specifications **(see illustration)**. By comparing the piston diameters with the bore diameters, an idea can be obtained of the clearances.

16  If the cylinder walls are badly scuffed or scored, or if they are excessively out-of-round or tapered, have the cylinder block rebored

**12.19a  A 'bottle-brush' hone will produce better results if you have never honed cylinders before**

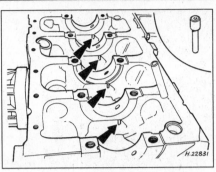

**12.9  Piston-cooling oil jet locations (arrowed)**

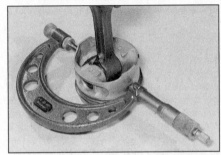

**12.15  Measure the piston skirt diameter at right-angles to the gudgeon pin axis, just above the base of the skirt**

(where possible) by an engine overhaul specialist. New pistons (oversize in the case of a rebore) will also be required.

17  If the cylinders are in reasonably good condition, then it may only be necessary to renew the piston rings.

18  If this is the case, the bores should be honed in order to allow the new rings to bed in correctly and provide the best possible seal. The conventional type of hone has spring-loaded stones, and is used with a power drill. You will also need some paraffin or honing oil and rags.

19  The hone should be moved up-and-down the cylinder to produce a crosshatch pattern, and plenty of honing oil should be used. Ideally, the crosshatch lines should intersect at approximately a 60° angle **(see illustrations)**.

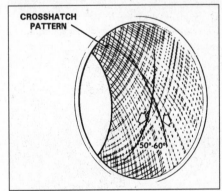

**12.19b  The cylinder hone should leave a smooth, cross-hatch pattern with the lines intersecting at approximately a 60° angle**

**13.2 Using feeler blades to remove piston rings**

**13.4 Piston ring grooves can be cleaned using a piece of an old ring**

**13.10 Checking the ring-to-groove clearance**

Do not take off more material than is necessary to produce the required finish. If new pistons are being fitted, the piston manufacturers may specify a finish with a different angle, so their instructions should be followed.

20 Do not withdraw the hone from the cylinder while it is still being turned, but stop it first (keep the hone moving up-and-down the bore while it slows down). After honing a cylinder, wipe out all traces of the honing oil. If equipment of this type is not available, or if you are not sure whether you are competent to undertake the task yourself, an engine overhaul specialist will carry out the work at a moderate cost.

21 Refit all external components and senders in their correct locations, as noted before removal.

## 13 Piston/connecting rod assemblies – inspection and reassembly

### Inspection

1 Before the inspection process can begin, the piston/connecting rod assemblies must be cleaned, and the original piston rings removed from the pistons.

2 Carefully expand the old rings over the top of the pistons. The use of two or three old feeler blades will be helpful in preventing the rings dropping into empty grooves **(see illustration)**. Note that the oil control scraper ring is in two sections.

3 Scrape away all traces of carbon from the

top of the piston. A hand-held wire brush or a piece of fine emery cloth can be used once the majority of the deposits have been scraped away.

4 Remove the carbon from the ring grooves in the piston by cleaning them using an old ring **(see illustration)**. Break the ring in half to do this. Be very careful to remove only the carbon deposits; do not remove any metal, or scratch the sides of the ring grooves. Protect your fingers – piston rings are sharp.

5 Once the deposits have been removed, clean the piston/connecting rod assembly with paraffin or a suitable solvent, and dry thoroughly. Make sure the oil return holes in the ring grooves are clear.

6 If the pistons and cylinder bores are not damaged or worn excessively, and if the cylinder block does not need to be rebored, the original pistons can be re-used. Normal piston wear appears as even vertical wear on the piston thrust surfaces, and slight looseness of the top ring in its groove. New piston rings, however, should always be used when the engine is reassembled.

7 Carefully inspect each piston for cracks around the skirt, at the gudgeon pin bosses, and at the piston ring lands (between the piston ring grooves).

8 Look for scoring and scuffing on the sides of the skirt, holes in the piston crown, and burned areas at the edge of the crown. If the skirt is scored or scuffed, the engine may have been suffering from overheating and/or abnormal combustion, which caused excessively-high operating temperatures. The cooling and lubricating systems should

be checked thoroughly. Scorch marks on the sides of the pistons show that blow-by has occurred and the rings are not sealing correctly. A hole in the piston crown is an indication that abnormal combustion has been occurring. If any of the above problems exist, the causes must be corrected, or the damage will occur again – incorrect injection pump timing or a faulty injector may be the cause.

9 Corrosion of the piston, in the form of small pits, indicates that coolant is leaking into the combustion chamber and/or the crankcase. Again, the cause must be corrected, or the problem may persist in the rebuilt engine.

10 If new rings are being fitted to old pistons, measure the piston ring-to-groove clearance by placing a new piston ring in each ring groove and measuring the clearance with a feeler blade. Check the clearance at three or four places around each groove **(see illustration)**. If the new ring is excessively tight, the most likely cause is dirt remaining in the groove.

11 Check the piston-to-bore clearance by measuring the cylinder bore and the piston diameter. Measure the piston across the skirt, at a 90° angle to the gudgeon pin, approximately half-way down the skirt. Subtract the piston diameter from the bore diameter to obtain the clearance. If this is greater than the figures given in the Specifications, the block will have to be rebored and new pistons and rings fitted.

12 Check the fit of the gudgeon pin by twisting the piston and connecting rod in opposite directions. Any noticeable play indicates excessive wear, which must be corrected. The gudgeon pins are secured by circlips, so the pistons and connecting rods can be separated without difficulty **(see illustration)**. Note the position of the piston relative to the rod before dismantling, and use new circlips on reassembly.

13 Before refitting the rings to the pistons, check their end gaps by inserting each of them in their cylinder bores. Use the piston to make sure that they are square. Using feeler blades, check that the gaps are within the tolerances given in the Specifications **(see illustration)**. Genuine rings are supplied pre-gapped; no attempt should be made to adjust the gaps by filing.

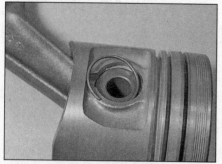

**13.12 Removing a gudgeon pin circlip**

**13.13 Measuring a piston ring end gap**

## Reassembly

**14** Install the new rings by fitting them over the top of the piston, starting with the oil control scraper ring sections. Use feeler blades in the same way as when removing the old rings. New rings generally have their top surfaces identified, and must be fitted the correct way round **(see illustration and illustration 10.2)**. Note that the first and second compression rings have different sections. Be careful when handling the compression rings; they will break if they are handled roughly or expanded too far. With all the rings in position, space the ring gaps at 120° to each other. The oil control scraper ring expander must also be positioned opposite to the actual ring.

## 14 Crankshaft – inspection

**1** Clean the crankshaft and dry it with compressed air if available. Be sure to clean the oil holes with a pipe cleaner or similar probe.

⚠️ *Warning: Wear eye protection when using compressed air.*

**2** Check the main and big-end bearing journals for uneven wear, scoring, pitting and cracking.
**3** If the crankshaft has been reground, check for burrs around the crankshaft oil holes (the holes are usually chamfered, so burrs should not be a problem unless regrinding has been carried out carelessly). Remove any burrs with a fine file or scraper, and thoroughly clean the oil holes as described previously.
**4** Accurate measuring of the crankshaft bearing journals requires special tools and the experience to use them. Consequently, it is recommended that the task be entrusted to an automotive engineering workshop or specialist. If the crankshaft requires machining, they will be able to carry out the work and supply suitable oversize bearing shells.
**5** Check the oil seal contact surfaces at each end of the crankshaft for wear and damage. If an excessive groove is evident in the surface of the crankshaft, consult an engine overhaul specialist who will be able to advise whether a repair is possible or if a new crankshaft is necessary.

## 15 Main and big-end bearings – inspection

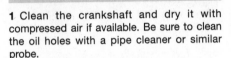

**1** Even though the main and big-end bearings should be renewed during the engine overhaul, the old bearings should be retained for close examination, as they may reveal valuable information about the condition of the engine. The size of the bearing shells is stamped on the back metal, and this information should be given to the supplier of the new shells.

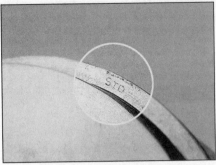

**13.14 Look for etched markings identifying the piston ring top surface**

**2** Bearing failure occurs because of lack of lubrication, the presence of dirt or other foreign particles, overloading the engine, and corrosion. Regardless of the cause of bearing failure, it must be corrected before the engine is reassembled, to prevent it from happening again **(see illustration)**.
**3** When examining the bearings, remove them from the engine block, the main bearing caps, the connecting rods and the rod caps, and lay them out on a clean surface in the same general position as their location in the engine. This will enable you to match any bearing problems with the corresponding crankshaft journal.
**4** Dirt and other foreign particles get into the engine in a variety of ways. Dirt may be left in the engine during assembly, or it may pass through filters or the crankcase ventilation system. It may get into the oil, and from there into the bearings. Metal chips from machining operations and normal engine wear are often present. Abrasives are sometimes left in engine components after reconditioning, especially when parts are not thoroughly

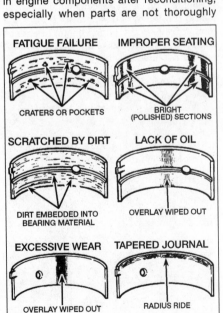

**15.2 Typical bearing shell failures**

cleaned using the proper cleaning methods. Whatever the source, these foreign objects often end up embedded in the soft bearing material, and are easily recognised. Large particles will not embed in the bearing, and will score or gouge the bearing and journal. The best prevention for this cause of bearing failure is to clean all parts thoroughly, and keep everything spotlessly-clean during engine assembly. Frequent and regular engine oil and filter changes are also recommended.
**5** Lack of lubrication (or lubrication breakdown) has a number of interrelated causes. Excessive heat (which thins the oil), overloading (which squeezes the oil from the bearing face) and oil leakage (from excessive bearing clearances, worn oil pump or high engine speeds) all contribute to lubrication breakdown. Blocked oil passages, which usually are the result of misaligned oil holes in a bearing shell, will also oil-starve a bearing and destroy it. When lack of lubrication is the cause of bearing failure, the bearing material is wiped or extruded from the steel backing of the bearing. Temperatures may increase to the point where the steel backing turns blue from overheating.
**6** Driving habits can have a definite effect on bearing life. Full-throttle, low-speed operation (labouring the engine) puts very high loads on bearings, which tends to squeeze out the oil film. These loads cause the bearings to flex, which produces fine cracks in the bearing face (fatigue failure). Eventually, the bearing material will loosen in pieces and tear away from the steel backing. Short-trip driving leads to corrosion of bearings, because insufficient engine heat is produced to drive off the condensed water and corrosive gases. These products collect in the engine oil, forming acid and sludge. As the oil is carried to the engine bearings, the acid attacks and corrodes the bearing material.
**7** Incorrect bearing installation during engine assembly will lead to bearing failure as well. Tight-fitting bearings leave insufficient bearing oil clearance, and will result in oil starvation. Dirt or foreign particles trapped behind a bearing shell result in high spots on the bearing which lead to failure.
**8** If new bearings are to be fitted, the bearing running clearances should be measured before the engine is finally reassembled, to ensure that the correct bearing shells have been obtained (see Sections 17 and 18). If the crankshaft has been reground, the engineering works which carried out the work will advise on the correct-size bearing shells to suit the work carried out.

## 16 Engine overhaul – reassembly sequence

**1** Before reassembly begins, ensure that all new parts have been obtained and that all necessary tools are available. Read through

**17.4a Fit the main bearing shells to their locations in the crankcase**

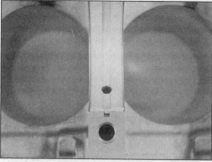

**17.4b Each bearing shell's tab engages the notch in the block or cap – shell oil holes must align with block oilways**

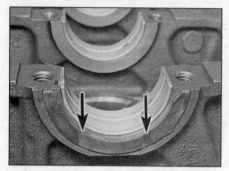

**17.5 Place the crankshaft thrustwashers into position with their oil grooves facing outwards**

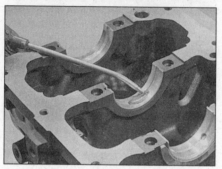

**17.6 Lubricate the upper shells before laying the crankshaft in place**

the entire procedure to familiarise yourself with the work involved, and to ensure that all items necessary for reassembly of the engine are at hand. In addition to all normal tools and materials, jointing and thread-locking compound will be needed during engine reassembly.

**2** Ford recommend a sealant to their specification SPM-4G-9112-F/G (see a Ford dealer) for the cylinder block/crankcase-to-sump/oil pump/oil seal carrier joints, and for No 1 camshaft bearing cap. In all other cases, provided the relevant mating surfaces are clean and flat, new gaskets will be sufficient to ensure joints are oil-tight.

**3** In order to save time and avoid problems, engine reassembly can be carried out in the following order:

a) Crankshaft and main bearings.
b) Pistons and connecting rods.

c) Oil pump.
d) Sump.
e) Flywheel.
f) Cylinder head.
g) Timing sprockets and belts.
h) Engine external components (including inlet and exhaust manifolds).

**4** Ensure that everything is clean prior to reassembly. As mentioned previously, dirt and metal particles can quickly destroy bearings and result in major engine damage. Use clean engine oil to lubricate during reassembly.

## 17 Crankshaft – refitting

**1** It is assumed at this point that the cylinder block/crankcase and crankshaft have been

cleaned and repaired or reconditioned as necessary. Position the engine upside-down.

**2** Remove the main bearing cap bolts, and lift out the caps. Lay the caps out in the proper order, to ensure correct installation.

**3** If they're still in place, remove the old bearing shells from the block and the main bearing caps. Wipe the bearing recesses of the block and caps with a clean, lint-free cloth. They must be kept spotlessly-clean.

**4** Wipe clean the backs of the bearing shells. Lightly oil the shells, and fit them into their respective positions in the crankcase. Note that the upper shells have grooves in them (the lower shells are plain). Where the old main bearings are being refitted, ensure that they are located in their original positions. Make sure that the tab on each bearing shell fits into the notch in the block or cap, and that the shell oil holes align with those on the block **(see illustrations)**.

*Caution: Don't hammer the shells into place, and don't damage the bearing faces.*

**5** Place the crankshaft thrustwashers into position in the crankcase, so that their oil grooves are facing outwards (away from the central web) **(see illustration)**. Hold them in position with a little grease.

**6** Apply a thin layer of clean engine oil to each shell **(see illustration)**. Coat the thrustwasher bearing surfaces as well.

**7** Make sure the crankshaft journals are clean, then lay the crankshaft in place in the block **(see illustration)**.

**8** Clean the bearing surfaces of the shells in the caps, then lubricate them with oil. Install the caps in their respective positions, with the arrows pointing to the timing belt end of the engine **(see illustration)**.

**9** Working on one cap at a time, from the centre main bearing outwards (and ensuring that each cap is tightened down squarely and evenly onto the block), tighten the main bearing cap bolts to the specified torque wrench setting. When all the bolts have been tightened to the Stage 1 torque, angle-tighten the bolts further in the same sequence using an angle-tightening adapter on a socket.

**10** Rotate the crankshaft a number of times by hand, to check for any obvious binding.

**11** Check the crankshaft endfloat (refer to Section 11).

**12** Refit the crankshaft left-hand/flywheel end oil seal housing and a new seal, as described in Chapter 2A.

**13** Refit the components removed in Section 11.

## 18 Piston/connecting rod assemblies – refitting

**1** Clean the backs of the big-end bearing shells and the recesses in the connecting rods and big-end caps. If new shells are being fitted, ensure that all traces of the protective

**17.7 Lowering the crankshaft onto the main bearings**

**17.8 Refitting the main bearing caps**

**18.2 The tab on each big-end bearing shell must engage with notch in connecting rod or cap**

**18.4a The arrow on the piston crown must point to the timing end of the engine**

**18.4b Drive the piston gently into the bore with the end of a wooden or plastic hammer handle**

grease are cleaned off using paraffin. Wipe the shells and connecting rods dry with a lint-free cloth.

**2** Press the big-end bearing shells into the connecting rods and caps in their correct positions. Make sure that the location tabs are engaged with the cut-outs in the connecting rods **(see illustration)**.

**3** Lubricate No 1 piston and piston rings, and check that the ring gaps are spaced at 120° intervals to each other.

**4** Fit a ring compressor to No 1 piston, then insert the piston and connecting rod into No 1 cylinder. Make sure that the arrow on the piston crown is facing the timing end of the engine. With No 1 crankpin at its lowest point, drive the piston carefully into the cylinder with the wooden handle of a hammer, at the same time guiding the connecting rod towards the crankpin **(see illustrations)**.

**5** Liberally lubricate the crankpin journals and big-end bearing shells. Fit the connecting rod onto the crankpin, then fit the corresponding big-end cap. Tighten the bearing cap bolts to the specified torque and angles, and turn the crankshaft each time to make sure that it is free before moving on to the next assembly.

**6** Repeat the above procedures on the remaining piston/connecting rod assemblies.

**7** On completion, refit the sump and cylinder head as described in Chapter 2A.

## 19 Engine – initial start-up after overhaul

**1** With the engine refitted in the car, double-check the engine oil and coolant levels (see *Weekly checks*). Make a final check that everything has been reconnected, and that there are no tools or rags left in the engine compartment.

**2** Remove the glow plugs, and disconnect the stop solenoid on the injection pump.

**3** Turn the engine over on the starter, until the oil pressure warning light goes out.

**4** Bleed the fuel system as described in Chapter 4A. Use the hand-priming pump, and turn the engine over several times, to assist with the bleeding process – at this stage, the engine will not start.

**5** Refit the glow plugs, and reconnect the stop solenoid.

**6** Turn the ignition key and wait for the pre-heating warning light to go out.

**7** Start the engine. Additional cranking may be necessary to completely bleed the fuel system before the engine starts.

**8** Once started, keep the engine running at fast tickover. Check that there are no leaks of oil, fuel and coolant. Check the power steering pipe/hose unions for leakage. Do not be alarmed if there are some odd smells and smoke from parts getting hot and burning off oil deposits.

**9** Keep the engine idling until hot coolant is felt circulating through the radiator top hose, indicating that the engine is at normal operating temperature, then stop the engine and allow it to cool.

**10** Recheck the oil and coolant levels, and top-up if necessary (see *Weekly checks*).

**11** Check the idle speed as described in Chapter 4A.

**12** If new pistons, rings or bearings have been fitted, the engine must be run-in at reduced speeds and loads for the first 500 miles or so. Do not operate the engine at full throttle, or allow it to labour in any gear during this period. It is recommended that the engine oil and filter be changed at the end of this period.

# Chapter 3
# Cooling, heating & ventilation systems

## Contents

Section number

Air conditioning system – general information and precautions . . . . 11
Air conditioning system components – removal and refitting . . . . . 12
Antifreeze – general information. . . . . . . . . . . . . . . . . . . . . . . . . . . . 2
Auxiliary drivebelt check and renewal . . . . . . . . . . . . . .See Chapter 1
Coolant level check . . . . . . . . . . . . . . . . . . . . . . . .See Weekly checks
Coolant renewal . . . . . . . . . . . . . . . . . . . . . . . . . . . . . .See Chapter 1
Cooling system checks (coolant leaks, hose condition) .See Chapter 1
Cooling system electrical switches and sensors – testing, removal and
   refitting . . . . . . . . . . . . . . . . . . . . . . . . . . . . . . . . . . . . . . . . . . . . 6
Cooling system hoses – disconnection and renewal . . . . . . . . . . . . 3

Section number

Cooling system servicing (draining, flushing and
   refilling) . . . . . . . . . . . . . . . . . . . . . . . . . . . . . . . . . . . .See Chapter 1
General information . . . . . . . . . . . . . . . . . . . . . . . . . . . . . . . . . . . . . 1
Heater/air conditioning controls – removal and refitting . . . . . . . . . 10
Heater/ventilation components – removal and refitting . . . . . . . . . . 9
Pollen filter renewal . . . . . . . . . . . . . . . . . . . . . . . . . . . .See Chapter 1
Radiator and expansion tank – removal, inspection and refitting . . . 7
Radiator electric cooling fan(s) – testing, removal and refitting . . . . . 5
Thermostat – removal, testing and refitting . . . . . . . . . . . . . . . . . . . 4
Water pump – checking, removal and refitting. . . . . . . . . . . . . . . . . 8

## Degrees of difficulty

| **Easy,** suitable for novice with little experience | **Fairly easy,** suitable for beginner with some experience | **Fairly difficult,** suitable for competent DIY mechanic | **Difficult,** suitable for experienced DIY mechanic | **Very difficult,** suitable for expert DIY or professional |
|---|---|---|---|---|

## Specifications

### Coolant
Mixture type . . . . . . . . . . . . . . . . . . . . . . . . . . . . . . . . . . . . . . . . . . .   See Lubricants and fluids on page 0•17
Cooling system capacity . . . . . . . . . . . . . . . . . . . . . . . . . . . . . . . . . .   See Chapter 1

### System pressure
Pressure test . . . . . . . . . . . . . . . . . . . . . . . . . . . . . . . . . . . . . . . . . . .   1.2 bars – should hold this pressure for at least 10 seconds

### Expansion tank filler cap
Pressure rating . . . . . . . . . . . . . . . . . . . . . . . . . . . . . . . . . . . . . . . . . .   1.2 bars approximately – see cap for actual value

### Thermostat
Starts to open. . . . . . . . . . . . . . . . . . . . . . . . . . . . . . . . . . . . . . . . . . .   92°C
Fully-open. . . . . . . . . . . . . . . . . . . . . . . . . . . . . . . . . . . . . . . . . . . . . .   106°C

### Radiator electric cooling fan
Switches on at:
   Single-speed fan and two-speed fan's first stage . . . . . . . . . . . . . .   100°C
   Two-speed fan's second stage. . . . . . . . . . . . . . . . . . . . . . . . . . . . .   103°C
Switches off at:
   Single-speed fan and two-speed fan's first stage . . . . . . . . . . . . . .   93°C
   Two-speed fan's second stage. . . . . . . . . . . . . . . . . . . . . . . . . . . . .   100°C

### Coolant temperature sensor
Resistance:
   At -40°C . . . . . . . . . . . . . . . . . . . . . . . . . . . . . . . . . . . . . . . . . . . . . .   860 to 900 kilohms
   At 20°C . . . . . . . . . . . . . . . . . . . . . . . . . . . . . . . . . . . . . . . . . . . . . . .   35 to 40 kilohms
   At 100°C . . . . . . . . . . . . . . . . . . . . . . . . . . . . . . . . . . . . . . . . . . . . . .   1.9 to 2.5 kilohms
   At 120°C . . . . . . . . . . . . . . . . . . . . . . . . . . . . . . . . . . . . . . . . . . . . . .   1.0 to 1.3 kilohms

### Air conditioning system
Refrigerant . . . . . . . . . . . . . . . . . . . . . . . . . . . . . . . . . . . . . . . . . . . . .   R134a

## Torque wrench settings

| | Nm | lbf ft |
|---|---|---|
| Air conditioning accumulator/dehydrator-to-subframe bolts . . . . . . . . | 7 | 5 |
| Air conditioning compressor mounting bolts . . . . . . . . . . . . . . . . . . . . | 25 | 18 |
| Air conditioning condenser mounting bolts . . . . . . . . . . . . . . . . . . . | 7 | 5 |
| Coolant drain plug . . . . . . . . . . . . . . . . . . . . . . . . . . . . . . . . | 23 | 17 |
| Coolant temperature sensor. . . . . . . . . . . . . . . . . . . . . . . . . . . | 23 | 17 |
| Coolant temperature gauge sender . . . . . . . . . . . . . . . . . . . . . . . | 8 | 6 |
| Radiator mounting bracket-to-subframe bolts: | | |
|   Pre-facelift models (1993 to October 1996) . . . . . . . . . . . . . . . . . | 23 | 17 |
|   Facelift models (October 1996 on) . . . . . . . . . . . . . . . . . . . . . | 10 | 7 |
| Thermostat cover/water outlet-to-thermostat housing bolts . . . . . . . . | 8 to 11 | 6 to 8 |
| Thermostat housing-to-cylinder head bolts. . . . . . . . . . . . . . . . . . . | 20 | 15 |
| Water pump bolts: | | |
|   Pre-facelift models (1993 to October 1996) . . . . . . . . . . . . . . . . . | 23 | 17 |
|   Facelift models (October 1996 on) . . . . . . . . . . . . . . . . . . . . . | 34 | 25 |

## 1  General information

### Cooling system

All models covered by this manual employ a pressurised engine cooling system with thermostatically-controlled coolant circulation. The coolant is circulated by an impeller-type water pump, bolted to the right-hand end of the cylinder block, and driven by the timing belt. The coolant flows through the cylinder block around each cylinder; in the cylinder head(s), cast-in coolant passages direct coolant around the inlet and exhaust ports, and close to the exhaust valve guides.

A wax pellet type thermostat is located in a housing at the transmission end of the engine. During warm-up, the closed thermostat prevents coolant from circulating through the radiator. Instead, it returns through the coolant metal pipe running across the front of the engine to the radiator bottom hose. The supply to the heater is made from the rear of the thermostat housing. As the engine nears normal operating temperature, the thermostat opens and allows hot coolant to travel through the radiator, where it is cooled before returning to the engine.

The radiator is of aluminium construction, and has plastic end tanks.

The cooling system is sealed by a pressure-type filler cap in the expansion tank. The pressure in the system raises the boiling point of the coolant, and increases the cooling efficiency of the radiator. When the engine is at normal operating temperature, the coolant expands, and the surplus is displaced into the expansion tank. When the system cools, the surplus coolant is automatically drawn back from the tank into the radiator.

⚠️ **Warning: DO NOT attempt to remove the expansion tank filler cap, or to disturb any part of the cooling system, while it or the engine is hot, as there is a very great risk of scalding. If the expansion tank filler cap must be removed before the engine and radiator have fully cooled down (even though this** is not recommended) the pressure in the cooling system must first be released. Cover the cap with a thick layer of cloth, to avoid scalding, and slowly unscrew the filler cap until a hissing sound can be heard. When the hissing has stopped, showing that pressure is released, slowly unscrew the filler cap further until it can be removed; if more hissing sounds are heard, wait until they have stopped before unscrewing the cap completely. At all times, keep well away from the filler opening.

⚠️ **Warning: Do not allow antifreeze to come in contact with your skin, or with the painted surfaces of the vehicle. Rinse off spills immediately with plenty of water. Never leave antifreeze lying around in an open container, or in a puddle in the driveway or on the garage floor. Children and pets are attracted by its sweet smell, but antifreeze is fatal if ingested.**

⚠️ **Warning: If the engine is hot, the electric cooling fan may start rotating even if the engine is not running, so be careful to keep hands, hair and loose clothing well clear when working in the engine compartment.**

### Heating/ventilation system

The heating system consists of a blower fan and heater matrix (radiator) located in the heater unit, with hoses connecting the heater matrix to the engine cooling system. Hot engine coolant is circulated through the heater matrix. When the heater temperature control on the facia is operated, a flap door opens to expose the heater box to the passenger compartment. When the blower control is operated, the blower fan forces air through the unit according to the setting selected. On models without air conditioning, the heater control is linked to the flap door by a Bowden cable.

Incoming fresh air for the ventilation system passes through a pollen filter mounted below the windscreen cowl panel (see Chapter 1) – this ensures that most particles will be removed before the air enters the cabin. However, it is vital that the pollen filter is changed regularly, since a blocked filter will significantly reduce airflow to the cabin, leading to reduced demisting.

The ventilation system air distribution is controlled by a number of vacuum-operated flap doors on the heater housing. Vacuum supply is taken from the engine, through a one-way valve, to a vacuum reservoir. From there, the vacuum is taken through a vacuum distribution block to the three vacuum units on the heater housing. The vacuum hoses are colour-coded as follows:

a) Black – main vacuum supply
b) White – supply to recirculation flap
c) Grey and blue – supply/return to floor level flap
d) Red and yellow – supply/return to demister flap

### Air conditioning system

See Section 11.

## 2  Antifreeze – general information

The cooling system should be filled with a water/ethylene glycol-based antifreeze solution, of a strength which will prevent freezing down to at least -25°C, or lower if the local climate requires it. Antifreeze also provides protection against corrosion, and increases the coolant boiling point.

The cooling system should be maintained according to the schedule described in Chapter 1. Old or contaminated coolant mixtures are likely to cause damage, and encourage the formation of corrosion and scale in the system. Use distilled water with the antifreeze, if available – if not, be sure to use only soft water. Clean rainwater is suitable.

Before adding antifreeze, check all hoses and hose connections, because antifreeze tends to leak through very small openings. Engines don't normally consume coolant, so if the level goes down, find the cause and correct it.

The exact mixture of antifreeze-to-water which you should use depends on the relative weather conditions. The mixture should contain at least 40% antifreeze, but not more than 70%. Consult the mixture ratio chart on the antifreeze container before adding coolant. Hydrometers are available at most automotive accessory shops to test the coolant. Use antifreeze which meets the vehicle manufacturer's specifications.

## 3 Cooling system hoses – disconnection and renewal

**Note:** *Refer to the warnings given in Section 1 of this Chapter before starting work.*
1 If the checks described in Chapter 1 reveal a faulty hose, it must be renewed as follows.
2 First drain the cooling system (see Chapter 1); if the antifreeze is not due for renewal, the drained coolant may be re-used, if it is collected in a clean container.
3 To disconnect any hose, use a pair of pliers to release the spring clamps (or a screwdriver to slacken screw-type clamps), then move them along the hose clear of the union. Carefully work the hose off its stubs. The hoses can be removed with relative ease when new – on an older car, they may have stuck.
4 If a hose proves stubborn, try to release it by rotating it on its unions before attempting to work it off. Gently prise the end of the hose with a blunt instrument (such as a flat-bladed screwdriver), but do not apply too much force, and take care not to damage the pipe stubs or hoses. Note in particular that the radiator hose unions are fragile; do not use excessive force when attempting to remove the hoses. If all else fails, cut the hose with a sharp knife, then slit it so that it can be peeled off in two pieces. While expensive, this is preferable to buying a new radiator. Check first, however, that a new hose is readily available.
5 When refitting a hose, first slide the clamps onto the hose, then work the hose onto its unions. If the hose is stiff, use soap (or washing-up liquid) as a lubricant, or soften it by soaking it in boiling water, but take care to prevent scalding.
6 Work each hose end fully onto its union, then check that the hose is settled correctly and is properly routed. Slide each clip along

the hose until it is behind the union flared end, before tightening it securely.
7 Refill the system with coolant (see Chapter 1).
8 Check carefully for leaks as soon as possible after disturbing any part of the cooling system.

## 4 Thermostat – removal, testing and refitting

**Note:** *Refer to the warnings given in Section 1 of this Chapter before starting work.*
1 As the thermostat ages, it will become slower to react to changes in water temperature ('lazy'). Ultimately, the unit may stick in the open or closed position, and this causes problems. A thermostat which is stuck open will result in a very slow warm-up; a thermostat which is stuck shut will lead to rapid overheating.
2 Before assuming the thermostat is to blame for a cooling system problem, check the coolant level. If the system is draining due to a leak, or has not been properly filled, there may be an airlock in the system (refer to the coolant renewal procedure in Chapter 1).
3 If the engine seems to be taking a long time to warm up (based on heater output), the thermostat could be stuck open. Don't necessarily believe the temperature gauge reading – some gauges never seem to register very high in normal driving.
4 A lengthy warm-up period might suggest that the thermostat is missing – it may have been removed or inadvertently omitted by a previous owner or mechanic. Don't drive the car without a thermostat – the engine will then stay in warm-up mode for longer than necessary, causing emissions and fuel economy to suffer.
5 If the engine runs hot, use your hand to check the temperature of the radiator top hose. If the hose isn't hot, but the engine clearly is, the thermostat is probably stuck closed, preventing the coolant inside the engine from escaping to the radiator – renew the thermostat. Again, this problem may also be due to an airlock (refer to the coolant renewal procedure in Chapter 1).

6 If the radiator top hose is hot, it means that the coolant is flowing (at least as far as the radiator) and the thermostat is open. Consult the *Fault diagnosis* section at the end of this manual to assist in tracing possible cooling system faults, but a lack of heater output would now definitely suggest an airlock or a blockage.
7 To gain a rough idea of whether the thermostat is working properly when the engine is warming up, without dismantling the system, proceed as follows.
8 With the engine completely cold, start the engine and let it idle, while checking the temperature of the radiator top hose. Periodically check the temperature indicated on the coolant temperature gauge – if overheating is indicated, switch the engine off immediately.
9 The top hose should feel cold for some time as the engine warms up, and should then get warm quite quickly as the thermostat opens.
10 The above is not a precise or definitive test of thermostat operation, but if the system does not perform as described, remove and test the thermostat as described below.

### Removal

11 Drain the cooling system (see Chapter 1). If the coolant is relatively new or in good condition, drain it into a clean container and re-use it.
12 On early models, remove the air cleaner resonator as described in Chapter 4A for improved access.
13 Unscrew the securing bolts, and lift off the thermostat cover **(see illustrations)**.
14 Note how the thermostat is installed (which end is facing outwards). Lift out the thermostat and recover the sealing ring **(see illustration)**.

### Testing

**Note:** *Frankly, if there is any question about the operation of the thermostat, it's best to renew it – they are not usually expensive items. Testing involves heating in, or over, an open pan of boiling water, which carries with it the risk of scalding. A thermostat which has seen more than five years' service may well be past its best already.*
15 If the thermostat remains in the open

**4.13a Unscrew the thermostat cover bolts . . .**

**4.13b . . . and remove it for access to the thermostat**

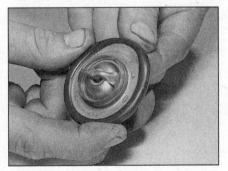

**4.14 Removing the thermostat sealing ring**

**5.9a  Fan shroud is secured at top by mounting nut (A), at bottom by clip (B) . . .**

position at room temperature, it is faulty, and must be renewed as a matter of course.

**16**  Check to see if there's a open temperature marking stamped on the thermostat.

**17**  Using a thermometer and container of water, heat the water until the temperature corresponds with the temperature marking stamped on the thermostat. If no marking is found, start the test with the water hot, and heat slowly until it boils.

**18**  Suspend the (closed) thermostat on a length of string in the water, and check that maximum opening occurs within two minutes, or before the water boils.

**19**  Remove the thermostat and allow it to cool down; check that it closes fully.

**20**  If the thermostat does not open and close as described, or if it sticks in either position, it must be renewed.

### Refitting

**21**  Refitting is the reverse of the removal procedure, noting the following points:

a) Clean the mating surfaces carefully, and renew the thermostat's sealing ring.

b) Fit the thermostat in the same position as noted on removal – where applicable, the bleed hole should be positioned at the top.

c) Tighten the thermostat cover/housing bolts to the specified torque wrench setting.

d) Remake all the coolant hose connections, then refill the cooling system as described in Chapter 1.

e) Start the engine and allow it to reach normal operating temperature, then check for leaks and proper thermostat operation.

**6.1  Temperature gauge sender location**

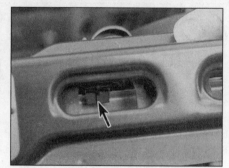

**5.9b  . . . and is hooked over radiator top edge (one point arrowed)**

## 5  Radiator electric cooling fan(s) – testing, removal and refitting

**Note:** Refer to the warnings given in Section 1 of this Chapter before starting work.

### Testing

**1**  The radiator cooling fan is controlled by the switch fitted to the base of the thermostat housing. Where twin fans or two-speed fans are fitted, control is through a resistor assembly, secured to the bottom left-hand corner of the fan shroud – this can be renewed separately if faulty.

**2**  First, check the relevant fuses and relays (see Chapter 12).

**3**  To test the fan motor, unplug the electrical connector, and use fused jumper wires to connect the fan directly to the battery. If the fan still does not work, renew the motor.

**4**  If the motor proved sound, the fault lies in the fan switch (see Section 6 for testing details), or in the wiring loom (see Chapter 12 for testing details).

### Removal

**5**  Where applicable, to improve access, remove the air cleaner resonator as described in Chapter 4A.

**6**  Drain the cooling system (see Chapter 1).

**7**  Remove the radiator top hose completely. Disconnect the metal coolant pipe/hose from the thermostat, and unbolt the coolant pipe from the exhaust manifold heat shield.

**8**  Unplug the cooling fan electrical connector(s), then release all wiring and hoses from the fan shroud.

**9**  Unscrew the two nuts securing the fan shroud, then lift the assembly to disengage it from its bottom mountings and from the radiator top edge **(see illustrations)**.

**10**  Withdraw the fan and shroud as an assembly **(see illustration)**.

**11**  At the time of writing, the fan, motor and shroud are available only as a complete assembly, and must be renewed together if faulty.

### Refitting

**12**  Refitting is the reverse of the removal procedure, noting the following points:

**5.10  Removing the radiator electric cooling fan and shroud assembly**

a) Ensure that the shroud is settled correctly at all four mounting points before refitting and tightening the nuts.

b) Refill the cooling system as described in Chapter 1.

## 6  Cooling system electrical switches and sensors – testing, removal and refitting

**Note:** Refer to the warnings given in Section 1 of this Chapter before starting work.

### Temperature gauge sender

**1**  The sender is screwed into the front of the thermostat housing **(see illustration)**.

### Testing

**2**  If the coolant temperature gauge is inoperative, check the fuses first (see Chapter 12).

**3**  If the gauge indicates hot at any time, consult the Fault finding Section at the end of this manual, to assist in tracing possible cooling system faults.

**4**  If the gauge indicates hot shortly after the engine is started from cold, unplug the coolant temperature sender's electrical connector. If the gauge reading now drops, renew the sender. If the reading remains high, the wire to the gauge may be shorted to earth, or the gauge is faulty.

**5**  If the gauge fails to indicate after the engine has been warmed up (approximately 10 minutes) and the fuses are known to be sound, switch off the engine. Unplug the sender's electrical connector, and use a jumper wire to connect the white/red wire to a clean earth point (bare metal) on the engine. Switch on the ignition without starting the engine. If the gauge now indicates hot, renew the sender.

**6**  If the gauge still does not work, the circuit may be open, or the gauge may be faulty. See Chapter 12 for additional information.

### Removal

**7**  Drain the cooling system (see Chapter 1).

**8**  Where applicable, to improve access, remove the air cleaner resonator as described in Chapter 4A.

**9**  Unplug the electrical connector from the sender, then unscrew the sender and withdraw it.

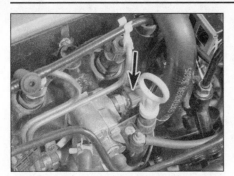

**6.12  Coolant temperature sensor location**

**6.25  Radiator fan switch location**

**6.27  Removing the radiator fan switch (thermostat housing removed)**

### Refitting

**10**  Clean any traces of old sealant from the sender location, then apply a light coat of sealant to the sender's threads. Screw in the sender and tighten it securely, and plug in its electrical connector.

**11**  Reconnect and refit any hoses and components removed for access. Refill the cooling system as described in Chapter 1 and run the engine. Check for leaks and proper gauge operation.

### *Coolant temperature sensor*

**12**  The temperature sensor is distinct from the gauge sender, in that it provides the engine management system with coolant temperature information. The sensor is screwed into the left-hand side of the thermostat housing (left as seen from the driver's seat) **(see illustration)**.

### Testing

**13**  Where applicable, to improve access, remove the air cleaner resonator as described in Chapter 4A.

**14**  Unplug the electrical connector from the sensor.

**15**  Using an ohmmeter, measure the resistance between the sensor terminals. Depending on the temperature of the sensor tip, the resistance measured will vary, but should be within the broad limits given in the Specifications Section of this Chapter. If the sensor's temperature is varied – by removing it (see below) and placing it in a freezer for a while, or by warming it gently – its resistance should alter accordingly.

**16**  Provided the sensor resistance falls significantly as the temperature rises, the sensor is likely to be performing well enough. However, if the results obtained show the sensor to be faulty, renew it.

**17**  On completion, plug in the connector and refit the components removed for access.

### Removal

**18**  It is not absolutely essential to drain the cooling system, providing the system is completely cool. Remove the expansion tank filler cap to release any pressure, then refit the cap. Provided you work swiftly and plug the opening as soon as the sensor is unscrewed, coolant loss will be minimised.

**19**  Gain access to the sensor as described in the *Testing* Section above.

**20**  Unscrew the sensor and withdraw it. If the cooling system has not been drained, plug the opening as quickly as possible.

### Refitting

**21**  Clean any traces of old sealant from the sensor location, then apply a light coat of sealant to the sensor's threads. Remove the material used to plug the sensor hole (where applicable), and quickly install the sensor to prevent coolant loss. Tighten the sensor securely, and plug in its electrical connector.

**22**  Refit the components removed for access, then refill or top-up the cooling system (see Chapter 1 or *Weekly checks*). Run the engine, checking for leaks.

### *Radiator fan switch*

### Testing

**23**  See Section 5.

### Removal

**24**  Drain the cooling system as described in Chapter 1. Alternatively, be prepared for some loss of coolant when the switch is removed.

**25**  The switch is located in the base of the thermostat housing **(see illustration)**.

**26**  Disconnect the wiring multi-plug from the switch.

**27**  Unscrew the switch from its location, and recover the sealing washer **(see illustration)**.

### Refitting

**28**  Refitting is a reversal of removal, but fit a new sealing washer and tighten the switch securely. Refill (or top-up) the cooling system as described in Chapter 1.

### *Coolant low level switch*

### Testing

**29**  The switch is a reed-type unit mounted in the bottom of the cooling system expansion tank, activated by a magnetic float. If the coolant level falls to the MIN level or less, the appropriate bulb lights in the warning display.

**30**  If the bulb fails to light during the 5-second bulb test when the ignition is switched on, check the bulb, and renew if necessary as described in Chapter 12.

**31**  To check the switch itself, unplug its electrical connector, and use an ohmmeter to measure the resistance across the switch terminals. With the float up, a resistance of 90 ohms should be measured; when it is down, the resistance should increase to approximately 150 kilohms.

**32**  If the results obtained from the check are significantly different from those expected, the switch is faulty, and must be renewed.

**33**  If the switch and bulb are proven to be sound, the fault must be in the wiring or in the auxiliary warning control assembly (see Chapter 12).

### Removal

**34**  Remove the expansion tank (see Section 7). The tank need not be drained, if preferred – we found that the switch could be removed without risk of spillage.

**35**  Unplug the switch electrical connector **(see illustration)**.

**36**  Release the switch by twisting it anti-clockwise, then withdraw it **(see illustrations)**.

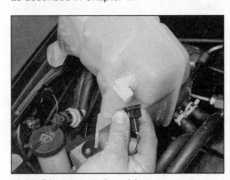

**6.35  Disconnect the wiring connector . . .**

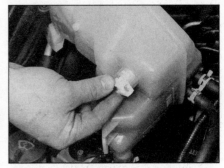

**6.36a  . . . then twist the level switch anti-clockwise . . .**

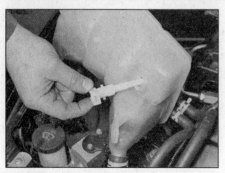

6.36b ... and withdraw it from the expansion tank

## Refitting

**37** Refitting is the reverse of the removal procedure. If it was drained, refill the cooling system (see Chapter 1). Start the engine, and check for coolant leaks when it is fully warmed-up.

## 7 Radiator and expansion tank – removal, inspection and refitting

**Note:** *Refer to the warnings given in Section 1 of this Chapter before starting work.*

## Radiator

**Note:** *If leakage is the reason for removing the radiator, bear in mind that minor leaks can often be cured using a radiator sealant added to the coolant with the radiator in situ.*

### Removal

**1** Remove the radiator fan and shroud assembly (see Section 5).
**2** To provide greater clearance for the radiator to be lowered and removed, ensure that the handbrake is firmly applied, then raise and support the front of the car on axle stands (see *Jacking and vehicle support*). Remove the radiator lower cover.
**3** Disconnect the bottom hose from the radiator, and the top hose, if not already done.
**4** If the car has air conditioning, unscrew the condenser mounting nuts or bolts, detach the condenser from the radiator, and tie it to the engine compartment front crossmember. Disconnect the wiring from the air conditioning compressor, and from the low pressure switch.

⚠ **Warning: Do not disconnect any of the refrigerant hoses.**

**5** Unbolt the radiator mounting brackets from the subframe – note that they are handed, and are marked to ensure correct refitting.

Collect the bottom mounting rubbers, noting which way up they are fitted, and store them carefully **(see illustrations)**.
**6** Carefully lower the radiator from the car, and withdraw it **(see illustration)**.

### Inspection

**7** With the radiator removed, it can be inspected for leaks and damage. If it needs repair, have a radiator specialist or dealer service department perform the work, as special techniques are required.
**8** Insects and dirt can be removed from the radiator with a garden hose or a soft brush. Don't bend the cooling fins as this is done.

### Refitting

**9** Refitting is the reverse of the removal procedure, noting the following points:
a) *Be sure the mounting rubbers are seated properly at the base of the radiator.*
b) *After refitting, refill the cooling system with the proper mixture of antifreeze and water (see Chapter 1).*
c) *Start the engine, and check for leaks. Allow the engine to reach normal operating temperature, indicated by the radiator top hose becoming hot.*
d) *Once the engine has cooled (ideally, leave overnight), recheck the coolant level, and add more if required.*

7.5a Radiator mounting bracket-to-subframe bolts (A), air conditioning system condenser mounting bolt (B)

7.5b Remove the radiator bottom mounting rubbers, noting their fitted direction

7.6 Lower the radiator out of the car

7.12a Unscrew the expansion tank mounting bolts ...

7.12b ... and disconnect the level switch wiring plug

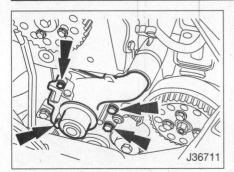

8.10a Water pump securing bolts (arrowed)

8.10b Removing the water pump

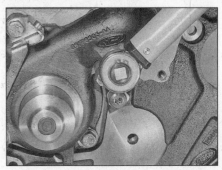

8.11 Tighten the water pump bolts to the specified torque

## Expansion tank

### Removal

10 With the engine completely cool, remove the expansion tank filler cap to release any pressure, then refit the cap.

11 Disconnect the hoses from the tank, upper hose first. As each hose is disconnected, drain the tank's contents into a clean container. If the antifreeze is not due for renewal, the drained coolant may be re-used, if it is kept clean.

12 Unscrew the tank's two mounting bolts and withdraw it, unplugging the coolant low level switch electrical connector (where fitted) **(see illustrations)**.

13 Wash out the tank, and inspect it for cracks and chafing – renew it if damaged.

### Refitting

14 Refitting is the reverse of the removal procedure. Refill the cooling system with the proper mixture of antifreeze and water (see Chapter 1), then start the engine and allow it to reach normal operating temperature, indicated by the radiator top hose becoming hot. Recheck the coolant level and add more if required, then check for leaks.

## 8 Water pump –
checking, removal and refitting

**Note:** *Refer to the warnings given in Section 1 of this Chapter before starting work.*

### Checking

1 A failure in the water pump can cause serious engine damage due to overheating.

2 There are three ways to check the operation of the water pump while it's installed on the engine. If the pump is defective, use a new or rebuilt unit.

3 With the engine running at normal operating temperature, squeeze the radiator top hose. If the water pump is working properly, a pressure surge should be felt as the hose is released.

⚠ *Warning: Keep your hands away from the radiator electric cooling fan blades.*

4 Water pumps are equipped with weep or vent holes. If a failure occurs in the pump

seal, coolant will leak from the hole. In most cases you'll need a torch to find the hole on the water pump from underneath to check for leaks. A white stain under the weep hole is a sign that coolant has been leaking.

5 The water pump is at the timing belt end of the engine – to check for a leak, it may be helpful to remove the timing belt covers, as described in Chapter 2A.

6 If the water pump shaft bearings fail, there may be a howling or a scraping sound at the drivebelt end of the engine while it's running. Shaft wear can be felt if the water pump pulley is rocked up-and-down.

7 Don't mistake drivebelt slippage, which causes a squealing sound, for water pump bearing failure.

### Removal

8 Drain the cooling system as described in Chapter 1.

9 Remove the timing belt as described in Chapter 2A. On early models, there may be a timing belt inner shield, secured by two bolts, which has to be removed for access.

10 Unscrew the four water pump securing bolts and withdraw the pump. Recover the gasket **(see illustrations)**.

### Refitting

11 Clean the pump mating surfaces carefully; the gasket must be renewed whenever it is disturbed. Use a little grease to stick the new gasket in place, refit the pump and tighten the bolts to the specified torque wrench setting **(see illustration)**.

12 The remainder of the refitting procedure is

the reverse of dismantling, noting the following points:

a) *Tighten all fixings to the specified torque wrench settings.*

b) *Fit a new timing belt as described in Chapter 2A.*

c) *On completion, refill the cooling system as described in Chapter 1.*

## 9 Heater/ventilation components –
removal and refitting

## Heater blower motor

### Removal

1 Disconnect the battery negative (earth) lead (see Chapter 5A, Section 1).

2 Release the four clips (by pulling them out) securing the passenger side footwell upper trim panel, then withdraw the panel.

3 Unplug the motor's electrical connector.

4 Lift the motor's retaining lug slightly, twist the motor anti-clockwise (seen from beneath) through approximately 30°, then withdraw the assembly.

5 The motor's control resistor can be removed by sliding a slim screwdriver into the slot provided in one end. Press the screwdriver in approximately 5 mm against spring pressure, and prise the resistor out **(see illustration)**.

### Refitting

6 Refitting is the reverse of the removal procedure. Refit the motor, and twist it clockwise until the retaining lug engages securely **(see illustration)**.

9.5 Heater blower motor control resistor can be prised out of heater unit

9.6 Ensure the blower motor retaining lug (arrowed) engages securely in the heater unit on reassembly

**9.9a Coolant pipes to the heater matrix must be disconnected . . .**

**9.9b . . . but can be reached best from below (arrowed)**

**9.11 Remove the screw to release the air duct in the base of the heater unit . . .**

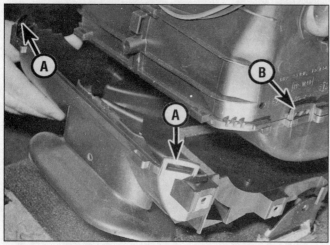

**9.12 . . . release the clips (A) to free the air distributor from the heater unit – note the clips (B) securing . . .**

**9.13 . . . the heater unit's bottom cover, complete with matrix**

### Heater matrix

#### Removal

**7** Disconnect the battery negative (earth) lead (see Chapter 5A, Section 1).

**8** Apply the handbrake, then raise and support the front of the car on axle stands. Drain the cooling system (see Chapter 1).

**9** Disconnect the coolant hoses from the heater matrix unions protruding through the engine compartment bulkhead – this is most easily done from underneath **(see illustrations)**.

**10** Working inside the passenger compart-

**9.14 Remove the clamp (one screw) to separate the matrix from heater unit's bottom cover**

ment, remove the trim panels from each footwell, just in front of the centre console. Each panel is secured by two screws. If additional clearance is required, the centre console can be removed as well (see Chapter 11), but this is not essential.

**11** Remove the single screw to release the air duct in the base of the heater unit **(see illustration)**.

**12** Remove the three Torx-type screws (size T20) securing the air distributor to the heater unit bottom cover, then release the clips. There is a single plastic clip on each side, and additional metal clips may be found. Push the duct up to retract it, and withdraw the air distributor **(see illustration)**.

**13** Release the clips – there are two plastic clips on each side, and additional metal clips may be found – then withdraw the heater unit's bottom cover, complete with the matrix **(see illustration)**.

**14** Undo the screw and withdraw the clamp to separate the matrix from the bottom cover **(see illustration)**.

#### Refitting

**15** Refitting is the reverse of the removal procedure. Additional metal clips may be required to secure the heater unit's bottom cover and the air distributor. Ensure that the

duct is lowered from the air distributor and secured with its screw.

**16** Refill the cooling system with the proper mixture of antifreeze and water (see Chapter 1). Start the engine and allow it to reach normal operating temperature, indicated by the radiator top hose becoming hot. Recheck the coolant level and add more if required, then check for leaks. Check the operation of the heater.

### Pollen filter

**17** Refer to Chapter 1.

### Facia vents

#### Driver's side and centre vents

**18** The driver's side and centre vents are removed complete with the instrument panel surround. Refer to Chapter 12.

#### Passenger side vent

**19** Remove the glovebox as described in Chapter 11.

**20** Using a suitable screwdriver, and a pad to protect the facia, prise out the vent from the end of the facia panel.

**21** Working through the glovebox aperture, detach the ventilation duct from the base of the vent, and remove the vent.

**22** Refitting is a reversal of removal.

10.6 Remove the screws (arrowed) securing each end of the heater control unit

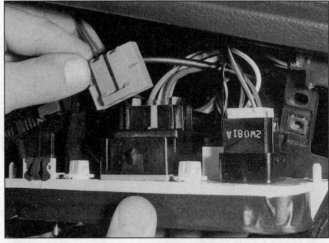

10.7a Disconnect the wiring and vacuum connections from the rear of the control panel

## 10 Heater/air conditioning controls – removal and refitting

### Heater control panel

1 Disconnect the battery negative (earth) lead (see Chapter 5A, Section 1).

2 Remove the ashtray, and prise off the cigar lighter bezel. Referring to the relevant Sections of Chapter 11, remove all the centre console securing screws, and slide the console to the rear.

3 Remove the radio/cassette player as described in Chapter 12.

#### Pre-facelift models (up to October 1996)

4 Pull out the cassette storage compartment below the radio/cassette player.

5 Pull the heater control/radio bezel out of the three clips securing its top edge, and pull it forwards.

6 Pull off the heater control knobs, and remove the screw securing each end of the heater control unit (see illustration). Pull the control unit out of the facia.

7 Taking careful note of all their locations, disconnect the various wiring and vacuum connections from the rear of the panel. On

10.7b Unhook the operating cable from the temperature control – note retaining screw (arrowed)

models without air conditioning, unhook the operating cable from the temperature control (see illustrations).

8 Make sure that nothing remains attached to the panel, then withdraw it from the facia.

#### Facelift models (October 1996 on)

9 Remove the two screws (one each side) inside the radio/cassette aperture (see illustration).

10 Pull the heater control/radio bezel out of the three clips securing its top edge, and pull it forwards.

11 Taking careful note of all their locations, disconnect the various wiring and vacuum

10.9 Remove the two screws inside the radio/cassette aperture

connections from the rear of the panel (see illustrations). On models without air conditioning, unhook the operating cable from the temperature control.

12 Make sure that nothing remains attached to the panel, then withdraw it from the facia.

### Blower/air conditioning control and temperature control

13 Remove the heater control panel as described above.

14 If not already done, pull off the control knob. Remove the retaining screw and withdraw the control, twisting it to release it from the panel (see illustrations).

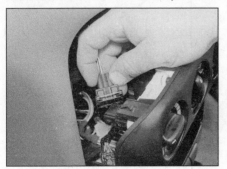

10.11a Disconnect the wiring . . .

10.11b . . . and vacuum connections from the control panel

10.14a Remove the retaining screw . . .

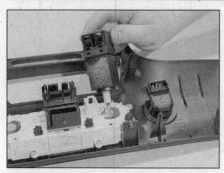

**10.14b** . . . and remove the control from the bayonet fitting

**10.17a** Pull off the control knob (facelift model shown) . . .

**10.17b** . . . release the clips using a small screwdriver . . .

**10.17c** . . . and remove the air distribution control

**15** Refitting is the reverse of the removal procedure. Check the operation of the control on completion.

### Air distribution control

**16** Remove the heater control panel as described above.

**17** If not already done, pull off the control knob. Use a pair of slim screwdrivers to release the clips on each side of the control, then withdraw the control from the unit **(see illustrations)**.

**18** Refitting is the reverse of the removal procedure. Check the operation of the controls on completion.

## 11 Air conditioning system – general information and precautions

### General information

The air conditioning system consists of a condenser mounted in front of the radiator, an evaporator mounted adjacent to the heater matrix, a compressor driven by an auxiliary drivebelt, an accumulator/dehydrator, and the plumbing connecting all of the above components – this contains a choke (or 'venturi') mounted in the inlet to the

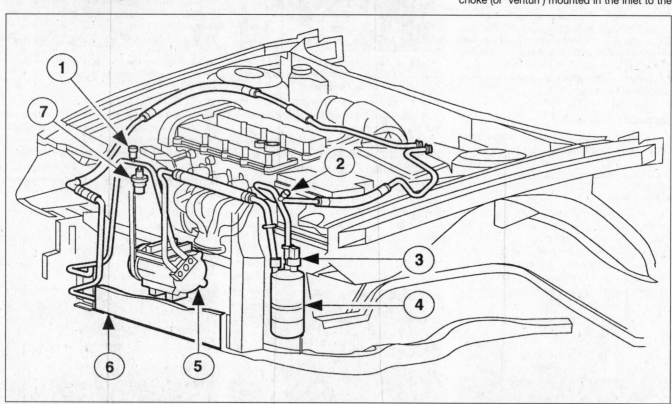

**11.1 Air conditioning system components**

| | | |
|---|---|---|
| 1 Quick-release Schrader valve-type coupling – high-pressure side | 3 Pressure-cycling switch – low-pressure side | 5 Compressor |
| | 4 Accumulator/dehydrator | 6 Condenser |
| 2 Quick-release Schrader valve-type coupling – low-pressure side | | 7 Pressure-regulating switch – high-pressure side |

evaporator, which creates the drop in pressure required to produce the cooling effect **(see illustration)**.

A blower fan forces the warmer air of the passenger compartment through the evaporator core (rather like a radiator in reverse), transferring the heat from the air to the refrigerant. The liquid refrigerant boils off into low-pressure vapour, taking the heat with it when it leaves the evaporator.

## Precautions

⚠️ *Warning: The air conditioning system is under high pressure. Do not loosen any fittings or remove any components until after the system has been discharged. Air conditioning refrigerant should be properly discharged into an approved type of container, at a dealer service department or an automotive air conditioning repair facility capable of handling R134a refrigerant. Always wear eye protection when disconnecting air conditioning system fittings.*

When an air conditioning system is fitted, it is necessary to observe the following special precautions whenever dealing with any part of the system, its associated components, and any items which necessitate disconnection of the system:

a) *While the refrigerant used – R134a – is less damaging to the environment than the previously-used R12, it is still a very dangerous substance. It must not be allowed into contact with the skin or eyes, or there is a risk of frostbite. It must also not be discharged in an enclosed space – while it is not toxic, there is a risk of suffocation. The refrigerant is heavier than air, and so must never be discharged over a pit.*

b) *The refrigerant must not be allowed to come in contact with a naked flame, otherwise a poisonous gas will be created – under certain circumstances, this can form an explosive mixture with air. For similar reasons, smoking in the presence of refrigerant is highly dangerous, particularly if the vapour is inhaled through a lighted cigarette.*

c) *Never discharge the system to the atmosphere – R134a is not an ozone-depleting ChloroFluoroCarbon (CFC) as is R12, but is instead a hydrofluorocarbon, which causes environmental damage by contributing to the 'greenhouse effect' if released into the atmosphere.*

d) *R134a refrigerant must not be mixed with R12; the system uses different seals (now green-coloured, previously black) and has different fittings requiring different tools, so that there is no chance of the two types of refrigerant becoming mixed accidentally.*

e) *If for any reason the system must be disconnected, entrust this task to your Ford dealer or a refrigeration engineer.*

f) *It is essential that the system be*

*professionally discharged prior to using any form of heat-welding, soldering, brazing, etc – in the vicinity of the system, before having the car oven-dried at a temperature exceeding 70°C after repainting, and before disconnecting any part of the system.*

## 12 Air conditioning system components – removal and refitting

⚠️ *Warning: The air conditioning system is under high pressure. Do not loosen any fittings or remove any components until after the system has been discharged. Air conditioning refrigerant should be properly discharged into an approved type of container, at a dealer service department or an automotive air conditioning repair facility capable of handling R134a refrigerant. Cap or plug the pipe lines as soon as they are disconnected, to prevent the entry of moisture. Always wear eye protection when disconnecting air conditioning system fittings.*

**Note:** *This Section refers to the components of the air conditioning system itself – refer to Sections 9 and 10 for details of components common to the heating/ventilation system.*

### Condenser

**1** Have the refrigerant discharged at a dealer service department or an automotive air conditioning repair facility.

**2** Remove the radiator undershield (see Chapter 1, Section 28).

**3** Using the Ford service tool 34-001, disconnect the refrigerant lines from the condenser. Immediately cap the open fittings, to prevent the entry of dirt and moisture.

**4** Remove the radiator as described in Section 7. Alternatively, just remove the radiator support brackets (note that the condenser is also mounted on the brackets), and have a jack or pair of axle stands ready to support the weight.

**5** Disengage the condenser upper mountings, then push it rearwards and remove it from below. Store it upright, to prevent oil loss.

**6** Refitting is the reverse of removal. If a new condenser was installed, add 20 cc of refrigerant oil to the system.

**7** Have the system evacuated, charged and leak-tested by the specialist who discharged it.

### Evaporator

**8** The evaporator is mounted with the heater matrix. Apart from the need to have the refrigerant discharged, and to use Ford service tools 34-001 and 34-003 to disconnect the lines, the procedure is as described in Section 9 of this Chapter.

**9** On reassembly, if a new evaporator was installed, add 20 cc of refrigerant oil to the system.

**10** Have the system evacuated, charged and leak-tested by the specialist who discharged it.

### Compressor

**11** Have the refrigerant discharged at a dealer service department or an automotive air conditioning repair facility.

**12** Remove the radiator undershield and the auxiliary drivebelt as described in Chapter 1, Sections 28 and 5 respectively.

**13** Unbolt the compressor from the cylinder block/crankcase, press it to one side, and unscrew the clamping bolt to disconnect the refrigerant lines.

**14** Plug the line connections, swing the compressor upright, unplug its electrical connector, then withdraw the compressor from the car. **Note:** *Keep the compressor level during handling and storage. If the compressor has seized, or if you find metal particles in the refrigerant lines, the system must be flushed out by an air conditioning technician, and the accumulator/dehydrator must be renewed.*

**15** Prior to installation, turn the compressor clutch centre six times, to disperse any oil that has collected in the head.

**16** Refit the compressor in the reverse order of removal; renew all seals disturbed.

**17** If you are installing a new compressor, refer to the compressor manufacturer's instructions for adding refrigerant oil to the system.

**18** Have the system evacuated, charged and leak-tested by the specialist that discharged it.

### Accumulator/dehydrator

**19** Have the refrigerant discharged at a dealer service department or an automotive air conditioning repair facility.

**20** The accumulator/dehydrator, which acts as a reservoir and filter for the refrigerant, is located in the left-hand front corner of the engine compartment. Using the Ford service tool 34-003, disconnect the refrigerant line next to the accumulator/dehydrator from the compressor. Immediately cap the open fittings, to prevent the entry of dirt and moisture, then unplug the pressure-cycling switch electrical connector **(see illustration)**.

**12.20 Unplug the pressure-cycling switch electrical connector (arrowed)**

**12.29 Unplug the pressure-regulating switch electrical connector (arrowed)**

21 Remove the radiator undershield (see Chapter 1, Section 28).

22 Unbolt the accumulator/dehydrator from the front suspension subframe.

23 Using the Ford service tool 34-003, disconnect the lower refrigerant line from the accumulator/dehydrator. It may be necessary to unscrew the pressure-cycling switch to allow the use of the tool. Immediately cap the open fittings, to prevent the entry of dirt and moisture.

24 Withdraw the accumulator/dehydrator.

25 Refit the accumulator/dehydrator in the reverse order of removal; renew all seals disturbed.

26 If you are installing a new accumulator/dehydrator, refer to the manufacturer's instructions for adding refrigerant oil to the system.

27 Have the system evacuated, charged and leak-tested by the specialist that discharged it.

### Pressure-cycling and pressure-regulating switches

28 Have the refrigerant discharged at a dealer service department or an automotive air conditioning repair facility.

29 Unplug the switch electrical connector, and unscrew it **(see illustration)**.

30 Refitting is the reverse of the removal procedure; there is no need to top-up the refrigerant oil.

31 Have the system evacuated, charged and leak-tested by the specialist that discharged it.

# Chapter 4  Part A:
# Fuel and exhaust systems

## Contents

| | Section number | | Section number |
|---|---|---|---|
| Accelerator cable – removal, refitting and adjustment | 4 | Fuel injection pump – removal and refitting | 8 |
| Accelerator pedal – removal and refitting | 5 | Fuel injectors – removal, testing and refitting | 9 |
| Air cleaner and associated components – removal and refitting | 3 | Fuel shut-off (stop) solenoid – removal and refitting | 10 |
| Catalytic converter – removal and refitting | See Chapter 4B | Fuel system – bleeding and cleaning | 2 |
| Cold start cable – adjustment, removal and refitting | 13 | Fuel tank – removal and refitting | 17 |
| Engine management system – description and component renewal | 20 | General information and precautions | 1 |
| Exhaust Gas Recirculation (EGR) system | See Chapter 4B | Idle-up control system – checking, adjustment and renewal | 12 |
| Exhaust system – general information and component renewal | 19 | Injection pump – adjustments | 6 |
| Fuel filter renewal | See Chapter 1 | Injection pump timing – general | 7 |
| Fuel filter water draining | See Chapter 1 | Intercooler – removal and refitting | 15 |
| Fuel gauge sender unit – removal and refitting | 16 | Manifolds – removal and refitting | 18 |
| Fuel heater – removal and refitting | 11 | Turbocharger – removal and refitting | 14 |

## Degrees of difficulty

| Easy, suitable for novice with little experience  | Fairly easy, suitable for beginner with some experience | Fairly difficult, suitable for competent DIY mechanic | Difficult, suitable for experienced DIY mechanic | Very difficult, suitable for expert DIY or professional  |
|---|---|---|---|---|

## Specifications

### General

| | |
|---|---|
| Injection (firing) order | 1-3-4-2 |
| No 1 cylinder position | Timing belt end |
| Idle speed: | |
|     Pre-facelift models (1993 to October 1996) | 830 ± 20 rpm |
|     Facelift models (October 1996 on) | 850 ± 50 rpm |
| Anti-stall speed (with 4 mm spacer – see text) | 900 to 1000 rpm |
| Maximum no-load speed | 5200 ± 50 rpm |
| Fuel type | Commercial diesel fuel for road vehicles (DERV) |

### Injection pump

| | |
|---|---|
| Make and type: | |
|     Pre-facelift models (1993 to October 1996) | Lucas DPC F18 ITCI 20 |
|     Facelift models (October 1996 on) | Lucas DPCN |
| Rotation (viewed from crankshaft pulley end) | Clockwise |
| Drive | By toothed belt from crankshaft |
| Injection pump timing | By timing pegs, at TDC |

### Injectors

| | |
|---|---|
| Make and type | Lucas, pintle, single-stage |
| Colour code | Purple |
| Injection pressure | 2200 to 2400 psi (150 to 165 bar) |

## Torque wrench settings

| | Nm | lbf ft |
|---|---|---|
| Exhaust front pipe to turbocharger | 40 | 30 |
| Exhaust manifold: | | |
| Studs | 10 to 14 | 7 to 10 |
| Nuts and bolts | 18 to 25 | 13 to 18 |
| Manifold-to-turbocharger nuts | 38 | 28 |
| Fuel filter bracket to cylinder head/lifting eye | 23 | 17 |
| Fuel injection pump: | | |
| Pump to engine front plate | 18 to 28 | 13 to 21 |
| Pump to rear support bracket | 18 to 22 | 13 to 16 |
| Pump support bracket to cylinder block | 18 to 27 | 13 to 20 |
| Pump pulley bolts | 20 to 25 | 15 to 18 |
| Pump pulley to flange | 23 | 17 |
| Pump belt tensioner to cylinder block | 45 | 33 |
| Fuel injectors: | | |
| Injectors | 70 | 52 |
| Injector line to injector(s) and pump | 25 | 18 |
| Fuel pipe banjo union bolts | 16 to 20 | 12 to 15 |
| Fuel regulating thermostat to thermostat housing | 23 | 17 |
| Fuel shut-off (stop) solenoid | 16 to 20 | 12 to 15 |
| Inlet manifold: | | |
| Studs | 10 to 14 | 7 to 10 |
| Nuts and bolts | 18 to 25 | 13 to 18 |
| Intercooler to bracket | 18 | 13 |
| Turbocharger: | | |
| Turbocharger oil return hose clip | 5 | 4 |
| Turbocharger-to-exhaust manifold nuts | 38 | 28 |
| Turbocharger to oil feed line | 18 | 13 |
| Turbocharger oil feed line bracket to cylinder block | 48 | 35 |
| Turbocharger/cylinder block bracket to turbocharger | 23 | 17 |
| Turbocharger/cylinder block bracket to cylinder block | 47 | 35 |

## 1 General information and precautions

### General information

The fuel system comprises a rear-mounted fuel tank, a fuel filter, fuel injection pump, injectors and associated components.

Fuel is drawn from the tank by the transfer pump incorporated in the injection pump. En route it passes through the fuel filter, located in the engine bay, where foreign matter and water are removed. A fuel heater is incorporated into the filter housing, to eliminate fuel 'waxing' which used to occur in cold weather, before the advent of 'winter' diesel fuel.

The distributor-type injection pump is driven by a toothed belt from the crankshaft, and supplies fuel under very high pressure to each injector in turn as it is needed. The amount of fuel delivered is determined by the pump governor, which reacts to throttle position and to engine speed. Injection timing is varied automatically to suit the prevailing speed and load.

Two systems, both automatic, assist cold starting. A cold start advance device on the injection pump alters the injection timing and causes fuel delivery to be increased during cold starts. It contains a heating element which is energised when the engine is running. Preheater or 'glow' plugs are fitted to each swirl chamber: they are electrically heated before, during and immediately after a cold start (see Chapter 5).

Rigid pipes connect the pump and injectors. There are four injectors, situated where spark plugs would be found on a petrol engine. Each injector sprays fuel into a pre-combustion or 'swirl' chamber as its piston approaches TDC on the compression stroke. This system is known as indirect injection. The injectors only open under very high pressure. Lubrication is provided by allowing a small quantity of fuel to leak back past the injector internal components. The leaked-back fuel is returned to the pump and then to the fuel tank.

To stop the engine, a solenoid valve at the rear of the fuel pump is used. The valve is of the 'fail safe' type, so it must be energised to allow the engine to run. When power is removed from the valve, its plunger moves under spring pressure and interrupts fuel delivery.

The fuel system on diesel engines is normally very reliable. Provided that clean fuel is used and the specified maintenance is conscientiously carried out, no problems should be experienced. The injection pump and injectors may require overhaul after a high mileage has been covered, but this cannot be done on a DIY basis.

### Precautions

**⚠ Warning: Exercise extreme caution when working on the fuel system. Do not attempt to test the fuel injectors or disconnect the high-pressure lines with the engine running. Never expose the hands or any part of the body to injector spray, as the high working pressure can cause the fuel to penetrate the skin, with possibly fatal results. You are strongly advised to have any work which involves testing the injectors under pressure carried out by a dealer or fuel injection specialist.**

**⚠ Warning: Many of the procedures given in this Chapter involve the disconnection of fuel pipes and system components, which may result in some fuel spillage. Before carrying out any operation on the fuel system, refer to the precautions given in Safety first! at the beginning of this manual, and follow them implicitly.**

**Caution: When working on fuel system components, scrupulous cleanliness must be observed, and care must be taken not to introduce any foreign matter into fuel lines or components. Care should be taken not to disturb any components unnecessarily. Before attempting work, ensure that the relevant spares are available. If persistent problems are encountered, it is recommended that the advice of a Ford dealer or a specialist is sought.**

**Caution: Do not allow diesel fuel to leak into the clutch bellhousing, or it will contaminate the clutch disc friction material which will cause severe clutch slip – curable only by the renewal of the clutch disc and the degreasing of all fouled surfaces. Similarly, diesel fuel should never**

*be allowed to contaminate components such as the alternator and starter motor, the coolant hoses and engine mountings, and any wiring.*

## 2 Fuel system –
bleeding and cleaning

### Bleeding

**1** If the system is thought to have been emptied of fuel, the fuel filter may also be empty. One of the best ways to reduce the amount of cranking needed to start the engine is to remove the filter, and fill it with clean fuel.

**2** This system is fitted with a hand-priming pump, operated by depressing repeatedly the black button on the top of the filter assembly.

**3** To bleed air from the system as far as the fuel filter, disconnect the pipe from the filter outlet union, and operate the hand-priming pump until fuel emerges free from air bubbles. Mop-up any spilt fuel, and operate the hand-priming pump until increased resistance is felt.

**4** If air has entered the system, purge it from the pump union and the injector pipes. Ensure that rags are placed underneath the bleeding point to catch the spilt fuel. Diesel fuel must not be allowed to contaminate vulnerable components, especially the clutch, alternator and starter motor.

**5** Slacken each union at the injectors in turn, and crank the engine until fuel emerges. Tighten securely the union and mopup the spilt fuel, before moving on to the next one.

**6** If air has reached the fuel injection pump, energise the fuel shut-off solenoid by switching on the ignition to position II, slacken the pump's fuel return union and operate the hand-priming pump until fuel emerges free from air bubbles. Tighten securely the union banjo bolt, mop-up any spilt fuel and operate the hand-priming pump until increased resistance is felt. Switch off the ignition.

**7** To minimise the strain on the battery and starter motor when trying to start the engine, crank it in 10-second bursts, pausing for 30 seconds each time, until the engine starts. Apart from the risk of flattening the battery, the starter motor will overheat and may be damaged if abused.

**8** If you are trying to bleed air from the injector pipes or pump, it may be necessary to repeat the operations in paragraphs 5 and 6 after cranking the engine a few times.

**9** When the engine starts, keep it running for approximately 5 minutes to ensure that all air is removed from the system.

### Cleaning

**10** If, at any time, sudden fuel filter blockage, poor starting or otherwise unsatisfactory engine performance should be traced to the appearance of black sludge or slime within the fuel system, this may be due to corrosion

caused by the presence of various micro-organisms in the fuel. These can live in the fuel tank if water is allowed to remain there in significant quantities, their waste products causing corrosion of steel and other metallic components of the fuel system.

**11** If the fuel system is thought to be contaminated in this way, immediately seek the advice of a Ford dealer or diesel specialist. Thorough treatment is required to cure the problem and to prevent it from occurring again.

**12** If you are considering treating the car on a DIY basis, proceed as follows. Do not re-use contaminated fuel.

**13** First drain and remove the fuel tank, flush it thoroughly with clean diesel fuel and use an electric torch to examine as much as possible of its interior. If the contamination is severe, the tank must be steam-cleaned internally and then flushed again with clean diesel fuel.

**14** Disconnect the fuel feed and return hoses from the injection pump, remove the fuel filter element and flush through the system's feed and return lines with clean diesel fuel.

**15** Renew the filter element, refit the fuel tank and reconnect the fuel lines, then fill the tank with clean diesel fuel and bleed the system as described previously in this Section. Watch carefully for signs of the problem occurring again.

**16** While it is unlikely that such contamination will be found beyond the fuel filter, if it is thought to have reached the injection pump, the pump may require cleaning. This is a task only for a Lucas agent or diesel specialist. Do not attempt to disturb any part of the pump (other than the few adjustments detailed in this manual) or to clean it yourself.

**17** The most common cause of excessive quantities of water being in the fuel is condensation from the water vapour in the air. Diesel tanks (whether underground storage tanks or that in the car) are more susceptible to this problem than petrol tanks because of petrol's higher vapour pressure. Water formation in the car's fuel tank can be minimised by keeping the tank as full as possible at all times, and by using the car regularly.

**18** Note that proprietary additives are available to inhibit the growth of micro-organisms in car fuel tanks or storage tanks.

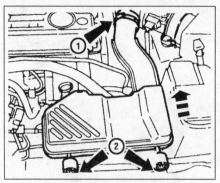

**3.1 Removing the air resonator –
early models**

*1 Hose clip        2 Retainers*

**19** If you buy all your fuel from the same source, and suspect that to be the source of the contamination, the owner or operator should be advised. Otherwise, the risk of taking on contaminated fuel can be minimised by using only reputable filling stations which have a good turnover.

## 3 Air cleaner and
associated components –
removal and refitting

**1** Early models may be fitted with a resonator box which is mounted on the front crossmember. To remove the resonator, first loosen the hose retaining clip next to the mass airflow sensor. Remove the resonator by pulling the body rearwards into the engine compartment, to detach its two locating pegs form the retainers on the crossmember **(see illustration)**.

**2** On all models, disconnect the multi-plug from the mass airflow (MAF) sensor. Release the two over-centre wire clips, and detach the sensor assembly from the casing cover **(see illustration)**. This operation may prove difficult, due to resistance from the rubber retaining ring.

**3** Unplug the vent pipe from the casing cover. Remove the air cleaner casing by first releasing the rubber retaining band, releasing the casing from the end bellows and pulling it from the base retaining spigots **(see illustrations)**.

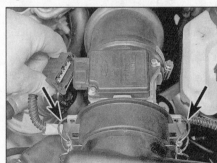

**3.2 Disconnecting the MAF sensor
multi-plug – over-centre wire clips arrowed**

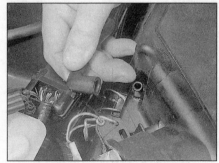

**3.3a Remove the breather hose . . .**

3.3b . . . then release the retaining band (arrowed) . . .

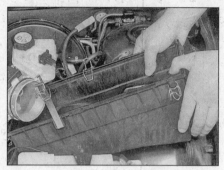

3.3c . . . and remove the air cleaner casing

**4** If the air cleaner is being removed to access other components, it may be advisable to also remove the mass airflow sensor as well – loosen the hose clip and withdraw it from the inlet duct.

**5** If the inlet duct is also to be removed, trace it down to the turbocharger inlet, disconnect the hose clip, and remove the duct – pack the turbocharger inlet with clean rag or paper towel, to stop dirt falling inside.

**6** Refit in the reverse order of removal, lightly greasing the mating surface of the mass airflow (MAF) sensor rubber retaining ring.

## 4 Accelerator cable – removal, refitting and adjustment

### Removal

**1** Where applicable, gain access to the cable by removing the air cleaner resonator box, as described in Section 3.

**2** Free the cable outer from the pump bracket by pulling out the retaining clip **(see illustration)**. If this proves difficult *in situ*, unbolt the bracket from the pump and remove it with the cable.

**3** Free the cable inner from the pump by prising off the end fitting **(see illustration)**.

### Models with traction control

**4** Disconnect the actuator wiring plug, then prise off its cover **(see illustration)**.

**5** Noting which cable section is connected

to which pulley, disconnect the first cable end nipple from the actuator's upper pulley, then slide the cable outer upwards out of the actuator housing. Disconnect the second cable in the same way from the actuator's lower pulley.

### All models

**6** Inside the car, reach up to the top of the accelerator pedal. Pull the end fitting and collar out of the pedal, then release the cable inner through the slot in the pedal. Tie a length of string to the end of the cable.

**7** Back in the engine compartment, pull the cable through the bulkhead until the string can be untied and the cable (or pedal-to-actuator cable, on models with traction control) can be removed.

### Refitting

**8** Refitting is a reversal of removal. Adjust the cable if necessary as described below.

### Adjustment

#### Models without traction control

**9** Adjustment is carried out by repositioning the cable outer retaining clip **(see illustration 4.2)**. With the pedal released, there should be a small amount of slack in the cable. Have an assistant operate the accelerator pedal, and check that the lever on the pump moves through its full range of travel (as limited by the idle and maximum speed adjusting screws). Adjust further if necessary.

### Models with traction control

**Note:** *Both sections of the cable must be adjusted together, even if only one has been disturbed.*

**10** Remove the metal clip from the adjuster of each cable section, and lubricate the adjusters' grommets with soapy water.

**11** Remove any slack by pulling both outer cables as far as possible out of their respective adjusters.

**12** Unplug the TCS throttle actuator's electrical connector, and prise off its cover. Lock both pulleys together by pushing a locking pin (a pin punch or a similar tool of suitable size) into their alignment holes. Disconnect the actuator-to-throttle housing cable's end nipple from the throttle linkage.

**13** Have an assistant depress the accelerator pedal fully. The pedal-to-actuator cable outer will move back into the adjuster; hold it there, and refit the clip.

**14** Connect the actuator-to-pump cable end nipple to the throttle linkage, and check that the outer cable grommet is correctly secured in the housing bracket.

**15** Again have the assistant depress the accelerator pedal fully. The actuator-to-pump cable outer will move back into the adjuster; hold it there, and refit the clip.

**16** Remove the locking pin from the pulleys. Check that the pump lever moves smoothly and easily from the fully-closed to the fully-open position and back again, as the assistant depresses and releases the accelerator pedal. Re-adjust the cable(s) if required.

**17** When the setting is correct, refit the actuator's cover and electrical connector.

## 5 Accelerator pedal – removal and refitting

### Removal

**1** Inside the car, reach up to the top of the accelerator pedal. Pull the end fitting and collar out of the pedal, then release the cable inner through the slot in the pedal.

**2** Undo the pedal mounting nuts and bolt,

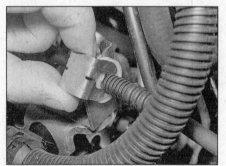

4.2 Pull out the cable outer retaining clip

4.3 Pull off the cable inner end fitting from the pump

4.4 Unplug the traction control actuator wiring plug (A) and prise off the cover at points B

**5.2  Removing the accelerator pedal**

then withdraw the pedal assembly **(see illustration)**.

### Refitting

**3** Refitting is a reversal of removal. Check the operation of the pedal, and adjust the cable if necessary, as described in Section 4.

---

## 6  Injection pump – adjustments

**1** The usual type of tachometer (rev counter), which works from ignition system pulses, cannot be used on diesel engines. If it is not felt that adjusting the idle speed 'by ear' is satisfactory, one of the following alternatives must be used:
  a) *Purchase or hire of an appropriate tachometer.*
  b) *Delegation of the job to a Ford dealer or other specialist.*
  c) *Timing light (strobe) operated by a petrol engine running at the desired speed. If the timing light is pointed at a chalk mark on the diesel engine crankshaft pulley, the mark will appear stationary when the two engines are running at the same speed (or multiples of that speed).*
  d) *Calculating the mph/rpm relationship for a particular gear and running the engine, in that gear, with the front wheels free. The speedometer accuracy may not be adequate, especially at low speeds. Stringent safety precautions must be observed.*

**2** The adjustment must be carried out with the engine at normal operating temperature. If necessary, take the car on a short run.

### Idle speed and anti-stall speed

#### Checking

**3** Check that there is 2.0 mm of play on the cold start cable at the pump end. If necessary, use the cable adjuster to alter the amount of play **(see illustrations)**.
**4** Take a note of the idle speed.
**5** Insert a 4.0 mm gauge (feeler blade, or twist drill), between the anti-stall screw and throttle lever **(see illustration)**.
**6** Rotate the stop lever in a clockwise direction

and insert a 3.0 mm diameter pin, or twist drill, through the idle lever **(see illustration)**.
**7** Take a note of the idle speed once more.
**8** If the idle speed is correct, open the throttle lever to obtain the engine maximum speed, then quickly release it. The time taken to decelerate to idle should be no more than 5 seconds, and the idle speed to drop by no more than 50 rpm below the specified idle speed, before stabilising. If adjustment is required, proceed as follows:

#### Setting

**9** Insert a 4.0 mm feeler blade between the anti-stall screw and the throttle lever.
**10** Rotate the stop lever in a clockwise direction, and insert a 3.0 mm diameter pin through the idle lever.
**11** Adjust the anti-stall screw to give the specified anti-stall speed.
**12** Remove the feeler blade and pin.
**13** Using the idle speed adjuster screw, set the idle speed to the specified figure.
**14** Repeat the check in paragraph 8.
**15** If the engine stalls, turn the anti-stall screw **anti-clockwise** (viewed from the rear of the pump) one quarter-turn.
**16** If the deceleration time exceeds 5 seconds, turn the anti-stall screw clockwise (viewed from the rear of the pump) one quarter-turn.
**17** If adjustments were made, recheck all operations from paragraph 9.
**18** With the engine idling, check the operation of the manual stop lever, by turning it anti-clockwise – the engine should stop immediately.

**19** Disconnect the tachometer, and refit any components removed for access.

### Manual stop lever

**20** The injection pump has a manual stop lever, which allows the fuel supply to be cut in an emergency. The operation of this lever should be checked regularly.
**21** The lever is at the front of the pump, below the idle lever. To check its operation, start the engine and allow it to idle; turn the stop lever anti-clockwise, and the engine should stop immediately. If the engine keeps running, check the anti-stall adjustment as described previously in this Section. If adjustment fails to restore the correct operation of the lever, this indicates a problem with the pump – consult a Ford dealer or diesel specialist.

### Maximum speed

**22** The maximum speed adjusting screw is sealed in production. Adjustment should only be made by a Ford dealer or authorised fuel injection specialist.
**23** The maximum no-load speed may be checked if wished, but do not hold the engine at this speed for more than 5 seconds. Keep well clear of the water pump/alternator drivebelt and pulleys.
**24** The engine speed should drop from maximum to idle within 5 seconds when the throttle is released. If not, check that the throttle linkage is not binding or obstructed. If this is in order, seek specialist advice.

**6.3a  Check for play in the cold start cable at the pump end . . .**

**6.3b  . . . and, if necessary, use the cable adjuster to alter the amount of play**

**6.5  Insert a 4.0 mm gauge or drill between the anti-stall screw and throttle lever**

**6.6  Rotate the stop lever clockwise, and insert a 3.0 mm diameter drill through the idle lever**

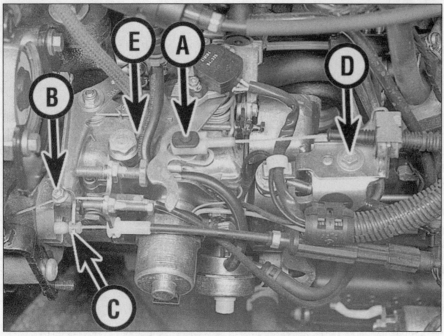

**8.4  Fuel injection pump connections**

A  Accelerator cable end fitting
B  Anti-stall cable end clamp
C  Cold start cable grommet
D  Throttle cable bracket bolt
E  Fuel supply connection

## 7  Injection pump timing – general

The injection pump mountings are fixed, and no adjustment of the pump relative to the engine is possible. The only way to ensure that the pump timing is correct is to first set the engine to TDC as described in Chapter 2A. In this position, it should be possible to insert a 6 mm pin or drill bit through the injection pump toothed pulley timing hole, down the slot in the pulley hub and into the hole in the pump body. Misalignment of these holes indicates that the drivebelt (and/or the pump itself) has been badly fitted.

If excessive smoke, noise or fuel consumption have been noticed, the pump timing is often suspected, but the injectors are more likely to be responsible – it is not unusual

for injectors to need reconditioning after a high mileage. Just as likely is a problem with the EGR valve, especially if the engine will not idle smoothly. Refer the car to a Ford dealer or diesel specialist for accurate diagnosis.

## 8  Fuel injection pump – removal and refitting

### Removal

1  To improve access, remove the air cleaner as described in Section 3.
2  Remove the timing belt and injection pump drivebelt as described in Chapter 2A.
3  Disconnect the fuel pipes from the pump and the injectors. Blank off all open connections to prevent the ingress of dirt and moisture.

4  Detach the accelerator, anti-stall and cold start cables from the pump **(see illustration)**.
5  Undo the accelerator cable support bracket bolt, and detach the bracket from the pump.
6  Disconnect the pump electrical connections by separating the multi-plugs.
7  Disconnect the fuel supply line and the remaining pipes from the pump **(see illustration)**.
8  Disconnect the turbocharger pipes in front of the pump.
9  With reference to Chapter 10, disconnect the hose and rigid pipe from the power steering pump, remove the pump drivebelt cover and loosen the locking bolt to slacken the drivebelt. Remove the drivebelt and the drive pulley.
10  Remove the pump sprocket retaining bolts, remove the timing pin, followed by the sprocket and belt.
11  Unscrew and remove the bolts from the pump's left-hand mounting **(see illustration)**.
12  Support the pump, then remove the three pump mounting screws behind the sprocket, and withdraw the pump from the engine **(see illustration)**.

### Refitting

13  Refitting the pump is a reversal of the removal procedure, noting the following points:
a) Before fitting a new pump, remove the blanking plugs and prime it with clean fuel, poured in through the return port.
b) Align the peg cut-outs of the pump body and drive flange before fitting.
c) Ensure that the mounting surfaces are clean before bolting the pump into position.
d) Tighten the pump mounting bolts to the specified torque **(see illustration)**.
e) When refitting the injection pump sprocket, check that the pump timing hole is visible through the sprocket hole **(see illustrations)**.
f) Tighten the sprocket retaining bolts finger-tight only, until the drivebelt is tensioned.
g) Refit the timing belt and injection pump drivebelt as described in Chapter 2A.
h) With all the pins removed, rotate the engine two full turns clockwise. Reinsert

**8.7  Fuel pipe unions at the injection pump**

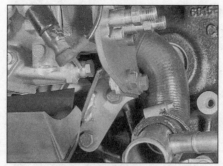

**8.11  Remove the pump's left-hand mounting bolts**

**8.12  Removing the injection pump**

**8.13a Tightening the three pump mounting screws behind the sprocket**

**8.13b When refitting the injection pump sprocket . . .**

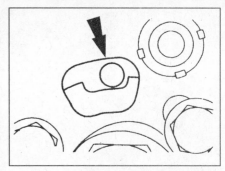

**8.13c . . . ensure that the timing hole is visible**

the pins to confirm the timing. If the pins cannot be inserted, then repeat the timing procedure.

i) Tighten all fasteners to the specified torque loading figures.

j) Refer to Chapter 1 when refilling the cooling system.

k) Clean all electrical connectors before reconnection.

l) On completion, check for correct accelerator cable operation and signs of fuel leakage.

## 9 Fuel injectors – removal, testing and refitting

> **Warning: Exercise extreme caution when working on the fuel injectors. Never expose the hands or any part of the body to injector spray, as**

the high working pressure can cause the fuel to penetrate the skin, with possibly fatal results. You are strongly advised to have any work which involves testing the injectors under pressure carried out by a dealer or fuel injection specialist.

### Removal

**1** Where applicable, remove the air cleaner resonator box as described in Section 3. Clean around the injectors and the injection pipe unions.

**2** Remove the fuel return hoses from the injectors **(see illustration)**.

**3** Unclip the pipes and wiring from the front of the cylinder head, then remove the support bracket from the head. Unclip the fuel supply pipe from the injector pipes, then disconnect the return pipe from the pump.

**4** Unscrew the injector pipe unions from the pump and injectors, using one spanner to

hold the union, and one to loosen the nut **(see illustrations)**. Remove the pipes completely.

**5** On later models only, disconnect the needle lift sensor wiring plug from No 3 injector **(see illustration)**.

**6** Unscrew and remove the injectors. A 27 mm box spanner or deep socket will be required – on later models, a cutaway socket will be needed to unscrew the injector with the needle lift sensor **(see illustration)**.

**7** Retrieve the flame washers from the injector bores **(see illustration)**. Obtain new washers for reassembly.

**8** Take care not to drop the injectors, nor allow the needles at their tips to become damaged.

### Testing

**9** Testing of injectors is quite simple, but requires a special high-pressure pump and gauge – also refer to the warning at the start of this Section.

**9.2 Pull off the injector return (leak-off) hoses**

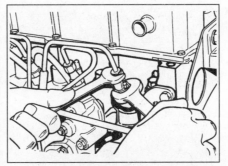

**9.4a Hold the injector body while unscrewing the injector unions**

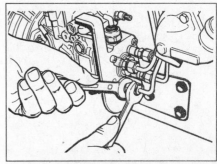

**9.4b Hold the pump adapters with one spanner while unscrewing the unions**

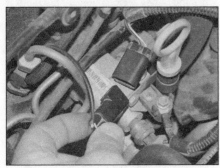

**9.5 Disconnect the needle lift sensor wiring plug from No 3 injector**

**9.6 Removing an injector**

**9.7 Retrieve the flame washers from the cylinder head**

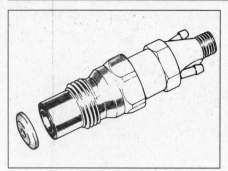

**9.11 Fit the new flame washers with the domed faces downwards**

10 Defective injectors should be renewed or professionally repaired. DIY repair is not a practical proposition.

### Refitting

11 Commence refitting by inserting new flame washers, domed faces downwards, to the injector bores **(see illustration)**.

12 Insert the injectors and screw them in by hand, then tighten them to the specified torque **(see illustration)**. No outer sealing washer is used, and the injectors are a taper fit in the head. On later models, the injector with the needle lift sensor is No 3 (No 1 is at the timing belt end of the engine).

13 Reconnect the fuel return hoses – make sure that a blanking cap is fitted to the unused connector on No 4 injector. Reconnect the needle lift sensor wiring plug, where applicable.

14 Refit the injection pipes, using two spanners as for removal.

**10.4 Fuel shut-off solenoid wiring connector**

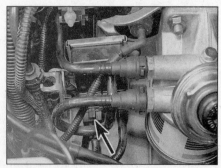

**11.2 Fuel heater wiring plug location (arrowed)**

**9.12 Tighten the injectors to the specified torque**

15 Reconnect the battery, then bleed the system as described in Section 2. When the engine is running, check for leaks around the disturbed components.

### 10 Fuel shut-off (stop) solenoid – removal and refitting

1 If the fuel shut-off solenoid is disconnected, the engine will not run. The same applies if the solenoid is defective. If the plunger jams in the raised position, the engine will not stop. A defective solenoid should be removed for inspection or renewal as follows.

### Removal

2 Disconnect the battery negative lead, and move the lead clear of the terminal. Check that the ignition is switched off (take out the key).

**10.6 Solenoid, spring and plunger (O-ring is arrowed)**

**12.1 Idle-up device (viewed from beneath car)**

3 Where applicable, remove the air cleaner resonator box as described in Section 3.

4 Disconnect the lead from the solenoid terminal, then clean the exterior of the solenoid **(see illustration)**.

5 Using a deep socket or box spanner, unscrew and remove the solenoid from the injection pump.

### Refitting

6 Refitting is a reversal of removal, but use a new O-ring if the old one is in anything but perfect condition **(see illustration)**. Tighten the solenoid to its specified torque wrench setting.

### 11 Fuel heater – removal and refitting

### Removal

1 Where applicable, remove the air cleaner resonator box as described in Section 3.

2 Disconnect the battery negative (earth) lead, then disconnect the wiring plug from the base of the fuel heater **(see illustration)**.

3 Obtain a container in which to catch any fuel spillage. Separate the quick-release connectors on the fuel inlet and outlet lines to the heater, catching any fuel spillage.

4 Remove the two plastic rivets and detach the heater from the engine.

### Refitting

5 Refitting is the reverse of the removal procedure. On completion, bleed the fuel system as described in Section 2, and carry out leak checks directly after the engine is first started.

### 12 Idle-up control system – checking, adjustment and renewal

### Checking

1 An idle-up device may be fitted to automatically raise the engine speed and prevent stalling when reverse gear is selected. The unit is attached to a bracket on the left-hand inner wing panel in the engine compartment **(see illustration)**.

2 The control unit operates in conjunction with the reversing light circuit and the brake vacuum system. It differs according to the fuel injection type.

3 To check the idle-up speed system for satisfactory operation, first check that the system wiring and vacuum hoses are in good condition and securely connected.

### Adjustment

4 Ensure that the idle operating cable is fully released and there is no vacuum in the servo, then check that there is a clearance of 0.5 to 1.0 mm between the idle-up speed

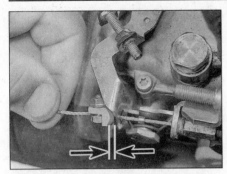

**12.4  Check the clearance between the cable clamp and lever**

**15.2  Remove the elbow retaining clips**

**15.3a  Remove the intercooler retaining screws from the right . . .**

operating cable clamp and the idle lever **(see illustration)**. If necessary, loosen off the adjuster clamp screw and move the clamp to set the clearance, then retighten the screw.

**5** If adjustment is required on either system, loosen off the cable clamp screw and set the clamp as required.

**6** Start the engine and allow it to idle for a period of 5 minutes, then engage reverse gear. The idle speed should rise and then level off within three seconds of reverse gear being engaged. Now disengage reverse gear and check that the idle speed drops and levels off within three seconds of disengagement.

### Renewal

**7** To remove the idle-up device, first disconnect the battery earth lead.

**8** Unplug the electrical connector, and pull off the lower vacuum pipe from the device.

**9** Disconnect the idle-up operating cable from the fuel injection pump.

**10** Remove the retaining bolts and withdraw the idle-up device from the car.

**11** Refitting is the reverse of the removal procedure. Adjust the cable as described above.

### 13  Cold start cable – adjustment, removal and refitting

### Adjustment

**1** The cold start cable is fitted to models without air conditioning only. It is located on the cylinder head side of the injection pump. The adjustment must be carried out with the engine cold.

**2** Release the clip securing the cold start cable to the support bracket.

**3** Hold the idle lever fully against its stop, then position the outer cable so that there is between 1.0 and 2.0 mm play in the inner cable. With the cable held in this position, refit the clip to the support bracket.

### Removal

**4** Drain the cooling system (see Chapter 1).

**5** Release the clip securing the cold start cable to the support bracket.

**6** Disconnect the inner cable from the idle lever on the injection pump.

**15.3b  . . . and left-hand sides . . .**

**7** Unscrew the cold start cable wax element from the thermostat housing and withdraw the cable from the engine compartment. Be prepared for some loss of coolant – place cloth rags beneath the thermostat housing.

### Refitting

**8** Refitting is a reversal of removal, but adjust the cable as described in paragraphs 1 to 3. Refill the cooling system as described in Chapter 1.

### 14  Turbocharger – removal and refitting

The turbocharger is removed with the exhaust manifold – on later models, it is part of the manifold. Refer to Chapter 2A, Section 7.

### 15  Intercooler – removal and refitting

### Removal

**1** Disconnect the battery earth lead.

**2** Loosen the two clips which hold the rubber elbow to the inlet manifold and intercooler assembly, and remove the elbow **(see illustration)**.

**3** Remove the four intercooler retaining screws and lift the cooler clear of the engine, taking care to avoid damaging the O-rings on the cooler-to-compressor joint **(see illustrations)**.

**15.3c  . . . then remove the intercooler, taking care to avoid damaging the O-rings (arrowed)**

### Refitting

**4** Refitting is a reversal of the removal procedure, noting the following points:
  a) Renew any O-ring or seal that is damaged.
  b) Ensure that all mating surfaces are clean.
  c) Tighten all fasteners to the specified torque settings.

### 16  Fuel gauge sender unit – removal and refitting

### Removal

**1** Disconnect the battery negative (earth) lead.

**2** Unbolt or fold forwards (as appropriate) the rear seat base cushion. Withdraw from the car floor the grommet covering the fuel sender

**16.2  Unplugging the sender unit electrical connector (arrowed)**

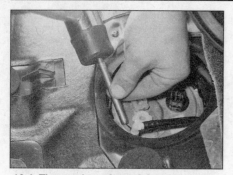

**16.4 The sender unit retaining ring can be tapped round to loosen it**

unit. Unplug the fuel sender unit electrical connector **(see illustration).**

3 Disconnect the fuel supply and return pipes from the stubs by squeezing the quick-release lugs – note that the fuel supply pipe is coded white, while the return pipe is red.

4 Unscrew and remove the special retaining ring, either by unscrewing it with the Ford tool, or by carefully tapping it round until it can be unscrewed by hand **(see illustration).** If care is taken, the ring could also be loosened using an oil filter removal chain- or strap-wrench.

5 Take out the rubber seal, then carefully lift out the fuel pump/gauge sender unit from the tank. Take care that the sender unit float and arm are not damaged as the unit is removed.

### Refitting

6 Refitting is a reversal of removal, but fit a

**17.8 Unbolt rear anti-roll bar mounting clamps (one arrowed) when preparing to remove the fuel tank**

**17.9b ... on Estate models, it is immediately above rear anti-roll bar**

new rubber seal and tighten the retaining ring securely. Before refitting the grommet to the floor, start the engine and check for leaks from the sender unit connections.

## 17 Fuel tank –
### removal and refitting

⚠️ **Warning: Carry out removal of the fuel tank only when it is nearly empty. If not used, fuel can be syphoned or hand-pumped from the tank whilst observing normal fire precautions.**

### Removal

1 Because a fuel tank drain plug is not provided, it is therefore preferable to carry out the removal operation when the tank is nearly empty.

2 Disconnect the battery negative (earth) lead.

3 Syphon or hand-pump any remaining fuel from the tank.

4 Unbolt or fold forwards (as appropriate) the rear seat base cushion. Withdraw from the car floor the grommet covering the fuel sender unit. Unplug the fuel sender unit electrical connector.

5 Disconnect the fuel supply and return pipes from the stubs by squeezing the quick-release lugs – note that the fuel supply pipe is coded white, while the return pipe is red.

6 Chock the front wheels, then raise the rear

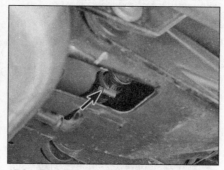

**17.9a Fuel filler vent hose clamp (arrowed) is accessible through rear crossmember (Saloon/Hatchback) ...**

**17.10 Tank retaining strap front bolt locations (arrowed) – remove heat shield for access**

of the car and support it securely on axle stands (see *Jacking and vehicle support*). Familiarise yourself with the layout of the fuel tank assembly before proceeding.

7 Unhook the exhaust system rubber mountings. Lower the system onto a suitable support, so that the front downpipe-to-exhaust manifold joint is not strained, or remove it completely.

8 Unbolt the rear suspension anti-roll bar mounting clamps **(see illustration).** Swing the bar down as far as possible. If clearance is very restricted, it is advisable to remove the bar completely.

9 On pre-facelift models (up to October 1996), disconnect the flexible vent hose from the moulded plastic fuel tank filler neck as follows:

a) On Saloon and Hatchback models, reach up into the right-hand side aperture in the rear suspension crossmember, slacken the clamp, and work the hose off the filler neck stub. This is a job for someone with small hands, good tools and a lot of patience! **(see illustration).**

b) On Estate models, slacken the clamp immediately above the rear anti-roll bar, and work the hose off the filler neck stub **(see illustration).**

10 Unscrew the six retaining nuts, and withdraw the exhaust system's rear heat shield from the underbody **(see illustration).**

11 Support the tank with a trolley jack or similar. Place a sturdy plank between the support and the tank, to protect the tank.

12 Unscrew the bolt at the front of each retaining strap and pivot the straps down until they are hanging out of the way. Note the earth lead under the left-hand strap bolt and clean its mating surfaces before the tank is refitted, so that clean, metal-to-metal contact is ensured.

13 Lower the tank enough to release the pipes from its top. If in doubt, clearly label all fuel lines and hoses and their respective unions. Plug the hoses, to prevent contamination of the fuel system.

14 Remove the tank from the car, releasing it from the filler neck stub.

15 With the tank removed, unhook the retaining straps (twist them through 90° to do so) and check that they and their locations in the underbody are in good condition.

### Refitting

16 Refitting is the reverse of the removal procedure, noting the following points:

a) Renew any hose or pipeline that is damaged.

b) Ensure that all mating surfaces are clean.

c) Ensure that all hoses are correctly routed.

d) Tighten all fasteners to the specified torque settings.

e) Carry out leak checks directly after the engine is first started.

## 18 Manifolds –
removal and refitting

Refer to Chapter 2A.

## 19 Exhaust system –
general information
and component renewal

⚠️ **Warning: Inspection and repair of exhaust system components should be done only after the system has cooled completely. This applies particularly to the catalytic converter, which runs at very high temperatures.**

### General information

**1** The catalytic converter (see Chapter 4B) is mounted at the rear of the front section, with a flanged joint connecting to the factory-fitted one-piece rear section, which contains the centre and rear silencers. To fit a new rear silencer, the original one-piece rear section has to be cut (by now, most models covered by this manual will have had this done) – the original and new sections are then sleeved together.

**2** The system is suspended throughout its entire length by rubber mountings.

**3** To remove a part of the system, first jack up the front or rear of the car, and support it on axle stands (see *Jacking and vehicle support*). Alternatively, position the car over an inspection pit, or on car ramps.

**4** Ford recommend that all nuts (such as flange joint nuts, clamp joint nuts, or converter-to-manifold nuts) are renewed on reassembly – given that they may be in less-than-perfect condition as a result of corrosion, this seems a good idea, especially as it will make subsequent removal easier.

**5** Make sure that the mating faces of the exhaust system joints are cleaned thoroughly before assembling, and use new gaskets where applicable.

### Component renewal

**6** If any section of the exhaust is damaged or deteriorated, excessive noise and vibration will occur.

**7** Carry out regular inspections of the exhaust system, to check security and condition. Look for any damaged or bent parts, open seams, holes, loose connections, excessive corrosion, or other defects which could allow exhaust fumes to enter the car. Deteriorated sections of the exhaust system should be renewed.

**8** If the exhaust system components are extremely corroded or rusted together, it may not be possible to separate them. In this case, simply cut off the old components with a hacksaw, and remove any remaining corroded pipe with a cold chisel. Be sure to wear safety glasses to protect your eyes, and wear gloves to protect your hands.

**9** Here are some simple guidelines to follow when repairing the exhaust system:

a) *Work from the back to the front when removing exhaust system components.*

b) *Apply penetrating fluid to the flange nuts before unscrewing them.*

c) *Use new gaskets and rubber mountings when installing exhaust system components.*

d) *Apply anti-seize compound (copper brake grease will suffice) to the threads of all exhaust system studs during reassembly.*

e) *Note that on some models, the downpipe is secured to the manifold by two coil springs, spring seats and a self-locking nut on each. Where fitted, tighten the nuts until they stop on the bolt shoulders; the pressure of the springs will then be sufficient to make a leak-proof connection. Do not overtighten the nuts to cure a leak – the studs will shear. Renew the gasket and the springs if a leak is found.*

f) *Be sure to allow sufficient clearance between newly-installed parts and all points on the underbody, to avoid overheating the floorpan, and possibly damaging the interior carpet and insulation. Pay particularly close attention to the catalytic converter and its heat shield.*

g) *The heat shields are secured to the underside of the body by special nuts, or by bolts. They are fitted above the exhaust, to reduce radiated heat affecting the cabin or fuel tank. Each shield can be removed separately, but note that some overlap each other, making it necessary to loosen another section first. If a shield is being removed to gain access to a component located behind it, it may prove sufficient in some cases to remove the retaining nuts and/or bolts, and simply lower the shield, without disturbing the exhaust system. Otherwise, remove the exhaust section as described earlier.*

## 20 Engine management system
– description and
component renewal

### General information

**1** An engine management system is fitted to all models. On models up to October 1996, the system was known as EDC (electronic diesel control), but the facelifted models after this date had a more sophisticated system, controlled by the Ford EEC V module.

**2** The heart of the system is the engine management ECU (also known as the powertrain control module), which works with a number of sensors and actuators **(see illustration overleaf)**. The sensors supply the ECU with input signals relating to the engine operating conditions. Once the ECU has processed all the information, it sends out signals to the actuators as necessary to control various engine functions.

**3** The ECU also has control over the emissions system components – these are dealt with in more detail in Chapter 4B.

### Exhaust gas recirculation system

**4** Refer to Chapter 4B.

### Engine coolant temperature sensor

**5** Information from the coolant temperature sensor used to operate the temperature gauge is also used by the ECU as a means of determining engine operating temperature. The coolant temperature sensor is screwed into the thermostat housing at the front of the engine – refer to Chapter 3 for more details.

### Crankshaft position sensor

**6** The inductive head of the sensor runs just above the engine flywheel, and scans a series of 36 protrusions on the flywheel periphery. As the crankshaft rotates, the sensor transmits a pulse to the ECU every time a protrusion passes it. There is one missing protrusion in the flywheel periphery at a point corresponding to 90° BTDC. The ECU recognises the absence of a pulse from the crankshaft position sensor at this point to establish a reference mark for crankshaft position. Similarly, the time interval between absent pulses is used to determine engine speed.

### Mass airflow sensor

**7** The mass airflow sensor is based on a 'hot-wire' system, sending the ECU a constantly-varying (analogue) voltage signal corresponding to the mass of air passing into the engine. Since air mass varies with temperature (cold air being denser than warm), measuring air mass provides the ECU with a very accurate means of determining the correct amount of fuel required to achieve the ideal air/fuel mixture ratio.

### Cold start system (waxstat)

**8** All models except those with air conditioning are fitted with a separate cold start system. A wax element inside the thermostat housing is linked to a control cable attached to the idle lever on the injection pump. This system is intended to provide a stable idle under cold conditions.

### Cold start system (solenoid)

**9** On models with air conditioning, a cold advance solenoid is fitted to the base of the injection pump. The solenoid regulates the pump timing during cold running, under the control of the engine management ECU.

### Needle lift sensor

**10** Later models have a needle lift (injection pulse) sensor fitted to No 3 injector. The sensor, which is not available separately, informs the ECU of the exact moment when injection starts.

### Advance solenoid (turbo boost)

**11** When the engine is running at full boost, additional fuel is required. The advance

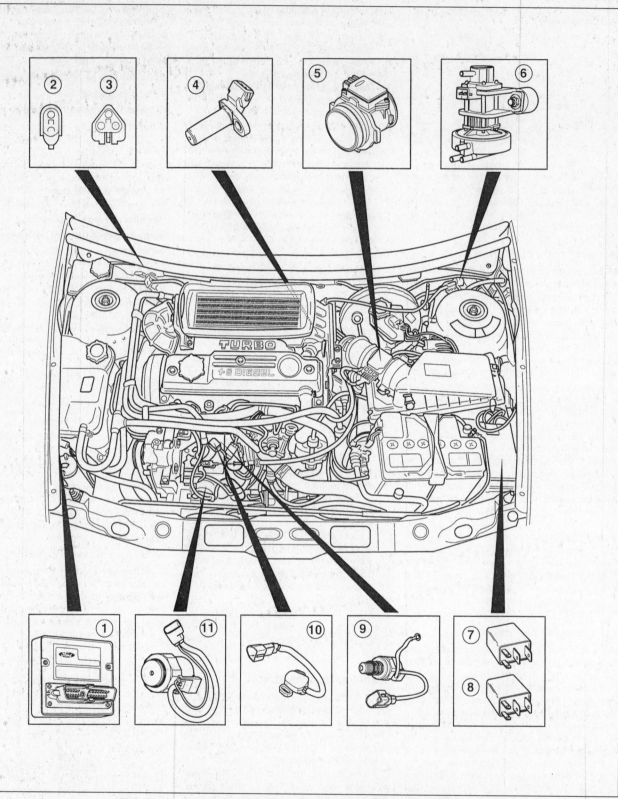

**20.2 Diesel engine management and emissions control components**

1  Engine management ECU
2  Diagnostic connector (Ford
   FDS 2000)
3  Diagnostic connector (Ford STAR)

4  Crankshaft speed/position sensor
5  Mass airflow sensor
6  EGR solenoid valve
7  Cold advance relay

8   Air conditioning relay
9   Advance solenoid (turbo boost)
10  Throttle lever position sensor
11  Advance solenoid (cold start)

solenoid allows the ECU to control the fuelling to a finer degree.

### Throttle lever position sensor

12 Fitted to the throttle lever on the injection pump, the sensor allows the ECU to take account of the lever position and rate of change, to improve fuelling. It also signals the ECU when the lever is in the idle position.

### Vehicle speed sensor

13 The vehicle speed sensor informs the ECU of the car's speed, and is driven by a worm gear inside the transmission. On pre-facelift models (up to October 1996), the speed sensor is part of the speedometer drive pinion (which drives the speedometer cable). On models after October 1996, the speed sensor is in the same place, but a cable is no longer fitted, as the speedometer is electronic.

### Power steering pressure switch

14 When the steering is turned anywhere near full lock, increased fluid pressure is required, which loads up the power steering pump. As the pump is driven by the engine, if the extra load happened at idle speed (such as when parking the car), the engine may stall. A pressure switch is fitted into the hydraulic pipe, which signals the ECU when pressure is high – if this happens at idle, the idle speed is temporarily increased by the ECU to prevent a stall.

## Component removal and refitting

### Engine management ECU

15 Disconnect the battery negative lead – this is **essential**, as the ECU may be damaged if its wiring plug is disconnected while 'live'.
16 On pre-facelift models (up to October 1996), the unit is located at the front of the right-hand inner wing, behind the screenwash reservoir filler neck. Disconnect the unit wiring plug, then remove the retaining bolts and remove the ECU **(see illustration)**.
17 On facelift models (October 1996 onwards), carefully lift out the power steering fluid reservoir, then unscrew the wiring plug retaining bolt (where applicable, remove the riveted tamperproof cover first). Inside the car, remove the footwell trim panels for access, then unscrew the ECU support bracket bolt, and withdraw the unit into the car **(see illustrations)**.
18 Refitting is a reversal of removal. Make sure that the wiring plug is securely connected, and that the ECU itself is also secure.

### EGR valve

19 Refer to Chapter 4B.

### EGR solenoid valve

20 Refer to Chapter 4B.

### Crankshaft position sensor

21 The crankshaft position sensor is located

at the rear of the engine, just in front of the right-hand driveshaft (right as seen from the driver's seat).
22 Access to the sensor is best gained from below. Jack up the front of the car, and support it on axle stands (see *Jacking and vehicle support*).
23 Reach up between the driveshaft and the engine, and disconnect the sensor wiring plug **(see illustration)**.
24 Unscrew the single bolt securing the sensor, and remove it.
25 Refitting is a reversal of removal. Make sure that the sensor is clean, and tighten its mounting bolt securely.

### Mass airflow sensor

26 Refer to Section 3.

### Advance solenoid (turbo boost)

27 The solenoid is fitted to the top of the pump. With the ignition switched off, disconnect the solenoid wiring plug.
28 Unscrew the solenoid from the pump, and recover the sealing washer – a new one should be used when refitting.
29 Refitting is a reversal of removal. Use a new sealing washer, and tighten the solenoid securely.

### Throttle lever position sensor

30 The sensor is attached to the throttle lever on the injection pump. Its position is set in production, and should not be disturbed – if a

20.16 Disconnect the ECU wiring plug

20.17a Lift out the power steering reservoir (keep it level, to avoid fluid spillage) . . .

20.17b . . . then unscrew the ECU wiring plug securing bolt

20.17c Inside the car, unscrew the ECU support bracket bolt . . .

20.17d . . . and withdraw the ECU into the driver's footwell

20.23 Disconnecting the crankshaft position sensor wiring plug

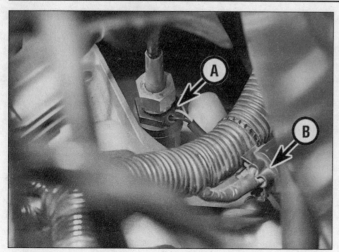

**20.33 Vehicle speed sensor (A) and wiring plug (B) – early models**

**20.38 Power steering pressure switch is screwed into the fluid pipe**

new sensor is required, mark the fitted position of the old one before removing it, and align the new sensor with the marks. Have the car checked by a Ford dealer or diesel specialist on completion.

### Advance solenoid (cold start)

**31** The solenoid is part of the injection pump, and is not intended to be removed. Consult a Ford dealer or diesel specialist if renewal is thought to be necessary.

### Needle lift sensor

**32** The sensor is an integral part of No 3 injector, and is not available separately – refer to Section 9 for injector removal and refitting.

### Vehicle speed sensor

**33** The sensor is located on top of the transmission, at the rear – on pre-facelift models, it will be at the end of the speedometer drive cable **(see illustration)**. Access to the sensor will be improved by removing the air cleaner as described in Section 3.

**34** Where applicable, unscrew the speedometer cable from the sensor, and move it clear, noting how it is fitted.

**35** Trace the wiring from the sensor back to its wiring plug, and disconnect it.

**36** Unscrew the mounting bolt(s), and remove the sensor from the transmission. Check the sensor's O-ring – if in poor condition, it should be renewed.

**37** Refitting is a reversal of removal. Check the operation of the speedometer on completion.

### Power steering pressure switch

**38** The pressure switch is screwed into the rigid high-pressure pipe at the rear of the engine compartment, next to the right-hand suspension strut (right as seen from the driver's seat) **(see illustration)**.

**39** Disconnect the wiring plug from the top of the switch.

**40** Place some absorbent cloth or paper towel under the switch, then unscrew and withdraw it from the fluid pipe. Recover the sealing washer – a new one should ideally be used when refitting.

**41** Refitting is a reversal of removal. Tighten the switch securely, then top-up the power steering fluid and bleed the system as described in Chapter 10.

# Chapter 4 Part B:
# Emission control systems

## Contents

| | Section number | | | Section number |
|---|---|---|---|---|
| Catalytic converter – precautions | 3 | General information | | 1 |
| Emission control systems – testing and component renewal | 2 | | | |

## Degrees of difficulty

| Easy, suitable for novice with little experience  | Fairly easy, suitable for beginner with some experience | Fairly difficult, suitable for competent DIY mechanic | Difficult, suitable for experienced DIY mechanic | Very difficult, suitable for expert DIY or professional  |
|---|---|---|---|---|

## Specifications

| Torque wrench settings | Nm | lbf ft |
|---|---|---|
| EGR pipe flange bolts | 15 | 11 |
| EGR valve mounting bolts (models up to October 1996) | 20 | 15 |

## 1 General information

1 All diesel engine models are designed to meet strict emission requirements, and are also equipped with a crankcase emission control system. In addition to this, all models are fitted with a two-way 'oxidation' catalytic converter to reduce harmful exhaust emissions.

2 To further reduce emissions, an exhaust gas recirculation (EGR) system is fitted.

3 The engine management system described in Chapter 4A also electronically controls the operation of the EGR system.

4 The emission control systems function as follows.

### Crankcase emission control

5 To reduce the emission of unburned hydrocarbons from the crankcase into the atmosphere, the engine is sealed and the blow-by gases and oil vapour are drawn from inside the crankcase, through a hose located on the rear of the engine, into the inlet manifold to be burned by the engine during normal combustion. A further hose from the cylinder head cover to the crankcase ensures the blow-by gases are circulated freely. Since the inlet manifold depression does not vary on a diesel engine, there is no regulating valve as fitted to petrol engines.

### Exhaust emission control

6 To minimise the level of exhaust pollutants released into the atmosphere, a catalytic converter is fitted in the exhaust system of all models.

7 The catalytic converter consists of a canister containing a fine mesh impregnated with a catalyst material, over which the hot exhaust gases pass. The catalyst speeds up the oxidation of harmful carbon monoxide, unburnt hydrocarbons and soot, effectively reducing the quantity of harmful products released into the atmosphere via the exhaust gases.

### Exhaust gas recirculation system

8 The EGR system consists of the vacuum-operated EGR valve, controlled by a solenoid valve. The EGR valve is linked to the inlet and exhaust manifolds by steel pipes. When the solenoid valve fitted in the left-hand rear corner of the engine compartment is activated by the engine management ECU, vacuum is applied to the EGR valve, which opens the pipe joining the inlet and exhaust manifolds.

9 Under the control of the engine management ECU, the EGR valve allows a proportion of exhaust gas back into the inlet air – this reduces combustion temperatures, and in turn reduces the amount of oxides of nitrogen emitted by the vehicle. Reducing combustion temperatures is particularly important on turbocharged engines.

## 2 Emission control systems – testing and component renewal

### Crankcase emission control

1 The components of this system require no attention other than to check that the hoses are clear and undamaged at regular intervals.

### Exhaust emission control

#### Testing

2 The performance of the catalytic converter can be checked only by measuring the exhaust gases using a good-quality, carefully-calibrated exhaust gas analyser.

3 Before assuming that the catalytic converter is faulty, it is worth checking the problem is not due to a faulty injector. Refer to your Ford dealer for further information.

#### Catalytic converter renewal

4 The converter is an integral part of the front downpipe – for general information on exhaust system repair, refer to Chapter 4A.

### Exhaust gas recirculation system

#### Testing

5 Start the engine and allow it to idle.

6 Detach the vacuum hose from the EGR valve, and attach a hand vacuum pump in its place.

7 Apply vacuum to the EGR valve. Vacuum should remain steady, and the engine should run poorly or stall.

   a) If the vacuum doesn't remain steady and the engine doesn't run poorly, renew the EGR valve and recheck it.

   b) If the vacuum remains steady but the engine doesn't run poorly, remove the EGR valve, and check the valve and the inlet manifold for blockage. Clean or renew parts as necessary, and recheck.

8 Any further checking of the system requires special tools and test equipment. Take the car to a Ford dealer or diesel specialist for checking.

**2.10 Disconnect the EGR valve vacuum hose (arrowed) – pre-facelift model shown**

## EGR valve renewal

**Note 1:** *These components will be very hot when the engine is running. Always allow the engine to cool down fully before starting work, to prevent the possibility of burns.*

**Note 2:** *On facelift models (October 1996 onwards), the EGR valve is an integral part of the inlet manifold. Refer to Chapter 2A.*

**9** Loosen/release the clips and disconnect the air inlet duct from the air cleaner. Although not essential, removing the intercooler (where applicable) as described in Chapter 4A will also improve access.

**10** Disconnect the vacuum pipe from the valve body **(see illustration)**.

**11** Unscrew the mounting bolts and remove the valve from the inlet manifold and transfer tube flange. Recover the gaskets.

**12** Clean the mating faces of the valve and inlet manifold.

**13** Refitting is a reversal of removal. Use new gaskets, and tighten the bolts to the specified torque.

## EGR pipe renewal

**14** Remove the intercooler as described in Chapter 4A.

**15** Disconnect the vacuum hose from the EGR valve.

**16** Unscrew the three bolts securing the pipe to the inlet manifold and to the valve (early models) or exhaust manifold (later models), and withdraw the pipe.

**17** Collect and discard the gaskets – these must always be renewed.

**18** Refitting is a reversal of removal. Tighten the bolts to the specified torque wrench setting.

## EGR solenoid valve renewal

**19** The solenoid valve is located at the rear of the engine compartment, behind the left-hand suspension strut mounting (left as seen from the driver's seat).

**20** Release the wire clip and unplug the electrical connector from the valve. Remove the two retaining screws, and withdraw the valve from the bulkhead mounting bracket, then label and disconnect the vacuum hoses.

**21** Refitting is the reverse of the removal procedure, but ensure that the hoses are correctly reconnected.

## 3 Catalytic converter – precautions

**1** The catalytic converter is a reliable and simple device, which needs no maintenance in itself, but there are some facts of which an owner should be aware if the converter is to function properly for its full service life.

**2** The catalytic converter fitted to diesel models is simpler than that fitted to petrol models, but it still needs to be treated with respect to avoid problems:

a) DO NOT use fuel or engine oil additives – these may contain substances harmful to the catalytic converter.

b) DO NOT continue to use the car if the engine burns (engine) oil to the extent of leaving a visible trail of blue smoke.

c) Remember that the catalytic converter operates at very high temperatures. DO NOT, therefore, park the car in dry undergrowth, over long grass or piles of dead leaves after a long run.

d) Driving through deep water should be avoided if possible. The sudden cooling effect will fracture the ceramic honeycomb, damaging it beyond repair.

e) Remember that the catalytic converter is FRAGILE – do not strike it with tools during servicing work, and take care handling it when removing it from the car for any reason.

f) If a substantial loss of power is experienced, remember that this could be due to the converter being blocked. This can occur simply as a result of contamination after a high mileage, but may be due to the ceramic element having fractured and collapsed internally. A new converter is the only cure in this instance.

g) The catalytic converter, used on a well-maintained and well-driven car, should last at least 100 000 miles – if the converter is no longer effective, it must be renewed.

# Chapter 5
# Engine electrical systems

## Contents

Section number

Alternator – removal and refitting. . . . . . . . . . . . . . . . . . . . . . . . . . . 6
Alternator brushes and voltage regulator – renewal. . . . . . . . . . . . . 7
Alternator/charging system – testing . . . . . . . . . . . . . . . . . . . . . . . 5
Auxiliary drivebelt check and renewal . . . . . . . . . . . . . . See Chapter 1
Battery – removal and refitting. . . . . . . . . . . . . . . . . . . . . . . . . . . . . 3
Battery – testing and charging . . . . . . . . . . . . . . . . . . . . . . . . . . . . . 2
Battery check, maintenance and charging. . . . . . . . . . . See Chapter 1
Battery leads – check and renewal . . . . . . . . . . . . . . . . . . . . . . . . . 4
Engine compartment wiring check. . . . . . . . . . . . . . . . See Chapter 1

Section number

Engine management system components. . . . . . . . . . .See Chapter 4A
General information and precautions. . . . . . . . . . . . . . . . . . . . . . . . . 1
Glow plug (preheating) system – description and testing . . . . . . . . 12
Glow plugs – removal, inspection and refitting . . . . . . . . . . . . . . . . 13
Starter motor – overhaul. . . . . . . . . . . . . . . . . . . . . . . . . . . . . . . . . 11
Starter motor – removal and refitting . . . . . . . . . . . . . . . . . . . . . . . . 10
Starting system – general information and precautions. . . . . . . . . . . 8
Starting system – testing . . . . . . . . . . . . . . . . . . . . . . . . . . . . . . . . . 9

## Degrees of difficulty

| **Easy,** suitable for novice with little experience  | **Fairly easy,** suitable for beginner with some experience | **Fairly difficult,** suitable for competent DIY mechanic | **Difficult,** suitable for experienced DIY mechanic | **Very difficult,** suitable for expert DIY or professional |
| --- | --- | --- | --- | --- |

## Specifications

### Battery

| | |
| --- | --- |
| Type . . . . . . . . . . . . . . . . . . . . . . . . . . . . . . . . . . . . . . . . . . . . . . . . . | Lead-acid |
| Rating – cold cranking/reserve capacity . . . . . . . . . . . . . . . . . . . . . | 500 A/75 RC, 590 A/95 RC, or 650 A/130 RC |

### Alternator

| Type: | Model | Rated output |
| --- | --- | --- |
| Bosch . . . . . . . . . . . . . . . . . . . . . . . . . . . . . . . . . . . . . . . . . . . . . | NC 14V 60-90A | 90A |
| Mitsubishi . . . . . . . . . . . . . . . . . . . . . . . . . . . . . . . . . . . . . . . . . . | A004T | 90A |
| Lucas/Magneti Marelli . . . . . . . . . . . . . . . . . . . . . . . . . . . . . . . . | - | 95A |
| Ford . . . . . . . . . . . . . . . . . . . . . . . . . . . . . . . . . . . . . . . . . . . . . . | EFHD 3G | 95A |
| Minimum brush length . . . . . . . . . . . . . . . . . . . . . . . . . . . . . . . . . . . | 5.0 mm | |
| Regulated voltage @ 4000 rpm . . . . . . . . . . . . . . . . . . . . . . . . . . . . | 13.5 to 14.6 volts | |

### Starter motor

| Type: | Model | Rated output |
| --- | --- | --- |
| Bosch . . . . . . . . . . . . . . . . . . . . . . . . . . . . . . . . . . . . . . . . . . . . . | DW | 1.1 or 1.4 kW |
| Bosch . . . . . . . . . . . . . . . . . . . . . . . . . . . . . . . . . . . . . . . . . . . . . | EV | 2.2 kW |
| Lucas/Magneti Marelli . . . . . . . . . . . . . . . . . . . . . . . . . . . . . . . . | M79 | 1.0 kW |
| Ford . . . . . . . . . . . . . . . . . . . . . . . . . . . . . . . . . . . . . . . . . . . . . . | EFHD | 1.4 kW |
| Minimum brush length . . . . . . . . . . . . . . . . . . . . . . . . . . . . . . . . . . . | 8.0 mm | |
| Commutator minimum diameter: | | |
| Bosch . . . . . . . . . . . . . . . . . . . . . . . . . . . . . . . . . . . . . . . . . . . . . | 32.8 mm | |
| Lucas/Magneti Marelli . . . . . . . . . . . . . . . . . . . . . . . . . . . . . . . . | Not available | |
| Armature endfloat: | | |
| Bosch . . . . . . . . . . . . . . . . . . . . . . . . . . . . . . . . . . . . . . . . . . . . . | 0.30 mm | |
| Lucas/Magneti Marelli . . . . . . . . . . . . . . . . . . . . . . . . . . . . . . . . | 0.25 mm | |

### Torque wrench settings

| | Nm | lbf ft |
| --- | --- | --- |
| Alternator mounting bolts. . . . . . . . . . . . . . . . . . . . . . . . . . . . . . . . . | 50 | 37 |
| Glow plugs . . . . . . . . . . . . . . . . . . . . . . . . . . . . . . . . . . . . . . . . . . . | 28 | 21 |
| Starter motor mounting bolts. . . . . . . . . . . . . . . . . . . . . . . . . . . . . . | 35 | 26 |

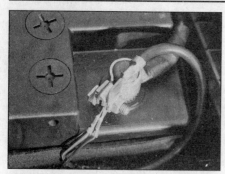

**1.2 Always disconnect battery – negative (earth) lead first – to prevent the possibility of short-circuits**

## 1 General information and precautions

### General information

The engine electrical systems include all charging and starting components, and the glow plug system. Because of their engine-related functions, these components are discussed separately from body electrical devices such as the lights, the instruments, etc (which are included in Chapter 12). Other engine-related items relating to the engine management system are classed as electronic components, and are covered in Chapters 4A and 4B.

### Precautions

Always observe the following precautions when working on the electrical system:

a) *Be extremely careful when servicing engine electrical components. They are easily damaged if checked, connected or handled improperly.*

b) *Never leave the ignition switched on for long periods of time when the engine is not running.*

c) *Don't disconnect the battery leads while the engine is running.*

d) *Maintain correct polarity when connecting a battery lead from another vehicle during jump starting – see the Jump starting Section at the front of this manual.*

e) *When working on the alternator, starter or glow plugs, the battery negative lead should **always** be disconnected (see illustration). The supply wiring to these components is taken straight from the battery, and will be live – if it touches the engine or bodywork when disconnected, there will be a dead short and a large amount of sparks.*

f) *Always disconnect the negative lead first, and reconnect it last, or the battery may be shorted by the tool being used to loosen the lead clamps. Don't leave tools lying across the battery terminals for the same reason.*

It's also a good idea to review the safety-related information regarding the engine electrical systems shown in the Safety first! section at the front of this manual, before beginning any operation included in this Chapter.

### Battery disconnection

Refer to *Disconnecting the battery* at the end of this manual.

## 2 Battery – testing and charging

### Testing

1 The simplest way to test a battery is with a voltmeter (or multi-meter set to voltage testing) – connect the voltmeter across the battery terminals, observing the correct polarity. The test is only accurate if the battery has not been subjected to any kind of charge for the previous six hours. If this is not the case, switch on the headlights for 30 seconds, then wait four to five minutes before testing the battery after switching off the headlights. All other electrical circuits must be switched off, so check that the doors and tailgate/boot lid are fully shut when making the test.

2 If the voltage reading is less than 12.0 volts, then the battery is less than healthy. Under 11.5 volts, and the battery needs charging. However, as little as 11.0 volts will still usually be enough to start the engine, though a battery in this condition could not be relied on. A reading of around 10.0 volts suggests that one of the six battery cells has died – a common way for modern batteries to fail.

3 If the battery is to be charged, remove it from the car (Section 3) and charge it as described later in this Section.

### Low-maintenance battery

4 If the car covers a small annual mileage, it is worthwhile checking the specific gravity of the electrolyte every three months to determine the state of charge of the battery. Use a hydrometer to make the check, and compare the results with the tool maker's instructions (typically, there will be a colour-coded scale on hydrometers sold for battery testing).

5 If the battery condition is suspect, first check the specific gravity of electrolyte in each cell. A significant variation between any cells indicates loss of electrolyte, or deterioration of the internal plates.

6 If the cell variation is satisfactory but the battery is discharged, it should be charged as described later in this Section.

### Maintenance-free battery

7 In cases where a 'sealed for life' maintenance-free battery is fitted, topping-up and testing of the electrolyte in each cell is not possible. The condition of the battery can therefore only be tested using a battery condition indicator or a voltmeter.

### Charging

**Note:** *The following is intended as a guide only. Always refer to the manufacturer's recommendations (often printed on a label attached to the battery), and always disconnect both terminal leads before charging a battery.*

### Low-maintenance battery

8 It is advisable to remove the cell caps or covers if possible during charging, but note that the battery will be giving off potentially-explosive hydrogen gas while it is being charged. Small amounts of acidic electrolyte may also escape as the battery nears full charge – keep your face and hands clear. Removing the cell caps will allow you to check whether all six cells are receiving charge – after a while, the electrolyte should start to bubble. If any cell does not bubble, this may indicate that it has failed, and the battery is no longer fit for use.

9 Charge the battery at a rate of 3.5 to 4 amps, and continue to charge the battery at this rate until no further rise in specific gravity is noted over a four-hour period.

10 Alternatively, a trickle charger charging at the rate of 1.5 amps can safely be used overnight.

11 Specially rapid 'boost' charges which are claimed to restore the power of the battery in 1 to 2 hours are not recommended, as they can cause serious damage to the battery plates through overheating.

12 While charging the battery, note that the temperature of the electrolyte should never exceed 38°C.

### Maintenance-free battery

13 This battery type takes considerably longer to fully recharge than the standard type, the time taken being dependent on the extent of discharge, but it can take anything up to three days.

14 A constant-voltage type charger is required, to be set, when connected, to 13.9 to 14.9 volts with a charger current below 25 amps. Using this method, the battery should be usable within three hours, giving a voltage reading of 12.5 volts, but this is for a partially-discharged battery and, as mentioned, full charging can take considerably longer.

15 If the battery is to be charged from a fully-discharged state (condition reading less than 12.2 volts), have it recharged by your local automotive electrician, as the charge rate is higher and constant supervision during charging is necessary.

## 3 Battery – removal and refitting

**Note:** *Refer to Section 1 of this Chapter before starting work.*

### Removal

1 Before removing the battery, refer to *Disconnecting the battery* in the reference section of this manual.

2 Disconnect the battery leads, negative

3.3a Unscrew hold-down nuts (one of two arrowed) . . .

3.3b . . . and withdraw hold-down clamp to release the battery

(earth) lead first. Move the leads well clear of the battery terminals.

3 Remove the battery hold-down clamp **(see illustrations)**.

4 Lift out the battery. Be careful – it's heavy (use the carrying handle, if the battery has one).

5 While the battery is out, inspect the tray for corrosion.

6 If you are renewing the battery, make sure that you get one that's identical, with the same dimensions, amperage rating, cold cranking rating, etc. Batteries for diesel engines have to be heavier-duty items than most petrol-engine ones, and cost more – buying a cheaper battery could leave you stranded.

7 Dispose of the old battery in a responsible fashion. Most local authorities have facilities for the collection and disposal of such items – batteries contain sulphuric acid, which must be treated with respect.

### Refitting

8 Refitting is a reversal of removal, noting the following points:
   a) Clean the battery tray if necessary.
   b) Tighten the battery hold-down clamp securely.
   c) Reconnect the battery leads, positive first, negative last.
   d) Re-activate the radio, re-program the electric windows, etc, as described in Disconnecting the battery.

### 4  Battery leads – check and renewal

**Note:** Refer to Section 1 of this Chapter before starting work.

1 Periodically inspect the entire length of each battery lead for damage, cracked or burned insulation, and corrosion. Poor battery lead connections can cause starting problems and decreased engine performance.

2 Check the lead-to-terminal connections at the ends of the leads for cracks, loose wire strands and corrosion. The presence of white, fluffy deposits under the insulation at the lead terminal connection is a sign that the lead is corroded and should be renewed. Check the terminals for distortion, missing clamp bolts, and corrosion.

3 When removing the leads, always disconnect the negative lead first, and reconnect it last (see Section 1). Even if only the positive lead is being renewed, be sure to disconnect the negative lead from the battery first.

4 Disconnect the old leads from the battery, then trace each of them to their opposite ends, and detach them from the starter solenoid and earth terminals. Note the routing of each lead, to ensure correct installation.

5 If you are renewing either or both of the old leads, take them with you when buying new leads. It is vitally important that you replace the leads with identical parts. Leads have characteristics that make them easy to identify: positive leads are usually red, larger in cross-section, and have a larger-diameter battery post clamp; earth leads are usually black, smaller in cross-section and have a slightly smaller-diameter clamp for the negative post.

6 Clean the threads of the solenoid or earth connection with a wire brush to remove rust and corrosion.

7 Attach the lead to the solenoid or earth connection, and tighten the mounting nut/bolt securely.

8 Before connecting a new lead to the battery, make sure that it reaches the battery post without having to be stretched.

9 Connect the positive lead first, followed by the negative lead.

 **Apply a light coat of battery terminal corrosion inhibitor, or petroleum jelly, to the terminals, to prevent future corrosion.**

### 5  Alternator/charging system – testing

**Note:** Refer to Section 1 of this Chapter before starting work.

1 If the charge warning light fails to illuminate when the ignition is switched on, first check the alternator wiring connections for security. If the light still fails to illuminate, check the continuity of the warning light feed wire from the alternator to the instrument panel. Check the condition of the auxiliary drivebelt. If all is satisfactory, the alternator is at fault and should be renewed or taken to an auto-electrician for testing and repair.

2 Similarly, if the charge warning light comes on with the ignition, but is then slow to go out when the engine is started, this may indicate an impending alternator problem. Check all the items listed in the preceding paragraph, and refer to an auto-electrical specialist if no obvious faults are found.

3 If the charge warning light illuminates when the engine is running, stop the engine and check that the drivebelt is correctly tensioned (see Chapter 1) and that the alternator connections are secure. If all is so far satisfactory, check the alternator brushes and slip-rings as described in Section 7. If the fault persists, the alternator should be renewed, or taken to an auto-electrician for testing and repair.

4 If the alternator output is suspect even though the warning light functions correctly, the regulated voltage may be checked as follows.

5 Connect a voltmeter across the battery terminals, and start the engine.

6 Increase the engine speed until the voltmeter reading remains steady; the reading should be approximately 12 to 13 volts, and no more than 14 volts.

7 Switch on as many electrical accessories (such as the headlights, heated rear window and heater blower) as possible, and check

that the alternator maintains the regulated voltage at around 13 to 14 volts.

**8** If the regulated voltage is not as stated, this may be due to worn brushes, weak brush springs, a faulty voltage regulator, a faulty diode, a severed phase winding or worn or damaged slip-rings. The brushes and slip-rings may be checked (see Section 7), but if the fault persists, the alternator should be renewed or taken to an auto-electrician.

### 6 Alternator – removal and refitting

**Note:** *Refer to Section 1 of this Chapter before starting work.*

### Removal

**1** Disconnect the battery negative (earth) lead.

**2** Remove the intercooler as described in Chapter 4A.

**3** Where applicable, detach and remove the alternator rear cover/heat shield – this is either clipped in place, or secured with screws.

**4** Disconnect the wiring from the alternator, noting the location of each wire/plug. On some models, the main wiring plug is retained by a wire clip, which hinges to one side. Where a nut and washer arrangement is used, loosely refit the nut and washer once the wire has been disconnected, to avoid losing them.

**5** Remove the auxiliary drivebelt as described in Chapter 1.

**6** Unscrew and remove the alternator lower mounting bolt.

**7** Unscrew the remaining mounting bolts, and withdraw the alternator from the engine – take care not to drop it as it is removed.

**8** If a new alternator is to be fitted, make sure that an exact replacement is obtained. Bear in mind that some exchange units may not come with a pulley fitted, which presents the problem of changing one over – most auto-electrical specialists will perform this free of charge if necessary.

### Refitting

**9** Refitting is the reverse of the removal procedure, noting the following points:
   a) Tighten the alternator mountings securely.
   b) Ensure that the alternator wiring is correctly and securely reconnected.
   c) Refit the auxiliary drivebelt as described in Chapter 1.
   d) On completion, check the charging voltage to verify proper operation of the alternator (see Section 5).

### 7 Alternator brushes and voltage regulator – renewal

**Note:** *This procedure assumes that parts of the correct type have been obtained. At the time of writing, no individual alternator components were available as separate Ford parts. An auto-electrical specialist should be able to supply parts such as brushes. The following procedure is for the Bosch unit fitted to the project car – details may vary for other alternator types.*

**1** Remove the alternator from the car (see Section 6) and place it on a clean workbench.

**2** Remove the three screws, and withdraw the plastic end cover **(see illustration)**.

**3** Remove the two voltage regulator/brush holder mounting screws.

**4** Remove the regulator/brush holder from the end frame **(see illustration)**. If you are renewing the assembly, proceed to paragraph 8, install the new unit, reassemble the alternator, and refit it to the engine (see Section 6). If you are going to check the brushes, proceed to the next paragraph.

**5** Measure the exposed length of each brush – if the length of either brush is less than the specified minimum, renew the assembly.

**6** Make sure that each brush moves smoothly in the brush holder.

**7** Check that the slip-rings – the ring of copper on which each brush bears – are clean. Wipe them with a solvent-moistened cloth; if either appears scored or blackened, take the alternator to a repair specialist for advice.

**8** Refit the voltage regulator/brush holder, ensuring that the brushes bear correctly on the slip-rings, and that they compress into their holders. Tighten the screws securely.

**9** Install the rear cover, and tighten the screws securely.

**10** Refit the alternator (see Section 6).

### 8 Starting system – general information and precautions

### General information

The sole function of the starting system is to turn over the engine quickly enough to allow it to start.

The starting system consists of the battery, the starter motor, the starter solenoid, and the wires connecting them. The solenoid is mounted directly on the starter motor.

The solenoid/starter motor assembly is installed on the rear upper part of the engine, next to the transmission bellhousing.

When the ignition key is turned to position III, the starter solenoid is actuated through the starter control circuit. The starter solenoid then connects the battery to the starter. The battery supplies the electrical energy to the starter motor, which does the actual work of cranking the engine.

If the alarm system is armed or activated, the starter motor cannot be operated. The same applies with the engine immobiliser system (where fitted).

### Precautions

Always observe the following precautions when working on the starting system:
   a) Excessive cranking of the starter motor

**7.2 Remove three screws and withdraw end cover . . .**

**7.4 . . . then remove regulator/brush holder assembly (secured by two screws)**

can overheat it, and cause serious damage. Never operate the starter motor for more than 15 seconds at a time without pausing to allow it to cool for at least two minutes.
b) The starter is connected directly to the battery, and could arc or cause a fire if mishandled, overloaded or shorted-out.
c) Always detach the lead from the negative terminal of the battery before working on the starting system (see Section 1).

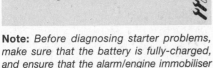

## 9 Starting system – testing

**Note:** Before diagnosing starter problems, make sure that the battery is fully-charged, and ensure that the alarm/engine immobiliser system is not activated.

1 If the starter motor does not turn at all when the switch is operated, make sure that the battery is fully-charged, and that all leads, both at the battery and starter solenoid terminals, are clean and secure.

2 If the starter motor spins but the engine is not cranking, the overrunning clutch or (when applicable) the reduction gears in the starter motor may be slipping, in which case the starter motor must be overhauled or renewed. (Other possibilities are that the starter motor mounting bolts are very loose, or that teeth are missing from the flywheel ring gear.)

3 If, when the switch is actuated, the starter motor does not operate at all but the solenoid clicks, then the problem lies with either the battery, the main solenoid contacts, or the starter motor itself (or the engine is seized). If the car has been driven through deep water, the engine may be full of water, and unable to turn over.

4 If the solenoid plunger cannot be heard to click when the switch is actuated, the battery is faulty, there is a fault in the circuit, or the solenoid itself is defective.

5 To check the solenoid, connect a fused jumper lead between the battery (+) and the ignition switch terminal (the small terminal) on the solenoid. If the starter motor now operates, the solenoid is OK, and the problem is in the ignition switch, or in the wiring.

6 If the starter motor still does not operate, remove it (see Section 10). The brushes and commutator may be checked (see Section 11), but if the fault persists, the motor should be renewed, or taken to an auto-electrician for testing and repair.

7 If the starter motor cranks the engine at an abnormally-slow speed, first make sure that the battery is charged, and that all terminal connections are tight. If the engine is partially seized, or has the wrong viscosity oil in it, it will crank slowly.

8 Run the engine until normal operating temperature is reached, then switch off and disable the injection pump by disconnecting the stop solenoid wiring connector.

9 Connect a voltmeter positive lead to the battery positive terminal, and connect the negative lead to the negative terminal.

10 Crank the engine, and take the voltmeter readings as soon as a steady figure is indicated. Do not allow the starter motor to turn for more than 15 seconds at a time. A reading of 10.5 volts or more, with the starter motor turning at normal cranking speed, is normal. If the reading is 10.5 volts or more but the cranking speed is slow, the solenoid contacts are burned, the motor is faulty, or there is a bad connection. If the reading is less than 10.5 volts and the cranking speed is slow, the starter motor is faulty or there is a problem with the battery.

## 10 Starter motor – removal and refitting

**Note:** Refer to Section 1 of this Chapter before starting work.

### Removal

1 Disconnect the battery negative (earth) lead.

2 Remove the air cleaner as described in Chapter 4A.

3 Apply the handbrake, then jack up the front of the car, and support it on axle stands (see Jacking and vehicle support). Remove the engine undershield and radiator lower cover.

4 Remove the nuts and through-bolt from the engine front mounting, and remove the mounting from the subframe and transmission.

5 Remove the cover caps, then unscrew the nuts to disconnect the wiring from the starter/ solenoid terminals (see illustration).

6 Unscrew the two starter motor mounting bolts, noting that one also secures an engine/ transmission earth lead.

7 Unscrew the starter support bracket bolt (see illustration), then withdraw the unit from the transmission.

### Refitting

8 Refitting is the reverse of the removal procedure. Tighten the bolts to the specified torque wrench settings.

## 11 Starter motor – overhaul

If the starter motor is thought to be defective, it should be removed from the car and taken to an auto-electrician for assessment. In the majority of cases, new starter motor brushes can be fitted at a reasonable cost. However, check the cost of repairs first, as it may prove more economical to purchase a new or exchange motor.

10.5 The starter supply lead retaining nut is under a cover cap

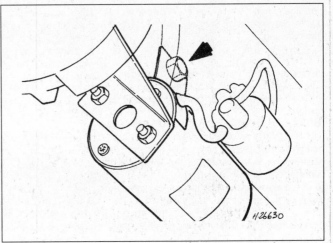

10.7 Unscrew the starter support bracket bolt (arrowed)

**13.2 Glow plug feed wire connection**

**13.3 Unscrewing a glow plug terminal nut**

**13.4 Glow plug removed from cylinder head**

## 12 Glow plug (preheating) system – description and testing

### Description

1 Each swirl chamber has a heater plug (commonly called a glow plug) screwed into it. The plugs are electrically operated before, during, and a short time after start-up when the engine is cold. Electrical feed to the glow plugs and glow plug warning light are controlled by the engine ECU.

2 The glow plugs are energised when the ignition is switched on, and they remain on, together with the warning light, for a period varying between 1 and 10 seconds, depending on the temperature of the engine coolant. After the warning light is extinguished, the glow plugs remain energised for a period up to 3 seconds, however if the engine is started in this period the glow plugs will remain on for a period up to 40 seconds depending on the engine coolant temperature. With the coolant at 80°C the period is 0 seconds and with the coolant at -40°C the period is 40 seconds.

3 A warning light in the instrument panel tells the driver that preheating is taking place. When the light goes out, the engine is ready to be started. If no attempt is made to start, the timer then cuts off the supply in order to avoid draining the battery and overheating of the glow plugs.

### Testing

4 If the system malfunctions, testing is ultimately by substitution of known good units, but some preliminary checks may be made as follows.

5 Connect a voltmeter or 12 volt test light between the glow plug supply cable and earth (engine or bodywork). Make sure that the live connection is kept clear of the engine and bodywork.

6 Have an assistant switch on the ignition and check that voltage is applied to the glow plugs. Note the time for which the warning light is lit and the total time for which voltage is applied before the system cuts out. Switch off the ignition.

7 If the results of the check do not come within the periods indicated in paragraph 2, refer to Chapters 3 and 12 and check the relevant temperature sensor and power supply.

8 If an ammeter of suitable range (0 to 50 amps approximately) is available, connect it between the glow plug feed wire and the bus bar. During the preheating period the ammeter should show a current draw of approximately 8 amps per working plug, ie. 32 amps if all four plugs are working. If one or more plugs appear not to be drawing current, remove the bus bar and check each plug separately with a continuity tester or self-powered test light.

9 If there is no supply at all to the glow plugs, the associated wiring is at fault.

10 To locate a defective glow plug, disconnect the main supply cable and the interconnecting wire or strap from the top of the glow plugs. Be careful not to drop the nuts and washers.

11 Use a continuity tester, or a 12 volt test light connected to the battery positive terminal, to check for continuity between each glow plug terminal and earth. The resistance of a glow plug in good condition is very low (less than 1 ohm), so if the test light does not come on or the continuity tester shows a high resistance, the glow plug is certainly defective.

12 If an ammeter is available, the current draw of each glow plug can be checked. After an initial surge of around 15 to 20 amps, each plug should draw around 10 amps. Any plug which draws much more or less than this is probably defective.

13 As a final check, the glow plugs can be removed and inspected as described in Section 13.

## 13 Glow plugs – removal, inspection and refitting

**Caution: If the preheating system has just been energised, or if the engine has been running, the glow plugs may be very hot.**

### Removal

1 Disconnect the battery negative (earth) lead (see Section 1).

2 Disconnect the feed wire from the bus bar **(see illustration)**.

3 Unscrew the terminal nut from each plug to be removed. Remove the nuts, washers and bus bar **(see illustration)**.

4 Clean around the glow plug seats then unscrew and remove them **(see illustration)**.

### Inspection

5 Inspect the glow plugs for damage. Burnt or eroded glow plug tips can be caused by a bad injector spray pattern. Have the injectors checked if this sort of damage is found.

6 If the glow plugs are in good physical condition, check them electrically using a 12 volt test lamp or continuity tester as described in the previous Section.

7 The glow plugs can be energised by applying 12 volts to them to verify that they heat up evenly and in the required time. Observe the following precautions:

a) Support the glow plug by clamping it carefully in a vice or self-locking pliers. Remember it will become red-hot.

b) Make sure that the power supply or test lead incorporates a fuse or overload trip to protect against damage from a short-circuit.

c) After testing, allow the glow plug to cool for several minutes before attempting to handle it.

8 A glow plug in good condition will start to glow red at the tip after drawing current for 5 seconds or so. Any plug which takes much longer to start glowing, or which starts glowing in the middle instead of at the tip, is defective.

### Refitting

9 When refitting, apply a little anti-seize compound to the glow plug threads. Screw the glow plugs into place and tighten them to the specified torque.

10 Refit the bus bar and washers, and secure with the nuts. Make sure that the clamping areas are clean.

11 Reconnect the feed wire and the battery earth lead.

# Chapter 6
# Clutch

## Contents

Section number

Clutch – description and checking. . . . . . . . . . . . . . . . . . . . . . . . . 2
Clutch adjustment – check. . . . . . . . . . . . . . . . . . . . . . . . . . . . . . 3
Clutch cable – removal and refitting. . . . . . . . . . . . . . . . . . . . . . . 4
Clutch components – removal, inspection and refitting. . . . . . . . . . 7
Clutch hydraulic system – bleeding . . . . . . . . . . . . . . . . . . . . . . . 10
Clutch master cylinder – removal and refitting. . . . . . . . . . . . . . . 5

Section number

Clutch pedal – removal and refitting. . . . . . . . . . . . . . . . . . . . . . . 6
Clutch release bearing (and slave cylinder) – removal, inspection and
   refitting . . . . . . . . . . . . . . . . . . . . . . . . . . . . . . . . . . . . . . . . 8
Clutch release shaft and bush – removal and refitting. . . . . . . . . . . 9
General information . . . . . . . . . . . . . . . . . . . . . . . . . . . . . . . . . . . 1

## Degrees of difficulty

| Easy, suitable for novice with little experience |  | Fairly easy, suitable for beginner with some experience | | Fairly difficult, suitable for competent DIY mechanic | | Difficult, suitable for experienced DIY mechanic | | Very difficult, suitable for expert DIY or professional | |

## Specifications

### General

Lining thickness (new):
   Cable-operated clutch . . . . . . . . . . . . . . . . . . . . . . . . . . . . . . . . . 8.8 mm
   Hydraulically-operated clutch. . . . . . . . . . . . . . . . . . . . . . . . . . . . 7.3 mm
Pedal stroke:
   Cable-operated clutch . . . . . . . . . . . . . . . . . . . . . . . . . . . . . . . . . 145 ± 5.0 mm
   Hydraulically-operated clutch. . . . . . . . . . . . . . . . . . . . . . . . . . . . 130 ± 3.0 mm

### Torque wrench settings

| | Nm | lbf ft |
|---|---|---|
| Master/slave cylinder mounting nuts/bolts | 10 | 7 |
| Pressure plate to flywheel | 29 | 21 |
| Release lever clamp bolt | 25 | 18 |

## 1 General information

All models covered by this manual are fitted with a pedal-operated single dry plate clutch system. When the clutch pedal is depressed, effort is transmitted to the clutch release mechanism either mechanically, by means of a cable, or hydraulically, via a master cylinder. The release mechanism transfers effort to the pressure plate diaphragm spring, which withdraws from the flywheel and releases the driven friction plate (disc).

The flywheel is mounted on the crankshaft, with the pressure plate bolted to it. Removal of the flywheel is described in Chapter 2A.

Since many of the procedures covered in this Chapter involve working under the car, make sure that it is securely supported on axle stands placed on a firm, level floor (see *Jacking and vehicle support*).

⚠ *Warning: On models with a hydraulic clutch, the fluid used in the system is brake fluid, which is poisonous. Take care to keep it off bare skin, and in particular not to get splashes in your eyes. The fluid also attacks paintwork, and may discolour carpets, etc – keep spillages to a minimum, and wash any off immediately with cold water. Finally, brake fluid is highly inflammable, and should be handled with the same care as petrol.*

## 2 Clutch – description and checking

### Description

1 The clutch assembly consists of a pressure plate or 'cover' with diaphragm spring (dowelled and bolted to the flywheel right-hand face), the friction disc, and a release bearing.
2 The friction disc is free to slide along the splines of the transmission input shaft, and is held in position between the flywheel and the pressure plate by the pressure of the diaphragm spring. Lining material is riveted to the friction disc, which has a spring-cushioned hub, to absorb transmission shocks and help ensure a smooth take-up of the drive.
3 The clutch release bearing contacts the fingers of the diaphragm spring. Depressing the clutch pedal pushes the release bearing against the diaphragm fingers, so moving the centre of the diaphragm spring inwards. As the centre of the spring is pushed inwards, the outside of the spring pivots outwards, so moving the pressure plate backwards and disengaging its grip on the clutch disc.
4 When the pedal is released, the diaphragm spring forces the pressure plate back into contact with the linings on the friction disc. The disc is now firmly held between the pressure

plate and the flywheel, thus transmitting engine power to the transmission.
5 On early Mondeos (up to 1994 approximately), the clutch is actuated by a cable. The cable runs from the pedal to a release arm, mounted on the transmission housing. Depressing the clutch pedal actuates the release arm, and the arm pushes the release bearing against the diaphragm fingers.
6 Unlike some other models in the Ford range, the cable clutch is not of the self-adjusting type, although it uses the same serrated quadrant fitted to models with a self-adjusting pedal. The normal self-adjusting spring-tensioned pawl is not fitted to the quadrant, although the pedal moves the quadrant when it contacts the end stops. This arrangement means that pedal adjustment must be carried out manually.
7 Mondeos from approximately 1994 onwards have a hydraulically-operated clutch. A master cylinder is mounted below the clutch pedal, and takes its hydraulic fluid supply from a separate chamber in the brake fluid reservoir. Depressing the clutch pedal operates the master cylinder pushrod, and the fluid pressure is transferred along the fluid lines to a slave cylinder mounted inside the bellhousing. The slave cylinder is incorporated into the release bearing – when the slave cylinder operates, the release bearing moves against the diaphragm spring fingers and disengages the clutch.
8 The hydraulic clutch offers several advantages over the cable type previously used – it is self-adjusting, requires less pedal effort, and is less subject to wear problems.

### Checking

9 The following checks may be performed to diagnose a clutch problem:

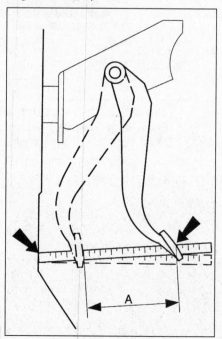

**3.4 Clutch pedal stroke (A)**

a) On models with a cable clutch, first check the entire length of the clutch cable in the engine compartment for obvious damage. Check also that it is located correctly, without any sharp turns.
b) Similarly, on models with a hydraulic clutch, check the fluid lines from the clutch master cylinder into the bellhousing for damage, signs of leakage, or for kinks or dents which might restrict fluid flow.
c) To check 'clutch spin down time', run the engine at normal idle speed with the transmission in neutral (clutch pedal up). Disengage the clutch (pedal down), wait several seconds, then engage reverse. No grinding noise should be heard. A grinding noise would most likely indicate a problem in the pressure plate or the clutch disc. Remember, however, that the transmission reverse gear has synchromesh fitted to it, so the probable symptom of a clutch fault would be a slight rearwards movement (or attempted movement) of the car. If the check is made on level ground with the handbrake released, the movement would be more noticeable.
d) To check for complete clutch release, run the engine at idle, and hold the clutch pedal approximately half an inch from the floor. Shift between 1st gear and reverse several times. If the shift is not smooth, or if the car attempts to move forwards or backwards, component failure is indicated. Check the pedal adjustment as described in Section 3.
e) On models with a hydraulic clutch, slow or poor operation may be due to air being present in the fluid. The system can be bled of air as described in Section 10.
f) Check the clutch pedal for excessive wear of the bushes, and for any obstructions which may restrict the pedal movement.

## 3 Clutch adjustment – check

### Cable-operated clutch

1 If this check is being made after fitting a new clutch cable, the pedal should be depressed fully 10 times first.
2 Fully depress and hold down the clutch pedal, then place a steel rule against the bulkhead, and measure and record the distance to the middle of the rubber pad (dimension C).
3 Release the pedal, and measure the distance from the bulkhead to the middle of the rubber pad again (dimension B). Do not lift the pedal when making the measurement.
4 Subtract dimension C from dimension B to determine the clutch pedal stroke – A **(see illustration)**:

A (stroke) = B (released dimension) minus C (depressed dimension)

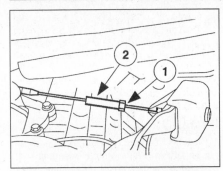

3.7 Locknut (1) and adjustment sleeve (2) for the clutch pedal stroke adjustment

3.10 To obtain the pedal stroke, measure from steering wheel to pedal with the pedal released . . .

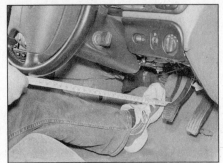

3.11 . . . and with it fully depressed

3.14 Remove the facia lower trim panel to the right of the steering wheel

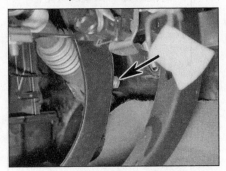

3.15a Clutch pedal stop bolt

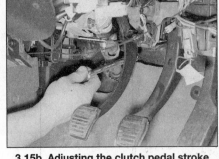

3.15b Adjusting the clutch pedal stroke

**5** Check that the dimension is within the tolerance given in the Specifications. If adjustment is required, proceed as follows.
**6** Remove the air cleaner assembly as described in Chapter 4A.
**7** Loosen the locknut on the clutch cable adjuster sleeve near the release arm on the transmission **(see illustration)**. Turn the sleeve until the correct clutch pedal stroke is obtained. On completion, tighten the locknut. Refit the air cleaner assembly as described in Chapter 4A.

### Hydraulically-operated clutch

**8** Turn the steering wheel (from the straight-ahead position) to the left by about 30°.
**9** Using tape or a cable-tie, attach the end lip of a measuring tape to the clutch pedal rubber. Alternatively, have an assistant hold the measuring tape in place – either way, make sure that the end of the tape does not move from one measurement to the next.
**10** Without touching the pedal, read off and record the distance measured from the pedal to the front of the steering wheel rim (dimension C) **(see illustration)**.
**11** Now press the pedal down to its stop, and record the new distance (dimension B) **(see illustration)**. Make sure that the pedal action is not hindered by the carpets or floormats, or by incorrect fitting of the master cylinder.
**12** The pedal stroke A is obtained by subtracting dimension C from dimension B:

$A$ (stroke) = $B$ (depressed dimension) minus $C$ (released dimension).

**13** Check that the dimension is within the

tolerance given in the Specifications. If adjustment is required, proceed as follows.
**14** Remove the facia lower trim panel to the right of the steering wheel **(see illustration)**. Refer to Chapter 11, Section 29, if necessary.
**15** Loosen the locknut on the clutch pedal stop bolt (on the master cylinder mounting bracket). Turn the stop bolt in or out to alter the pedal stroke as required **(see illustrations)**. On completion, tighten the locknut securely.

### 4 Clutch cable – removal and refitting

#### Removal

**1** Remove the air cleaner assembly as described in Chapter 4A.
**2** Disengage the clutch cable from the release

4.3 Rubber cushion (arrowed) on the end of the outer cable

arm, by gripping the inner cable with pliers and pulling it forwards to disengage the cable nipple from the release arm. Take care not to damage the cable, if it is to be re-used.
**3** Disengage the outer cable from the support lug on top of the transmission bellhousing. Note the rubber cushion on the end of the outer cable **(see illustration)**.
**4** Working inside the car, remove the facia lower trim panel from beneath the steering column for access to the clutch pedal. Refer to Chapter 11, Section 29, if necessary.
**5** Disconnect the clutch pedal return spring from the pedal and bracket. Note where the spring is attached to the bracket, as the small hole is not easy to see.
**6** Unhook the inner cable from the pedal quadrant **(see illustration)**.
**7** Pull the cable through the aperture in the bulkhead. Detach the cable from the support stay near the brake servo unit, and

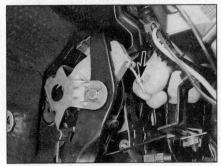

4.6 Unhooking the clutch inner cable (arrowed) from the pedal segment

**4.7 Clutch cable support stay (arrowed) located next to the brake servo unit**

**4.8 Inner cable (arrowed) fitted to the pedal segment**

withdraw it from the engine compartment **(see illustration)**.

### Refitting

**8** To refit the cable, thread it through the bulkhead from the engine compartment side. Fit the inner cable over the quadrant, engaging the end stop to secure it **(see illustration)**.
**9** Reconnect the pedal return spring, making sure that it is correctly fitted in the small hole.
**10** Reconnect the cable at the transmission end, passing it through the support lug on the

top of the transmission, and engaging it with the release arm.
**11** Locate the rubber grommet in the clutch cable support stay. Renew the grommet if necessary.
**12** Adjust the pedal stroke as described in Section 3.
**13** Check the operation of the clutch.
**14** Refit the trim panel under the steering column.
**15** Refit the air cleaner assembly as described in Chapter 4A.

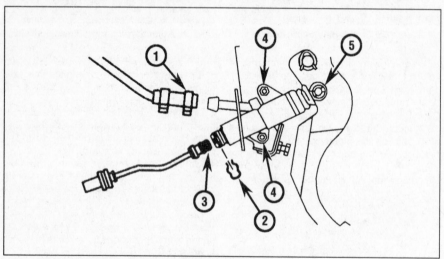

**5.6a Clutch master cylinder and related fittings**

| | |
|---|---|
| 1  Fluid supply (low-pressure) hose | 4  Master cylinder mounting nuts |
| 2  Hose retaining clip | 5  Master cylinder-to-pedal circlip |
| 3  High-pressure fluid pipe | |

**5.6b Disconnect the low-pressure fluid supply hose**

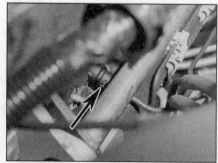

**5.7 Pull out the spring clip (arrowed) from the high-pressure pipe**

## 5 Clutch master cylinder – removal and refitting

**Note:** *Refer to the warning in Section 1 concerning the dangers of hydraulic fluid before proceeding.*

### Removal

**1** Disconnect the battery negative lead, and position the lead away from the terminal.
**2** Working inside the car, move the driver's seat fully to the rear, to allow maximum working area. Remove the fasteners securing the driver's side lower facia trim panel, and remove the panel from the car.
**3** Before proceeding, anticipate some spillage of hydraulic (brake) fluid – most will occur on the engine compartment side. However, if sufficient fluid comes into contact with the carpet, it may be discoloured or worse. Place a good quantity of clean rags below the clutch pedal, and have a container ready in the engine compartment.
**4** Remove the brake fluid reservoir cap, and then tighten it down over a piece of polythene or cling film, to obtain an airtight seal. This may help to reduce the spillage of fluid when the lines are disconnected.
**5** To gain access to the fluid connections where they pass through the engine compartment bulkhead, move any wiring and hoses to one side as necessary. Remove the air cleaner inlet hose and plenum chamber as described in the relevant Part of Chapter 4.
**6** Working in the engine compartment, release the hose clips and disconnect the low-pressure (upper) hose from the clutch master cylinder **(see illustrations)**. Plug or clamp the hose end if possible, to reduce fluid loss and to prevent dirt entry.
**7** To remove the high-pressure (lower) fluid pipe, pull out the spring clip to the side, then pull the pipe fitting out of the base of the cylinder **(see illustration)**. Again, plug or tape over the pipe end, to avoid losing fluid, and to prevent dirt entry.
**8** Returning to the driver's footwell, prise off the circlip which secures the top of the master cylinder to the clutch pedal.
**9** Remove the two master cylinder mounting nuts, and withdraw the master cylinder through the bulkhead and from the footwell, taking care to avoid spilling any remaining fluid onto the interior fittings.

### Refitting

**10** Refitting is a reversal of removal, noting the following points:
   a) Tighten the mounting nuts to the specified torque.
   b) Use new clips when refitting the fluid feed hose.
   c) Refit any components removed for access.
   d) Remove the polythene from under the fluid reservoir cap, and top-up the fluid level (see Weekly checks).

e) Refer to Section 10 and bleed the clutch hydraulic system.

f) If the fluid level in the reservoir fell sufficiently, it may be necessary to bleed the braking system also – refer to Chapter 9.

## 6 Clutch pedal – removal and refitting

### Removal

**1** Remove the brake pedal (see Chapter 9).

**2** Remove the blue nylon spacer from the pedal pivot shaft.

**3** Unhook and remove the clutch pedal return spring.

#### Cable-operated clutch

**4** Remove the air cleaner assembly as described in Chapter 4A.

**5** Disconnect the clutch cable from the release arm as described in Section 4.

**6** Working inside the car, release the inner cable from the pedal quadrant on the clutch pedal.

#### Hydraulically-operated clutch

**7** Prise off the circlip which secures the top of the clutch master cylinder to the clutch pedal.

#### All models

**8** Withdraw the pedal pivot shaft through the mounting bracket, and remove the pedal together with the blue nylon spacer. Note that this spacer is additional to the spacer located next to the brake pedal.

**9** With the pedal removed, prise out the bushes from each side. Also remove the rubber pad. On models with the cable-operated clutch, remove the cable quadrant **(see illustrations)**. Renew the components as necessary.

### Refitting

**10** Prior to refitting the pedal, apply a little grease to the pivot shaft and pedal bushes.

**11** Refitting is a reversal of the removal procedure, making sure that the bushes and spacers are correctly located.

**12** Adjust the clutch pedal stroke as described in Section 3.

## 7 Clutch components – removal, inspection and refitting

⚠️ **Warning: Dust created by clutch wear and deposited on the clutch components may contain asbestos, which is a health hazard. DO NOT blow it out with compressed air, and do not inhale any of it. DO NOT use petrol or petroleum-based solvents to clean off the dust. Brake system cleaner or methylated spirit should be used to flush the dust into a suitable receptacle. After the clutch components are wiped clean with rags,**

6.9a Removing the clutch pedal bushes

6.9b Removing the cable quadrant from the clutch pedal

**dispose of the contaminated rags and cleaner in a sealed, marked container.**

### Removal

**1** Access to the clutch may be gained in one of two ways. The engine/transmission can be removed, as described in Chapter 2B, and the transmission separated from the engine on the bench. Alternatively, the engine may be left in the car and the transmission removed independently, as described in Chapter 7. If the latter course of action is taken, note that the transmission need only be moved to the left of the engine compartment – it is not necessary to remove it completely **(see illustration)**.

**2** Having separated the transmission from the engine, check if there are any marks identifying the relation of the clutch pressure plate to the flywheel. If not, make your own marks using a dab of paint or a scriber **(see**

illustration). These marks will be used if the original pressure plate is refitted, and will help to maintain the balance of the unit. A new pressure plate may be fitted in any position allowed by the locating dowels.

**3** Unscrew the six clutch pressure plate retaining bolts, working in a diagonal sequence, and slackening the bolts only a turn at a time **(see illustration)**. If necessary, the flywheel may be held stationary using a wide-bladed screwdriver inserted in the teeth of the starter ring gear and resting against part of the cylinder block.

**4** Ease the clutch pressure plate off its locating dowels. Be prepared to catch the clutch disc, which will drop out as the pressure plate is removed **(see illustration)**. Note which way round the disc is fitted.

### Inspection

**5** The most common problem which occurs

7.1 Clutch is accessible with the transmission moved to one side

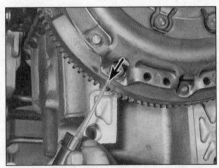

7.2 Marking the clutch cover and flywheel with a dab of paint (arrowed)

7.3 Unscrewing the clutch cover bolts

7.4 Removing the clutch cover and disc

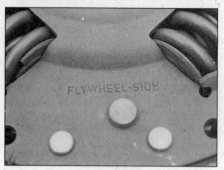

7.12 FLYWHEEL-SIDE marking on the clutch disc

7.16 Using a clutch-aligning tool to centralise the clutch disc

in the clutch is wear of the clutch disc (driven plate). However, all the clutch components should be inspected at this time, particularly if the engine has covered a high mileage. Unless the clutch components are known to be virtually new, it is worth renewing them all as a set (disc, pressure plate and release bearing). Renewing a worn clutch disc by itself is not always satisfactory, especially if the old disc was slipping and causing the pressure plate to overheat.

6 Examine the linings of the clutch disc for wear and loose rivets, and the disc hub and rim for distortion, cracks, broken torsion springs, and worn splines. The surface of the friction linings may be highly glazed, but as long as the friction material pattern can be clearly seen, and the rivet heads are at least 1 mm below the lining surface, this is satisfactory. The disc must be renewed if the lining thickness has worn down to, or just above, the level of the rivet heads.

7 If there is any sign of oil contamination, indicated by shiny black discoloration, the disc must be renewed, and the source of the contamination traced and rectified. This will be a leaking crankshaft oil seal or transmission input shaft oil seal. The renewal procedure for the former is given in Chapter 2A. Renewal of the transmission input shaft oil seal should be entrusted to a Ford dealer, as it involves dismantling the transmission, and (where applicable) the renewal of the clutch release bearing guide tube, using a press.

8 Check the machined faces of the flywheel and pressure plate. If either is grooved, or heavily scored, renewal is necessary. The pressure plate must also be renewed if any cracks are apparent, or if the diaphragm spring is damaged or its pressure suspect. Pay particular attention to the tips of the spring fingers, where the release bearing acts upon them.

9 With the transmission removed, it is also advisable to check the condition of the release bearing, as described in Section 8. Having got this far, it is almost certainly worth renewing it.

### Refitting

10 It is important that no oil or grease is allowed to come into contact with the friction material of the clutch disc or the pressure plate and flywheel faces. To ensure this, it is advisable to refit the clutch assembly with clean hands, and to wipe down the pressure plate and flywheel faces with a clean dry rag before assembly begins.

11 Ford technicians use a special tool for centralising the clutch disc at this stage. The tool holds the disc centrally on the pressure plate, and locates in the middle of the diaphragm spring fingers. If the tool is not available, it will be necessary to centralise the disc after assembling the pressure plate loosely on the flywheel, as described in the following paragraphs.

12 Place the clutch disc against the flywheel, ensuring that it is the right way round. It should be marked FLYWHEEL-SIDE, but if not, position it so that the raised hub with the cushion springs is facing away from the flywheel (see illustration).

13 Place the clutch pressure plate over the dowels. Refit the retaining bolts, and tighten

them finger-tight so that the clutch disc is gripped lightly, but can still be moved.

14 The clutch disc must now be centralised so that, when the engine and transmission are mated, the splines of the transmission input shaft will pass through the splines in the centre of the clutch disc hub.

15 Centralisation can be carried out by inserting a round bar through the hole in the centre of the clutch disc, so that the end of the bar rests in the hole in the rear end of the crankshaft. Move the bar sideways or up-and-down, to move the clutch disc in whichever direction is necessary to achieve centralisation. Centralisation can then be checked by removing the bar and viewing the clutch disc hub in relation to the diaphragm spring fingers, or by viewing through the side apertures of the pressure plate, and checking that the disc is central in relation to the outer edge of the pressure plate.

16 An alternative and more accurate method of centralisation is to use a commercially-available clutch-aligning tool, obtainable from most accessory shops (see illustration).

17 Once the clutch is centralised, progressively tighten the pressure plate bolts in a diagonal sequence to the specified torque.

18 Ensure that the input shaft splines, clutch disc splines and release bearing guide sleeve are clean. Apply a thin smear of high melting-point grease to the input shaft splines and the release bearing guide sleeve.

19 Refit the transmission to the engine.

## 8 Clutch release bearing (and slave cylinder) – removal, inspection and refitting

### Removal

1 Separate the engine and transmission as described in the previous Section.

#### Cable-operated clutch

2 Withdraw the release bearing from its guide sleeve by turning the release arm (see illustrations).

#### Hydraulically-operated clutch

3 The release bearing and slave cylinder are combined into one unit (see illustrations).

8.2a Clutch release bearing in place on the guide sleeve

8.2b Release bearing removed from the transmission

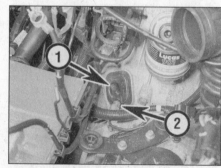

8.3a Bleed screw (1) and fluid pipe quick-release fitting (2) – hydraulic clutch

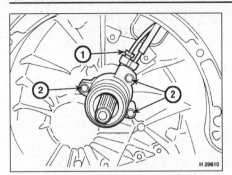

**8.3b Combined release bearing and slave cylinder – hydraulic clutch**

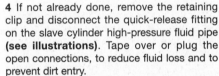

*1 Fluid pipe*      *2 Mounting bolts*

**4** If not already done, remove the retaining clip and disconnect the quick-release fitting on the slave cylinder high-pressure fluid pipe **(see illustrations)**. Tape over or plug the open connections, to reduce fluid loss and to prevent dirt entry.

**5** Remove the bleed screw dust cap, and prise out the grommet from the top of the transmission housing **(see illustrations)**.

**6** Remove the three mounting bolts, and withdraw the slave cylinder and release bearing **(see illustrations)**.

### Inspection

**7** Check the bearing for smoothness of operation, and renew it if there is any sign of harshness or roughness as the bearing is spun. Do not attempt to dismantle, clean or lubricate the bearing.

**8** It is worth renewing the release bearing as

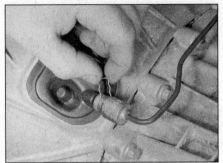

**8.4a Remove the retaining clip . . .**

a matter of course, unless it is known to be in perfect condition.

**9** On models with the hydraulic clutch, check the condition of all O-ring seals, and renew if necessary **(see illustrations)**. Considering the difficulty in gaining access to some of the seals if they fail, it would be wise to renew these as a precaution.

### Refitting

**10** Refitting of the clutch release bearing is a reversal of the removal procedure, noting the following points:

a) *On cable clutch models, make sure that the bearing is correctly located on the release arm fork. It is helpful to slightly lift the release arm while locating the bearing on its guide sleeve. Keep the fork in contact with the plastic shoulders on the bearing as the bearing is being located.*

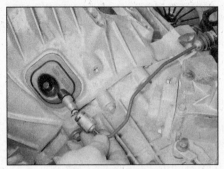

**8.4b . . . and disconnect the fluid pipe from the slave cylinder**

b) *On hydraulically-operated clutch models, tighten the mounting bolts to the specified torque. Reconnect the fluid pipe, and bleed the system on completion.*

## 9 Clutch release shaft and bush – removal and refitting

**Note:** *This Section does not apply to models with the hydraulic clutch.*

### Removal

**1** Remove the clutch release bearing as described in the previous Section.

**2** Unscrew the clamp bolt securing the release arm to the shaft. Mark the relative position of the shaft to the arm, then withdraw the arm

**8.5a Take off the bleed screw cap . . .**

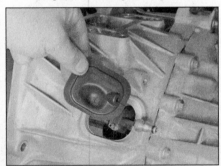

**8.5b . . . then prise out the grommet from the transmission housing**

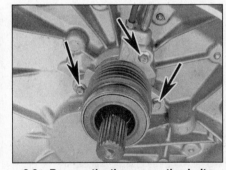

**8.6a Remove the three mounting bolts (arrowed) . . .**

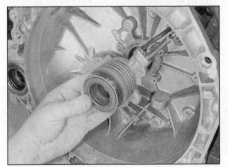

**8.6b . . . and withdraw the slave cylinder/ release bearing assembly**

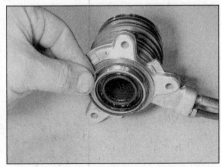

**8.9a Check the condition of the large O-ring on the slave cylinder . . .**

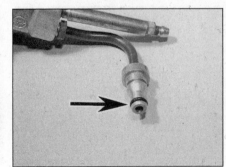

**8.9b . . . and of the smaller pipe connection O-rings**

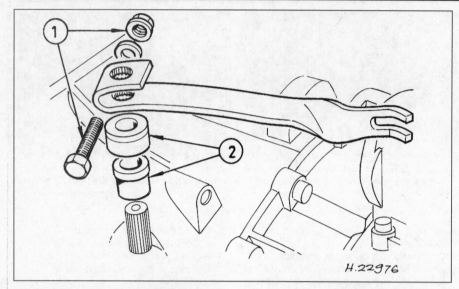

H.22976

**9.2a Clutch release arm removal**

1 Clamp bolt
2 Protective cap and bearing bush

from the shaft. The shaft has a master spline, to ensure that the arm is fitted correctly **(see illustrations)**.

**3** Remove the protective cap from around the top of the release shaft splines, to allow access to the bush.

**4** Extract the bush by gently levering it from the housing, using grips or a pair of screwdrivers **(see illustration)**, then lift it out over the splines of the shaft.

**5** With the bush removed, the release shaft can be removed by lifting it from its lower bearing bore, manoeuvring it sideways and withdrawing it **(see illustration)**.

## Refitting

**6** Refitting is a reversal of the removal procedure. Apply a little grease to the bearing surfaces, both in the transmission and in the bush.

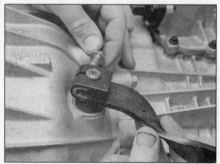

**9.2b Removing the clamp bolt**

**9.2c Master spline (arrowed) on the shaft**

## 10 Clutch hydraulic system – bleeding

**1** The clutch hydraulic system will not normally require bleeding, and this task should only be necessary when the system has been opened for repair work. However, as with the brake pedal, if the clutch pedal feels at all soggy or unresponsive in operation, this may indicate the need for bleeding.

**2** The system bleed screw is located on top of the transmission bellhousing.

**3** Remove the battery as described in Chapter 5, and the air cleaner as described in Chapter 4A. Move the pipework and wiring harness to one side as necessary to reach the access cover.

**4** Remove the bleed screw cap **(see illustration)**.

**5** Bleeding the clutch is much the same as bleeding the brakes – refer to Chapter 9 for the various methods which may be used **(see illustration)**. Ensure that the level in the brake/clutch fluid reservoir is maintained well above the MIN mark at all times, otherwise the clutch and brake hydraulic systems will both need bleeding.

**6** On completion, tighten the bleed screw securely, and top-up the fluid level to the MAX mark. If possible, test the operation of the clutch before refitting all the components removed for access.

**7** Failure to bleed correctly may point to a leak in the system, or to a worn master or slave cylinder. At the time of writing, it appears that the master and slave cylinders are only available as complete assemblies – overhaul is not possible.

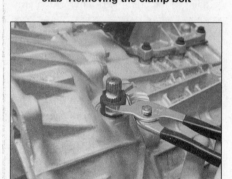

**9.4 Removing the bush using grips**

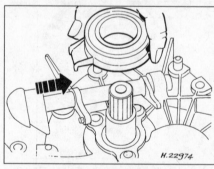

H.22974

**9.5 Removing the clutch release arm shaft**

**10.4 Remove the bleed screw cap**

**10.5 Bleeding the clutch using a one-man bleed kit**

# Chapter 7
# Manual transmission

## Contents

| | Section number | | Section number |
|---|---|---|---|
| Gearchange linkage – adjustment | 2 | Reversing light switch – removal and refitting | 6 |
| Gearchange linkage and gear lever – removal and refitting | 3 | Speedometer drive pinion – removal and refitting | 4 |
| General information | 1 | Transmission – removal and refitting | 7 |
| Manual transmission overhaul – general | 9 | Transmission mounting – checking and renewal | 8 |
| Oil seals – renewal | 5 | Transmission oil level check | See Chapter 1 |

## Degrees of difficulty

| Easy, suitable for novice with little experience | Fairly easy, suitable for beginner with some experience | Fairly difficult, suitable for competent DIY mechanic | Difficult, suitable for experienced DIY mechanic | Very difficult, suitable for expert DIY or professional |
|---|---|---|---|---|

## Specifications

### Gear ratios

| | |
|---|---|
| 1st | 3.666:1 |
| 2nd | 2.047:1 |
| 3rd | 1.258:1 |
| 4th | 0.864:1 |
| 5th | 0.674:1 |
| Reverse | 3.460:1 |
| Final drive ratio | 4.06:1 |

### Torque wrench settings

| | Nm | lbf ft |
|---|---|---|
| **All models** | | |
| Reversing light switch mounting bolts | 10 | 7 |
| Transmission to engine | 40 | 30 |
| **Pre-October 1996 models** | | |
| Gearchange assembly rear mounting | 44 | 32 |
| Gearchange linkage clamp bolt | 11 | 8 |
| Gearchange linkage to selector shaft | 23 | 17 |
| Gearchange support rod | 55 | 41 |
| **October 1996-on models** | | |
| Bearing housing | 10 | 7 |
| Gear lever assembly to floor | 10 | 7 |
| Selector and shift cable bush | 10 | 7 |

---

## 1 General information

The transmission is a compact, two-piece, lightweight aluminium alloy housing, containing both the transmission and differential assemblies. The transmission code name is MTX-75, MT standing for Manual Transmission, X for transaXle (front-wheel-drive), and 75 being the distance (in mm) between the input and output shafts.

Note that facelifted models (from October 1996 onwards) have a cable-operated gear linkage instead of the rod gearchange used previously.

Because of the complexity of the assembly, possible unavailability of parts and special tools necessary, internal repair procedures for the transmission are not recommended for the home mechanic. The bulk of the information in this Chapter is devoted to removal and refitting procedures.

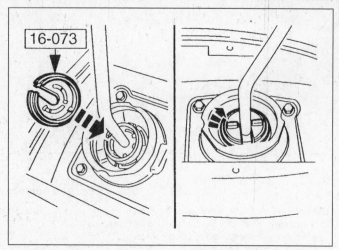

2.4 Ford special tool 16-073 used to lock the gear lever in neutral

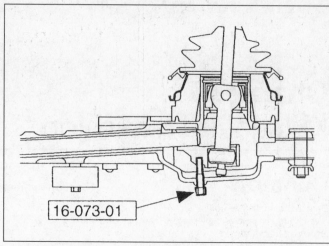

2.5 Ford special tool 16-073-01 screwed in to align gear linkage in neutral

## 2 Gearchange linkage – adjustment

### Rod gearchange (up to October 1996)

**Note:** *The special Ford tools 16-073 and 16-073-01 will be required in order to carry out the following adjustment. If these are not available, adjustment is still possible by proceeding on a trial-and-error basis, preferably with the help of an assistant to hold the gear lever in the neutral position.*

1 Prise out the gear lever gaiter frame and pull the gaiter up onto the gear knob.

2 Apply the handbrake, jack up the front of the car and support it on axle stands (see *Jacking and vehicle support*). Select neutral.

3 Working beneath the car, loosen the clamp bolt on the gearchange linkage located behind the transmission, then check that the linkage front section can slide freely in the rear section.

4 With the gear lever still in neutral, fit the special Ford tool 16-073 over the gear lever, and locate it in the recess in the lever retaining housing on top of the transmission. Twist the tool clockwise to lock the lever in the neutral position **(see illustration)**. Take care during the adjustment not to move the gear lever or displace the adjustment tool.

5 Screw in the special Ford tool 16-073-01 to the underside of the gear lever until it stops – do not force it **(see illustration)**.

6 Check that the front part of the gear-change linkage from the transmission is in neutral. It will be necessary to move the linkage slightly forwards and backwards to determine that it is in the correct position. Recheck that the adjustment tools are still correctly fitted, then tighten to the specified torque wrench setting the gearchange linkage clamp bolt.

7 Remove the adjustment tools.

8 Lower the car to the ground and refit the gear lever gaiter.

### Cable gearchange (October 1996 on)

**Note:** *The special Ford tool 16-088 will be required in order to carry out the following adjustment. This tool locks the gear lever in the neutral position during adjustment. If the tool is not available, adjustment is still possible by proceeding on a trial-and-error basis, preferably with the help of an assistant to hold the gear lever in the neutral position.*

9 Remove the air cleaner assembly as described in Chapter 4A.

10 On the transmission, release the adjusters on the cables by depressing the tabs on the sides of the red plastic locking sliders **(see illustration)**.

11 Inside the car, prise out the gear lever gaiter frame and pull the gaiter up onto the gear knob.

12 Lock the gear lever in neutral using the special tool 16-088 **(see illustration)**.

2.10 Release the cable adjusters by depressing the tabs on the sides of the red plastic locking sliders

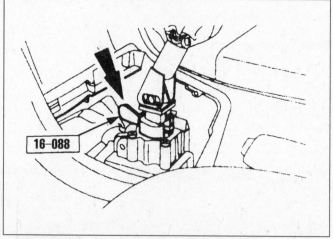

2.12 Ford special tool 16-088 used to lock the gear lever in neutral

**13** With the levers on the transmission in neutral, lock the red plastic locking sliders by pressing them in.

**14** Remove the special tool, and refit the gaiter to the gearchange lever.

**15** Refit the air cleaner assembly with reference to Chapter 4A.

## 3 Gearchange linkage and gear lever – removal and refitting

### Rod gearchange (up to October 1996)

#### Removal

**1** Prise out the gear lever gaiter frame and pull the gaiter up onto the gear knob **(see illustration)**.

**2** Apply the handbrake, jack up the front of the car and support it on axle stands (see *Jacking and vehicle support*). Select neutral.

**3** Working beneath the car, unscrew the bolt and disconnect the gearchange linkage from the selector shaft on the rear of the transmission.

**4** Mark the position of the gearchange linkage front and rear sections in relation to each other. Loosen the clamp bolt and remove the front section.

**5** Unscrew the bolt securing the gearchange support rod to the bracket on the rear of the transmission.

**6** Remove the heat shield. Support the weight of the gearchange linkage assembly, unscrew

**3.1 View of the top of the gearchange assembly – centre console removed**

the nuts from the rear mounting bracket, and lower the assembly from the underbody **(see illustration)**.

**7** Remove the insulator rubber from the rear of the assembly.

**8** Examine the insulator rubber and the stabiliser bar mounting rubber for wear and deterioration, and if necessary obtain new ones.

#### Refitting

**9** Refitting is a reversal of the removal procedure, but adjust the linkage as described in Section 2.

### Cable gearchange (October 1996 on)

#### Removal

**10** Disconnect the battery negative (earth) lead (see Chapter 5).

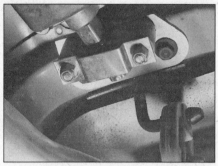

**3.6 Gearchange linkage assembly rear mounting**

**11** Loosen the front wheel nuts, then apply the handbrake. Jack up the front of the car and support it on axle stands (see *Jacking and vehicle support*). Remove both wheels.

**12** Remove the engine undershield and left-hand wheel arch liner.

**13** At the transmission, remove the cables from the support brackets by twisting the spring-loaded knurled collars anti-clockwise from each other (ie, in different directions). Prise off the retaining clips and release the cables from the transmission levers – note their fitted locations. Withdraw the cables downwards from the engine compartment **(see illustrations)**.

**14** Make sure that the levers on the transmission are both vertical (ie, in neutral).

**15** Remove the air cleaner as described in Chapter 4A.

**16** Remove the gear lever knob. On early

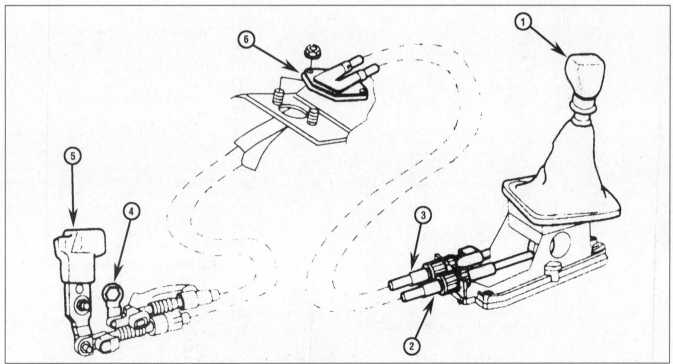

**3.13a Cable gearchange components – October 1996-on models**

| | | |
|---|---|---|
| 1 Gear lever | 3 Selector cable | 5 Shift lever on the transmission |
| 2 Shift cable | 4 Selector lever on the transmission | 6 Bulkhead adapter |

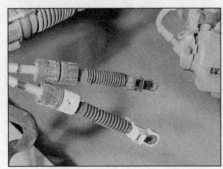

**3.13b The cable ends disconnected from the transmission and mounting bracket**

models the knob is pressed on, but on later models it is screwed on.

**17** Unclip and remove the gear lever gaiter.

**18** Remove the centre console as described in Chapter 11.

**19** Prise the cable end fittings from the gear lever stubs, then detach the cable ferrules from the bracket by turning the serrated collars anti-clockwise to each other.

**20** Unscrew the bolt and lift the air duct up from the centre channel.

**21** Cut the carpet if necessary, and fold it away from the area over the cable adapter.

**22** Unscrew the nuts and release the adapter from the floor, then withdraw the cables through the bulkhead and into the car.

**23** To remove the gear lever assembly, extract the circlip from the end of the bearing bolt and remove the spacer, spring and lever **(see illustration)**.

**24** Unscrew the bolts and remove the bearing housing and plate, reverse gear lockout, and the bearing shell.

**25** If necessary, bend back the lugs and remove the brackets and studs.

## Refitting

**26** Refitting is a reversal of removal, but adjust the cables as described in Section 2.

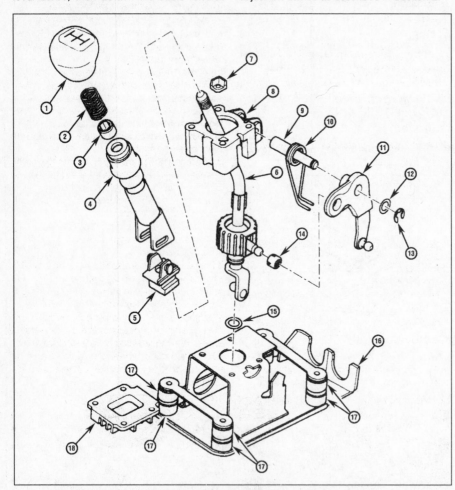

**3.23 Gear lever assembly components**

| | | |
|---|---|---|
| 1 *Knob* | 7 *Reverse gear lockout* | 13 *Circlip* |
| 2 *Spring* | 8 *Bearing housing* | 14 *Bearing shell* |
| 3 *Damping sleeve* | 9 *Bearing bolt* | 15 *O-ring* |
| 4 *Reverse gear release* | 10 *Spring* | 16 *Housing bracket* |
| 5 *Stop sleeve* | 11 *Lever* | 17 *Damping rings* |
| 6 *Gear lever* | 12 *Spacer* | 18 *Plate* |

## 4 Speedometer drive pinion – removal and refitting

### Removal

**1** Access to the speedometer drive pinion may be gained from the top of the engine (after removing the air cleaner – see Chapter 4A), or from below by raising the front of the car and reaching up over the top of the transmission. If the latter method is used, make sure that the car is supported adequately on axle stands (see *Jacking and vehicle support*).

**2** On early models, unscrew the nut and disconnect the speedometer cable from the vehicle speed sensor on the transmission. Use two spanners to loosen the nut – one to counterhold the sensor, and the other to unscrew the cable nut.

**3** Disconnect the wiring from the vehicle speed sensor, then unscrew the sensor from the top of the drive pinion.

**4** Using a pair of grips, pull out the drive pinion retaining roll-pin from the transmission casing.

**5** Withdraw the speedometer drive pinion and bearing from the top of the transmission.

**6** Using a small screwdriver, prise the O-ring from the groove in the bearing; obtain a new one for reassembly.

**7** Wipe clean the drive pinion and bearing, also the seating bore in the transmission casing.

### Refitting

**8** Refitting is a reversal of the removal procedure, but lightly oil the new O-ring before inserting the assembly in the transmission casing. Drive in the retaining roll-pin using a hammer.

## 5 Oil seals – renewal

**1** Oil leaks frequently occur due to wear or deterioration of the differential side gear seals and/or the gearchange selector shaft oil seal and speedometer drive pinion O-ring. Renewal of these seals is relatively easy, since the repairs can be performed without removing the transmission from the car.

### Differential side gear oil seals

**2** The differential side gear oil seals are located at the sides of the transmission, where the driveshafts enter the transmission. If leakage at the seal is suspected, raise the car and support it securely on axle stands. If the seal is leaking, oil will be found on the side of the transmission below the driveshaft.

**3** Refer to Chapter 8 and remove the appropriate driveshaft. If removing the right-hand driveshaft, it will be necessary to remove the intermediate shaft as well.

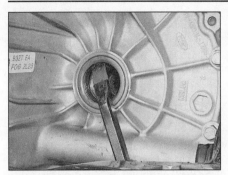

**5.4a Prise out the oil seal with a suitable lever**

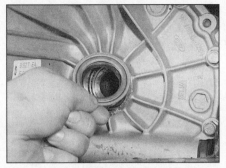

**5.4b Removing the oil seal from the transmission casing**

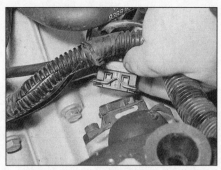

**6.2 Disconnecting the reversing light switch**

**4** Using a large screwdriver or lever, carefully prise the oil seal out of the transmission casing, taking care not to damage the transmission casing **(see illustrations)**.

**5** Wipe clean the oil seal seating in the transmission casing.

**6** Dip the new oil seal in clean oil, then press it a little way into the casing by hand, making sure that it is square to its seating.

**7** Using suitable tubing or a large socket, carefully drive the oil seal fully into the casing until it contacts the seating.

**8** Refit the driveshaft with reference to Chapter 8.

### Gearchange selector shaft oil seal

**9** Apply the handbrake, jack up the front of the car and support it on axle stands (see *Jacking and vehicle support*).

**10** Unscrew the bolt securing the gearchange linkage to the shaft on the rear of the transmission. Pull off the linkage and remove the rubber boot.

**11** Using a suitable tool or grips, pull the oil seal out of the transmission casing. Ford technicians use a slide hammer with an end fitting which locates over the oil seal extension. In the absence of this tool, if the oil seal is particularly tight, drill one or two small holes in the oil seal, and screw in self-tapping screws. The oil seal can then be removed from the casing by pulling on the screws.

**12** Wipe clean the oil seal seating in the transmission.

**13** Dip the new oil seal in clean oil, then press it a little way into the casing by hand, making sure that it is square to its seating.

**14** Using suitable tubing or a large socket, carefully drive the oil seal fully into the casing.

**15** Locate the rubber boot over the selector shaft.

**16** Refit the gearchange linkage to the shaft on the rear of the transmission, and tighten the bolt.

**17** If necessary, adjust the gearchange linkage as described in Section 2.

### Speedometer drive pinion oil seal

**18** The procedure is covered in Section 4.

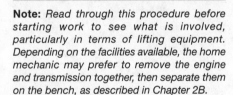

**6 Reversing light switch –** removal and refitting

### Removal

**1** Remove the air cleaner as described in Chapter 4A.

**2** Disconnect the wiring leading to the reversing light switch on the top of the transmission **(see illustration)**.

**3** Unscrew the mounting bolts and remove the reversing light switch from the cover housing on the transmission.

### Refitting

**4** Refitting is a reversal of the removal procedure.

**7 Transmission –** removal and refitting

**Note:** *Read through this procedure before starting work to see what is involved, particularly in terms of lifting equipment. Depending on the facilities available, the home mechanic may prefer to remove the engine and transmission together, then separate them on the bench, as described in Chapter 2B.*

### Removal

**1** Disconnect the battery negative (earth) lead (see Chapter 5). It is advisable to remove the battery completely, to improve access.

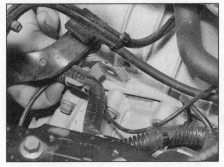

**7.6 Removing the wiring loom bracket from the top of the transmission**

**2** If necessary, the bonnet may be removed as described in Chapter 11 for better access, and for fitting the engine lifting hoist.

**3** Hold the radiator in its raised position by inserting split pins through the holes in the upper mounting extensions. This is necessary to retain the radiator when the subframe is removed.

**4** Remove the air cleaner and intercooler with reference to Chapter 4A – remove all the air ducts, and plug the turbocharger ports with clean rag to prevent dirt entry.

**5** Disconnect the wiring from the reversing light switch on the transmission.

**6** Unscrew the bolt and remove the wiring loom bracket from the top of the transmission **(see illustration)**.

**7** Detach the earth cable located between the transmission and the body.

**8** Disconnect the clutch cable or hydraulic line from the transmission, with reference to Chapter 6.

**9** Unscrew the three upper bolts securing the transmission to the engine.

**10** Unscrew the starter motor upper mounting bolt, noting that an earth cable is attached to it **(see illustration)**.

**11** Loosen the front wheel nuts, then apply the handbrake. Jack up the front of the car and support it on axle stands (see *Jacking and vehicle support*). Remove the front wheels.

**12** Remove the front lower cover from under the radiator by prising out the side clips and unscrewing the retaining bolts **(see illustration)**.

**13** Remove the wheel arch liner from the right-hand side of the car as described in Chapter 11.

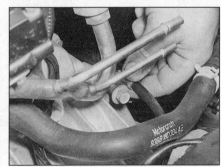

**7.10 Removing the starter motor bolt with the earth cable**

**7.12 Radiator front lower cover removal**

**7.20 Unscrew the gearchange link rod bolt on the rear of the transmission**

**7.21 Removing the gearchange linkage front section**

14 Unscrew the bolts and remove the auxiliary drivebelt cover.

15 Working on each side of the car in turn, unscrew the nut and disconnect the anti-roll bar link from the strut, noting that the flexible brake hose bracket is attached to the link stud.

**7.22 Unscrewing the gearchange support rod bolt from the transmission rear bracket**

16 Extract the split pins (where fitted), then unscrew the nut securing the track rod end to the hub carrier on each side. Release the balljoints from the hub carrier steering arms, using a balljoint separator tool.

17 Working on each side in turn, note which

way round the front suspension lower arm balljoint clamp bolt is fitted, then unscrew and remove it from the hub carrier. Lever the balljoint down from the hub carrier – if it is tight, prise the joint open carefully using a large flat-bladed tool. Take care not to damage the balljoint seal during the separation procedure.

18 Disconnect the cooling fan multi-plug on the subframe behind the radiator, and unclip the plug from the bracket.

19 Remove the complete exhaust system as described in Chapter 4A.

### Rod gearchange (up to October 1996)

20 Unscrew the bolt securing the gearchange linkage to the selector shaft on the rear of the transmission (see illustration).

21 Mark the position of the gearchange linkage front and rear sections, then unscrew the clamp bolt. Disconnect the linkage from the selector shaft on the rear of the transmission, and separate the front and rear sections of the linkage (see illustration).

22 Unscrew the mounting bolt, and disconnect the gearchange support rod from the bracket on the rear of the transmission (see illustration).

23 Remove the gear linkage heat shield from the underbody by unscrewing the nuts. Unscrew the gear linkage rear mounting bolts, swivel the linkage around to the rear, and tie it to the underbody (see illustrations).

### Cable gearchange (October 1996 on)

24 Disconnect the two gearchange cables from the transmission with reference to Section 3.

### All models

25 Unscrew the bolts securing the air conditioning receiver/dryer to the left-hand side of the subframe, and tie it to one side.

26 Unscrew the bolts securing the steering gear to the subframe. The bolts are difficult to reach using normal spanners; if possible, the special cranked Ford tool should be obtained (see Chapter 10).

27 Unscrew the through-bolt from the engine/transmission rear mounting, then unbolt the mounting from the subframe (see illustrations). To ensure correct refitting, note the fitted position of the mounting before removing it.

**7.23a Remove the gearchange linkage heat shield . . .**

**7.23b . . . unscrew the linkage rear mounting bolts . . .**

**7.23c . . . swivel the linkage around, and tie it to the underbody**

**7.27a Remove the through-bolt from the rear mounting . . .**

**7.27b . . . then unbolt the mounting from the subframe and remove it**

**28** On rod gearchange models, unscrew the nut and bolt and remove the support rod bracket from the rear of the transmission **(see illustrations)**.

**29** Unscrew the nuts and bolts and remove the engine/transmission rear mounting bracket from the transmission **(see illustrations)**. To ensure correct refitting, note the fitted position of the mounting before removing it.

**30** Unscrew the through-bolt from the engine front mounting **(see illustration)**.

**31** With the help of an assistant, support the weight of the subframe, using trolley jacks if possible. Unscrew the bolts securing the power steering fluid cooler pipes to the sub-frame. Mark the fitted position of the subframe, referring to Chapter 2B, Section 4. Unscrew the subframe mounting bolts, and lower the subframe to the ground **(see illustrations)**.

**32** Position a suitable container beneath the transmission, then unscrew the drain plug and drain the oil **(see illustration)**. Refit and tighten the plug on completion.

**33** Unscrew the bolts securing the right-hand driveshaft centre bearing to the cylinder block. Remove the heat shield, then pull out the right-hand strut so that the intermediate shaft is removed from the transmission differential gears. Be prepared for oil spillage.

**34** Support the right-hand driveshaft on axle stands, making sure that the inner tripod joint is not angled through more than 18° (damage may occur if the joint is turned through too great an angle).

**35** Insert a suitable lever between the left-hand driveshaft inner joint and the transmission case (with a thin piece of wood against the case), then prise free the joint from the differential. If it proves reluctant to move, strike the lever firmly with the palm of the hand. Be careful not to damage the adjacent components, and be prepared for oil spillage. As the right-hand driveshaft has already been removed, it is possible to release the left-hand driveshaft by inserting a forked drift from the right-hand side, but care must be taken to prevent damage to the differential gears.

**36** Support the left-hand driveshaft on axle stands, making sure that the inner tripod joint is not angled through more than 18° (damage may occur if the joint is turned through too great an angle).

**7.28a** Unscrew the nut and bolt . . .

**7.29a Nuts securing the rear mounting bracket to the transmission**

**37** Disconnect the multi-plug from the wiring leading to the vehicle speed sensor.

**38** On early models with a speedometer cable, unscrew the cable nut, and disconnect the speedometer cable from the top of the vehicle speed sensor. Hold the

**7.30 Removing the through-bolt from the engine front mounting bracket**

**7.28b . . . and remove the transmission support rod bracket – early models**

**7.29b Removing the rear mounting bracket**

sensor with a spanner while the cable nut is loosened. Disconnect the wiring from the speed sensor.

**39** If necessary, the car may be lowered to the ground at this stage, in order to connect an engine hoist. If an engine support bar

**7.31a Removing the steering fluid cooler pipes from the subframe**

**7.31b Unscrewing the subframe front . . .**

**7.31c . . . and rear mounting bolts**

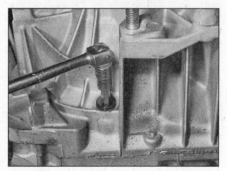

**7.32 Unscrewing the transmission oil drain plug**

**7.48 Removing the lower cover plate**

which locates over the engine compartment is to be used, then the car may be left in its raised position.

**40** Attach the hoist to diagonally-opposite positions on the engine, and take the weight of the engine and transmission.

**41** Unscrew the nuts from the engine right-hand mounting bracket. Note that, where a hydraulic mounting is fitted, the mounting must never be tilted by more than 5°. To ensure correct refitting, note the fitted position of the mounting before removing it.

**42** Unscrew the retaining nuts and remove the engine/transmission left-hand mounting from the transmission. To ensure correct refitting, note the fitted position of the mounting before removing it.

**43** Lower the engine until the air conditioning compressor is below the right-hand side-member.

**44** Lower the transmission until it is opposite the aperture on the left-hand side of the engine compartment.

**45** Support the weight of the transmission on a trolley jack. Use safety chains or a cradle to steady the transmission on the jack.

**46** Remove the remaining starter motor mounting bolts.

**47** Unscrew the lower bolts securing the transmission to the engine. Also unscrew the bolts securing the lower cover plate to the transmission.

**48** With the help of an assistant, withdraw the transmission squarely from the engine, taking care not to allow its weight to hang on the clutch friction disc. As the transmission is being withdrawn, remove the lower cover plate sandwiched between the transmission and engine, where applicable **(see illustration)**. Lower the transmission to the ground.

**49** The clutch components can now be inspected with reference to Chapter 6, and renewed if necessary. (Unless they are virtually new, it is worth renewing the clutch components as a matter of course, even if the transmission has been removed for some other reason.)

### Refitting

**50** If removed, refit the clutch components (see Chapter 6).

**51** With the transmission secured to the

trolley jack as on removal, raise it into position, and then carefully slide it onto the rear of the engine, at the same time engaging the input shaft with the clutch friction disc splines. Do not use excessive force to refit the transmission – if the input shaft does not slide into place easily, readjust the angle of the transmission so that it is level, and/or turn the input shaft so that the splines engage properly with the disc. If problems are still experienced, check that the clutch friction disc is correctly centred (Chapter 6).

**52** Refit the lower bolts securing the transmission to the engine, and tighten moderately at this stage.

**53** Insert and tighten the starter mounting bolts, noting that an earth cable is attached to one of them.

**54** Raise the transmission to its normal position.

**55** Refit the engine/transmission left-hand mounting, and tighten the nuts. Align the mounting as noted during removal.

**56** Refit the engine right-hand mounting bracket, and tighten the nuts. Align the mounting as noted during removal.

**57** If previously lowered, raise the front of the car, and support on axle stands.

**58** Refit the speedometer cable to the vehicle speed sensor, and tighten the cable nut.

**59** Reconnect the wiring to the speed sensor.

**60** Insert the left-hand driveshaft into the transmission, making sure that it is fully engaged with the internal circlip.

**61** Refit the right-hand driveshaft and intermediate shaft, and tighten the bolts.

**62** Refit and align the subframe, with reference to Chapter 2B, Section 4. Tighten the mounting bolts to the specified torque.

**63** Tighten the through-bolt in the engine front mounting.

**64** Refit the engine rear mounting bracket, and tighten the bolts.

**65** Where fitted, refit the transmission support rod and bracket, and tighten the bolts and nut.

**66** Refit the engine rear mounting to the subframe, and tighten the bolts.

**67** Refit the steering gear to the subframe, and tighten the mounting bolts.

**68** Refit the air conditioning receiver/dryer to the subframe, and tighten the mounting bolts.

**69** Refit the gear linkage and heat shield.

**70** Refit the transmission gearchange support rod to the rear of the transmission, and tighten the bolt. Adjust the gearchange linkage if necessary, with reference to Section 2.

**71** Refit the exhaust system, with reference to Chapter 4A.

**72** Reconnect and secure the cooling fan multi-plug.

**73** Refit the front suspension lower arm balljoints to the hub carriers, with reference to Chapter 10.

**74** Refit the track rod ends to the hub carrier steering arms on each side, with reference to Chapter 10.

**75** Refit the anti-roll bar links to the struts, and tighten the nuts.

**76** Refit the auxiliary drivebelt cover and the wheel arch liner.

**77** Refit the front lower cover beneath the radiator.

**78** Refit the wheels, and lower the car to the ground.

**79** Insert the upper bolts securing the transmission to the engine.

**80** Reconnect the clutch cable or hydraulic line with reference to Chapter 6.

**81** Refit the earth cable between the transmission and the body.

**82** Refit the wiring loom bracket to the top of the transmission.

**83** Reconnect the wiring to the reversing light switch.

**84** Tighten all transmission mounting bolts fully.

**85** Refit the air cleaner assembly with reference to Chapter 4A.

**86** Remove the split pins holding the radiator in its raised position.

**87** If removed, refit the bonnet.

**88** If removed, refit the battery and reconnect the leads.

**89** Fill the transmission with oil, and check the level as described in Chapter 1.

**90** Make a final check that all connections have been made, and all bolts tightened fully.

**91** Road test the car to check for proper transmission operation, then check the transmission visually for leakage of oil.

## 8  Transmission mounting – checking and renewal

This procedure is covered in Chapter 2A.

## 9  Manual transmission overhaul – general

Overhauling a transmission is a difficult job for the do-it-yourselfer. It involves the dismantling and reassembly of many small parts. Numerous clearances must be precisely measured and, if necessary, changed with selected spacers and circlips. As a result, if transmission problems arise, while the unit can be removed and refitted by a competent do-it-yourselfer, overhaul should be left to a transmission specialist. Rebuilt transmissions may be available – check with your dealer parts department, motor factors, or transmission specialists. At any rate, the time and money involved in an overhaul is almost sure to exceed the cost of a rebuilt unit.

Nevertheless, it's not impossible to rebuild a transmission, providing the special tools are available, and the job is done in a deliberate step-by-step manner so nothing is overlooked.

The tools necessary for an overhaul include: internal and external circlip pliers, a bearing puller, a slide hammer, a set of pin punches, a dial test indicator, and possibly a hydraulic press. In addition, a large, sturdy workbench and a vice or transmission stand will be required.

During dismantling of the transmission, make careful notes of how each part comes off, where it fits in relation to other parts, and what holds it in place.

Before taking the transmission apart for repair, it will help if you have some idea what area of the transmission is malfunctioning.

Certain problems can be closely tied to specific areas in the transmission, which can make component examination and renewal easier. Refer to the Fault finding Section at the end of this manual for information regarding possible sources of trouble.

# Chapter 8
# Driveshafts

## Contents

Section number

Driveshaft gaiter and CV joint check . . . . . . . . . . . . . . . . See Chapter 1
Driveshaft inner CV joint gaiter – renewal. . . . . . . . . . . . . . . . . . . 3
Driveshaft outer CV joint gaiter – renewal . . . . . . . . . . . . . . . . . . . 4

Section number

Driveshafts – inspection and joint renewal. . . . . . . . . . . . . . . . . . . . 5
Driveshafts – removal and refitting. . . . . . . . . . . . . . . . . . . . . . . . . . 2
General information . . . . . . . . . . . . . . . . . . . . . . . . . . . . . . . . . . . . . . 1

## Degrees of difficulty

| Easy, suitable for novice with little experience  | Fairly easy, suitable for beginner with some experience  | Fairly difficult, suitable for competent DIY mechanic 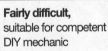 | Difficult, suitable for experienced DIY mechanic 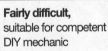 | Very difficult, suitable for expert DIY or professional  |
| --- | --- | --- | --- | --- |

## Specifications

| Torque wrench settings | Nm | lbf ft |
| --- | --- | --- |
| Anti-roll bar link nut | 47 | 35 |
| Driveshaft nut | 340 | 251 |
| Driveshaft support bearing bracket-to-cylinder block bolts | 48 | 35 |
| Lower arm balljoint-to-hub carrier clamp bolt | 83 | 61 |
| Right-hand intermediate shaft bearing and heat shield bolts | 27 | 20 |
| Roadwheel nuts | 85 | 63 |
| Suspension strut upper mounting nut (renew) | 46 | 34 |
| Track rod end balljoint nut | 28 | 21 |

### 1  General information

Drive is transmitted from the transmission differential to the front wheels by means of two driveshafts. The right-hand driveshaft is in two sections, and incorporates a support bearing.

Each driveshaft consists of three main components: the sliding (tripod type) inner joint, the actual driveshaft, and the outer CV (constant velocity) joint. The inner (male) end of the left-hand tripod joint is secured in the differential side gear by the engagement of a circlip. The inner (female) end of the right-hand driveshaft is held on the intermediate shaft by the engagement of a circlip. The intermediate shaft is held in the transmission by the support bearing, which in turn is supported by a bracket bolted to the rear of the cylinder block. The outer CV joint on both driveshafts is of ball-bearing type, and is secured in the front hub by the driveshaft nut.

## 2 Driveshafts – removal and refitting

### Removal

**1** Remove the wheel trim (or centre cover) from the wheel, apply the handbrake, and engage 1st gear. Loosen the driveshaft nut about half a turn **(see illustration)**. This nut is very tight – use only high-quality, close-fitting tools, and take adequate precautions against personal injury when loosening it.

**2** Loosen the front wheel retaining nuts. Apply the handbrake, jack up the front of the car and support it on axle stands (see *Jacking and vehicle support*). Remove the wheel.

**3** To avoid spillage when the driveshafts are separated from the transmission, drain the transmission oil as described in Chapter 1.

**4** Remove the front brake disc as described in Chapter 9.

**5** Completely unscrew the driveshaft nut. Note that the nut is of special laminated design – Ford state that it can be re-used up to 5 times, but owners may prefer to fit a new nut every time. When the nut is removed, check it carefully for signs of splitting – it is not unknown for these nuts to split during tightening, and it pays to have a new nut to hand.

**6** Retain the suspension strut piston with an Allen key, then loosen the strut upper mounting nut and unscrew it by five complete turns. It is not necessary to remove the nut at this stage, but note that a new one will be required on refitting. Where necessary, detach the ABS wiring from the strut.

**7** Unscrew the nut securing the anti-roll bar link to the front suspension strut, and position the link to one side.

**8** Extract the split pin from the track rod end balljoint nut. Unscrew the nut and detach the rod from the hub carrier steering arm using a conventional balljoint removal tool. Take care not to damage the balljoint seal.

**9** Note which way round the front suspension lower arm balljoint clamp bolt is fitted, then unscrew it from the hub carrier. Lever the balljoint down from the hub carrier; if it is tight, carefully prise the clamp open using a large flat-bladed tool. Take care not to damage the balljoint seal during the separation procedure.

**10** Using a universal puller located on the hub flange, press the driveshaft through the front hub and hub carrier by pulling the hub carrier outwards **(see illustrations)**. When the driveshaft is free, support it on an axle stand, making sure that the inner tripod joint is not angled through more than 18° (damage may occur if the joint is turned through too great an angle).

### Left-hand side

**11** Insert a lever between the inner driveshaft joint and the transmission case, with a thin piece of wood against the case. Prise free the inner joint from the differential **(see illustration)**. If it proves reluctant to move, strike the lever firmly with the palm of the hand.

**12** Be careful not to damage the adjacent components, and in particular, make sure that the driveshaft oil seal in the differential is not damaged. Especially if the transmission was not drained, be prepared for oil spillage.

**13** Note that if the right-hand driveshaft has already been removed, it is possible to release the left-hand driveshaft by inserting a forked drift from the right-hand side. However, care must be taken to prevent damage to the differential gears, particularly if the special Ford tool is not used.

**14** Withdraw the driveshaft from under the car.

**15** Extract the circlip from the groove on the inner end of the driveshaft, and obtain a new one.

### Right-hand side

**16** The right-hand driveshaft may either be removed complete with the intermediate shaft from the transmission, or it may be disconnected from the outer end of the intermediate shaft. If the latter course of action is taken, use a soft-faced mallet to sharply tap the inner CV joint housing from the intermediate shaft. The internal circlip will be released, and the driveshaft may be withdrawn from the splines.

**17** Extract the circlip from the groove on the outer end of the intermediate shaft. Obtain a new circlip for use when refitting.

**18** If the complete driveshaft is to be removed, proceed as follows. Unscrew the bolts securing the driveshaft support bearing bracket to the rear of the cylinder block, and remove the heat shield **(see illustration)**.

**19** Withdraw the complete driveshaft from the transmission and from the bearing bracket, and remove it from under the car **(see illustration)**. Especially if the transmission was not drained, be prepared for oil spillage.

**2.1 Loosen the driveshaft nut with the wheel on the ground**

**2.10a Using a puller on the hub flange . . .**

**2.10b . . . to press the driveshaft out of the front hub and hub carrier**

**2.11 Removing the left-hand driveshaft from the transmission**

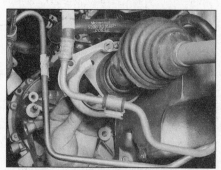

**2.18 Removing the heat shield from the right-hand driveshaft support bearing**

**2.19 Removing the complete right-hand driveshaft**

## Both sides

**20** Check the condition of the differential oil seals, and if necessary renew them as described in Chapter 7. Check the support bearing, and if necessary renew it as described in Section 5.

### *Refitting*

#### Right-hand side

**21** If the intermediate shaft has not been removed, proceed to paragraph 24. Otherwise, proceed as follows.
**22** Carefully refit the complete driveshaft in the support bearing and into the transmission, taking care not to damage the oil seal. Turn the driveshaft until it engages the splines on the differential gears.
**23** Tighten the bolts securing the support bearing to the bracket on the cylinder block to the specified torque. Proceed to paragraph 28.
**24** Locate the new circlip in the groove on the outer end of the intermediate shaft, then smear a little grease over the entire circumference of the intermediate shaft splines.
**25** Locate the right-hand driveshaft on the intermediate shaft splines, and push it on until the internal circlip is heard to engage with the groove in the shaft.

#### Left-hand side

**26** Locate the new circlip in the groove on the inner end of the driveshaft.
**27** Insert the driveshaft into the transmission, making sure that the circlip is fully engaged.

#### Both sides

**28** Pull the hub carrier outwards, and insert the outer end of the driveshaft through the hub. Turn the driveshaft to engage the splines in the hub, and fully push on the hub. Ford use a special tool to draw the driveshaft into the hub, but it is unlikely that the splines will be tight. However, if they are, it will be necessary to obtain the tool, or to use a similar home-made tool.
**29** Screw on the driveshaft nut finger-tight.
**30** Locate the front suspension lower arm balljoint stub in the bottom of the hub carrier. Insert the clamp bolt in the previously-noted position, screw on the nut, and tighten it to the specified torque.
**31** Refit the track rod end balljoint to the hub carrier steering arm and screw on the nut. Tighten the nut to the specified torque.
**32** Check that the balljoint nut split pin holes are aligned. If not, re-position the nut, but make sure that it is still tightened securely. Insert a new split pin, and bend its legs back to secure it.
**33** Locate the anti-roll bar link on the front suspension strut, and tighten the nut to the specified torque.
**34** Remove the suspension strut upper mounting nut and fit the new nut, tightening it to the specified torque. Where necessary, refit the ABS wiring to the strut bracket.
**35** Refit the front brake disc with reference to Chapter 9.

**36** Fill the transmission with oil, and check the level as described in Chapter 1.
**37** Refit the wheel, and lower the car to the ground. Tighten the wheel retaining nuts to the specified torque.
**38** Fully tighten the driveshaft nut to the specified torque **(see illustration)**. Finally, refit the wheel trim (or centre cover).

---

### 3  Driveshaft inner CV joint gaiter – renewal

**1** The inner CV joint gaiter is renewed by disconnecting the driveshaft from the inner CV joint housing at the transmission (left-hand side) or intermediate shaft (right-hand side). The work can be carried out either with the driveshaft removed from the car, or with it *in situ*. If it is wished to fully remove the driveshaft, refer to Section 2 first. Note that if both the inner and outer gaiters are being renewed at the same time, the outer gaiter can be removed from the inner end of the driveshaft.

### *Without removing driveshaft*

**2** Loosen the front wheel nuts on the appropriate side. Apply the handbrake, jack up the front of the car and support it on axle stands (see *Jacking and vehicle support*). Remove the wheel.
**3** Unscrew the nut securing the anti-roll bar link to the front suspension strut, and position the link to one side.
**4** Extract the split pin from the track rod end balljoint nut. Unscrew the nut and detach the rod from the hub carrier steering arm using a conventional balljoint removal tool. Take care not to damage the balljoint seal.
**5** Note which way round the front suspension lower arm balljoint clamp bolt is fitted, then unscrew it from the hub carrier. Lever the balljoint down from the hub carrier; if it is tight, prise the clamp open carefully using a large flat-bladed tool. Take care not to damage the balljoint seal during the separation procedure.
**6** Mark the driveshaft in relation to the joint housing, to ensure correct refitting.
**7** Note the fitted location of both of the inner joint gaiter retaining clips. Release the clips from the gaiter, and slide the gaiter back along the driveshaft (away from the transmission) a little way.
**8** Pull the front suspension strut outwards, while guiding the tripod joint out of the joint housing. As the joint tripod is being withdrawn from the housing, be prepared for some of the bearing rollers to fall out. Identify them for position with a dab of paint. Support the inner end of the driveshaft on an axle stand.
**9** Remove the support ring from the joint housing.
**10** Remove the remaining bearing rollers from the tripod, and identify them for position with a dab of paint.
**11** Check that the inner end of the driveshaft

**2.39 Torque-tightening the driveshaft nut**

is marked in relation to the splined tripod hub. If not, carefully centre-punch the two items, to ensure correct refitting. Alternatively, use dabs of paint on the driveshaft and one end of the tripod.
**12** Extract the circlip retaining the tripod on the driveshaft.
**13** Using a suitable puller, remove the tripod from the end of the driveshaft, and slide off the gaiter.
**14** If the outer gaiter is also to be renewed, remove it with reference to Section 4.
**15** Clean the driveshaft, and obtain a new tripod retaining circlip. The gaiter retaining clips and the steering track rod end split pin must also be renewed.
**16** Slide the new gaiter on the driveshaft, together with new clips. Also locate the support ring on the joint housing.
**17** Refit the tripod on the driveshaft splines, if necessary using a soft-faced mallet to drive it fully onto the splines. It must be fitted with the chamfered edge leading (towards the driveshaft), and with the previously-made marks aligned. Secure it in position using the new circlip. Ensure that the circlip is fully engaged in its groove.
**18** Locate the bearing rollers on the tripod in their previously-noted positions, using grease to hold them in place.
**19** With the front suspension strut pulled outwards, guide the tripod joint into the joint housing, making sure that the previously-made marks are aligned. Pack the joint with 180 grams of CV joint grease.
**20** Slide the gaiter along the driveshaft, and locate it on the support ring located on the joint housing. The small-diameter end of the gaiter must be located in the groove on the driveshaft.
**21** Ensure that the gaiter is not twisted or distorted, then insert a small screwdriver under the lip of the gaiter at the housing end. This will allow trapped air to escape during the next step.
**22** Push the tripod fully into the housing, then pull it out by 20 mm. Remove the screwdriver, then fit the retaining clips and tighten them.
**23** Reconnect the front suspension lower arm balljoint to the hub carrier. Refit and tighten the clamp nut and bolt.
**24** Reconnect the track rod end balljoint to the hub carrier steering arm and tighten the

**3.28 Removing the gaiter from the inner joint housing**

**3.31 Removing the support ring from the joint housing**

**3.32 Removing the bearing rollers**

nut to the specified torque. Check that the split pin holes are correctly aligned; if necessary, reposition the nut, making sure that it is still tightened securely. Insert a new split pin, and bend its legs back to secure it.

25 Refit the anti-roll bar link to the front suspension strut, and tighten the nut to the specified torque.

26 Refit the wheel, and lower the car to the ground. Tighten the wheel nuts to the specified torque.

### With driveshaft on bench

27 Mount the driveshaft in a vice.

28 Mark the driveshaft in relation to the joint housing, to ensure correct refitting.

29 Note the fitted location of both of the inner joint gaiter retaining clips, then release the clips from the gaiter, and slide the gaiter back along the driveshaft a little way **(see illustration)**.

30 Remove the inner joint housing from the tripod. As the housing is being removed, be prepared for some of the bearing rollers to fall out. Identify them for position with a dab of paint.

31 Remove the support ring from the joint housing **(see illustration)**.

32 Remove the remaining bearing rollers from the tripod, and identify them for position with a dab of paint **(see illustration)**.

33 Check that the inner end of the driveshaft is marked in relation to the splined tripod hub. If not, carefully centre-punch the two items, to ensure correct refitting. Alternatively, use dabs of paint on the driveshaft and one end of the tripod.

34 Extract the circlip retaining the tripod on the driveshaft **(see illustration)**.

35 Using a puller, remove the tripod from the end of the driveshaft, and slide off the gaiter **(see illustration)**.

36 If the outer gaiter is also to be renewed, remove it with reference to Section 4.

37 Clean the driveshaft, and obtain a new joint retaining circlip. The gaiter retaining clips must also be renewed.

38 Slide the new gaiter on the driveshaft, together with new clips **(see illustration)**.

39 Locate the support ring on the CV joint housing.

40 Refit the tripod on the driveshaft splines, if necessary using a soft-faced mallet and a suitable socket to drive it fully onto the splines **(see illustrations)**. It must be fitted with the chamfered edge leading (towards the driveshaft), and with the previously-made marks aligned. Secure it in position using a new circlip. Ensure that the circlip is fully engaged in its groove.

41 Locate the bearing rollers on the tripod in their previously-noted positions, using grease to hold them in place.

42 Guide the joint housing onto the tripod joint, making sure that the previously-made marks are aligned. Scoop out all of the old grease, then pack the joint with 180 grams of new CV joint grease.

43 Slide the gaiter along the driveshaft, and locate it on the support ring on the CV joint housing. The small-diameter end of the gaiter must be located in the groove on the driveshaft.

44 Ensure that the gaiter is not twisted or distorted, then insert a small screwdriver under the lip of the gaiter at the housing end. This will allow trapped air to escape during the next step.

**3.34 Circlip retaining the tripod on the driveshaft**

**3.35 Using a puller to remove the tripod**

**3.38 Slide the gaiter and clips onto the driveshaft**

**3.40a Locate the tripod on the splines . . .**

**3.40b . . . and drive it fully onto the driveshaft**

**3.45 Using pincers to tighten the retaining clips**

**4.4a Release the clips . . .**

**4.4b . . . and remove the gaiter**

45 Push the housing fully on the tripod, then pull it out by 20 mm. Remove the screwdriver, then fit the retaining clips and tighten them **(see illustration)**.

## 4 Driveshaft outer CV joint gaiter – renewal

1 The outer CV joint gaiter can be renewed by removing the inner gaiter first as described in Section 3, or after removing the driveshaft complete as described in Section 2. If the driveshaft is removed, then the inner gaiter need not necessarily be removed. It is impractical to renew the outer gaiter by dismantling the outer joint with the driveshaft in position in the car. The following paragraphs describe renewal of the gaiter on the bench.
2 Mount the driveshaft in a vice.
3 Mark the driveshaft in relation to the CV joint housing, to ensure correct refitting.
4 Note the fitted location of both of the outer joint gaiter retaining clips, then release the clips from the gaiter, and slide the gaiter back along the driveshaft a little way **(see illustrations)**.
5 Using a brass drift or a copper mallet, carefully drive the outer CV joint hub from the splines on the driveshaft **(see illustrations)**. Initial resistance will be felt until the internal circlips are released. Take care not to damage the bearing cage.
6 Extract the outer circlip from the end of the driveshaft **(see illustration)**.

7 Slide the gaiter over the remaining circlip, and remove it together with the clips.
8 Clean the driveshaft, and obtain new joint retaining circlips. The gaiter retaining clips must also be renewed.
9 Slide the new gaiter (together with new clips) onto the driveshaft and over the inner circlip **(see illustration)**.
10 Fit a new outer circlip to the groove in the driveshaft.
11 Scoop out all of the old grease, then pack the joint with 100 grams of new CV joint grease **(see illustration)**. If no new grease is supplied with the gaiter, use a good-quality molybdenum disulphide grease. Take care that the fresh grease does not become contaminated with dirt or grit as it is being applied.
12 Locate the CV joint on the driveshaft so that the splines are aligned, then push the joint until the internal circlips are fully engaged.

13 Move the gaiter along the driveshaft, and locate it over the joint and onto the outer CV joint housing. The small-diameter end of the gaiter must be located in the groove on the driveshaft.
14 Ensure that the gaiter is not twisted or distorted, then insert a small screwdriver under the lip of the gaiter at the housing end, to allow any trapped air to escape.
15 Remove the screwdriver, fit the retaining clips in their previously-noted positions, and tighten them.

## 5 Driveshafts – inspection and joint renewal

1 If any of the checks described in Chapter 1 reveal apparent excessive wear or play in any driveshaft joint, first remove the wheel trim (or

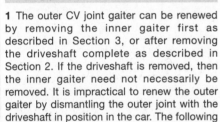

**4.5a Drive off the outer CV joint hub . . .**

**4.5b . . . and remove the joint from the driveshaft**

**4.6 Circlips fitted on the outer end of the driveshaft**

**4.9 Fitting the new gaiter and clips on the driveshaft**

**4.11 Packing the outer CV joint with new grease**

centre cover), and check that the driveshaft nut is tightened to the specified torque. Repeat this check on the other driveshaft nut.

**2** Road test the car, and listen for a metallic clicking from the front, as the car is driven slowly in a circle on full-lock. If a clicking noise is heard, this indicates wear in the outer constant velocity joint, which means that the joint must be renewed; reconditioning is not possible.

**3** To renew an outer CV joint, remove the driveshaft as described in Section 2, then separate the joint from the driveshaft with reference to Section 4. In principle, the gaiter can be left on the driveshaft, provided that it is in good condition; in practice, it makes sense to renew the gaiter in any case, having got this far.

**4** If vibration, consistent with roadspeed, is felt through the car when accelerating, there is a possibility of wear in the inner tripod joints.

**5** To renew an inner joint, remove the driveshaft as described in Section 2, then separate the joint from the driveshaft with reference to Section 3.

**6** Continual noise from the right-hand driveshaft, increasing with roadspeed, may indicate wear in the support bearing. To renew this bearing, the driveshaft and intermediate shaft must be removed, and the bearing extracted using a puller.

**7** Remove the bearing dust cover, and obtain a new one.

**8** Drive or press on the new bearing, applying the pressure to the inner race only. Similarly drive or press on the new dust cover.

# Chapter 9
# Braking system

## Contents

| | Section number |
|---|---|
| ABS hydraulic unit – removal and refitting | 20 |
| ABS relay box – removal and refitting | 22 |
| ABS wheel sensor – testing, removal and refitting | 21 |
| Brake check | See Chapter 1 |
| Brake fluid renewal | See Chapter 1 |
| Brake pedal – removal and refitting | 12 |
| Brake pedal-to-servo cross-link – removal and refitting | 13 |
| Front brake caliper – removal, overhaul and refitting | 3 |
| Front brake disc – inspection, removal and refitting | 4 |
| Front brake pads – renewal | 2 |
| General information | 1 |
| Handbrake cables – removal and refitting | 27 |
| Handbrake lever – removal and refitting | 26 |
| Hydraulic pipes and hoses – inspection, removal and refitting | 14 |
| Hydraulic system – bleeding | 15 |
| Master cylinder – removal and refitting | 11 |

| | Section number |
|---|---|
| Pressure-control relief valve (early ABS models) – removal and refitting | 19 |
| Pressure-control relief valve (non-ABS models) – removal and refitting | 18 |
| Rear brake caliper – removal, overhaul and refitting | 9 |
| Rear brake disc – inspection, removal and refitting | 10 |
| Rear brake drum – removal, inspection and refitting | 5 |
| Rear brake pads – renewal | 8 |
| Rear brake shoes – renewal | 6 |
| Rear wheel cylinder – removal, overhaul and refitting | 7 |
| Stop-light switch – removal, refitting and adjustment | 25 |
| Traction control system inhibitor switch – removal and refitting | 23 |
| Traction control system throttle actuator – removal and refitting | 24 |
| Vacuum pump – removal and refitting | 28 |
| Vacuum pump – testing and overhaul | 29 |
| Vacuum servo unit – testing, removal and refitting | 16 |
| Vacuum servo unit vacuum hose and non-return valve – removal, testing and refitting | 17 |

## Degrees of difficulty

| | | | | |
|---|---|---|---|---|
| **Easy,** suitable for novice with little experience | **Fairly easy,** suitable for beginner with some experience | **Fairly difficult,** suitable for competent DIY mechanic | **Difficult,** suitable for experienced DIY mechanic | **Very difficult,** suitable for expert DIY or professional |

## Specifications

### Front brakes

Disc thickness:
| | |
|---|---|
| New | 24.15 mm |
| Minimum | 22.20 mm |
| Maximum disc run-out (fitted) | 0.15 mm |
| Maximum disc thickness variation | 0.015 mm |
| Front hub face maximum run-out | 0.05 mm |

### Rear drum brakes

Diameter:
| | |
|---|---|
| New | 228.6 mm |
| Maximum | 229.6 mm |

### Rear disc brakes

Disc thickness:
| | |
|---|---|
| New | 20.0 mm |
| Minimum | 18.0 mm |
| Maximum disc run-out (fitted) | 0.15 mm |
| Maximum disc thickness variation | 0.015 mm |
| Rear hub face maximum run-out | 0.05 mm |

## Torque wrench settings

| | Nm | lbf ft |
|---|---|---|
| ABS hydraulic unit to bracket | 20 | 15 |
| Brake pipe unions | 13 | 10 |
| Front caliper carrier bracket | 120 | 89 |
| Front caliper guide bolts | 28 | 21 |
| Handbrake lever mountings | 23 | 17 |
| Master cylinder mountings | 25 | 18 |
| Rear caliper carrier bracket | 59 | 44 |
| Rear caliper guide bolts | 41 | 30 |
| Rear drum brake backplate | 50 | 37 |
| Roadwheel nuts | 85 | 63 |
| Splash shield bolts | 90 | 66 |
| Vacuum pump: | | |
| Bracket to cylinder block | 47 | 35 |
| Bracket to lifting eye | 23 | 17 |
| Pump to cylinder head bolts | 20 | 15 |
| Vacuum line bracket to cylinder head | 9 | 7 |
| Vacuum line to pump union | 16 | 12 |
| Vacuum servo unit | 40 | 30 |

## 1 General information

The braking system is of diagonally-split, dual-circuit design, with ventilated discs at the front, and drum or disc brakes (according to model) at the rear. The calipers are of floating single-piston design, using asbestos-free pads. The rear drum brakes are of the leading and trailing shoe type. They are self-adjusting during footbrake operation. The rear brake shoe linings are of different thicknesses, in order to allow for the different proportional rates of wear.

The vacuum servo unit boosts the effort applied by the driver at the brake pedal, and transmits this increased effort to the master cylinder pistons. It is direct-acting, with its input rod connected directly to the brake pedal, and is of the suspended-vacuum type. Because there is no throttling of the inlet manifold on a diesel engine, it is not a suitable source of vacuum for brake servo operation. Vacuum is therefore derived from a separate vacuum pump, driven by via a pushrod operated by an eccentric on the camshaft's left-hand end.

Pressure-control relief valves are fitted to the rear brakes, to prevent rear wheel lock-up under hard braking. The valves are sometimes referred to as pressure-conscious reducing valves. On non-ABS models, they are fitted in the master cylinder rear brake outlet ports; on models with ABS, they are located on the ABS hydraulic unit.

When rear disc brakes are fitted, the rear brake caliper is located on the front of the hub carrier on Saloon and Hatchback models, and on the rear of the hub carrier on Estate models.

The handbrake is cable-operated, and acts on the rear brakes. On rear drum brake models, the cables operate on the rear trailing brake shoe operating levers, while on rear disc brake models, they operate on levers on the rear calipers. The handbrake lever incorporates an automatic adjuster, which removes any slack from the cables when the lever is disengaged. Handbrake lever movement remains consistent at all times, and no adjustment is necessary or possible.

Where fitted, the anti-lock braking system (ABS) is of the four-channel low-pressure type. It uses the basic conventional brake system, together with an ABS hydraulic unit fitted between the master cylinder and the four wheel brakes. The hydraulic unit consists of a hydraulic actuator, an ABS brake pressure pump, an ABS module with built-in relay box, and two pressure-control relief valves. Braking at each of the four wheels is controlled by separate solenoid valves in the hydraulic actuator. If wheel lock-up is detected on a wheel when the vehicle speed is above 3 mph, the valve opens, releasing pressure to the relevant brake, until the wheel regains a rotational speed corresponding to the speed of the car. The cycle can be repeated many times a second. In the event of a fault in the ABS system, the conventional braking system is not affected. Diagnosis of a fault in the ABS system requires the use of special equipment, and this work should therefore be left to a Ford dealer. Diagnostic connectors are located on the side of the left-hand front suspension turret.

The traction control system is fitted as an option to some models, and uses the basic ABS system, with an additional pump and valves fitted to the hydraulic actuator. If wheelspin is detected at a speed below 30 mph, one of the valves opens, to allow the pump to pressurise the relevant brake, until the spinning wheel slows to a rotational speed corresponding to the speed of the car. This has the effect of transferring torque to the wheel with most traction. At the same time, the throttle lever is closed slightly, to reduce the torque from the engine. At speeds above 30 mph, the system operates by throttle lever adjustment only.

## Precautions

The car's braking system is one of its most important safety features. When working on the brakes, there are a number of points to be aware of, to ensure that your health (or even your life) is not being put at risk.

⚠️ *Warning: Brake fluid is poisonous. Take care to keep it off bare skin, and in particular not to get splashes in your eyes. The fluid also attacks paintwork and plastics – wash off spillages immediately with cold water. Finally, brake fluid is highly flammable, and should be handled with the same care as petrol.*

• *On models with ABS, make sure the ignition is off (take out the key) before disconnecting any braking system hydraulic union, and do not switch it on until after the hydraulic system has been bled. Failure to do this could lead to air entering the ABS hydraulic unit. If air enters the hydraulic unit pump, it will prove very difficult (in some cases impossible) to bleed the unit (see Section 15).*

• *When servicing any part of the system, work carefully and methodically – do not take short-cuts; also observe scrupulous cleanliness when overhauling any part of the hydraulic system.*

• *Always renew components in axle sets, where applicable – this means renewing brake pads, shoes, etc, on BOTH sides, even if only one set of pads is worn, or one wheel cylinder is leaking (for example). In the instance of uneven brake wear, the cause should be investigated and fixed (on disc brakes, sticking caliper pistons is a likely problem).*

• *Use only genuine Ford parts, or at least those of known good quality.*

• *Although genuine Ford brake pads and shoes are asbestos-free, the dust created by wear of non-genuine parts may contain asbestos, which is a health hazard. Never blow it out with compressed air, and don't inhale any of it.*

**2.2a  Disconnect the pad wear warning light wiring plug . . .**

**2.2b  . . . and detach the wiring plug from the clip on the caliper**

**2.3  Prising the pad retaining clip from the caliper – note the use of pliers**

• *DO NOT use petroleum-based solvents to clean brake parts; use brake cleaner or methylated spirit only.*
• *DO NOT allow any brake fluid, oil or grease to contact the brake pads or disc.*

## 2  Front brake pads – renewal

**Note:** *Refer to the precautions in Section 1 before proceeding.*

**1** Apply the handbrake. Loosen the front wheel nuts, then jack up the front of the car and support it on axle stands (see *Jacking and vehicle support*). Remove the front wheels. Work on one brake assembly at a time, using the assembled brake for reference if necessary.

**2** Disconnect the brake pad wear warning light wiring plug, and release the wiring from the clip on the brake caliper, noting its routing **(see illustrations)**. Only the inner pad is fitted with a wear warning light wire.

**3** Using a suitable screwdriver, prise the pad retaining clip from the caliper. Hold the clip with a pair of pliers as this is done, to avoid personal injury **(see illustration)**.

**4** Prise the plastic covers from the ends of the two guide pins, then using a 7 mm Allen key, unscrew the guide bolts securing the caliper to the carrier bracket **(see illustrations)**.

**5** Withdraw the caliper from the disc, and support it on an axle stand to avoid straining the hydraulic hose. The outer pad will normally remain in position against the disc, but the inner pad will stay attached to the piston in the caliper **(see illustration)**.

**6** Pull the inner pad from the piston in the caliper, then remove the outer pad from the carrier bracket, noting their fitted positions **(see illustrations)**.

> **HAYNES HiNT**
>
> *If the pads are wearing unevenly, the calipers are probably seized, which will also wear the discs prematurely. Just removing the pads and pushing the piston fully back into its bore (see paragraph 9) may unseize the piston enough to restore correct operation. If not, remove and overhaul the calipers as described in Section 3.*

**7** Brush all dust and dirt from the caliper, pads and disc, but do not inhale it, as it may be harmful to health. Scrape any corrosion from the edge of the disc, taking care not to damage the friction surface.

**8** Inspect the front brake disc for scoring and cracks. If a detailed inspection is necessary, refer to Section 4.

**9** The caliper piston must be pushed back into

**2.4a  Prise the plastic covers from the guide pins . . .**

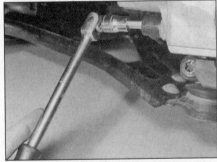

**2.4b  . . . using a 7 mm Allen key, unscrew . . .**

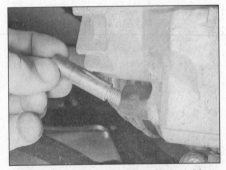

**2.4c  . . . and remove the caliper guide bolts**

**2.5  Withdrawing the caliper and inner pad**

**2.6a  Pull the inner pad out of the caliper piston . . .**

**2.6b  . . . then remove the outer pad from the carrier bracket**

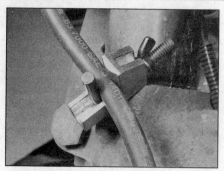

**3.2 Brake hose clamp fitted to the front flexible brake hose**

the caliper to make room for the new pads – this may require considerable effort. Either use a G-clamp, sliding-jaw (water pump) pliers, or suitable pieces of wood as levers.

*Caution: Pushing back the piston causes a reverse-flow of brake fluid, which has been known to 'flip' the master cylinder rubber seals, resulting in a total loss of braking. To avoid this, clamp the caliper flexible hose and open the bleed screw – as the piston is pushed back, the fluid can be directed into a suitable container using a hose attached to the bleed screw. Close the screw just before the piston is pushed fully back, to ensure no air enters the system.*

**10** If the recommended method of opening a bleed screw before pushing back the piston is not used, the fluid level in the reservoir will rise, and possibly overflow. Make sure that there is sufficient space in the brake fluid reservoir to accept the displaced fluid, and if necessary, syphon some off first. Any brake fluid spilt on paintwork should be washed off with clean water without delay – brake fluid is a highly-effective paint-stripper.

**11** Fit the new pads using a reversal of the removal procedure, but tighten the guide bolts to the torque wrench setting given in the Specifications at the beginning of this Chapter.

**12** On completion, firmly depress the brake pedal a few times, to bring the pads to their normal working position. Check the level of the brake fluid in the reservoir, and top-up if necessary.

**13** Give the car a short road test, to make sure that the brakes are functioning correctly,

**3.6 Removing the caliper carrier bracket**

and to bed-in the new pads to the contours of the disc. New pads will not provide maximum braking efficiency until they have bedded-in; avoid heavy braking as far as possible for the first hundred miles or so.

---

### 3  Front brake caliper –
removal, overhaul and refitting

**Note:** *Refer to the precautions in Section 1 before proceeding.*

#### Removal

**1** Apply the handbrake. Loosen the front wheel nuts, then jack up the front of the car and support it on axle stands (see *Jacking and vehicle support*). Remove the appropriate front wheel.

**2** Fit a brake hose clamp to the flexible hose leading to the caliper. This will minimise brake fluid loss during subsequent operations **(see illustration)**.

**3** Loosen the union on the caliper end of the flexible brake hose **(see illustration)**. Once loosened, do not try to unscrew the hose at this stage.

**4** Remove the brake pads as described in Section 2.

**5** Support the caliper in one hand, and prevent the hydraulic hose from turning with the other hand. Unscrew the caliper from the hose, making sure that the hose is not twisted unduly or strained. Once the caliper is detached, plug the open hydraulic unions in the caliper and hose, to keep out dust and dirt.

**6** If required, the caliper carrier bracket can be unbolted from the hub carrier **(see illustration)**.

#### Overhaul

**7** With the caliper on the bench, brush away all traces of dust and dirt, but take care not to inhale any dust, as it may be injurious to health.

**8** Pull the dust-excluding rubber seal from the end of the piston.

**9** Apply low air pressure to the fluid inlet union, and eject the piston. Only low air pressure is required for this, such as is produced by a foot-operated tyre pump.

*Caution: The piston may be ejected with some force. Position a thin piece of wood between the piston and the caliper body, to prevent damage to the end face of the piston, in the event of it being ejected suddenly.*

**10** Using a suitable blunt instrument (for instance a knitting needle or a crochet hook), prise the piston seal from the groove in the cylinder bore. Take care not to scratch the surface of the bore.

**11** Clean the piston and caliper body with methylated spirit, and allow to dry. Examine the surfaces of the piston and cylinder bore for wear, damage and corrosion. If the piston alone is unserviceable, a new piston must be

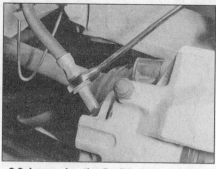

**3.3 Loosening the flexible brake hose at the caliper**

obtained, along with seals. If the cylinder bore is unserviceable, the complete caliper must be renewed. The seals must be renewed, regardless of the condition of the other components.

**12** Coat the piston and seals with clean brake fluid, then manipulate the piston seal into the groove in the cylinder bore.

**13** Push the piston squarely into its bore.

**14** Fit the dust-excluding rubber seal onto the piston and caliper, then depress the piston fully.

#### Refitting

**15** Refit the caliper, and where applicable the carrier bracket, by reversing the removal operations. Make sure that the flexible brake hose is not twisted. Tighten the mounting bolts and wheel nuts to the specified torque **(see illustration)**.

**16** Bleed the brake circuit according to the procedure given in Section 15, remembering to remove the brake hose clamp from the flexible hose. Make sure there are no leaks from the hose connections. Test the brakes carefully before returning the car to normal service.

---

### 4  Front brake disc –
inspection, removal and refitting

**Note:** *Refer to the precautions in Section 1 before proceeding.*

#### Inspection

**1** Apply the handbrake. Loosen the relevant wheel nuts, jack up the front of the car and

**3.15 Tightening the carrier bracket mounting bolts**

**4.4a Using a micrometer to measure the thickness of the front brake disc**

**4.4b Disc minimum thickness marking**

**4.5 Measuring the disc run-out with a dial gauge**

support it on axle stands. Remove the appropriate front wheel.

**2** Remove the front brake caliper and carrier bracket with reference to Section 3, but do not disconnect the flexible hose. Support the caliper on an axle stand, or suspend it out of the way with a piece of wire, taking care to avoid straining the flexible hose.

**3** Temporarily refit two of the wheel nuts to diagonally-opposite studs, with the flat sides of the nuts against the disc. Tighten the nuts progressively, to hold the disc firmly.

**4** Scrape any corrosion from the disc. Rotate the disc, and examine it for deep scoring, grooving or cracks. Using a micrometer, measure the thickness of the disc in several places. The minimum thickness is stamped on the disc hub **(see illustrations)**. Light wear and scoring is normal, but if excessive, the disc should be removed, and either reground by a specialist, or renewed. If regrinding is undertaken, the minimum thickness must be maintained. Obviously, if the disc is cracked, it must be renewed.

**5** Using a dial gauge or a flat metal block and feeler gauges, check that the disc run-out 10 mm from the outer edge does not exceed the limit given in the Specifications. To do this, fix the measuring equipment, and rotate the disc, noting the variation in measurement as the disc is rotated **(see illustration)**. The difference between the minimum and maximum measurements recorded is the disc run-out.

**6** If the run-out is greater than the specified amount, check for variations of the disc thickness as follows. Mark the disc at eight positions 45° apart, then using a micrometer, measure the disc thickness at the eight positions, 15 mm in from the outer edge. If the variation between the minimum and maximum readings is greater than the specified amount, the disc should be renewed.

**7** The hub face run-out can also be checked in a similar way. First remove the disc as described later in this Section, fix the measuring equipment, then slowly rotate the hub, and check that the run-out does not exceed the amount given in the Specifications. If the hub face run-out is excessive, this should be corrected (by renewing the hub bearings – see Chapter 10) before rechecking the disc run-out.

**4.10a Remove the special washers . . .**

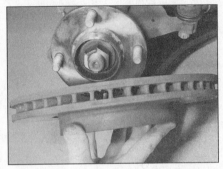

**4.10b . . . and withdraw the disc**

### Removal

**8** With the wheel and caliper removed, remove the wheel nuts which were temporarily refitted in paragraph 3.

**9** Mark the disc in relation to the hub, if it is to be refitted.

**10** Remove the two special washers (where fitted), and withdraw the disc over the wheel studs **(see illustrations)**.

### Refitting

**11** Make sure that the disc and hub mating surfaces are clean, then locate the disc on the wheel studs. Align the previously-made marks if the original disc is being refitted.

**12** Refit the two special washers, where fitted.

**13** Refit the brake caliper and carrier bracket with reference to Section 3.

**14** Refit the wheel, and lower the car to the ground. Tighten the wheel nuts to the specified torque.

**5.2a Releasing the automatic adjuster mechanism with a screwdriver through the backplate hole**

**15** Test the brakes carefully before returning the car to normal service.

---

## 5 Rear brake drum – removal, inspection and refitting

**Note:** *Refer to the precautions in Section 1 before proceeding.*

### Removal

**1** Chock the front wheels, release the handbrake and engage 1st gear. Loosen the relevant wheel nuts, jack up the rear of the car and support it on axle stands (see *Jacking and vehicle support*). Remove the appropriate rear wheel.

**2** Remove the two special clips (where fitted), and withdraw the brake drum over the wheel studs. If the drum will not pass over the shoes, it is possible to release the automatic adjuster mechanism by prising out the small rubber grommet near the centre of the backplate, and inserting a screwdriver through the small hole **(see illustrations)**. The self-adjusting ratchet can then be rotated, so that the brake shoes move to their lowest setting. Refit the rubber grommet before proceeding.

**3** With the brake drum removed, clean the dust from the drum, brake shoes, wheel cylinder and backplate, using brake cleaner or methylated spirit. Take care not to inhale the dust, as it may contain asbestos.

### Inspection

**4** Clean the inside surfaces of the brake

**5.2b Removing a rear brake drum**

drum, then examine the internal friction surface for signs of scoring or cracks. If it is cracked, deeply scored, or has worn to a diameter greater than the maximum given in the Specifications, then it should be renewed, together with the drum on the other side.

5 Regrinding of the brake drum is not recommended.

### Refitting

6 Locate the brake drum over the wheel studs, and (where fitted) refit the special clips. Make sure that the drum contacts the hub flange.

7 Refit the wheel, then check the remaining rear drum.

8 Lower the car to the ground, and tighten the wheel nuts to the specified torque. Depress the brake pedal several times, in order to operate the self-adjusting mechanism and set the shoes at their normal operating position.

**6.3b Removing the hold-down pins from the rear of the backplate**

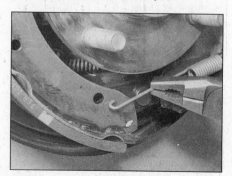

**6.5b . . . so that the lower return spring can be unhooked**

**6.2 Note the fitted position of all components**

9 Test the brakes carefully before returning the car to normal service.

## 6 Rear brake shoes – renewal

**Note:** *Refer to the precautions in Section 1 before proceeding.*

1 Remove the rear brake drums as described in Section 5. Work on one brake assembly at a time, using the assembled brake for reference if necessary.

2 Note the fitted position of the springs and the adjuster strut **(see illustration)**, then clean the components with brake cleaner, and allow to dry. Position a tray beneath the backplate, to catch the fluid and residue.

3 Remove the two shoe hold-down springs, using a pair of pliers to depress the upper ends

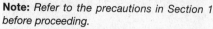

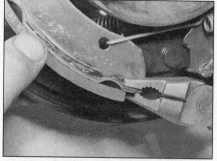

**6.4 Using pliers, pull the bottom end of the leading brake shoe from the bottom anchor**

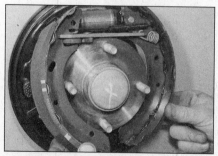

**6.6 Disconnect the shoes from the wheel cylinder, taking care not to damage the rubber boots**

**6.3a Using pliers to remove the two shoe hold-down springs**

so that they can be withdrawn downwards off the pins. Remove the hold-down pins from the backplate **(see illustrations)**.

4 Pull the bottom end of the leading (front) brake shoe from the bottom anchor (use pliers or an adjustable spanner over the edge of the shoe to lever it away) **(see illustration)**.

5 Release the trailing (rear) brake shoe from the anchor, then move the bottom ends of both shoes towards each other. Unhook the lower return spring from the shoes, noting the location holes **(see illustrations)**.

6 Move the bottom ends of the brake shoes together, and disconnect the top ends of the shoes from the wheel cylinder, taking care not to damage the rubber boots **(see illustration)**.

7 Unhook the upper return spring from the shoes, and withdraw the leading shoe from the backplate **(see illustrations)**.

8 To prevent the wheel cylinder pistons from

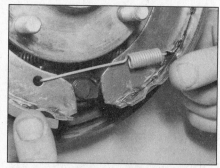

**6.5a Release the trailing brake shoe from the anchor, then move the shoes together . . .**

**6.7a Unhook the upper return spring . . .**

6.7b ... and withdraw the leading shoe

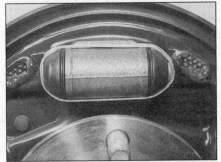

6.8 Elastic band fitted over the wheel cylinder, to prevent ejection of the pistons

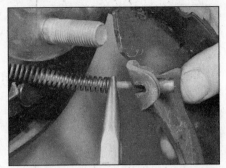

6.9 Using thin-nosed pliers, pull the handbrake cable spring and unhook the cable

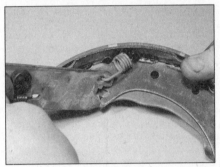

6.10a Unhook the automatic adjustment strut ...

6.10b ... and remove the small spring

6.12 Apply a little high melting-point brake grease to the brake shoe contact points

being accidentally ejected, fit a suitable elastic band or wire lengthways over the cylinder/pistons **(see illustration)**. Don't press the brake pedal while the shoes are removed.

**9** Pull the handbrake cable spring back from the operating lever on the rear of the trailing shoe **(see illustration)**. Unhook the cable end from the cut-out in the lever, and remove the shoe.

**10** Unhook the automatic adjustment strut from the trailing brake shoe, and remove the small spring **(see illustrations)**.

**11** If the wheel cylinder shows signs of fluid leakage, or if there is any reason to suspect it of being defective, inspect it now, as described in the next Section.

**12** Clean the backplate, and apply small amounts of high melting-point brake grease to the brake shoe contact points **(see illustration)**. Be careful not to get grease on any friction surfaces.

**13** Lubricate the sliding components of the automatic adjuster with a little high melting-point brake grease, but leave the serrations on the eccentric cam clean **(see illustration)**.

**14** Fit the new brake shoes using a reversal of the removal procedure, but set the eccentric cam at its lowest position before assembling it to the trailing shoe.

**15** Before refitting the brake drum, it should be checked as described in Section 5.

**16** With the drum in position, refit the wheel, then carry out the renewal procedure on the remaining rear brake.

**17** Lower the car to the ground, and tighten the wheel nuts to the specified torque.

**18** Depress the brake pedal several times, in order to operate the self-adjusting mechanism and set the shoes at their normal operating position.

**19** Make several forward and reverse stops, and operate the handbrake fully two or three times. Give the car a road test, to make sure that the brakes are functioning correctly, and to bed-in the new shoes to the contours of the drum. Remember that the new shoes will not give full braking efficiency until they have bedded-in.

**7 Rear wheel cylinder –**
removal, overhaul and refitting

**Note 1:** *Refer to the precautions in Section 1 before proceeding.*
**Note 2:** *If the brake shoes have been*

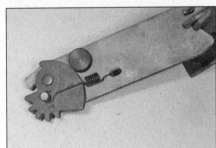

6.13 Lubricate the automatic adjuster, but leave the eccentric cam serrations shown here clean

*contaminated by fluid leaking from the wheel cylinder, they must be renewed. The shoes on BOTH sides of the car must be renewed, even if they are only contaminated on one side. The wheel cylinders fitted to Estate models are of larger diameter than those fitted to the Saloon and Hatchback. Be sure to order the correct parts, and be sure that the same size of wheel cylinder is fitted to both sides, or uneven braking could result.*

**Removal**

**1** Remove the brake drum as described in Section 5.

**2** Minimise fluid loss either by removing the master cylinder reservoir cap, and then tightening it down onto a piece of polythene to obtain an airtight seal, or by using a brake hose clamp, a G-clamp, or similar tool, to clamp the flexible hose at the nearest convenient point to the wheel cylinder.

**3** Pull the brake shoes apart at their top ends, so that they are just clear of the wheel cylinder. The automatic adjuster will hold the shoes in this position, so that the cylinder can be withdrawn.

**4** Wipe away all traces of dirt around the hydraulic union at the rear of the wheel cylinder, then undo the union nut.

**5** Unscrew the two bolts securing the wheel cylinder to the backplate **(see illustration)**.

**6** Withdraw the wheel cylinder from the backplate so that it is clear of the brake shoes. Plug the open hydraulic unions, to prevent the entry of dirt, and to minimise further fluid loss whilst the cylinder is detached.

**7.5 Wheel cylinder-to-backplate bolts (arrowed) – brake union nut and bleed screw cap also visible**

### Overhaul

**7** Clean the external surfaces of the cylinder, and unscrew the bleed screw.

**8** Carefully prise off the dust cover from each end of the cylinder.

**9** Tap the wheel cylinder on a block of wood to eject the pistons and seals, keeping them identified for location. Finally remove the spring.

**10** Clean the pistons and the cylinder by washing in methylated spirit or fresh hydraulic fluid. Do not use petrol, paraffin or any other mineral-based fluid. Remove and discard the old seals, noting which way round they are fitted.

**11** Examine the surfaces of the pistons and the cylinder bores, and look for any signs of rust or scoring. If such damage is evident, the complete wheel cylinder must be renewed.

**12** Reassemble by lubricating the first piston in clean hydraulic fluid, then manipulating a new seal into position, so that its raised lip

faces away from the brake shoe bearing face of the piston.

**13** Insert the piston into the cylinder. As the seal enters the bore, twist the piston back-and-forth so that the seal lip is not trapped.

**14** Insert the spring, then refit the remaining piston and seal, again making sure that the seal lip is not trapped as it enters the bore.

**15** Fit new dust covers to the grooves in the pistons and wheel cylinder body.

**16** Refit the bleed screw.

### Refitting

**17** Wipe clean the backplate and remove the plug from the end of the hydraulic pipe. Fit the cylinder onto the backplate and screw in the hydraulic union nut by hand, being careful not to cross-thread it.

**18** Tighten the mounting bolts, then fully tighten the hydraulic union nut.

**19** Retract the automatic brake adjuster mechanism, so that the brake shoes engage with the pistons of the wheel cylinder. To do this, prise the shoes apart slightly, turn the automatic adjuster to its minimum position, and release the shoes.

**20** Remove the clamp from the flexible brake hose, or the polythene from the master cylinder (as applicable).

**21** Refit the brake drum with reference to Section 5.

**22** Bleed the brake hydraulic system as described in Section 15. Providing suitable precautions were taken to minimise loss of fluid, it should only be necessary to bleed the relevant rear brake.

**23** Test the brakes carefully before returning the car to normal service.

## 8 Rear brake pads – renewal

**Note:** *Refer to the precautions in Section 1 before proceeding.*

**1** Chock the front wheels, and engage 1st gear. Loosen the rear wheel nuts, then jack up the rear of the car and support it on axle stands (see *Jacking and vehicle support*). Remove the rear wheels, and release the handbrake.

**2** Work on one brake assembly at a time, using the assembled brake for reference if necessary.

**3** Disconnect the brake pad wear warning light wiring plug, and release the wiring from the clip on the brake caliper, noting its routing **(see illustrations)**. Only the inner pad is fitted with a wear warning light wire.

**4** On Estate models only, to enable the caliper to pivot rearwards to allow pad removal, the handbrake cable must be disconnected from the caliper. Using pliers, compress the tangs on the cable outer retaining clip, and release the cable outer from the caliper bracket. Ensure that the handbrake is released, then swivel the caliper handbrake arm to obtain some slack in the cable, and use a pair of pliers to pull out and disconnect the cable inner from the arm **(see illustrations)**. Once the cable has been disconnected, don't operate the handbrake arm excessively, as this will make refitting the cable more difficult.

**8.3a Disconnect the pad wear warning light wiring plug . . .**

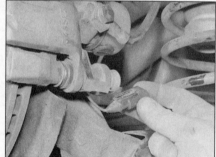

**8.3b . . . and detach the wiring plug from the clip on the caliper**

**8.4a Compress the retaining clip tangs to release the cable outer . . .**

**8.4b . . . then disconnect the cable inner end fitting from the handbrake arm**

**8.5a Extract the spring clip . . .**

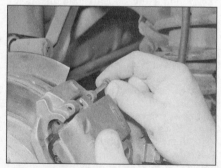

**8.5b . . . and withdraw the caliper retaining pin**

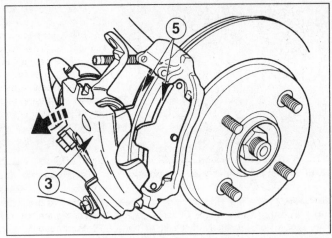

**8.6a  Rear brake pad removal –
Saloon/Hatchback models**

*4  Brake caliper*      *5  Brake pads*

**8.6b  Rear brake pad removal –
Estate models**

*3  Brake caliper*      *5  Brake pads*

**5** Extract the spring clip, and pull out the retaining pin securing the caliper to the carrier bracket **(see illustrations)**. Note that on Saloon and Hatchback models, the pin is at the bottom of the caliper, whereas on Estate models, it is at the top.

**6** Swivel the caliper away from the carrier bracket, to expose the brake pads **(see illustrations)**.

**7** On Saloon and Hatchback models, unbolt the brake hose bracket from the rear suspension strut, to avoid straining the flexible hose.

**8** On Estate models, the flexible hose cannot be readily detached to avoid straining it. To relieve the strain on the hose, place a jack below the suspension arm, and carefully compress the suspension a little.

**9** If necessary, the caliper may be completely removed by prising off the cap and unscrewing the pivot guide bolt. Support the caliper on an axle stand, or tie it to one side with wire. Do not allow it to hang down unsupported, as this will strain the brake hose.

**10** Remove the pads from the carrier bracket, noting their fitted positions (the inner pad is fitted with the wear warning light wire). Brush all dust and dirt from the caliper, pads and disc, but do not inhale it, as it may be harmful to health. Scrape any corrosion from the edge of the disc.

**11** Inspect the rear brake disc as described in Section 10.

**12** It will be necessary to retract the piston fully into the caliper bore, by rotating it in a clockwise direction. This can be achieved using sturdy circlip pliers, but note that as well as being turned, the piston has to be pressed in very firmly. Special tools are available from companies such as Draper to achieve this with less effort **(see illustration)**.

*Caution: Pushing back the piston causes a reverse-flow of brake fluid, which has been known to 'flip' the master cylinder rubber seals, resulting in a total loss of braking. To*

*avoid this, clamp the caliper flexible hose and open the bleed screw – as the piston is pushed back, the fluid can be directed into a suitable container using a hose attached to the bleed screw. Close the screw just before the piston is pushed fully back, to ensure no air enters the system.*

**13** If the recommended method of opening a bleed screw before pushing back the piston is not used, the fluid level in the reservoir will rise, and possibly overflow. Make sure that there is sufficient space in the brake fluid reservoir to accept the displaced fluid, and if necessary, syphon some off first. Any brake

fluid spilt on paintwork should be washed off with clean water, without delay – brake fluid is also a highly-effective paint-stripper.

**14** The caliper piston must be rotated so that one of the cut-outs is positioned to engage with the lug on the back of the inner pad, with the piston's round orientation drilling uppermost **(see illustration)**.

**15** Fit the new pads, noting that the inner pad has the wear warning light wire. Apply a little copper-based brake grease to the contact areas on the pad backing plates, taking care not to get any on the friction material **(see illustrations)**.

**8.12  Using a proprietary tool to screw the caliper piston back into the caliper**

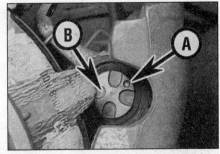

**8.14  Set piston drilling (A) uppermost, so one of the cut-outs (B) will engage the lug on the back of the inner pad**

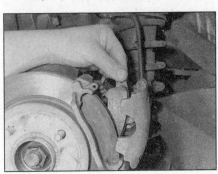

**8.15a  Fit the inner pad . . .**

**8.15b  . . . and the outer pad – note the brake grease applied to the backing plate**

**8.16 Swivel the caliper back into position**

**9.2 Fit a brake hose clamp to the rear brake hose**

**9.3 Loosen the union bolt on the caliper end of the brake hose**

16 Swivel the caliper back into position **(see illustration)**, engaging the piston cut-out with the lug on the back of the inner pad, and secure with the retaining pin and spring clip. Do not depress the brake pedal until the handbrake cable has been reconnected, since the extra pad-to-disc clearance makes reconnecting the cable easier.

17 Reconnect the cable to the caliper operating arm, noting the points made in Section 27.

18 Refit the brake hose bracket, or lower the jack under the suspension arm, as applicable.

19 Reconnect the brake pad wear warning light connector plug, and clip the plug onto the caliper. The wiring should not be under any strain – check the wire routing on the other rear brake if in doubt.

20 Firmly depress the brake pedal a few times, to bring the pads to their normal working position. Check the level of the brake fluid in the reservoir, and top-up if necessary.

21 Give the car a road test, to make sure that the brakes are functioning correctly, and to bed-in the new pads to the contours of the disc. Remember that full braking efficiency will not be obtained until the new pads have bedded-in.

**9 Rear brake caliper –** removal, overhaul and refitting

**Note:** *Refer to the precautions in Section 1 before proceeding.*

### Removal

1 Chock the front wheels, and engage 1st gear. Loosen the rear wheel nuts, then jack up the rear of the car and support it on axle stands (see *Jacking and vehicle support*). Remove the appropriate rear wheel.

2 Fit a brake hose clamp to the flexible hose leading to the caliper **(see illustration)**. This will minimise brake fluid loss during subsequent operations.

3 Loosen (but do not completely unscrew) the union on the caliper end of the flexible hose **(see illustration)**.

4 Remove the brake pads as described in Section 8.

5 On Saloon and Hatchback models, disconnect the handbrake cable from the caliper as described in Section 8, paragraph 4. On Saloon and Hatchback models, the handbrake lever faces away from the caliper, unlike Estate models where it faces towards the caliper **(see illustrations)**.

6 Prise off the cap, then unscrew the pivot guide bolt. Remove the caliper, and support it on an axle stand, or tie it to one side with wire **(see illustrations)**. Do not allow it to hang down unsupported, as this will strain the brake hose.

7 Unscrew the caliper from the hydraulic hose, making sure that the hose is not twisted or strained unduly. Plug the open hydraulic unions to keep dust and dirt out.

8 If necessary, unbolt the carrier bracket from the hub carrier.

### Overhaul

9 No overhaul procedures were available at the time of writing, so check availability of

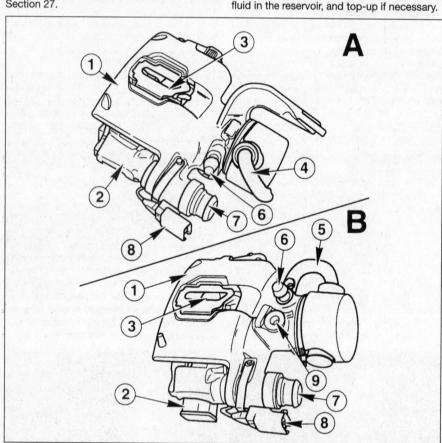

**9.5a Rear brake caliper –
Saloon/Hatchback models (A), Estate models (B)**

1 Caliper body
2 Frame
3 Brake pad spring clip
4 Handbrake cable lever facing away from caliper
5 Handbrake cable lever facing towards caliper
6 Bleed screw
7 Guide pin protective cap
8 Pad wear warning light connector
9 Flexible hydraulic hose connection

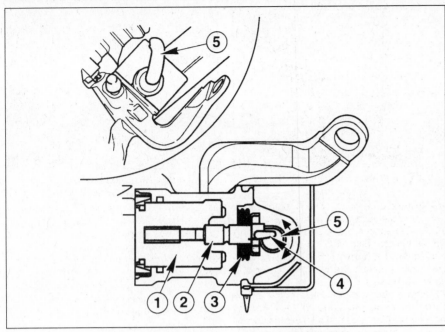

**9.5b Handbrake operation on the rear brake caliper**

1 Piston
2 Automatic adjusting screw
3 Spring washers
4 Cam
5 Handbrake cable lever

spares before dismantling the caliper. In principle, the overhaul information given for the front brake caliper will apply, noting that it will be necessary to unscrew the piston from the handbrake mechanism (see Section 8) before being able to expel the piston from the caliper. On reassembly, push the piston fully into the caliper, and screw it back onto the handbrake mechanism. Do not attempt to dismantle the handbrake mechanism; if the mechanism is faulty, the complete caliper assembly must be renewed.

**9.6a Prise off the bolt cap . . .**

**9.6b . . . unscrew and remove the guide bolt . . .**

**9.6c . . . and remove the caliper**

**11.2 Brake fluid reservoir and low level warning light multi-plug**

### Refitting

**10** Refit the caliper, and where applicable the carrier bracket, by reversing the removal operations. Refer to the points made in Section 27 when reconnecting the handbrake cable. Tighten the mounting bolts and wheel nuts to the specified torque, and do not forget to remove the brake hose clamp from the flexible brake hose.

**11** Bleed the brake circuit according to the procedure given in Section 15. Make sure there are no leaks from the hose connections. Test the brakes carefully before returning the car to normal service.

## 10 Rear brake disc – inspection, removal and refitting

Refer to Section 4. Once the rear caliper is removed (Section 9), the procedure is the same.

## 11 Master cylinder – removal and refitting

**Note:** Refer to the precautions in Section 1 before proceeding.

### Removal

**1** Exhaust the vacuum in the servo by pressing the brake pedal a few times, with the engine switched off.

**2** Disconnect the low fluid level warning light multi-plug from the fluid reservoir **(see illustration)**. Unscrew the cap.

**3** Draw off the hydraulic fluid from the reservoir, using an old battery hydrometer or a poultry baster.

**4** On models with a hydraulically-operated clutch, release the hose clip and disconnect the fluid supply hose from the rear of the brake fluid reservoir **(see illustration)**. Keeping the hose end uppermost, plug or cap the hose, to prevent fluid loss or dirt entry.

**5** Identify the locations of each brake pipe on the master cylinder. On non-ABS models, there are four pipes; the two rear brake pipes are attached to pressure-control relief valves on the master cylinder. On ABS models, there

**11.4 Disconnecting the clutch fluid supply hose from the rear of the fluid reservoir**

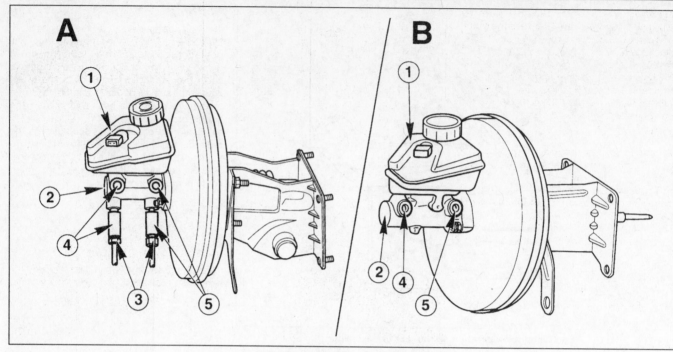

**11.5 Master cylinder connections -
non-ABS models (A), and models with ABS (B)**

1  Brake fluid reservoir
2  Master cylinder

3  Pressure-control relief valves
   for rear brakes

4  Primary brake hydraulic
   circuit (front right/rear left)

5  Secondary brake hydraulic
   circuit (front left/rear right)

are only two pipes, which lead to the ABS hydraulic unit **(see illustration)**.

**6** Place rags beneath the master cylinder to catch spilt hydraulic fluid.

**7** Clean around the hydraulic union nuts. Unscrew the nuts, and disconnect the hydraulic lines from the master cylinder.

**8** Unscrew the mounting nuts, and withdraw the master cylinder from the studs on the front of the servo unit. If the nuts are tight, a split ring spanner should be used in preference to an open-ended spanner. Plug or cap open unions, to keep dust and dirt out.

**9** Recover the gasket from the master cylinder.

**10** If the master cylinder is faulty, it must be renewed. At the time of writing, no overhaul kits were available.

### Refitting

**11** Clean the contact surfaces of the master

cylinder and servo, and locate a new gasket on the master cylinder.

**12** Position the master cylinder on the studs on the servo unit. Refit and tighten the nuts to the specified torque.

**13** Carefully insert the hydraulic lines in the apertures in the master cylinder, then tighten the union nuts. Make sure that the nuts enter their threads correctly.

**14** Where applicable, reconnect the clutch fluid supply hose, then fill the reservoir with fresh brake fluid.

**15** Bleed the brake hydraulic system as described in Section 15, and where applicable, the clutch hydraulic system as described in Chapter 6.

**16** Refit the reservoir filler cap, and reconnect the multi-plug for the low fluid level warning light.

**17** Test the brakes carefully before returning the car to normal service.

## 12 Brake pedal –
removal and refitting

### Removal

**1** Working inside the car, move the driver's seat fully to the rear, to allow maximum working area.

**2** Undo the screws and remove the facia lower panel.

**3** Prise the hairpin clip from the right-hand end of the pedal pivot shaft **(see illustration)** and remove the washer.

**4** Unscrew the nut securing the pedal trunnion to the pushrod. The nut is located near the top of the pedal **(see illustrations)**.

**5** Press the pedal pivot shaft to the left, through the mounting bracket, just far enough

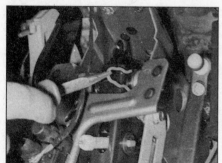

**12.3  Removing the hairpin clip from the right-hand end of the brake pedal pivot shaft**

**12.4a  Unscrew the nut securing the pedal trunnion to the pushrod . . .**

**12.4b  . . . and remove the tube from the pushrod**

to allow the pedal to be withdrawn – leave the blue nylon spacer (located between the clutch and brake pedals) on the pivot shaft (see illustration).

6 With the pedal removed, prise out the bushes from each side. If necessary, also remove the pushrod trunnion and the rubber pad (see illustrations). Renew the components as necessary.

## Refitting

7 Prior to refitting the pedal, apply a little grease to the pivot shaft, pedal bushes and trunnion.

8 Refitting is a reversal of the removal procedure, but make sure that the pedal bushes are correctly located, and that the pedal shaft D-section locates in the right-hand side of the pedal bracket. Also make sure that the hairpin clip is correctly located.

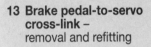

## 13 Brake pedal-to-servo cross-link –
removal and refitting

## Removal

1 Disconnect the battery negative (earth) lead (Chapter 5, Section 1).

2 Remove the master cylinder and the vacuum servo unit as described in Sections 11 and 16. If preferred, the master cylinder may be left attached to the servo unit.

3 Working inside the passenger compartment, fold down the covering from the front of both front footwells.

4 Have an assistant support the cross-link assembly from inside the engine compartment.

5 Unscrew the nuts and bolts on each side of the bulkhead and remove the link assembly from inside the engine compartment. If necessary, have the assistant hold the bolt heads from inside the engine compartment while the nuts are being loosened.

6 Clean the cross-link components, and examine the bushes for wear. Renew the bushes if necessary.

## Refitting

7 Refitting is a reversal of the removal procedure. Refer to Sections 11 and 16 when refitting the master cylinder and vacuum servo unit.

## 14 Hydraulic pipes and hoses –
inspection, removal and refitting

Note: Refer to the precautions in Section 1 before proceeding.

## Inspection

1 Jack up the front and rear of the car, and support on axle stands (see Jacking and vehicle support).

2 Check for signs of leakage at the pipe

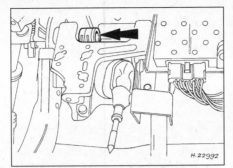

**12.5  Leave the nylon spacer (arrowed) in position on the pivot shaft**

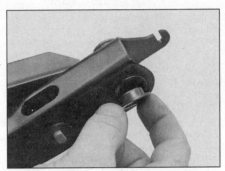

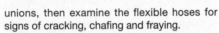

**12.6b  . . . from each side of the pedal . . .**

unions, then examine the flexible hoses for signs of cracking, chafing and fraying.

3 The brake pipes should be examined carefully for signs of dents, corrosion or other damage. Corrosion should be scraped off, and if the depth of pitting is significant, the pipes renewed. This is particularly likely in those areas underneath the car body where the pipes are exposed and unprotected.

4 Renew any defective brake pipes and/or hoses.

## Removal

5 If a section of pipe or hose is to be removed, loss of brake fluid can be reduced by unscrewing the filler cap, and completely sealing the top of the reservoir with cling film or adhesive tape. Alternatively, the reservoir can be emptied (see Section 11).

6 To remove a section of pipe, hold the adjoining hose union nut with a spanner to

**14.6a  Unscrewing a brake pipe union nut using a split ring spanner**

**12.6a  Prise out the bushes . . .**

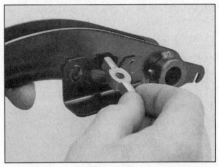

**12.6c  . . . and remove the pushrod trunnion**

prevent it from turning, then unscrew the union nut at the end of the pipe, and release it. Repeat the procedure at the other end of the pipe, then release the pipe by pulling out the clips attaching it to the body (see illustrations). Note that these clips are easily broken – treat them with care.

7 Where the union nuts are exposed to the full force of the weather, they can sometimes be quite tight. If an open-ended spanner is used, burring of the flats on the nuts is not uncommon, and for this reason, it is preferable to use a split ring (brake) spanner, which will engage all the flats. If such a spanner is not available, self-locking grips may be used as a last resort; these may well damage the nuts, but if the pipe is to be renewed, this does not matter.

8 To further minimise the loss of fluid when disconnecting a flexible brake line from a rigid pipe, clamp the hose as near as possible to

**14.6b  Pulling out a brake pipe mounting clip**

the pipe to be detached, using a brake hose clamp or a pair of self-locking grips with protected jaws.

**9** To remove a flexible hose, first clean the ends of the hose and the surrounding area, then unscrew the union nuts from the hose ends. Recover the spring clip, and withdraw the hose from the serrated mounting in the support bracket. Where applicable, unscrew the hose from the caliper.

**10** Brake pipes supplied with flared ends and union nuts can be obtained individually or in sets from Ford dealers or accessory shops. The pipe is then bent to shape, using the old pipe as a guide, and is ready for fitting. Be careful not to kink or crimp the pipe when bending it; ideally, a proper pipe-bending tool should be used.

### Refitting

**11** Refitting of the pipes and hoses is a reversal of removal. Make sure that all brake pipes are securely supported in their clips, and ensure that the hoses are not kinked. Check also that the hoses are clear of all suspension components and underbody fittings, and will remain clear during movement of the suspension and steering.

**12** On completion, bleed the brake hydraulic system as described in Section 15, and where applicable, the clutch hydraulic system as described in Chapter 6.

### 15  Hydraulic system – bleeding

*Note: Refer to the precautions in Section 1 before proceeding.*

**1** If the master cylinder has been disconnected and reconnected, then the complete system (both circuits) must be bled of air. If a component of one circuit has been disturbed, then only that particular circuit need be bled.

**2** Bleeding should commence on one front brake, followed by the diagonally-opposite rear brake. The remaining front brake should then be bled, followed by its diagonally-opposite rear brake.

**3** There is a variety of do-it-yourself 'one-man' brake bleeding kits available from motor accessory shops, and it is recommended that one of these kits be used wherever possible, as they greatly simplify the brake bleeding operation. Follow the kit manufacturer's instructions in conjunction with the following procedure. If a pressure-bleeding kit is obtained, then it will not be necessary to depress the brake pedal in the following procedure.

**4** During the bleeding operation, do not allow the brake fluid level in the reservoir to drop below the minimum mark. If the level is allowed to fall so far that air is drawn in, the whole procedure will have to be started again from scratch. Only use new fluid for topping-up, preferably from a freshly-opened container. Never re-use fluid bled from the system.

**5** Before starting, check that all rigid pipes and flexible hoses are in good condition, and that all hydraulic unions are tight. Take great care not to allow hydraulic fluid to come into contact with the paintwork, otherwise the finish will be seriously damaged. Wash off any spilt fluid immediately with cold water.

**6** If a brake bleeding kit is not being used, gather together a clean jar, a length of plastic or rubber tubing which is a tight fit over the bleed screw, and a new container of the specified brake fluid (see *Lubricants and fluids*). The help of an assistant will also be required.

**7** Clean the area around the bleed screw on the front brake unit to be bled (it is important that no dirt be allowed to enter the hydraulic system), and remove the dust cap. Connect one end of the tubing to the bleed screw, and immerse the other end in the jar, which should be filled with sufficient brake fluid to keep the end of the tube submerged **(see illustrations)**.

**8** Open the bleed screw by one or two turns, and have the assistant depress the brake pedal to the floor. Tighten the bleed screw at the end of the downstroke, then have the assistant release the pedal. Continue this procedure until clean brake fluid, free from air bubbles, can be seen flowing into the jar. Finally tighten the bleed screw with the pedal in the fully-depressed position.

**9** Remove the tube, and refit the dust cap. Top-up the master cylinder reservoir if necessary, then repeat the procedure on the diagonally-opposite rear brake.

**10** Repeat the procedure on the remaining circuit, starting with the front brake, and followed by the diagonally-opposite rear brake.

**11** Check the feel of the brake pedal – it should be firm. If it is spongy, there is still some air in the system, and the bleeding procedure should be repeated.

**12** When bleeding is complete, top-up the master cylinder reservoir and refit the cap.

**13** On models with a hydraulically-operated clutch, check the clutch operation on completion; it may be necessary to bleed the clutch hydraulic system as described in Chapter 6.

### 16  Vacuum servo unit – testing, removal and refitting

### Testing

**1** To test the operation of the servo unit, depress the footbrake four or five times to dissipate the vacuum, then start the engine while keeping the footbrake depressed. As the engine starts, there should be a noticeable 'give' in the brake pedal as vacuum builds-up. Allow the engine to run for at least two minutes, and then switch it off. If the brake pedal is now depressed again, it should be possible to hear a hiss from the servo when the pedal is depressed. After four or five applications, no further hissing should be heard, and the pedal should feel harder.

**2** Before assuming that a problem exists in the servo unit itself, inspect the non-return valve as described in the next Section.

### Removal

**3** Refer to Section 11 and remove the master cylinder.

**4** Remove the air cleaner assembly as described in Chapter 4A.

**5** Unbolt the air conditioning refrigerant pipe brackets in the vicinity of the servo unit, and move the brackets aside.

**6** Disconnect the vacuum hose adaptor at the servo unit by pulling it free from the rubber grommet. If it is reluctant to move, prise it free, using a screwdriver with its blade inserted under the flange.

**7** Inside the passenger compartment, remove the driver's side facia lower panel for access to the brake pedal.

**8** Unscrew the nut securing the pedal trunnion to the servo unit pushrod. The nut is located near the top of the pedal, and is accessible through an access hole.

**9** Again inside the passenger compartment, remove the four servo unit mounting bracket nuts above the pedals.

**10** Unscrew the four nuts securing the servo unit to the mounting brackets on the bulkhead in the engine compartment **(see illustration)**.

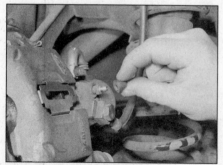

**15.7a  Remove the bleed screw dust cap . . .**

**15.7b  . . . and connect up the bleeding equipment**

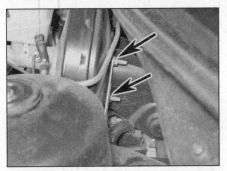

**16.10 Two of the servo unit mounting nuts**

**11** Remove the servo unit mounting bracket from inside the engine compartment.
**12** Withdraw the servo unit from the bulkhead, and remove it from the engine compartment, taking care not to damage the bulkhead rubber grommet as the pushrod passes through it.
**13** Note that the servo unit cannot be dismantled for repair or overhaul and, if faulty, must be renewed.

### Refitting

**14** Refitting is a reversal of the removal procedure. Refer to Section 11 for details of refitting the master cylinder.

## 17 Vacuum servo unit vacuum hose and non-return valve – removal, testing and refitting

### Removal

**1** With the engine switched off, depress the brake pedal four or five times, to dissipate any remaining vacuum from the servo unit.
**2** Disconnect the vacuum hose adapter at the servo unit, by pulling it free from the rubber grommet **(see illustration)**. If it is reluctant to

move, prise it free, using a screwdriver with its blade inserted under the flange.
**3** Unscrew the union nut and disconnect the vacuum line from the top of the pump.
**4** If the hose or the fixings are damaged or in poor condition, they must be renewed.

### Testing

**5** Examine the non-return valve for damage and signs of deterioration, and renew it if necessary. The valve may be tested by blowing through its connecting hoses in both directions. It should only be possible to blow from the servo end towards the inlet manifold.

### Refitting

**6** Refitting is a reversal of the removal procedure. If fitting a new non-return valve, ensure that it is fitted the correct way round. Tighten the vacuum line union nut at the pump to the specified torque.

## 18 Pressure-control relief valve (non-ABS models) – removal and refitting

**Note:** *Refer to the precautions in Section 1 before proceeding.*

### Removal

**1** On non-ABS models up to October 1996, the two pressure-control relief valves are located on the master cylinder outlets to the rear brake circuits. Later non-ABS models have the valves incorporated further down the rear brake circuits.
**2** Unscrew the fluid reservoir filler cap, and draw off the fluid – see Section 11.
**3** Position some rags beneath the master cylinder, to catch any spilled fluid.
**4** Clean around the valve to be removed. Hold the valve stationary with one spanner, and unscrew the hydraulic pipe union nut with

**17.2 Removing the plastic adapter from the servo unit**

another spanner. Pull out the pipe, and bend it slightly away from the valve.
**5** Unscrew the valve from the master cylinder.
**6** On models up to October 1996, note that the primary and secondary (front and rear locations on the master cylinder) valves have different thread diameters, to prevent incorrect fitment **(see illustration)**.

### Refitting

**7** Refitting is a reversal of the removal procedure. On completion, bleed the hydraulic system as described in Section 15.

## 19 Pressure-control relief valve (early ABS models) – removal and refitting

**Note 1:** *Refer to the precautions in Section 1 before proceeding.*
**Note 2:** *The valves are only removable on models with the early Mecatronic ABS system (see Section 20). On other ABS systems, the function of the valves is built into the unit itself.*

### Removal

**1** The pressure-control relief valves are located on the ABS hydraulic unit **(see illustration)**.

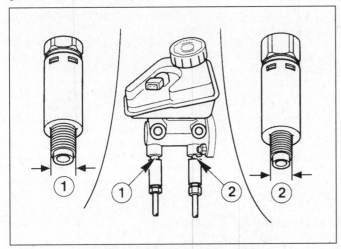

**18.6 Pressure-control relief valve locations – on master cylinder (early models)**

1  *Primary (front) valve (12 mm) – rear left circuit*
2  *Secondary (rear) valve (10 mm) – rear right circuit*

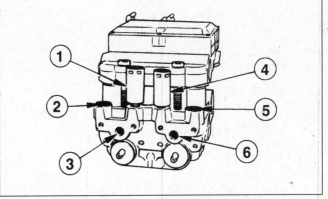

**19.1 Pressure-control relief valve locations – on ABS hydraulic unit**

1  *Pressure-control relief valve, rear right brake circuit*
2  *Outlet, front left brake circuit*
3  *Inlet, from brake master cylinder secondary circuit*
4  *Pressure-control relief valve, rear left brake circuit*
5  *Outlet, front right brake circuit*
6  *Inlet, from brake master cylinder primary circuit*

**2** Disconnect the battery negative (earth) lead (see Chapter 5, Section 1).
**3** Remove the air cleaner assembly as described in Chapter 4A.
**4** Disconnect the low fluid level warning multi-plug from the brake fluid reservoir. Where applicable, detach the clutch fluid supply hose from its bracket, and move it aside, if possible without disconnecting the hose.
**5** Unscrew the brake fluid reservoir filler cap, and completely seal the top of the reservoir using cling film or adhesive tape. This will reduce loss of fluid when the valve is removed.
**6** Unscrew the master cylinder mounting nuts, and carefully withdraw the cylinder from the servo unit, leaving the brake pipes still connected to it. Move the master cylinder over to the left-hand side of the engine compartment, to rest against the left-hand suspension turret.
**7** Unscrew the servo unit mounting nuts, and move the unit away from the bulkhead.
**8** Position some rags beneath the ABS hydraulic unit, to catch spilled fluid.
**9** Clean around the valve to be removed. Hold the valve stationary with one spanner, and unscrew the hydraulic pipe union nut with another spanner. Pull out the pipe, and bend it slightly away from the valve.
**10** Unscrew the valve from the ABS hydraulic unit.

### Refitting

**11** Refitting is a reversal of the removal procedure. On completion, bleed the hydraulic system as described in Section 15.

---

## 20 ABS hydraulic unit – removal and refitting

**Note:** *If any part of the ABS hydraulic unit is defective, it must be renewed as an assembly. Apart from the relay box (Section 22), individual spare parts are not available.*
**1** Models up to December 1997 are equipped with one of two 'generations' of Mecatronic ABS system, while models after this date have a Bosch 5.3 system. It is unclear at the time of writing at what point the changeover was made from the early to the later type of Mecatronic system. Removal and refitting procedures for all units are broadly similar, at least in terms of the preliminary dismantling required. Refer to the relevant sub-section below.

### Removal

#### Early Mecatronic system

**2** Remove both pressure-control relief valves as described in Section 19.
**3** Unscrew the nut securing the pedal trunnion to the servo unit pushrod inside the passenger compartment. The nut is located near the top of the pedal, and is accessible through an access hole. For improved access, remove

the facia lower panel first (see Chapter 11, Section 29).
**4** Remove the vacuum servo unit, together with the pushrod, from the engine compartment. Take care not to damage the rubber grommet in the bulkhead.
**5** Identify the location of the remaining brake hydraulic pipes on the ABS hydraulic unit, then unscrew the union nuts and pull out the pipes. Carefully bend the pipes away from the hydraulic unit, to allow the unit to be removed.
**6** Disconnect the multi-plugs from the hydraulic unit. To disconnect the main 22-pin multi-plug, push the locktab, then swivel the multi-plug outwards and unhook it.
**7** Unscrew the pump mounting nut, and the unit retaining nuts, as applicable.
**8** Raise the left-hand side of the ABS hydraulic unit, then swivel the unit out of the right-hand mounting. Take care not to lose the bracket studs and insulator ring.

#### Later Mecatronic system

**9** Disconnect the battery negative (earth) lead (see Chapter 5, Section 1).
**10** Remove the air cleaner assembly as described in Chapter 4A.
**11** Disconnect the low fluid level warning multi-plug from the brake fluid reservoir. Detach the clutch fluid supply hose from its bracket, and move it aside, if possible without disconnecting the hose.
**12** Unscrew the brake fluid reservoir filler cap, and completely seal the top of the reservoir using cling film or adhesive tape. This will reduce loss of fluid when the hydraulic pipes are disconnected.
**13** Unscrew the master cylinder mounting nuts, and carefully withdraw the cylinder from the servo unit, leaving the brake pipes still connected to it. Move the master cylinder over to the left-hand side of the engine compartment, to rest against the left-hand suspension turret.
**14** Unscrew the servo unit mounting nuts, and move the unit away from the bulkhead.
**15** Unscrew the nut securing the pedal trunnion to the servo unit pushrod inside the passenger compartment. The nut is located near the top of the pedal, and is accessible through an access hole. For improved access, remove the facia lower panel first, disconnecting the diagnostic plug from the panel as it is removed.
**16** Remove the vacuum servo unit, together with the pushrod, from the engine compartment. Take care not to damage the rubber grommet in the bulkhead.
**17** Disconnect the multi-plug from the hydraulic unit.
**18** Position some rags beneath the ABS hydraulic unit, to catch spilled fluid.
**19** Identify the location of the brake hydraulic pipes on the ABS hydraulic unit, then unscrew the union nuts and pull out the pipes. Carefully bend the pipes away from the hydraulic unit, to allow the unit to be removed.

**20** Unscrew the four mounting bracket bolts and remove the hydraulic unit, complete with brackets, from the engine compartment.

#### Bosch system

**21** Disconnect the battery negative (earth) lead (see Chapter 5, Section 1).
**22** Remove the air cleaner assembly as described in Chapter 4A. Also remove the air cleaner support bracket.
**23** Disconnect the low fluid level warning multi-plug from the brake fluid reservoir. Detach the clutch fluid supply hose from its bracket, and move it aside, if possible without disconnecting the hose.
**24** Unscrew the brake fluid reservoir filler cap, and completely seal the top of the reservoir using cling film or adhesive tape. This will reduce loss of fluid when the hydraulic pipes are disconnected.
**25** Unscrew the master cylinder mounting nuts, and carefully withdraw the cylinder from the servo unit, leaving the brake pipes still connected to it. Move the master cylinder over to the left-hand side of the engine compartment, to rest against the left-hand suspension turret.
**26** Unscrew the servo unit mounting nuts, and move the unit away from the bulkhead.
**27** Unscrew the nut securing the pedal trunnion to the servo unit pushrod inside the passenger compartment. The nut is located near the top of the pedal, and is accessible through an access hole. For improved access, remove the facia lower panel first, disconnecting the diagnostic plug from the panel as it is removed.
**28** Remove the vacuum servo unit, together with the pushrod, from the engine compartment. Take care not to damage the rubber grommet in the bulkhead.
**29** Remove the nuts around the base of the steering column securing the servo unit mounting bracket, and withdraw the mounting bracket from the bulkhead.
**30** Move the air conditioning pipe bracket to one side.
**31** Unbolt the brake servo side support brackets.
**32** Disconnect the multi-plug from the hydraulic unit.
**33** Position some rags beneath the ABS hydraulic unit, to catch spilled fluid.
**34** Identify the location of the brake hydraulic pipes on the ABS hydraulic unit, then unscrew the union nuts and pull out the pipes. Carefully bend the pipes away from the hydraulic unit, to allow the unit to be removed.
**35** Remove the two mounting nuts, and slide the hydraulic unit off its locating peg and out of the mounting brackets.

### Refitting

#### Early Mecatronic system

**36** Locate the insulator ring on the pump end, and fit the stud cap to the insulator ring.
**37** Lower the ABS hydraulic unit into position, right-hand end first.

**38** Fit the right-hand bracket studs onto the insulators.

**39** Lower the left-hand end of the ABS hydraulic unit onto the bracket. Fit and tighten the pump mounting nut and the remaining unit mountings, as applicable.

**40** Locate the vacuum servo unit and pushrod on the bulkhead bracket, taking care not to damage the rubber grommet.

**41** Insert the pushrod in the pedal trunnion, and tighten the nut.

**42** Refit the facia lower panel if it was removed.

**43** The remainder of refitting is a reversal of removal. Ensure that the multi-plugs are securely connected, and that the brake pipe unions are tightened to the specified torque. Refit both pressure-control relief valves, with reference to Section 19.

### Later Mecatronic system

**44** Refitting is a reversal of removal. Ensure that the multi-plug is securely connected, and that the brake pipe unions are tightened to the specified torque.

### Bosch system

**45** Refitting is a reversal of removal. Ensure that the multi-plug is securely connected, and that the brake pipe unions are tightened to the specified torque.

---

## 21 ABS wheel sensor –
testing, removal and refitting

### Testing

**1** Checking of the sensors is done before removal, connecting a voltmeter to the disconnected sensor multi-plug. Using an analogue (moving coil) meter is not practical, since the meter does not respond quickly enough. A digital meter having an AC facility may be used to check that the sensor is operating correctly.

**2** To do this, raise the relevant wheel then disconnect the wiring to the ABS sensor and connect the meter to it.

**3** Spin the wheel and check that the output voltage is between 1.5 and 2.0 volts, depending on how fast the wheel is spun.

**4** Alternatively, an oscilloscope may be used to check the output of the sensor – an alternating current will be traced on the screen, of magnitude depending on the speed of the rotating wheel.

**5** If the sensor output is low or zero, renew the sensor.

### Removal

#### Front wheel sensor

**6** Apply the handbrake and loosen the relevant front wheel nuts. Jack up the front of the car and support it on axle stands (see *Jacking and vehicle support*). Remove the relevant wheel.

**7** Unscrew the sensor mounting bolt from

**21.7 Unscrew the mounting bolt and remove the ABS sensor**

the hub carrier and withdraw the sensor **(see illustration)**.

**8** Remove the sensor wiring loom from the support brackets on the front suspension strut and wheel arch.

**9** Prise out the stud clips, and remove the Torx screws and screw clips holding the wheel arch liner in position. Withdraw the liner.

**10** Disconnect the multi-plug, and withdraw the sensor and wiring loom.

#### Rear wheel sensor

**11** Chock the front wheels, and engage 1st gear. Loosen the relevant rear wheel nuts, then jack up the rear of the car and support it on axle stands (see *Jacking and vehicle support*). Remove the relevant wheel.

**12** Unscrew the sensor mounting bolt, located on the brake backplate (drum brakes) or rear suspension hub carrier (disc brakes), and withdraw the sensor.

**13** On disc brake models, prise out the stud clips, and remove the Torx screws and screw clips holding the wheel arch liner in position. Withdraw the liner.

**14** Disconnect the sensor wiring loom from the supports on the rear suspension strut (or hub carrier) and wheel arch.

**15** Working inside the car, lift the rear seat cushion, then disconnect the multi-plug for the sensor wiring loom **(see illustration)**.

**16** Withdraw the sensor and wiring loom through the rubber grommet in the rear floor.

### Refitting

**17** Refitting is a reversal of the removal procedure.

---

## 22 ABS relay box –
removal and refitting

**Note:** *This Section only applies to the Mecatronic ABS systems fitted up to December 1997. On the Bosch system fitted after this date, the system relays are integral with the hydraulic unit.*

### Removal

**1** Disconnect the battery negative (earth) lead (see Chapter 5, Section 1).

**2** Detach the vacuum hose from the inlet manifold connection, pressing in the collar

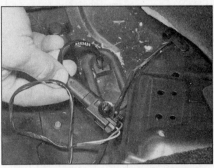

**21.15 Rear ABS sensor wiring multi-plug located beneath the rear seat**

to disengage the tabs, then withdrawing the collar slowly.

**3** To improve access, remove the air cleaner and intercooler as described in Chapter 4A.

**4** Free the heater hose from its retaining clips, and position it clear of the relay box.

**5** Disconnect the wiring connector(s) from the relay box and, where necessary, from the vehicle speed sensor.

**6** Unscrew the four Torx retaining screws and withdraw the relay box from the hydraulic unit **(see illustration)**.

### Refitting

**7** Refitting is a reversal of the removal procedure. Do not overtighten the relay box retaining screws, as the plastic is easily cracked.

---

## 23 Traction control system inhibitor switch –
removal and refitting

Refer to Chapter 12.

---

## 24 Traction control system throttle actuator –
removal and refitting

### Removal

**1** The throttle actuator is located in the front right-hand corner of the engine compartment. First disconnect the battery negative (earth) lead (see Chapter 5, Section 1).

**2** To improve access to the actuator, unbolt

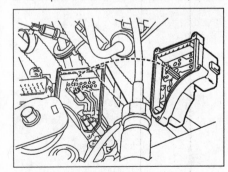

**22.6 Removing the ABS relay box**

**24.3a Disconnect the throttle actuator upper . . .**

**24.3b . . . and lower wiring plugs**

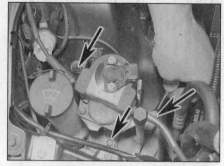

**24.4a Remove the three mounting bolts (arrowed) . . .**

**24.4b . . . and lift out the throttle actuator for cable removal**

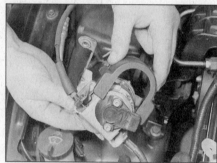

**24.5 Unclip the actuator cover for access to the cables**

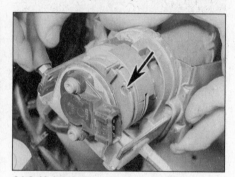

**24.6 Unhook the cable inner end fitting . . .**

the coolant expansion tank (refer to Chapter 3 if necessary), and carefully lift it on top of the engine, without disturbing any of the hoses. Ensure that the tank cap is securely fastened, to prevent leaks.

**3** Disconnect the upper and lower wiring plugs from the throttle actuator **(see illustrations)**.

**4** Unscrew the mounting bolts, and lift out the throttle actuator **(see illustrations)**.

**5** Unclip the motor cover **(see illustration)**.

**6** Turn the upper throttle control segment, to provide some play in the accelerator cable from the accelerator pedal, then disconnect the cable by unhooking the end fitting **(see illustration)**.

**7** Prise back the retaining catch, and slide the cable guide upwards from the motor housing **(see illustration)**.

**8** Turn the lower accelerator control segment, to provide play in the accelerator cable leading

to the throttle lever, then disconnect the cable by unhooking the end fitting. Release the cable from the motor housing as described in paragraph 6 **(see illustrations)**.

### Refitting

**9** Refitting is a reversal of the removal procedure. If necessary, check the accelerator cable adjustment as described in Chapter 4A.

## 25 Stop-light switch – removal, refitting and adjustment

### Removal

**1** Disconnect the battery negative (earth) lead (see Chapter 5, Section 1).

**2** Remove the facia lower panel, with reference to Chapter 11, Section 29.

**3** Disconnect the wiring multi-plug from the switch. On models with cruise control, note that the stop-light switch is the lower of the two switches above the brake pedal **(see illustration)**.

**4** On models without cruise control, rotate the switch anti-clockwise by a quarter-turn, and withdraw it from the pedal bracket **(see illustration)**. Where cruise control is fitted, the switch is rotated clockwise to remove it.

### Refitting and adjustment

**5** With the switch removed, reset it by fully extending its plunger.

**6** Depress the brake pedal until the distance between the pedal and mounting bracket is as shown **(see illustration)**.

**7** Hold the pedal in this position, and refit the stop-light switch to the mounting bracket.

**8** With the switch securely clipped in

**24.7 . . . then unclip the cable outer from the actuator housing**

**24.8a Unhook the cable inner end fitting . . .**

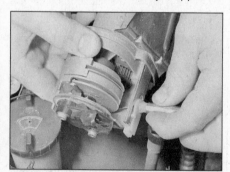

**24.8b . . . and disconnect the cable outer guide**

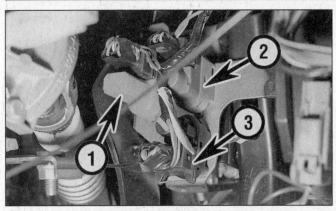

**25.3 On models with cruise control, there are three switches on the pedal bracket**

*1 Clutch pedal position switch*  *2 Brake pedal deactivator switch*
*3 Stop-light switch*

**25.4 Removing the stop-light switch**

position, release the brake pedal, and gently pull it fully back to the at-rest position. This will automatically set the adjustment of the stop-light switch.

**9** Reconnect the wiring connector and the battery, and check the operation of the switch prior to refitting the facia lower panel.

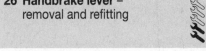

## 26 Handbrake lever – removal and refitting

### Removal

**1** Raise the front and rear of the car, and support it on axle stands (see *Jacking and vehicle support*). Fully release the handbrake lever.

**2** Remove the centre console as described in Chapter 11.

**3** Working beneath the car, release the exhaust system from the rubber mountings. Lower the exhaust system as far as possible, supporting it on blocks or more axle stands.

**4** Detach the exhaust heat shield from the underbody.

**5** Unhook the secondary (rear) handbrake cables from the equaliser bar **(see illustration)**.

**6** Working inside the car, unscrew the two mounting bolts securing the handbrake lever to the floor **(see illustration)**.

**7** Turn the handbrake lever upside-down, then disconnect the primary cable end from the segment.

**8** Withdraw the handbrake from inside the car.

### Refitting

**9** If a new lever is being fitted, the self-adjust mechanism is pre-set to the correct position. When refitting the old lever, it may be necessary to reset the mechanism, as follows.

**10** Lift the lever to the fully-raised position, then sit down and grip the cable and equaliser bracket between your feet.

**11** Release the pawl from the adjuster

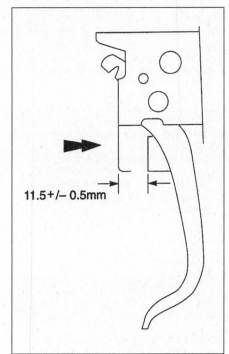

11.5+/– 0.5mm

**25.6 Position the brake pedal as shown prior to refitting the switch to its mounting bracket**

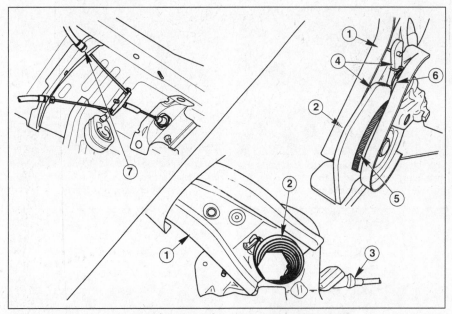

**26.5 Handbrake lever and associated components**

*1 Handbrake lever*
*2 Clock spring*
*3 Handbrake cable*
*4 Toothed segment and pawl to lock the handbrake lever*
*5 Fine-toothed segment for the clock spring*
*6 Pawl for the clock spring*
*7 Underbody bracket, secondary cables and equaliser bar*

**26.6 Handbrake lever mounting bolts**

mechanism, lift the lever, and pull out approximately 40 mm of cable **(see illustration)**. Allow the pawl to engage the mechanism, and release the cable. The mechanism should now be in the correct position for refitting.

**12** Make sure that the primary cable is correctly located in the segment.

**13** Check the operation of the handbrake before returning the car to normal service.

## 27 Handbrake cables – removal and refitting

### Removal

#### Primary (front)

**1** Remove the handbrake lever as described in Section 26.

**2** Prise the grommet from the underbody, and withdraw the cable from beneath the car.

#### Secondary (rear)

**3** Chock the front wheels, and engage 1st gear. Loosen the wheel nuts on the relevant rear wheel, then jack up the rear of the car and support it on axle stands (see *Jacking and vehicle support*). Fully release the handbrake lever.

**4** Remove the relevant rear wheel.

**5** Working beneath the car, release the exhaust system from the rubber mountings. Lower the exhaust system as far as possible, supporting it on blocks or more axle stands.

**6** Unbolt the exhaust heat shield(s) from the underbody.

**7** Unhook the relevant cable from the equaliser bar.

**8** On drum brake models, remove the rear brake shoes on the relevant side as described in Section 6, then remove the cable outer from the backplate by compressing the three retaining lugs (use a suitable ring spanner) and pushing the cable through **(see illustration)**.

**9** On disc brake models, swivel the caliper handbrake arm towards the front of the car, and unhook the end of the cable inner from the arm **(see illustration)**. Compress the tangs of the cable outer retaining clip, and release the cable from the caliper bracket.

**10** Release the lugs securing the cable outer to the underbody brackets, then release the cable from the clips, and withdraw it from under the car **(see illustrations)**.

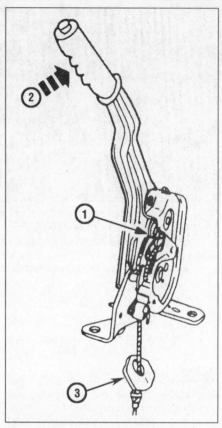

**26.11 Release the pawl (1), lift the lever (2) and pull out the cable (3)**

### Refitting

**11** Refitting is a reversal of the removal procedure, noting the following points:
  a) *The handbrake cables are self-adjusting, using a ratchet and pawl mechanism on the base of the handbrake lever. When reconnecting the cables to the rear brakes, don't be alarmed by any clicking noises heard.*
  b) *Make sure that the cable end fittings are correctly located.*
  c) *Check the operation of the handbrake. The cables will adjust themselves to the optimum setting once the handbrake has been applied and released a few times. Make sure that both wheels are locked, then free to turn, as the handbrake is operated.*

## 28 Vacuum pump – removal and refitting

### Removal

**1** Remove the cylinder head cover as described in Chapter 2A.

**2** Using a suitable socket or spanner on the crankshaft pulley bolt, turn the crankshaft

**27.8 Using a ring spanner to compress the retaining lugs securing the cable outer to the backplate**

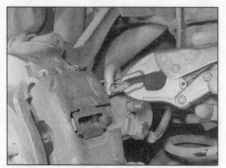

**27.9 Disconnect the cable inner from the caliper handbrake arm**

**27.10a Release the lugs using a ring spanner . . .**

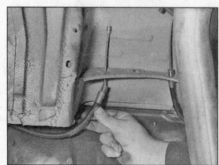

**27.10b . . . and remove the cable outer from the underbody brackets**

**28.2 Vacuum pump pushrod (1) must be fully retracted – pushrod resting on lowest point of eccentric (2)**

**28.3 Disconnecting the vacuum line from the vacuum pump**

until the vacuum pump pushrod (operated by the eccentric on the camshaft end) is fully retracted into the cylinder head **(see illustration)**.

**3** Unscrew the union nut and disconnect the vacuum line from the top of the pump **(see illustration)**.

**4** Release the retaining clip and disconnect the oil return hose from the base of the pump **(see illustration)**. Be prepared for some oil spillage as the hose is disconnected and mop-up any spilt oil.

**5** Unscrew the bolt securing the fuel heater bracket to the side of the cylinder head **(see illustration)**. Move the fuel heater to one side for access to the vacuum pump lower securing bolt.

**6** Evenly and progressively slacken the bolts securing the pump to the front of the cylinder head. Note that there is no need completely to remove the lower bolt, as the lower end of the pump is slotted **(see illustrations)**.

**7** Remove the pump from the engine compartment, along with its sealing ring. Discard the sealing ring, a new one should be used on refitting **(see illustration)**.

### Refitting

**8** Ensure the pump and cylinder head mating

surfaces are clean and dry and fit the new sealing ring to the pump recess.

**9** Manoeuvre the pump into position, ensuring the sealing ring remains correctly seated, then tighten the pump mounting bolts to the specified torque wrench setting.

**10** Reconnect the oil return hose to the base of the pump and secure it in position with the retaining clip.

**11** Reconnect the vacuum line to the pump, tightening its union nut to the specified torque wrench setting.

**12** Refit the fuel heater bracket and tighten the securing bolt.

**13** Refit the cylinder head cover with reference to Chapter 2A. Start the engine and check for correct operation of the pump as described in Section 16.

## 29 Vacuum pump – testing and overhaul

**Note:** *A vacuum gauge will be required for this check.*

**1** The operation of the braking system vacuum pump can be checked using a vacuum gauge.

**28.4 Disconnecting the oil return hose from the vacuum pump**

**28.5 Unscrew the bolt (arrowed) securing the fuel heater bracket**

**28.6a Vacuum pump lower securing bolt location (arrowed)**

**28.6b Unscrewing the vacuum pump upper securing bolt**

**28.7 Use a new sealing ring (arrowed) when refitting the vacuum pump**

**2** Disconnect the vacuum pipe from the pump, and connect the gauge to the pump union using a suitable length of hose.

**3** Start the engine and allow it to idle, then measure the vacuum created by the pump. As a guide, after one minute, a minimum of approximately 500 mm Hg should be recorded. If the vacuum registered is significantly less than this, it is likely that the pump is faulty. However, seek the advice of a Ford dealer before condemning the pump.

**4** Overhaul of the vacuum pump is not possible, since no components are available separately for it. If faulty, the complete pump assembly must be renewed.

# Chapter 10
# Suspension and steering

## Contents

Section number

Front anti-roll bar and links – removal and refitting . . . . . . . . . . . . . . 6
Front hub and bearings – inspection and renewal . . . . . . . . . . . . . . . 3
Front hub carrier and hub assembly – removal and refitting . . . . . . . 2
Front lower arm – removal, overhaul and refitting . . . . . . . . . . . . . . 7
Front lower arm balljoint – renewal . . . . . . . . . . . . . . . . . . . . . . . . . 8
Front strut – overhaul . . . . . . . . . . . . . . . . . . . . . . . . . . . . . . . . . . . . 5
Front strut – removal and refitting . . . . . . . . . . . . . . . . . . . . . . . . . . 4
General information . . . . . . . . . . . . . . . . . . . . . . . . . . . . . . . . . . . . . 1
Rear anti-roll bar and links (Estate) – removal and refitting . . . . . . . 20
Rear anti-roll bar and links (Saloon/Hatchback) – removal and
  refitting . . . . . . . . . . . . . . . . . . . . . . . . . . . . . . . . . . . . . . . . . . . . . . 13
Rear coil spring (Estate) – removal and refitting . . . . . . . . . . . . . . . . 21
Rear crossmember (Estate) – removal and refitting . . . . . . . . . . . . . . 26
Rear crossmember (Saloon/Hatchback) – removal and refitting . . . . 16
Rear hub and bearings (Estate) – inspection and renewal . . . . . . . . 17
Rear hub and bearings (Saloon/Hatchback) – inspection and
  renewal . . . . . . . . . . . . . . . . . . . . . . . . . . . . . . . . . . . . . . . . . . . . . . 9
Rear hub carrier (Estate) – removal and refitting . . . . . . . . . . . . . . . . 18
Rear hub carrier (Saloon/Hatchback) – removal and refitting . . . . . . 10
Rear lower arm (front) (Estate) – removal and refitting . . . . . . . . . . . 23
Rear lower arm (rear) (Estate) – removal and refitting . . . . . . . . . . . 22

Section number

Rear lower arms (Saloon/Hatchback) – removal and refitting . . . . . . 14
Rear shock absorber (Estate) – removal, testing and refitting . . . . . . 19
Rear strut (Saloon/Hatchback) – overhaul . . . . . . . . . . . . . . . . . . . . 12
Rear strut (Saloon/Hatchback) – removal and refitting . . . . . . . . . . . 11
Rear tie-bar (Estate) – removal and refitting . . . . . . . . . . . . . . . . . . . 25
Rear tie-bar (Saloon/Hatchback) – removal and refitting . . . . . . . . . 15
Rear upper arm (Estate) – removal and refitting . . . . . . . . . . . . . . . . 24
Steering column – removal, inspection and refitting . . . . . . . . . . . . . 28
Steering column flexible coupling – removal and refitting . . . . . . . . . 29
Steering fluid cooler – removal and refitting . . . . . . . . . . . . . . . . . . . 34
Steering fluid level check . . . . . . . . . . . . . . . . . . . . . . . See Weekly checks
Steering gear – removal and refitting . . . . . . . . . . . . . . . . . . . . . . . . 30
Steering gear rubber gaiters – renewal . . . . . . . . . . . . . . . . . . . . . . . 31
Steering hydraulic system – bleeding . . . . . . . . . . . . . . . . . . . . . . . . 32
Steering pump – removal and refitting . . . . . . . . . . . . . . . . . . . . . . . 33
Steering pump drivebelt . . . . . . . . . . . . . . . . . . . . . . . . . . See Chapter 1
Steering wheel – removal and refitting . . . . . . . . . . . . . . . . . . . . . . . 27
Steering, suspension and roadwheel check . . . . . . . . . . See Chapter 1
Track rod end – renewal . . . . . . . . . . . . . . . . . . . . . . . . . . . . . . . . . . 35
Tyre condition and tyre pressure checks . . . . . . . . . See Weekly checks
Wheel alignment and steering angles – general information . . . . . . . 36

## Degrees of difficulty

| Easy, suitable for novice with little experience 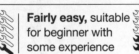 | Fairly easy, suitable for beginner with some experience | Fairly difficult, suitable for competent DIY mechanic | Difficult, suitable for experienced DIY mechanic | Very difficult, suitable for expert DIY or professional  |
|---|---|---|---|---|

## Specifications

### Front wheel alignment

Toe setting:
Tolerance allowed before resetting required . . . . . . . . . . . . . . . . . . . 1.5 mm toe-in to 1.5 mm toe-out (0°15' to -0°15')
Adjustment setting (if required) . . . . . . . . . . . . . . . . . . . . . . . . . . . . . 0 mm ± 1.0 mm (0°00' ± 0°10')

### Rear wheel alignment

Toe setting:
Tolerance allowed before resetting required:
  Saloon/Hatchback . . . . . . . . . . . . . . . . . . . . . . . . . . . . . . . . . . . . . 3.9 mm toe-in to 0.1 mm toe-out (0°39' to -0°01')
  Estate . . . . . . . . . . . . . . . . . . . . . . . . . . . . . . . . . . . . . . . . . . . . . . 2.7 mm toe-in to 1.3 mm toe-out (0°27' to -0°13')
Adjustment setting (if required):
  Saloon/Hatchback . . . . . . . . . . . . . . . . . . . . . . . . . . . . . . . . . . . . . 1.9 mm toe-in ± 1.2 mm (0°18' ± 0°12')
  Estate . . . . . . . . . . . . . . . . . . . . . . . . . . . . . . . . . . . . . . . . . . . . . . 0.7 mm toe-in ± 1.2 mm (0°07' ± 0°12')

### Roadwheels and tyres

Wheel sizes:
  Steel . . . . . . . . . . . . . . . . . . . . . . . . . . . . . . . . . . . . . . . . . . . . . . . 14x5.5, 15x5.5, or 15x6
  Alloy* . . . . . . . . . . . . . . . . . . . . . . . . . . . . . . . . . . . . . . . . . . . . . . . 14x5.5, 15x6, 16x6, or 16x6.5
Tyre sizes (depending on model) . . . . . . . . . . . . . . . . . . . . . . . . . . . 185/65/14, 195/60/14, 195/60/15, 195/55/15, 195/50/16, 205/55/15, or 205/50/16
Tyre pressures . . . . . . . . . . . . . . . . . . . . . . . . . . . . . . . . . . . . . . . . . See end of Weekly checks on page 0•17

* On some models with alloy wheels, a steel spare wheel may be provided

## Torque wrench settings

| | Nm | lbf ft |
|---|---|---|
| **Front suspension** | | |
| Anti-roll bar clamp bolts.................................... | 24 | 18 |
| Anti-roll bar link ......................................... | 47 | 35 |
| Driveshaft/hub retaining nut................................ | 340 | 251 |
| Front subframe............................................. | 130 | 96 |
| Lower arm balljoint to lower arm (service replacement, bolted on) .... | 58 | 43 |
| Lower arm balljoint-to-hub carrier clamp bolt .................... | 83 | 61 |
| Lower arm to subframe: | | |
|    Stage 1 ............................................. | 50 | 37 |
|    Stage 2 ............................................. | Tighten through a further 90° | |
| Suspension strut thrust bearing retaining nut .................... | 59 | 44 |
| Suspension strut upper mounting nut (renew)................... | 46 | 34 |
| Suspension strut-to-hub carrier pinch-bolt .................... | 84 | 62 |
| **Rear suspension (Saloon/Hatchback)** | | |
| Anti-roll bar............................................... | 25 | 18 |
| Anti-roll bar link ......................................... | 35 | 26 |
| Crossmember mounting bolts ................................ | 120 | 89 |
| Disc brake splash shield................................... | 90 | 66 |
| Drum brake backplate ..................................... | 50 | 37 |
| Front lower arm to hub carrier and to crossmember .............. | 84 | 62 |
| Hub nut................................................... | 290 | 214 |
| Rear lower arm to crossmember ............................ | 84 | 62 |
| Rear lower arm to hub carrier.............................. | 120 | 89 |
| Suspension strut to hub carrier ........................... | 84 | 62 |
| Suspension strut upper mounting bolts....................... | 27 | 20 |
| Suspension strut upper nut ............................... | 50 | 37 |
| Tie-bar and tie-bar bracket ............................... | 120 | 89 |
| **Rear suspension (Estate)** | | |
| *As for Saloon/Hatchback, except for the following.* | | |
| Anti-roll bar.............................................. | 23 | 17 |
| Front lower arm to hub carrier and to crossmember .............. | 120 | 89 |
| Hub assembly-to-hub carrier retaining bolts .................... | 65 | 48 |
| Shock absorber lower mounting bolt........................... | 120 | 89 |
| Shock absorber upper mounting bolt ......................... | 84 | 62 |
| Tie-bar bracket to underbody .............................. | 120 | 89 |
| Tie-bar to bracket........................................ | 120 | 89 |
| Tie-bar to hub carrier .................................... | 84 | 62 |
| Upper arm to crossmember................................. | 84 | 62 |
| Upper arm to hub carrier .................................. | 120 | 89 |
| **Steering** | | |
| Flexible coupling-to-pinion shaft clamp bolt (renew).............. | 28 | 21 |
| Steering pipe unions to valve body ........................... | 31 | 23 |
| Steering column mounting bolts ............................. | 24 | 18 |
| Steering column-to-flexible coupling clamp bolt (renew)........... | 24 | 18 |
| Steering gear mounting bolts................................ | 137 | 101 |
| Steering pump mounting bolts................................ | 24 | 18 |
| Steering pump pressure line to pump ......................... | 65 | 48 |
| Steering wheel bolt........................................ | 50 | 37 |
| Track rod end locknut...................................... | 41 | 30 |
| Track rod end to front hub carrier........................... | 28 | 21 |
| Track rod locknuts ........................................ | 110 | 81 |
| **Roadwheel nuts** ......................................... | 85 | 63 |

---

## 1  General information

The independent front suspension is of MacPherson strut type, incorporating coil springs, integral telescopic shock absorbers and an anti-roll bar. The struts are attached to hub carriers at their lower ends and the hub carriers are in turn attached to the lower arm by balljoints. The anti-roll bar is bolted to the rear of the subframe and is connected to the front struts by links **(see illustration)**.

On Saloon/Hatchback models, the independent rear suspension is of 'Quadralink' type, having four mounting points on each side of the car. The two lower arms are attached

### 1.1 Front suspension components

1  MacPherson strut
2  Front hub carrier
3  Lower arm
4  Lower arm rear rubber bush
5  Anti-roll bar
6  Front subframe
7  Subframe front rubber bush
8  Subframe rear rubber bush

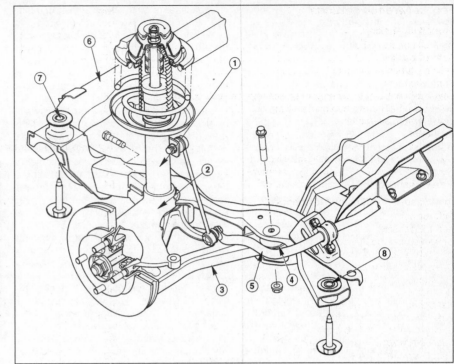

to the rear hub carrier at their outer ends and to the rear crossmember at their inner ends. A tie-bar, located between the bottom of the hub carrier and the floor, counteracts braking and acceleration forces on each side **(see illustration)**.

On Estate models, the independent rear suspension is of 'SLA' (Short and Long Arm) type. This allows a larger load area, since there are no suspension points projecting into the luggage area. There are three side arms on each side: one forged upper arm and two pressed-steel lower side arms. A tie-bar on each side supports the rear hub carriers.

### 1.2 Rear suspension components – Saloon/Hatchback models

1  Wheel housing
2  Upper mounting bracket and coil spring seat
3  Strut
4  Adaptive damping solenoid (petrol models)
5  Rear suspension crossmember
6  Eccentric bolt for rear toe setting
7  Anti-roll bar
8  Link
9  Front lower arm
10 Rear lower arm
11 Hub carrier (drum brake models)
12 ABS wheel sensor (drum brake models)
13 Tie-bar
14 Backplate
15 Hub and bearing assembly
16 Hub nut
17 Grease cap
18 Brake drum
19 Tie-bar mounting bracket
20 Brake disc
21 Splash shield (disc brake models)
22 Brake caliper (disc brake models)
23 Hub carrier (disc brake models)
24 ABS wheel sensor (disc brake models)

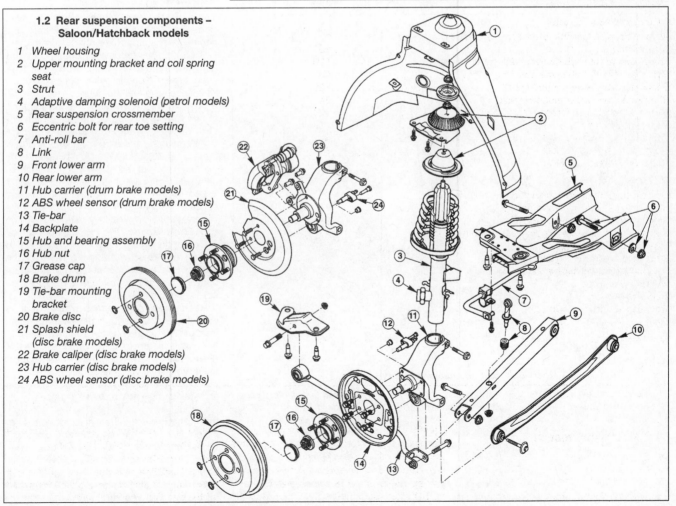

The coil springs are separate from the shock absorbers **(see illustration)**.

A rear anti-roll bar is fitted to all models. Self-levelling rear shock absorbers are available on Estate models.

A variable-ratio type rack-and-pinion steering gear is fitted, together with a conventional column and telescopic coupling, incorporating two universal joints. Power-assisted steering is fitted to all models. A fluid cooler is fitted to the steering system, in front of the cooling system radiator on the crossmember (see Section 34).

## Seized nuts/bolts

When working on the suspension or steering system components, you may come across fasteners which seem impossible to loosen. These fasteners on the underside of the car are continually subjected to water, road grime, mud, etc, and can become rusted or 'seized', making them extremely difficult to remove. In order to unscrew these stubborn fasteners without damaging them (or other components), first use a wire brush to clean exposed threads. Afterwards, use lots of penetrating oil or a maintenance spray such as WD-40, and allow it to soak in for a while.

Sometimes a sharp blow with a hammer and punch is effective in breaking the bond between a nut and bolt threads, but care must be taken to prevent the punch from slipping off the fastener and ruining the threads. Impact drivers can also be successful in freeing a stubborn fastener, but make sure a close-fitting socket is used.

A fastener which has rounded off may still be loosened, by tapping on a socket which is slightly smaller than the original size – it's useful to have a set of old imperial-size sockets for this, as they often fall between the metric sizes. Hex sockets (ones with six 'sides') are preferable to bi-hex ones, as they are less likely to round off corners – 'surface-drive' sockets are also available, which grip on the flats, not the corners.

Heating the stuck fastener and surrounding area sometimes helps too, but isn't always recommended because of the obvious dangers associated with fire – take care if rubber or plastic components, or fuel/brake pipes, are close by. Heat may also ignite the penetrating oil or maintenance spray.

Long breaker bars and extension pipes will increase leverage (an extension pipe is any strong piece of metal tube, slipped over a socket handle, to make it 'longer'). Don't

use an extension pipe on a ratchet handle – the ratchet mechanism could be damaged. Wear gloves if a great amount of force is being applied – these will protect your hands if something 'lets go'. Sometimes, turning the nut or bolt in the tightening (usually clockwise) direction first will help to break it loose.

Fasteners that require drastic measures to loosen should always be renewed.

 **Warning: Since most of the procedures that are dealt with in this Chapter involve jacking up the car and working underneath it, a good pair of axle stands will be needed. A trolley jack is the preferred type of jack to lift the car, and it can also be used to support other components during certain operations. Do not rely on a trolley jack alone to support the car, as they can 'creep' down – once the car is raised on the jack, place at least one axle stand underneath as a precaution.**

## 2 Front hub carrier and hub assembly – removal and refitting

### Removal

**1** Remove the wheel cover (or centre cover) from the wheel, apply the handbrake and engage 1st gear. Loosen the hub nut about half a turn. This nut is very tight – use only high-quality, close-fitting tools and take adequate precautions against personal injury when loosening the hub nut.

**2** Working inside the engine compartment, remove the strut cap (if fitted). Retain the strut piston with an Allen key, then loosen the strut upper mounting nut and unscrew it by five complete turns. Do not remove the nut completely at this stage, but note that, on completion, a new nut should be fitted.

**3** Loosen the relevant front wheel nuts and chock the rear wheels. Jack up the front of the car and support it on axle stands (see *Jacking and vehicle support*). Remove the front wheel.

**4** Extract the split pin from the track rod end balljoint nut. Unscrew the nut and detach the rod from the hub carrier steering arm using a conventional balljoint removal tool. Take care not to damage the balljoint seal.

**5** Remove the ABS sensor (when fitted) as described in Chapter 9; disconnect the wiring from the clip on the hub **(see illustrations)**.

**6** Remove the brake caliper and brake disc as described in Chapter 9, but do not disconnect the flexible hose from the caliper. Suspend the caliper from a suitable point under the wheel arch, taking care not to strain the hose.

**7** Completely unscrew the driveshaft nut. Note that the nut is of special laminated design – Ford state that it can be re-used up to 5 times, but owners may prefer to fit a new nut every time. When the nut is removed, check it carefully for signs of splitting – it is not unknown for these nuts to split during tightening, and it pays to have a new nut to hand.

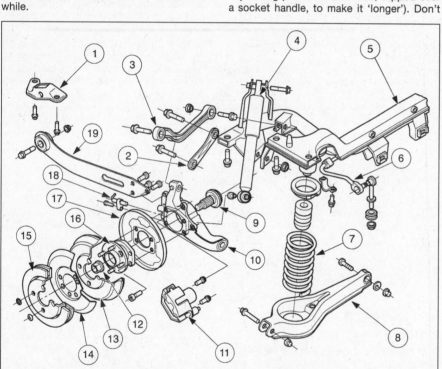

**1.3 Rear suspension components – Estate models**

| | | |
|---|---|---|
| 1  *Tie-bar bracket* | 8  *Rear lower arm* | 14 *Splash guard (disc brake* |
| 2  *Short front lower* | 9  *Stub axle (part of hub and* | *models)* |
|    *arm* |    *bearing assembly)* | 15 *Brake disc* |
| 3  *Long front upper* | 10 *Hub carrier* | 16 *Hub and bearing* |
|    *arm* | 11 *Brake caliper (disc brake* |    *assembly* |
| 4  *Shock absorber* |    *models)* | 17 *Backplate (drum brake* |
| 5  *Crossmember* | 12 *Hub nut* |    *models)* |
| 6  *Anti-roll bar* | 13 *Brake drum* | 18 *ABS wheel sensor* |
| 7  *Coil spring* | | 19 *Tie-bar* |

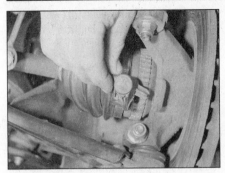

**2.5a Remove the ABS wheel sensor . . .**

**2.5b . . . and unclip the wiring harness from the hub**

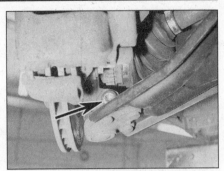

**2.8a Lower arm balljoint clamp bolt . . .**

**8** Note which way round the lower arm balljoint clamp bolt is fitted, then unscrew its nut and remove it from the hub carrier (see illustrations). Lever the balljoint down from the hub carrier; if it is tight, prise the clamp open using a large flat-bladed tool. Take care not to damage the balljoint seal during the separation procedure.

**9** Unscrew the pinch-bolt securing the hub carrier to the front strut, noting which way round it is fitted (see illustration). Prise open the clamp using a wedge-shaped tool and release the hub carrier from the strut. If necessary, tap the hub carrier downwards with a soft-headed mallet to separate the two components. Support the hub carrier on an axle stand.

**10** Pull the hub carrier and hub assembly from the driveshaft splines. If it is tight, connect a universal puller to the hub flange and withdraw it from the driveshaft. When the driveshaft is free, support it on an axle stand, or suspend it from a suitable point under the wheel arch, making sure that the inner constant velocity joint is not turned through more than 18°. (Damage may occur if the joint is turned through too great an angle.)

### Refitting

**11** Lift the hub carrier and hub assembly onto the driveshaft splines and support the assembly on an axle stand.

**12** Locate the assembly on the front strut. Insert the pinch-bolt with its head facing forwards. Fit the nut and tighten it to the specified torque.

**13** Refit the lower arm balljoint to the hub carrier assembly, and insert the clamp bolt with its head facing forwards. Refit the nut and tighten it to the specified torque.

**14** Fit the driveshaft/hub nut and tighten it moderately at this stage. Final tightening of the nut is made with the car lowered to the ground.

**15** Refit the brake caliper and brake disc as described in Chapter 9.

**16** Where applicable, refit the ABS sensor as described in Chapter 9. Clip the wiring back into place.

**17** Reconnect the track rod end balljoint to the steering arm and tighten the nut to the specified torque. Check that the split pin holes are aligned; if necessary, turn the nut to the nearest alignment, making sure that the nut is

**2.8b . . . and nut – note direction of fitting before removal**

still secure. Insert a new split pin and bend it back to secure.

**18** Refit the front wheel and lower the car to the ground. Tighten the wheel nuts to the specified torque.

**19** Tighten the driveshaft/hub nut to the specified torque and refit the wheel cover.

**20** Remove the strut upper mounting nut and fit a new one. Tighten the nut to the specified torque, while holding the piston rod with an 8 mm Allen key. If the adapter needed to do this is not available, the nut can be tightened initially with a ring spanner while the piston rod is held. Final tightening can then be carried out using a torque wrench and a conventional socket.

### 3 Front hub and bearings – inspection and renewal

### Inspection

**1** The front hub bearings are non-adjustable, and are supplied already greased (see illustration).

**2** To check the bearings for excessive wear, first chock the rear wheels and apply the handbrake. Jack up the front of the car and support it on axle stands (see Jacking and vehicle support).

**3** Grip the front wheel at top and bottom and attempt to rock it. If excessive movement is noted, it may be that the hub bearings are worn. Do not confuse wear in the driveshaft outer joint or front lower arm balljoint with

**2.9 Front hub carrier-to-strut pinch-bolt**

wear in the bearings. Hub bearing wear will show up as roughness or vibration when the wheel is spun; it will also be noticeable as a rumbling or growling noise when driving.

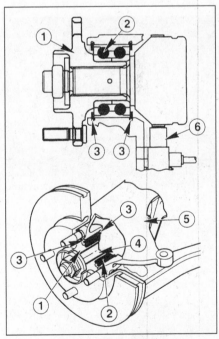

**3.1 Front hub and bearing**

| | |
|---|---|
| 1 Hub | 4 Stub axle |
| 2 Double-row ball-bearing | 5 Front hub carrier |
| 3 Circlips | 6 ABS sensor |

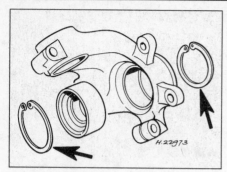

**3.8 Front wheel bearing retaining circlips**

## Renewal

**4** Remove the front hub carrier and hub assembly as described in Section 2.

**5** The hub must now be removed from the bearing inner races. It is preferable to use a press to do this, but it is possible to drive out the hub using a length of metal tube of suitable diameter.

**6** Part of the inner race will remain on the hub and this should be removed using a puller.

**7** Note that if this procedure is being used to renew the hub only (ie, it is not intended to renew the bearings), then it is important to check the condition of the bearing balls and races, to see if they are fit for re-use. It is difficult to be sure that no damage has occurred, especially if makeshift methods have been used during removal; in practice, it is probably false economy not to renew the bearings in any case, having got this far.

**8** Using circlip pliers, extract the inner and

**4.2 Front suspension strut upper mounting nut**

**4.4b . . . or unclip the brake hose from the bracket**

outer circlips securing the hub bearing in the hub carrier **(see illustration)**.

**9** Press or drive out the bearing, using a length of metal tubing of diameter slightly less than the bearing outer race.

**10** Clean the bearing seating faces in the hub carrier.

**11** Locate one of the circlips in the outer groove of the hub carrier.

**12** Press or drive the new bearing into the hub carrier until it contacts the circlip, using a length of metal tube of diameter slightly less than the outer race. Do not apply any pressure to the inner race.

**13** Locate the remaining circlip in the inner groove of the hub carrier.

**14** Support the inner race on a length of metal tube, then press or drive the hub fully into the bearing.

**15** Refit the front hub carrier and hub assembly as described in Section 2.

### 4  Front strut –
### removal and refitting

## Removal

**1** Remove the wheel cover (or centre cover) from the wheel, apply the handbrake and engage 1st gear. Loosen the hub nut about half a turn. This nut is very tight – use only high-quality, close-fitting tools and take adequate precautions against personal injury when loosening the hub nut.

**2** Working inside the engine compartment,

**4.4a Either unbolt the brake hose support bracket from the suspension strut . . .**

**4.6 Removing the anti-roll bar link and wiring bracket**

remove the strut cap (if fitted). Retain the strut piston with an Allen key, then loosen the strut upper mounting nut and unscrew it by five complete turns **(see illustration)**. Do not remove the nut completely at this stage, but note that, on completion, a new nut should be fitted.

**3** Loosen the relevant front wheel nuts and chock the rear wheels. Jack up the front of the car and support it on axle stands. Remove the front wheel.

**4** Unbolt the brake hose support bracket from the front of the strut. Alternatively, unclip the hose from the bracket **(see illustrations)**.

**5** Remove the ABS sensor (when fitted) as described in Chapter 9.

**6** Remove the nut and disconnect the anti-roll bar link from the strut. Note that the ABS wheel sensor and pad wear warning light wiring support bracket is located beneath the nut **(see illustration)**.

**7** Remove the brake caliper and brake disc as described in Chapter 9, but do not disconnect the flexible hose from the caliper. Suspend the caliper from a suitable point under the wheel arch, taking care not to strain the hose.

**8** Extract the split pin from the track rod end balljoint nut. Unscrew the nut and detach the rod from the hub carrier steering arm using a conventional balljoint removal tool. Take care not to damage the balljoint seal.

**9** Completely unscrew the driveshaft nut. Note that the nut is of special laminated design – Ford state that it can be re-used up to 5 times, but owners may prefer to fit a new nut every time. When the nut is removed, check it carefully for signs of splitting – it is not unknown for these nuts to split during tightening, and it pays to have a new nut to hand.

**10** Note which way round the lower arm balljoint clamp bolt is fitted, then unscrew its nut and remove it from the hub carrier. Lever the balljoint down from the hub carrier; if it is tight, prise the clamp open using a large flat-bladed tool. Take care not to damage the balljoint seal during the separation procedure.

**11** Unscrew the pinch-bolt securing the hub carrier to the front strut, noting which way round it is fitted **(see illustration)**. Prise open the clamp using a wedge-shaped tool and release the hub carrier from the strut. If necessary, tap the hub carrier downwards with a soft-headed mallet to separate the two components. Support the hub carrier on an axle stand.

**12** Pull the front hub carrier and hub assembly from the driveshaft splines. If it is tight, connect a universal puller to the hub flange and withdraw it from the driveshaft. When the driveshaft is free, support it on an axle stand, or suspend it from a suitable point under the wheel arch, making sure that the inner constant velocity joint is not turned through more than 18°. (Damage may occur if the joint is turned through too great an angle.)

**13** Holding the strut body with one hand, fully unscrew the front strut upper mounting nut. Lower the strut out from under the wheel arch.

## Refitting

**14** Lift the strut into position, feeding the threaded end of the piston rod up through the hole in the inner wing. Fit the new upper mounting nut and tighten it by a few threads so that the weight of the strut is supported.

**15** Lift the front hub carrier and hub assembly onto the driveshaft splines and support the assembly on an axle stand.

**16** Locate the assembly on the front strut. Insert the pinch-bolt with its head facing forwards. Fit the nut and tighten it to the specified torque.

**17** Refit the lower arm balljoint to the hub carrier and insert the clamp bolt with its head facing forwards. Refit the nut and tighten it to the specified torque.

**18** Fit the driveshaft/hub nut and tighten it moderately at this stage. Final tightening of the nut is made with the car lowered to the ground.

**19** Reconnect the track rod end balljoint to the steering arm and tighten the nut to the specified torque. Check that the split pin holes are aligned; if necessary, turn the nut to the nearest alignment, making sure that the nut is still secure. Insert a new split pin and bend it back to secure.

**20** Refit the brake caliper and brake disc as described in Chapter 9.

**21** Reconnect the anti-roll bar link to the strut and tighten the nut to the specified torque. Do not forget to locate the wiring support bracket beneath the nut.

**22** Where applicable, refit the ABS sensor as described in Chapter 9.

**23** Refit the brake hose support bracket to the front of the strut.

**24** Refit the front wheel and lower the car to the ground. Tighten the wheel nuts to the specified torque.

**25** Tighten the driveshaft/hub nut to the specified torque and refit the wheel cover.

**26** Tighten the strut upper mounting nut to the specified torque, while holding the piston rod with an 8 mm Allen key. If the adapter needed to do this is not available, the nut can be tightened initially with a ring spanner while the piston rod is held. Final tightening can then be carried out using a torque wrench and a conventional socket **(see illustration)**.

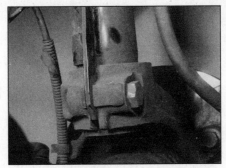

**4.11 Front hub carrier-to-strut pinch-bolt**

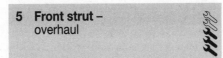

## 5  Front strut – overhaul

⚠️ **Warning: Before attempting to dismantle the front strut, a tool to hold the coil spring in compression must be obtained. Do not attempt to use makeshift methods. Uncontrolled release of the spring could cause damage and personal injury. Use a high-quality spring compressor, and carefully follow the tool manufacturer's instructions provided with it. After removing the coil spring, store it with the compressor still fitted in a safe area.**

**1** If the front struts exhibit signs of wear (leaking fluid, loss of damping capability, sagging or cracked coil springs) then they should be dismantled and overhauled as necessary. The struts themselves cannot be serviced and

**4.26 Final tightening of the front suspension strut upper mounting nut**

should be renewed if faulty, but the springs and related components can be renewed. To maintain balanced characteristics on both sides of the car, the components on both sides should be renewed at the same time.

**2** With the strut removed from the car, clean away all external dirt, then mount it in a vice.

**3** Fit the coil spring compressor tools (ensuring that they are fully engaged) and compress the spring until all tension is relieved from the upper mounting **(see illustration)**.

**4** Hold the strut piston with an Allen key and unscrew the thrust bearing retaining nut with a ring spanner **(see illustration)**.

**5** Withdraw the top mounting, thrust bearing, upper spring seat and spring, followed by the gaiter and the bump stop **(see illustrations)**.

**6** If a new spring is to be fitted, the original spring must now be carefully released from the compressor. If it is to be re-used, the spring can be left in compression.

**5.3 Coil spring compressor tools fitted to the coil spring**

**5.4 Unscrewing the nut from the top of the strut**

**5.5a Removing the top mounting from the strut**

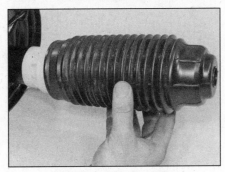

**5.5b Removing the gaiter**

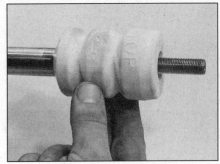

**5.5c Removing the bump stop**

6.2a Unscrew the nut . . .

6.2b . . . and disconnect the anti-roll bar link and the wiring support bracket

6.3 Front anti-roll bar-to-subframe bolts

**7** With the strut assembly now completely dismantled, examine all the components for wear and damage and check the bearing for smoothness of operation. Renew components as necessary.

**8** Examine the strut for signs of fluid leakage. Check the strut piston for signs of pitting along its entire length and check the strut body for signs of damage.

**9** Test the operation of the strut, while holding it in an upright position, by moving the piston through a full stroke and then through short strokes of 50 to 100 mm. In both cases, the resistance felt should be smooth and continuous. If the resistance is jerky, uneven, or if there is any visible sign of wear or damage to the strut, renewal is necessary.

**10** Reassembly is a reversal of dismantling, noting the following points:
a) *Make sure that the coil spring ends are correctly located in the upper and lower seats before releasing the compressor.*
b) *Check that the bearing is correctly fitted to the piston rod seat.*
c) *Tighten the thrust bearing retaining nut to the specified torque.*

### 6 Front anti-roll bar and links – removal and refitting

#### Removal

**1** Apply the handbrake and chock the rear wheels. Loosen the front wheel nuts, then jack up the front of the car and support it on axle stands. Remove the front wheels.

**2** Unscrew the nuts and disconnect the anti-roll bar links from the front struts on both sides of the car. Note the wiring support brackets located beneath the nuts **(see illustrations).**

**3** Unscrew the anti-roll bar mounting bolts from the engine subframe on both sides of the car **(see illustration)**.

**4** Withdraw the anti-roll bar from one side of the car, taking care not to damage the surrounding components.

**5** If necessary, unscrew the nuts and remove the links from the anti-roll bar.

#### Refitting

**6** Refitting is a reversal of the removal procedure.

### 7 Front lower arm – removal, overhaul and refitting

**Note:** *Removal of the left-hand lower arm is hampered by the fact that the bolts are inserted from the top of the arm – this means that the bolts must be removed upwards. The proximity of the transmission housing means that the front of the two bolts cannot be withdrawn upwards* **(see illustrations)**. *As a result, the engine/transmission assembly must be disconnected from its mountings and raised sufficiently to permit withdrawal of the front bolt. Some mechanics refit this bolt from below, to make*

*future removal easier, but note that washers may be needed under the bolt head, to ensure the bolt's threaded end does not contact the transmission housing when tightened.*

#### Removal

##### Right-hand lower arm

**1** Apply the handbrake and chock the rear wheels. Loosen the front wheel nuts, then jack up the front of the car and support it on axle stands (see *Jacking and vehicle support*). Remove the front wheels.

**2** Remove the auxiliary drivebelt cover where necessary.

**3** Unscrew the nuts and bolts securing the lower arm to the subframe **(see illustration)**.

**4** Unscrew the nut and disconnect the anti-roll bar link from the anti-roll bar.

**5** Extract the split pin from the track rod end balljoint nut. Unscrew the nut and detach the rod from the hub carrier steering arm using a conventional balljoint removal tool. Take care not to damage the balljoint seal.

**6** Using the information in Chapter 8, disconnect the right-hand driveshaft from the transmission. Support the inner end of the driveshaft on an axle stand.

**7** Note which way round the front lower arm balljoint clamp bolt is fitted, then unscrew it from the hub carrier. Lever the balljoint down from the hub carrier; if it is tight, prise the joint open carefully using a large flat-bladed tool. Take care not to damage the balljoint seal during the separation procedure **(see illustrations)**.

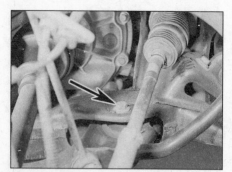

7.0a While the left-hand arm rear bolt can be withdrawn . . .

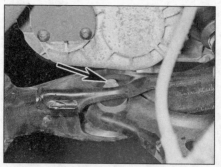

7.0b . . . the front bolt is prevented from doing so by the transmission

7.3 One of the nuts and bolts securing the lower arm to the subframe

**7.7a Unscrew the lower arm balljoint clamp bolt . . .**

**7.7b . . . and disconnect the balljoint from the hub carrier**

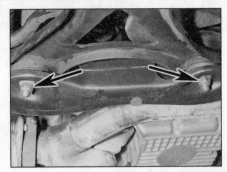

**7.19 Remove the lower arm bolt nuts from below**

**8** Remove the lower arm from the subframe and withdraw it from the car.

### Left-hand lower arm

**9** Working inside the engine compartment, remove the strut cap (if fitted). Retain the strut piston with an Allen key, then loosen the strut upper mounting nut and unscrew it by five complete turns. Do not remove the nut completely at this stage, but note that, on completion, a new nut should be fitted.

**10** Remove the air cleaner as described in Chapter 4A.

**11** Apply the handbrake and chock the rear wheels. Loosen the front wheel nuts, then jack up the front of the car and support it on axle stands (see *Jacking and vehicle support*). Remove the front wheels.

**12** On models up to October 1996, disconnect the gearchange linkage and support rods from the transmission, as described in Chapter 7. On later models with a cable gearchange, ensure that the cables are not placed under strain as the transmission is lifted.

**13** Disconnect the left-hand driveshaft from the transmission, using the information in Chapter 8. Support the inner end of the driveshaft on an axle stand.

**14** Note which way round the front lower arm balljoint clamp bolt is fitted, then unscrew its nut and remove it from the hub carrier assembly. Lever the balljoint down from the hub carrier; if it is tight, prise the joint open carefully using a large flat-bladed tool. Take care not to damage the balljoint seal during the separation procedure.

**15** The weight of the engine and transmission must now be supported, as the engine mountings must be disconnected. Either use an engine crane or hoist, or if available, an engine support bar mounted on the inner wing flanges. Given that you will be working under the car, supporting from below is not recommended.

**16** Unbolt and separate the front and rear engine mountings from the subframe, noting the fitted position of all components. Make accurate alignment marks for refitting the front mounting.

**17** With the weight of the engine and transmission supported, unbolt and separate the engine right- and left-hand mountings.

**18** Carefully raise the engine and transmission by approximately 50 mm, taking care that no pipes, cables or wiring are strained excessively as this is done.

**19** Remove the lower arm-to-subframe nuts and bolts, then remove the lower arm **(see illustration)**.

### Overhaul

**20** Examine the rubber bushes and the balljoint for wear and damage. The balljoint may be renewed as described in Section 8. The rubber bushes may be removed using a press, or a length of metal tubing together with a long bolt, washers and nut. However, most owners renew the lower arm complete.

**21** Note that the front and rear bushes are different. The front one has a solid rubber bush with a cylindrical inner tube, whereas the rear one has a voided rubber bush with a barrel-shaped inner tube **(see illustration)**.

**22** Press the new bushes into the lower arm, using the same method as used for removal. Note that, when fitting the rear bush, the voids must be in line with the front bush location. On later models, a pip on the rear bush must be aligned with a triangular alignment mark on the arm.

### Refitting

#### Right-hand lower arm

**23** Locate the lower arm on the subframe and insert the mounting bolts. Fit the nuts and tighten them in stages, first to the specified torque and then through the angle specified.

**24** Refit the inner end of the right-hand driveshaft as described in Chapter 8.

**25** Refit the front lower arm balljoint to the hub carrier and insert the clamp bolt with its head facing forwards. Refit the nut and tighten to the specified torque.

**26** Refit the track rod end balljoint to the hub carrier and tighten the nut to the specified torque. Check that the split pin holes are aligned; if necessary, turn the nut to align the holes, making sure that the nut is still secure. Insert a new split pin and bend it back to secure.

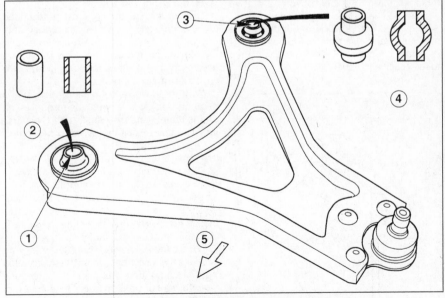

**7.21 Front suspension lower arm bushes**

1 *Front bush*  3 *Rear bush*  5 *Front of car*
2 *Cylindrical inner tube*  4 *Barrel-shaped inner tube*

**8.2 Original riveted front suspension lower arm balljoint**

**27** Swivel the anti-roll bar down, then reconnect the link to the bar and tighten the nut to the specified torque.

**28** Refit the auxiliary drivebelt cover where necessary.

**29** Refit the wheel and lower the car to the ground. Tighten the wheel nuts to the specified torque. Have the front wheel alignment checked as soon as possible, especially if non-genuine parts have been fitted.

### Left-hand lower arm

**30** Locate the lower arm on the subframe and insert the mounting bolts. Fit the nuts and tighten them in stages, first to the specified torque and then through the angle specified.

**31** Carefully lower the engine/transmission back into position and reconnect the left- and right-hand mountings. Do not fully tighten the mountings at this stage.

**32** Reconnect the front and rear mountings to the subframe, using the alignment marks made on removal.

**33** Tighten all the engine mountings to the specified torque (see Chapter 2A), then remove the engine hoist or support bar.

**34** Refit the front lower arm balljoint to the hub carrier and insert the clamp bolt with its head facing forwards. Refit the nut and tighten to the specified torque.

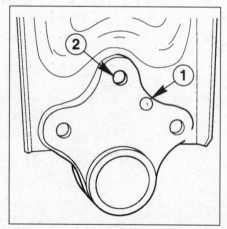

**8.5 Location lug (1) and bolt hole (2) in the front suspension lower arm balljoint**

**35** Refit the left-hand driveshaft to the transmission as described in Chapter 8 and reconnect the gearchange linkage as described in Chapter 7.

**36** Refit the front wheel and lower the car to the ground. Tighten the wheel nuts to the specified torque.

**37** Refit the air cleaner as described in Chapter 4A.

**38** Remove the strut upper mounting nut and fit a new one. Tighten the nut to the specified torque, while holding the piston rod with an 8 mm Allen key. If the adapter needed to do this is not available, the nut can be tightened initially with a ring spanner while the piston rod is held. Final tightening can then be carried out using a torque wrench and a conventional socket.

**39** Have the front wheel alignment checked as soon as possible, especially if non-genuine parts have been fitted.

## 8 Front lower arm balljoint – renewal

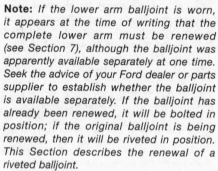

**Note:** *If the lower arm balljoint is worn, it appears at the time of writing that the complete lower arm must be renewed (see Section 7), although the balljoint was apparently available separately at one time. Seek the advice of your Ford dealer or parts supplier to establish whether the balljoint is available separately. If the balljoint has already been renewed, it will be bolted in position; if the original balljoint is being renewed, then it will be riveted in position. This Section describes the renewal of a riveted balljoint.*

**1** Remove the front lower arm as described in Section 7. It is not recommended that the balljoint be renewed with the lower arm in position on the car; the accurate drilling necessary may not be possible, and the holes in the arm may be enlarged.

**2** With the lower arm on the bench, use a 3 mm drill to make a pilot hole through each of the three rivets (see illustration). Now use a 9 mm drill to drill the rivets to a depth of 12 mm, then use a 7 or 8 mm drift to drive the rivets out of the arm.

**3** Clean any rust or dirt from the rivet holes.

**4** The new balljoint is supplied with a protective plastic cover over the rubber boot and stub, and it is recommended that this remains in position until it is time to connect the balljoint to the hub carrier.

**5** Locate the new balljoint on the lower arm and use three new bolts to secure it, inserting the bolts from the top of the arm. Tighten the nuts to the specified torque. Make sure that the location lug on the balljoint engages the hole in the lower arm (see illustration).

**6** Refit the front lower arm as described in Section 7.

## 9 Rear hub and bearings (Saloon/Hatchback) – inspection and renewal

**Note:** *Removal of the rear hub damages the bearings and renders them unserviceable for future use. The hub and bearing assembly must always be renewed if it is removed.*

### Inspection

**1** The rear hub bearings are non-adjustable, and are supplied complete with the hub. It is not possible to renew the bearings separately from the hub.

**2** To check the bearings for excessive wear, chock the front wheels, then jack up the rear of the car and support it on axle stands (see *Jacking and vehicle support*). Fully release the handbrake.

**3** Grip the rear wheel at the top and bottom and attempt to rock it (see illustration). If excessive movement is noted, or if there is any roughness or vibration felt when the wheel is spun, it is indicative that the hub bearings are worn.

### Renewal

**4** Remove the rear wheel.

**5** Remove the rear brake drum or disc as described in Chapter 9.

**6** Tap off the dust cap and unscrew the hub nut. Note that the nut is of special laminated design – Ford state that it can be re-used up to 5 times, but owners may prefer to fit a new nut every time. When the nut is removed, check it carefully for signs of splitting – it is not unknown for these nuts to split during tightening, and it pays to have a new nut to hand.

**7** Using a suitable puller, draw the hub and bearing assembly off the stub axle. Note that this procedure renders the bearings unserviceable for future use.

**8** Locate the new rear hub and bearing assembly on the stub axle, then fit the hub nut and tighten it to the specified torque.

**9** Tap the dust cap fully onto the hub.

**10** Refit the rear brake disc or drum as applicable, as described in Chapter 9.

**11** Refit the rear wheel and lower the car to the ground. Tighten the wheel nuts to the specified torque.

**9.3 Assessing rear wheel bearing play**

## 10 Rear hub carrier (Saloon/Hatchback) – removal and refitting

**Note:** *Removal of the rear hub from the hub carrier damages the bearings and renders them unserviceable for future use. The hub and bearing assembly must always be renewed if it is removed.*

### Removal

1 Chock the front wheels, engage 1st gear and loosen the relevant rear wheel nuts. Jack up the rear of the car and support it on axle stands (see *Jacking and vehicle support*). Remove the rear wheel.

2 When applicable, remove the ABS sensor from the hub carrier as described in Chapter 9.

3 Remove the rear hub and bearing assembly as described in Section 9.

### Drum brake models

4 Fit a brake hose clamp to the flexible brake hose, then release the clip and detach the flexible hose from the strut.

5 Unscrew the union nut and detach the rigid brake pipe from the wheel cylinder. If preferred (to eliminate any bleeding procedure during refitting) the rigid brake pipe may remain attached to the wheel cylinder, provided that care is taken to prevent damage to both the rigid and flexible brake pipes.

6 Unbolt the backplate from the rear hub carrier, and support it to one side on an axle stand **(see illustration)**. The brake shoes and handbrake cable can remain attached.

### Disc brake models

7 Unbolt the splash shield from the rear hub carrier.

### All models

8 Unscrew the bolt securing the tie-bar to the bottom of the hub carrier and move the tie-bar downwards.

9 Unscrew the bolts securing the front and rear lower arms to the hub carrier and move the arms to one side.

10 Support the hub carrier on an axle stand, then unscrew the clamp bolt securing the hub carrier to the strut.

11 Prise the top of the hub carrier apart carefully using a large flat-bladed tool and

**10.6 Two of the bolts securing the brake backplate to the rear hub carrier**

withdraw the hub carrier downwards from the strut. Withdraw the hub carrier from under the rear wheel arch.

### Refitting

12 Locate the hub carrier fully on the strut, then insert the clamp bolt and tighten to the specified torque.

13 Refit the front and rear lower arms to the hub carrier and insert the bolts finger-tight at this stage.

14 Refit the tie-bar to the bottom of the hub carrier and insert the bolt finger-tight at this stage.

15 Refit the backplate (or splash shield, as applicable) to the rear hub carrier and tighten the bolts to the specified torque.

### Drum brake models

16 Reconnect the rigid brake pipe to the wheel cylinder (if disconnected) and tighten the union nut.

17 Attach the flexible hose to the strut, refit the clip and remove the hose clamp.

### All models

18 Fit a new rear hub and bearing assembly as described in Section 9.

19 Where applicable, refit the ABS sensor as described in Chapter 9.

20 Refit the wheel and lower the car to the ground. Tighten the wheel nuts to the specified torque.

21 With the weight of the car on the suspension, fully tighten the mounting bolts for the tie-bar and lower arms.

22 Where applicable, bleed the hydraulic brake circuit as described in Chapter 9.

## 11 Rear strut (Saloon/Hatchback) – removal and refitting

**Note:** *In order to remove the rear strut, the coil spring must be temporarily compressed. This will enable the piston rod to be retracted into the strut, and will provide additional room for releasing the strut from the bump stop on top of the rear crossmember.*

⚠ **Warning: It is important to only use a high-quality spring compressor; carefully follow the tool manufacturer's instructions provided with it.**

### Removal

1 Chock the front wheels, engage 1st gear and loosen the relevant rear wheel nuts. Jack up the rear of the car and support it on axle stands (see *Jacking and vehicle support*). Remove the rear wheel.

2 Where fitted, unclip the ABS sensor wiring from the strut and remove the sensor from the hub carrier as described in Chapter 9 **(see illustration)**.

3 On drum brake models, fit a brake hose clamp to the rear flexible brake hose, then unscrew the union nut securing the rigid brake pipe to the flexible hose on the strut. Extract the clip and disconnect the flexible hose from the strut.

4 On models with rear disc brakes, unbolt the caliper from the hub carrier as described in Chapter 9, but leave the hydraulic hose attached. Support the caliper on an axle stand, making sure that the flexible hose is not strained.

5 Unscrew the nut securing the rear anti-roll bar link to the front lower arm on the appropriate side. Hold the actual link with an adjustable spanner or grips while unscrewing the nut, to prevent damage to the link joint.

6 Unscrew the bolt securing the tie-bar to the bottom of the hub carrier. Move the tie-bar downwards **(see illustrations)**.

7 Unscrew the bolts securing the front and rear lower arms to the hub carrier, and move the arms to one side **(see illustrations)**.

8 Support the hub carrier on a trolley jack, then unscrew the clamp bolt securing the hub carrier to the strut **(see illustrations)**.

**11.2 Unclipping the ABS sensor wiring from the strut**

**11.6a Tie-bar mounting bolt on hub carrier**

**11.6b Remove the bolt . . .**

11.6c . . . and move the tie-bar downwards

11.7a Unscrew the bolt . . .

11.7b . . . and remove the rear lower arm from the hub carrier

**9** Prise the clamp on the hub carrier apart using a large flat-bladed tool. Disconnect the hub carrier from the strut and lower it on the trolley jack as far as possible, taking care not to damage the handbrake cable **(see illustration)**.

**10** Fit the coil spring compressor tool (ensuring that it is fully engaged) and compress the coil spring until all tension is relieved from the upper and lower mountings **(see illustration)**. This will also release the bracket on the strut from the bump stop rubber on the top of the rear crossmember.

**11** Support the strut, then reach up under the wheel arch and unscrew the two bolts securing the upper mounting to the underbody **(see illustration)**.

**12** Slightly lift the strut, to force the piston into the shock absorber and release the strut bracket from the bump stop on the crossmember. Lower the strut assembly and withdraw it from under the car **(see illustration)**.

### Refitting

**13** Locate the strut assembly (together with the coil spring compressor tool) under the wheel arch, and locate the bracket on the bump stop on the rear crossmember. Insert the two bolts securing the upper mounting to the underbody tower and tighten them to the specified torque.

**14** Carefully release the coil spring compressor tool, making sure that the spring locates correctly in the upper and lower seats and that the strut bracket locates on the crossmember bump stop. The bump stop is tapered inwards, and the strut bracket should be fully engaged with it before releasing the coil spring.

**15** Raise the hub carrier and engage it with the strut, then insert the clamp bolt and tighten to the specified torque.

**16** Reconnect the front and rear lower arms to the hub carrier and finger-tighten the bolts at this stage.

**17** Reconnect the tie-bar to the bottom of the hub carrier and finger-tighten the bolt at this stage.

**18** Refit the anti-roll bar link to the lower arm and tighten the nut to the specified torque.

**19** On disc brake models, refit the caliper bracket to the hub carrier and tighten the mounting bolts to the specified torque (see Chapter 9). Make sure that the flexible brake hose is not twisted.

**20** On drum brake models, connect the flexible hose to the strut, insert the clip, then insert the rigid brake line and tighten the union nut. Remove the brake hose clamp, then

11.8a Support the hub carrier on a trolley jack . . .

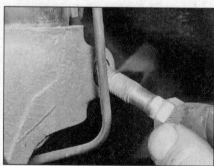

11.8b . . . and remove the hub carrier-to-strut clamp bolt

11.9 Separating the hub carrier from the strut

11.10 Compressor tools fitted to the rear coil spring

11.11 Bolts securing the strut upper mounting to the underbody

11.12 Removing the rear suspension strut

**12.1a  Rear strut dismantling – unscrew the upper mounting nut . . .**

**12.1b . . . remove the cup . . .**

**12.1c . . . upper mounting bracket and seat . . .**

bleed the hydraulic brake circuit as described in Chapter 9.

**21**  Where applicable, refit the ABS sensor as described in Chapter 9 and clip the wiring to the strut.

**22**  Refit the wheel and lower the car to the ground. Tighten the wheel nuts to the specified torque.

**23**  With the weight of the car on the rear suspension, fully tighten the lower arm and tie-bar mounting bolts.

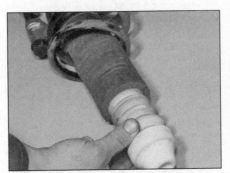

**12.1d . . . gaiter and bump stop . . .**

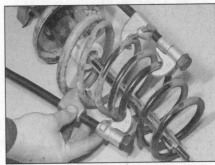

**12.1e . . . and coil spring**

## 12  Rear strut (Saloon/Hatchback) – overhaul

The procedure is similar to that for the front strut, and reference should be made to Section 5. Note that the spring compressor tools will already be in position on the coil spring following the removal operation. Refer also to the accompanying illustrations for details of the separate components **(see illustrations)**.

## 13  Rear anti-roll bar and links (Saloon/Hatchback) – removal and refitting

### Removal

**1**  Chock the front wheels, engage 1st gear and loosen the relevant rear wheel nuts. Jack up the rear of the car and support it on axle stands (see *Jacking and vehicle support*). Remove the rear wheel.

**2**  Unscrew the nuts securing the anti-roll bar links to the front lower arms on both sides. Hold the upper part of the links with a spanner while loosening the nuts. Recover the rubber bushes **(see illustrations)**.

**3**  Unscrew the bolts securing the anti-roll bar mounting clamps to the rear crossmember **(see illustration)**, then unhook the clamps and withdraw the anti-roll bar from under the car.

**4**  Examine the rubber bushes for the mounting clamps and links and if necessary renew them. The links are available individually.

### Refitting

**5**  Locate the anti-roll bar on the rear cross-

member, hook the mounting clamps in position and insert the bolts. Tighten the bolts to the specified torque.

**6**  Locate the anti-roll bar links in the front lower arms on both sides, making sure that

**13.2a  Loosen the nut . . .**

**13.2c . . . and remove the anti-roll bar link from the lower arm**

the rubber bushes are in position. Refit the nuts and tighten them to the specified torque.

**7**  Refit the rear wheels and lower the car to the ground. Tighten the wheel nuts to the specified torque.

**13.2b . . . remove the nut and rubber bush . . .**

**13.3  Rear anti-roll bar mounting clamp**

**14.9 Bolt securing the rear lower arm to the crossmember**

## 14 Rear lower arms (Saloon/Hatchback) – removal and refitting

### Removal

**1** Chock the front wheels, engage 1st gear and loosen the relevant rear wheel nuts. Jack up the rear of the car and support it on axle stands (see *Jacking and vehicle support*). Remove the rear wheel.

#### Front lower arm

**2** To remove the front lower arm, it is necessary to remove the fuel tank first. Refer to Chapter 4A for details.

**3** Unscrew the nut and disconnect the anti-roll bar link from the lower arm. Hold the link with an adjustable spanner or grips while unscrewing the nut, to prevent damage to the link joint. Recover the rubber bush.

**4** Unscrew the bolt securing the front lower arm to the hub carrier.

**5** Unscrew the bolt securing the front lower arm to the crossmember.

**6** Withdraw the front lower arm from under the car.

#### Rear lower arm

**7** Unscrew the bolt securing the rear lower arm to the hub carrier.

**8** The bolt securing the rear lower arm to the crossmember has an eccentric head and spacer, which are used to adjust the rear toe setting. Before removing this bolt, mark its position, using a scriber or similar sharp instrument through the aperture in the crossmember.

**15.4 Tie-bar bracket on the underbody**

**14.11 TOP marking on the rear lower arm**

**9** Unscrew the bolt securing the rear lower arm to the crossmember (see illustration). The bolt may be removed through the aperture in the crossmember. Recover the eccentric spacer.

**10** Withdraw the rear lower arm from under the car.

### Refitting

**11** Refitting is a reversal of the removal procedure, noting the following points:

a) *The arm mounting bolts should be finger-tightened initially and only fully tightened after the car is lowered to the ground, so that its weight is on the rear suspension. Note that the rear lower arm is marked TOP for correct refitting (see illustration).*

b) *The rear toe setting should be checked and if necessary adjusted, at the earliest opportunity.*

## 15 Rear tie-bar (Saloon/Hatchback) – removal and refitting

### Removal

**1** Chock the front wheels, engage 1st gear and loosen the relevant rear wheel nuts. Jack up the rear of the car and support it on axle stands (see *Jacking and vehicle support*). Remove the rear wheel.

**2** Disconnect the handbrake cable from the tie-bar bracket on the underbody.

**3** Unscrew the bolt securing the tie-bar bracket to the rear hub carrier.

**4** Unscrew the bolts securing the tie-bar

**16.8 One of the rear suspension crossmember mounting bolts**

bracket to the underbody and withdraw the bracket from the car (see illustration).

**5** Mount the bracket in a vice, then unscrew the bolt and remove the tie-bar from the bracket.

**6** It is not possible to renew the rubber bushes – if they are worn excessively, the tie-bar should be renewed complete.

### Refitting

**7** Refitting is a reversal of the removal procedure, noting the following points:

a) *The bracket-to-underbody bolts should be fully tightened to the specified torque before lowering the car.*

b) *The bolts securing the tie-bar to the bracket and hub carrier should be finger-tightened initially and only fully tightened after the car is lowered to the ground, so that its weight is on the rear suspension.*

## 16 Rear crossmember (Saloon/Hatchback) – removal and refitting

**Note:** *Before attempting to remove the rear crossmember, tools to hold the coil springs in compression must be obtained. Careful use of conventional coil spring compressors will prove satisfactory.*

### Removal

**1** Chock the front wheels, engage 1st gear and loosen the rear wheel nuts. Jack up the rear of the car and support it on axle stands, making sure that the car is supported high enough for the crossmember to be removed (see *Jacking and vehicle support*). Remove the rear wheels.

**2** Remove the complete exhaust system as described in Chapter 4A.

**3** Unscrew the bolts securing the tie-bars to the rear hub carriers and disconnect the tie-bars.

**4** Unscrew the nuts securing the rear anti-roll bar links to the front lower arms. Hold the actual links stationary while the nuts are being unscrewed, to prevent damage to the joints. Swivel the anti-roll bar upwards and recover the rubber bushes.

**5** Where applicable, remove the ABS wheel sensor from the rear hub carrier as described in Chapter 9.

**6** Unscrew the bolts and disconnect both lower arms from the rear hub carrier.

**7** To allow the rear struts to be released from the rubber stops on the top of the crossmember, it is necessary to fit coil spring compressor tools to both of the rear coil springs and compress them until all tension is removed from the upper and lower mountings. With the compressor tools fitted, support the struts to one side.

⚠️ **Warning: It is important to only use high-quality spring compressors, and to carefully follow the tool manufacturer's instructions provided with them.**

**8** Make accurate alignment markings between

the crossmember and the underbody, for use on refitting. Support the rear crossmember on a trolley jack, then unscrew the four mounting bolts from the underbody (see illustration).

9 Lower the crossmember to the ground.

10 Unscrew the bolts securing the anti-roll bar clamps to the crossmember, then remove the clamps and withdraw the anti-roll bar.

11 Remove the lower arms from the crossmember as described in Section 14.

### Refitting

12 Refitting is a reversal of the removal procedure, noting the following points:

a) Ford specify the use of a special tool (tool number 15-097) to accurately align the crossmember onto the underbody before tightening the mounting bolts. This tool should be obtained if possible, since inaccurate alignment would result in bad handling and excessive tyre wear. However, if the marks made on removal are accurately aligned, the crossmember should be refitted in exactly the same position as before.

b) The tie-bar and arm mounting bolts should be finger-tightened initially, and only fully tightened after the car is lowered to the ground, so that its weight is on the rear suspension.

c) The rear toe setting should be checked and if necessary adjusted, at the earliest opportunity.

## 17 Rear hub and bearings (Estate) – inspection and renewal

### Inspection

1 The rear hub bearings are non-adjustable, and are supplied complete with the hub. It is not possible to renew the bearings separately from the hub.

2 To check the bearings for excessive wear, chock the front wheels, then jack up the rear of the car and support it on axle stands (see Jacking and vehicle support). Fully release the handbrake.

3 Grip the rear wheel at the top and bottom and attempt to rock it. If excessive movement is noted, or if there is any roughness or vibration felt when the wheel is spun, it is indicative that the hub bearings are worn.

### Renewal

4 Remove the rear wheel.

5 Remove the rear brake drum or disc as described in Chapter 9.

6 Turning the hub as necessary, line up the hole in the flange with the each of the bolts securing the hub assembly to the rear hub carrier; unscrew the bolts (see illustration).

7 Withdraw the hub and bearing assembly. Refit two of the hub mounting bolts, to hold the backplate/splash shield in place.

8 If necessary, the stub shaft may be removed from the hub for inspection of the bearing, by unscrewing the hub nut. Note that the nut is of special laminated design – Ford state that it can be re-used up to 5 times, but owners may prefer to fit a new nut every time. When the nut is removed, check it carefully for signs of splitting – it is not unknown for these nuts to split during tightening, and it pays to have a new nut to hand. Tighten the nut to the specified torque on reassembly.

9 Fit the new hub and bearing assembly using a reversal of the removal procedure. Tighten all nuts and bolts to the specified torque.

## 18 Rear hub carrier (Estate) – removal and refitting

### Removal

1 Chock the front wheels, engage 1st gear and loosen the relevant rear wheel nuts. Jack up the rear of the car and support it on axle stands (see Jacking and vehicle support). Remove the rear wheel, then release the handbrake.

2 Position a trolley jack or axle stand beneath the rear lower arm, to keep the coil spring in compression.

3 Where applicable, remove the ABS sensor as described in Chapter 9.

#### Drum brake models

4 Remove the rear brake drum as described in Chapter 9.

5 Disconnect the flexible hydraulic brake hose at the bracket on the rear crossmember as described in Chapter 9.

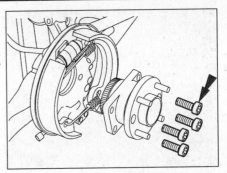

**17.6 Rear hub mounting bolts – Estate models**

#### Disc brake models

6 Remove the rear brake disc as described in Chapter 9.

#### All models

7 Remove the rear hub as described in Section 17.

8 Remove the backplate or splash shield, as applicable. On drum brake models, support the backplate assembly on an axle stand, to prevent damage to the handbrake cable.

9 Unscrew the shock absorber lower mounting bolt.

10 Unscrew the three bolts securing the tie-bar to the hub carrier.

11 Unscrew the bolt securing the front lower arm to the hub carrier (see illustration).

12 Unscrew the bolt securing the upper arm to the hub carrier (see illustration).

13 Support the hub carrier, then unscrew the bolt securing the rear lower arm to the hub carrier (see illustration) and withdraw the hub carrier.

### Refitting

14 Refitting is a reversal of the removal procedure, noting the following points:

a) Delay fully tightening the rubber bush mounting bolts until the weight of the car is on the suspension. Tighten all bolts to the specified torque.

b) Where the flexible rear brake hose was disconnected, bleed the hydraulic system as described in Chapter 9.

c) Finally check and if necessary adjust the rear wheel toe setting as described in Section 36.

**18.11 Front lower arm-to-hub carrier bolt**

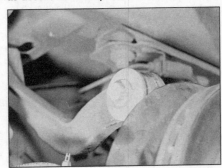

**18.12 Upper arm-to-hub carrier bolt**

**18.13 Rear lower arm-to-hub carrier bolt**

**19.3 Rear shock absorber lower mounting bolt – Estate models**

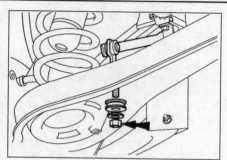

**20.3a Mounting nut and rubber bush securing the rear anti-roll bar link to the rear lower arm**

**20.3b View of the anti-roll bar link nut through the rear lower arm**

**20.4 Anti-roll bar mounting clamp on the rear suspension crossmember**

## 19 Rear shock absorber (Estate) – removal, testing and refitting

### Removal

**1** Chock the front wheels, engage 1st gear and loosen the relevant rear wheel nuts. Jack up the rear of the car and support it on axle stands (see *Jacking and vehicle support*). Remove the rear wheel.

**2** Position a trolley jack under the coil spring area of the rear lower arm, to keep the coil spring in compression.

**3** Unscrew the shock absorber lower mounting bolt **(see illustration)**.

**4** Unscrew the upper mounting bolt and withdraw the shock absorber from under the car.

### Testing

**5** Check the mounting rubbers for damage and deterioration. If they are worn, they may be renewed separately from the shock absorber body.

**6** Mount the shock absorber in a vice, gripping it by the lower mounting. Examine the shock absorber for signs of fluid leakage. Test the operation of the shock absorber by moving it through a full stroke and then through short strokes of 50 to 100 mm. In both cases, the resistance felt should be smooth and continuous. If the resistance is jerky or uneven, the shock absorber should be renewed.

### Refitting

**7** Refitting is a reversal of the removal procedure, tightening the mounting bolts to the specified torque.

## 20 Rear anti-roll bar and links (Estate) – removal and refitting

### Removal

**1** Chock the front wheels, engage 1st gear and loosen the rear wheel nuts. Jack up the rear of the car and support it on axle stands (see *Jacking and vehicle support*). Remove the rear wheels.

**2** Where applicable, remove the two bolts and disconnect the brake compensator operating arm from the anti-roll bar.

**3** Unscrew the nuts and remove the washers and bushes securing the anti-roll bar links to the rear lower arms **(see illustrations)**.

**4** Using a Torx key, unscrew the bolts securing the anti-roll bar mounting clamps to the rear crossmember **(see illustration)**; release the clamps and withdraw the anti-roll bar from under the car.

**5** Examine the rubber bushes for the mounting clamps and links and if necessary renew them. The links are available individually.

### Refitting

**6** Locate the anti-roll bar on the rear crossmember, then refit the clamps and tighten the bolts to the specified torque.

**7** Refit the anti-roll bar links to the rear lower arms, together with the bushes and washers. Tighten the nuts to the specified torque, while holding the links stationary in their central position.

**8** Refit the rear wheels and lower the car to the ground. Tighten the wheel nuts to the specified torque.

## 21 Rear coil spring (Estate) – removal and refitting

**Note:** *Before attempting to remove the rear coil spring, a tool to hold the coil spring in compression must be obtained. Careful use of conventional coil spring compressors will prove satisfactory.*

### Removal

**1** Chock the front wheels, engage 1st gear and loosen the relevant rear wheel nuts. Jack up the rear of the car and support it on axle stands (see *Jacking and vehicle support*). Remove the rear wheel.

**2** Support the weight of the rear lower arm beneath the coil spring position with a trolley jack.

**3** Fit the coil spring compressor tool (ensuring that it is fully engaged) and compress the coil spring until all tension is relieved from the upper mounting.

**4** Unscrew the nut and remove the washer and bush attaching the anti-roll bar link to the rear lower arm.

**5** Unscrew the bolt securing the rear lower arm to the hub carrier **(see illustration)**.

**21.5 Rear lower arm-to-hub carrier mounting bolt**

**21.6 Front lower arm-to-hub carrier mounting bolt**

**6** Unscrew the bolt securing the front lower arm to the hub carrier (see illustration).

**7** Lower the rear lower arm and withdraw the coil spring from under the car (see illustration). Take care to keep the compressor tool in full engagement with the coil spring.

**8** If a new coil spring is to be fitted, the original coil spring must be released from the compressor. If it is to be re-used, the coil spring can be left in compression.

### Refitting

**9** Refitting is a reversal of the removal procedure, noting the following points:

a) *Make sure that the coil spring is located correctly in the upper and lower seats* (see illustration).

b) *Delay fully tightening the two lower arm mounting bolts until the weight of the car is on the rear suspension.*

c) *Finally check and if necessary adjust the rear wheel toe setting as described in Section 36.*

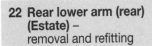

## 22 Rear lower arm (rear) (Estate) – removal and refitting

### Removal

**1** Remove the rear coil spring as described in Section 21.

**2** The bolt securing the rear lower arm to the crossmember has an eccentric head and spacer, which are used to adjust the rear toe setting. Before removing this bolt, mark its position, using a scriber or similar sharp instrument through the aperture in the crossmember.

**3** Unscrew the bolt securing the rear lower arm to the crossmember. The bolt may be removed through the aperture in the crossmember. Recover the eccentric spacer (see illustration).

**4** Withdraw the rear lower arm from under the car.

### Refitting

**5** Refitting is a reversal of the removal procedure, noting the following points:

a) *Delay fully tightening the lower arm mounting bolts until the weight of the car is on the rear suspension.*

b) *Finally check and if necessary adjust the rear wheel toe setting as described in Section 36.*

## 23 Rear lower arm (front) (Estate) – removal and refitting

### Removal

**1** Chock the front wheels, engage 1st gear and loosen the relevant rear wheel nuts. Jack up the rear of the car and support it on axle stands (see *Jacking and vehicle support*). Remove the rear wheel.

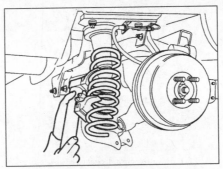

**21.7 Removing the coil spring, with compressor tool attached, from under the car**

**2** Unscrew the bolt securing the front lower arm to the crossmember (see illustration).

**3** Unscrew the bolt securing the front lower arm to the hub carrier and withdraw the arm from under the car (see illustration).

### Refitting

**4** Refitting is a reversal of the removal procedure, but delay fully tightening the mounting bolts until the weight of the car is on the rear suspension.

## 24 Rear upper arm (Estate) – removal and refitting

### Removal

**1** Chock the front wheels, engage 1st gear

**22.3 Bolts securing the rear lower arms to the crossmember – note the eccentric spacers**

**23.3 Front lower arm**

**21.9 Correct location (arrowed) of the coil spring in the upper seat**

and loosen the relevant rear wheel nuts. Jack up the rear of the car and support it on axle stands (see *Jacking and vehicle support*). Remove the rear wheel.

**2** Using a trolley jack, support the rear lower arm beneath the coil spring position.

**3** Unscrew the bolt securing the upper arm to the hub carrier (see illustration).

**4** Unscrew the bolt securing the upper arm to the crossmember and withdraw the arm from under the car.

### Refitting

**5** Refitting is a reversal of the removal procedure, but delay fully tightening the mounting bolts until the weight of the car is on the rear suspension.

**23.2 Front lower arm-to-crossmember securing bolt**

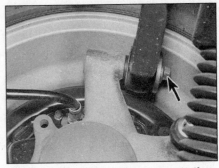

**24.3 Bolt securing the upper arm to the hub carrier**

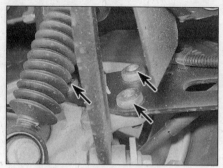

**25.7 Bolts securing the rear suspension tie-bar to the hub carrier**

**25.8a Tie-bar bracket front bolt on the underbody**

**25.8b Tie-bar bracket rear bolt on the underbody**

## 25 Rear tie-bar (Estate) – removal and refitting

### Removal

**1** Chock the front wheels, engage 1st gear and loosen the relevant rear wheel nuts. Jack up the rear of the car and support it on axle stands (see *Jacking and vehicle support*). Remove the rear wheel.

**2** Using a trolley jack, support the rear lower arm beneath the coil spring position.

**3** Unscrew the bolt securing the rear shock absorber to the hub carrier.

**4** Where applicable, release the ABS wheel sensor lead from the tie-bar.

**5** Detach the handbrake cable from the tie-bar bracket.

**6** Refer to Chapter 9 and disconnect the handbrake cable from the rear brake shoes or rear caliper, as applicable. Pass the cable through the hole in the tie-bar.

**7** Unscrew the three bolts securing the tie-bar to the hub carrier **(see illustration)**.

**8** Unbolt the tie-bar bracket from the underbody and withdraw the assembly from under the car **(see illustrations)**.

**9** Mount the tie-bar in a vice, then unscrew the bolt and separate the tie-bar from its bracket.

**10** It is not possible to renew the rubber bush in the tie-bar and if it is excessively worn, the complete tie-bar must be renewed.

### Refitting

**11** Refitting is a reversal of the removal procedure, noting the following points:
  a) *Delay fully tightening the bolt which secures the arm to the bracket until the weight of the car is on the rear suspension.*
  b) *On completion, check the operation of the handbrake.*

## 26 Rear crossmember (Estate) – removal and refitting

### Removal

**1** Chock the front wheels, engage 1st gear and loosen the rear wheel nuts. Jack up the rear of the car and support it on axle stands, making sure that the car is supported high enough for the crossmember to be removed (see *Jacking and vehicle support*). Remove the rear wheels.

**2** Disconnect the handbrake rear cables from the front primary cable, as described in Chapter 9.

**3** Where applicable, remove the ABS wheel sensors from the rear hub carriers and disconnect the wiring leads from the clips as described in Chapter 9.

**4** Disconnect the flexible brake hoses from the brackets on both sides of the crossmember, as described in Chapter 9.

**5** Working on each side of the car, unbolt the tie-bar brackets from the underbody.

**6** Support the rear crossmember on a trolley jack.

**7** Unscrew the mounting bolts and lower the crossmember to the ground **(see illustrations)**.

**8** If necessary, remove the suspension components from the crossmember as described in the appropriate Sections of this Chapter.

### Refitting

**9** Refitting is a reversal of the removal procedure, noting the following points:
  a) *When raising the crossmember, note that guide pins are provided to ensure correct alignment (see illustration).*
  b) *Delay fully tightening the suspension mounting bolts until the weight of the car is on the rear suspension.*
  c) *Tighten all bolts to the specified torque.*
  d) *If necessary, bleed the brake hydraulic system as described in Chapter 9.*
  e) *Check and if necessary adjust the rear wheel toe setting as described in Section 36.*

## 27 Steering wheel – removal and refitting

 *Warning: All models are equipped with an airbag system. Make sure that the safety recommendations given in Chapter 12 are followed, to prevent personal injury.*

**26.7a Rear suspension crossmember rear mounting bolt**

**26.7b Rear suspension crossmember front mounting bolt**

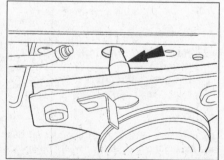

**26.9 Guide pin for correct alignment of the rear crossmember**

**27.5 Removing the steering wheel retaining bolt**

## Removal

**1** Disconnect the battery negative (earth) lead (refer to Chapter 5, Section 1).

 *Warning: Before proceeding, wait a minimum of 15 minutes, as a precaution against accidental firing of the airbag unit. This period ensures that any stored energy in the back-up capacitor is dissipated.*

**2** Turn the steering wheel so that the front wheels are in the straight-ahead position.

**3** Unscrew the screws (two above, three below) and remove the steering column upper and lower shrouds.

**4** Remove the airbag unit from the steering wheel as described in Chapter 12.

 *Warning: Position the airbag module in a safe place, with the cover facing upwards.*

**5** Make sure that the steering lock is not engaged. Unscrew the retaining bolt from the centre of the steering wheel (see illustration).

**6** Remove the steering wheel from the top of the column, while feeding the horn and airbag wiring through the hole in the steering wheel hub (see illustration).

## Refitting

**7** Make sure that the front wheels are still facing straight-ahead, then locate the steering wheel on the top of the steering column.

**8** Refit the retaining bolt and tighten it to the specified torque while holding the steering wheel (see illustration). Do not tighten the bolt with the steering lock engaged, as this may damage the lock.

**27.6 Feeding the horn and airbag wiring through the hole in the steering wheel hub**

**9** Reconnect the horn wiring connections and airbag multi-plug.

**10** Locate the airbag module/horn contact on the steering wheel, then insert the mounting screws and tighten them.

**11** Refit the steering column upper and lower shrouds, ensuring that the rubber ring around the lock barrel is fitted before offering the lower shroud into place and that the column switch gaiters engage correctly.

**12** Reconnect the battery negative lead.

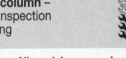

**28 Steering column –**
removal, inspection
and refitting

 *Warning: All models are equipped with an airbag system. Make sure that the safety recommendations given in Chapter 12 are followed, to prevent personal injury.*

**28.4a Unscrew the screws from the lower shroud . . .**

**27.8 Tightening the steering wheel retaining bolt**

## Removal

**1** Disconnect the battery negative (earth) lead (refer to Chapter 5, Section 1).

 *Warning: Before proceeding, wait a minimum of 15 minutes, as a precaution against accidental firing of the airbag unit. This period ensures that any stored energy in the back-up capacitor is dissipated.*

**2** Turn the steering wheel so that the front wheels are in the straight-ahead position.

**3** Remove the ignition key, then turn the steering wheel slightly as necessary until the steering lock engages.

**4** Unscrew the screws (two above, three below) and remove the steering column lower and upper shrouds. As the lower shroud is being removed, it will be necessary to remove the rubber ring from the ignition switch/steering lock (see illustrations).

**28.4b . . . remove the rubber ring . . .**

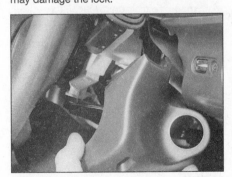

**28.4c . . . and remove the lower shroud**

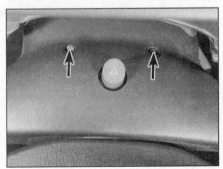

**28.4d Upper shroud retaining screws**

**28.4e Removing the upper shroud**

**28.5a On models with the PATS immobiliser, disconnect the wiring plug . . .**

**28.5b . . . then remove the mounting screw and remove the transceiver**

**28.7a Unscrew the clamp plate bolt . . .**

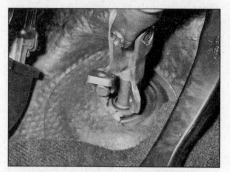

**28.7b . . . and swivel the clamp plate around**

**28.8a Disconnecting the multi-plug from the ignition switch**

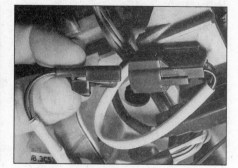

**28.8b Disconnecting the small multi-plug . . .**

5 On models with the PATS immobiliser (April 1995 onwards), remove the immobiliser transceiver from the ignition switch by disconnecting the wiring plug and removing the mounting screw **(see illustrations)**.

6 Remove the driver's side lower facia panel (see Chapter 11, Section 29).

7 Unscrew the clamp plate bolt securing the steering column shaft to the flexible coupling. Swivel the clamp plate around and disengage it from the flexible coupling stub **(see illustrations)**.

8 Release the cable-tie from the wiring loom at the steering column and disconnect the multi-plugs from both sides of the column, noting their locations as necessary **(see illustrations)**.

9 Remove the mounting nut and detach the column lower support brace.

10 Unscrew the steering column mounting bolts.

11 Taking care not to damage the column switches, slide the column upwards to disengage the retaining tab from the groove in the crossbeam bracket and withdraw it from inside the car **(see illustrations)**.

### Inspection

12 With the steering column removed, check the universal joints for wear and examine the column upper and lower shafts for any signs of damage or distortion **(see illustration)**. Where evident, the column should be renewed complete.

13 Examine the height adjustment lever mechanism for wear and damage **(see illustration)**.

14 With the steering lock disengaged, turn the inner column and check the upper and lower bearings for smooth operation. The bearings are obtainable separately and should be renewed if necessary. Dismantling and reassembly of the column assembly is a relatively easy operation.

### Refitting

15 Locate the steering column on its bracket,

**28.8c . . . and main multi-plug from the steering column**

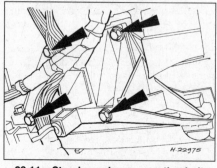

**28.11a Steering column mounting bolt locations**

**28.11b Removing the steering column**

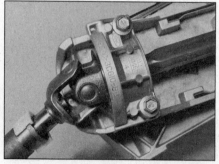

**28.12 Steering column and universal joint**

making sure that the tab slides down into the groove correctly.

**16** Insert the mounting bolts and tighten to the specified torque **(see illustration)**.

**17** Reconnect the column lower support brace and tighten the mounting nut.

**18** Reconnect the various multi-plugs to their correct locations and secure the wiring loom with a cable-tie.

**19** Locate the steering column shaft on the flexible coupling, swivel the clamp plate round, then insert a new bolt and tighten to the specified torque.

**20** Refit the driver's side lower trim panel.

**21** Where applicable, refit the PATS transceiver to the ignition switch.

**22** Refit the steering column upper and lower shrouds, ensuring that the rubber ring around the lock barrel is fitted before offering the lower shroud into place and that the column switch gaiters engage correctly.

**23** Reconnect the battery negative lead.

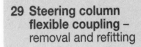

## 29 Steering column flexible coupling – removal and refitting

### Removal

**1** Disconnect the battery negative (earth) lead (refer to Chapter 5, Section 1).

**2** Turn the steering wheel so that the front wheels are in the straight-ahead position. Remove the ignition key, then turn the steering wheel slightly as necessary until the steering lock engages.

**3** Unscrew the clamp plate bolt securing the steering column shaft to the flexible coupling. Swivel the clamp plate around and disengage it from the flexible coupling stub.

**4** Carefully prise the rubber boot from the bulkhead and withdraw it into the passenger compartment. Take care not to damage the sealing lip of the boot.

**5** Using an Allen key, unscrew the clamp bolt securing the flexible coupling to the pinion shaft on the steering gear and withdraw the coupling from inside the car.

### Refitting

**6** Refitting is a reversal of the removal procedure, noting the following points:

a) Use new clamp bolts, tightened to the specified torque.

b) Make sure that the rubber boot engages correctly in the bulkhead and on the flexible coupling.

## 30 Steering gear – removal and refitting

### Removal

**1** Remove the steering column flexible coupling as described in Section 29.

**2** Apply the handbrake, then loosen the front

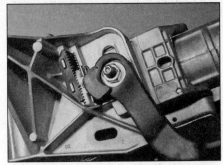

**28.13 Height adjustment lever mechanism**

wheel nuts. Jack up the front of the car and support it on axle stands (see *Jacking and vehicle support*). Remove both front wheels.

**3** Working beneath the car, unbolt the front and rear engine mountings from the subframe. Make accurate alignment markings for refitting the front mounting in particular.

**4** Although not essential, to improve access, remove the exhaust downpipe complete as described in Chapter 4A.

**5** Extract the split pins from the track rod end balljoint nuts, then unscrew the nuts and detach the rods from the hub carrier steering arms using a conventional balljoint removal tool. Take care not to damage the balljoint seals.

**6** Release the securing clips and screws and remove the auxiliary drivebelt cover from the right-hand wheel arch.

**7** Position a suitable container beneath the steering gear, then unscrew the union nuts securing the steering fluid supply, return and cooler lines to the steering gear. Identify the lines for position, then unbolt the clamps, disconnect the lines and allow the fluid to drain into the container. Cover the apertures in the steering gear and also the ends of the fluid pipes, to prevent the ingress of dust and dirt into the hydraulic circuit.

**8** Where applicable, remove the steering gear cover plate, then unscrew the mounting bolts. The bolts are located on top of the steering gear and are difficult to reach. Ideally, the special U-shaped Ford spanner should be used, but it is just possible to reach them with a normal spanner **(see illustration)**.

**9** Withdraw the steering gear through the

**30.8 Ford special tool for unscrewing the steering gear mounting bolts**

wheel arch. Take care that the pressure check valve does not fall out of its port as the gear is removed.

### Refitting

**10** If a new steering gear unit is being fitted, the new unit will be supplied together with union nuts already fitted. The new nuts must only be used with new feed and return lines – otherwise, they must be removed and discarded.

**11** If the original lines and union nuts are being used, the Teflon rings on the union nuts must be renewed. To do this, the rings must be expanded individually onto a fitting adapter, then located in the grooves of the union nuts **(see illustration)**.

**12** Locate the steering gear on the subframe and insert the two mounting bolts. Tighten the bolts to the specified torque. Note that, if the special Ford tool is being used, the bottom of the tool must be turned anti-clockwise in order to tighten the mounting bolts **(see illustration)**.

**13** Reconnect the fluid lines and tighten the union nuts to the specified torque. Refit the clamps and tighten the bolts. Where applicable, refit the steering gear cover and tighten the five bolts securely.

**14** Refit the engine front and rear mountings to the subframe, aligning the marks made on removal and tightening the bolts to the specified torque (see Chapter 2A).

**28.16 Tightening the steering column mounting bolts**

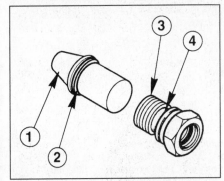

**30.11 Using an adapter to fit the Teflon rings to the union nuts**

1 Adapter
2 Teflon ring
3 Union nut

4 Groove location for the Teflon ring

**15** Refit the exhaust downpipe with reference to Chapter 4A.

**16** Refit the auxiliary drivebelt cover.

**17** Refit the track rod end balljoints to the hub carriers, and tighten the nuts to the specified torque. Check that the split pin holes are aligned; if necessary, turn the nuts to the nearest alignment, making sure that the nut is still secure. Insert new split pins and bend them back to secure.

**18** Refit the front wheels and lower the car to the ground. Tighten the wheel nuts to the specified torque.

**19** Refit the steering column flexible coupling with reference to Section 29.

**20** Fill and bleed the steering hydraulic system as described in Section 32.

**21** Have the front wheel alignment checked and if necessary adjusted, at the earliest opportunity (refer to Section 36).

## 31 Steering gear rubber gaiters – renewal

**1** Remove the track rod end and its locknut from the track rod, as described in Section 35. Make sure that a note is made of the exact position of the track rod end on the track rod, in order to retain the front wheel alignment setting on refitting.

**2** Release the outer retaining clip and inner plastic clamp band and disconnect the gaiter from the steering gear housing.

**3** Disconnect the breather from the gaiter, then slide the gaiter off the track rod.

**4** Scrape off all grease from the old gaiter and apply to the track rod inner joint. Wipe clean the seating areas on the steering gear housing and track rod.

**5** Slide the new gaiter onto the track rod and steering gear housing and reconnect the breather.

**6** Fit a new inner plastic clamp band and outer retaining clip.

**7** Refit the track rod end as described in Section 35.

**8** Have the front wheel alignment checked and if necessary adjusted, at the earliest opportunity (refer to Section 36).

## 32 Steering hydraulic system – bleeding

**1** Following any operation in which the steering system fluid lines have been disconnected, the system must be bled to remove any trapped air.

**2** With the front wheels in the straight-ahead position, check the steering fluid level in the reservoir and, if low, add fresh fluid until it reaches the MAX or MAX COLD mark. Pour the fluid slowly, to prevent air bubbles forming and use only the specified fluid (refer to *Weekly checks*).

**3** Start the engine and allow it to run at a fast

**30.12 Tightening the steering gear mounting bolts using the Ford special tool**

idle. Check the hoses and connections for leaks.

**4** Stop the engine and recheck the fluid level. Add more if necessary, up to the MAX or MAX COLD mark.

**5** Start the engine again, allow it to idle, then bleed the system by slowly turning the steering wheel from side to side several times. This should purge the system of all internal air. However, if air remains in the system (indicated by the steering operation being very noisy), leave the car overnight and repeat the procedure again the next day.

**6** If air still remains in the system, it may be necessary to resort to the Ford method of bleeding, which uses a vacuum pump. Turn the steering to the right until it is near the stop, then fit the vacuum pump to the fluid reservoir and apply 0.15 bars of vacuum. Maintain the vacuum for a minimum of 5 minutes, then repeat the procedure with the steering turned to the left.

**7** Keep the fluid level topped-up throughout the bleeding procedure; note that, as the fluid temperature increases, the level will rise.

**8** On completion, switch off the engine and return the front wheels to the straight-ahead position.

## 33 Steering pump – removal and refitting

### Removal

**1** Disconnect the fluid pressure switch wiring plug **(see illustration)**.

**33.1 Disconnect the wiring plug from the steering fluid pressure switch**

**2** Unscrew the bolt securing the hydraulic fluid line support to the engine lifting bracket on the right-hand side of the engine, and a further bolt securing the line to the pump mounting bracket.

**3** Position a suitable container beneath the steering pump to catch spilt fluid.

**4** Loosen the clip and disconnect the fluid supply hose from the pump inlet. Plug the hose, to prevent the ingress of dust and dirt.

**5** Unscrew the union nut and disconnect the high-pressure line from the pump. Allow the fluid to drain into the container.

**6** Apply the handbrake, then jack up the front of the car and support it on axle stands. Remove the right-hand front wheel.

**7** Unbolt the lower drivebelt cover.

**8** Using a spanner, rotate the drivebelt tensioner in a clockwise direction to release the belt tension, then slip the drivebelt off the pulleys. Refer to Chapter 1 if necessary.

**9** Unscrew the four mounting bolts and withdraw the steering pump from its bracket. Access to the bolts on the right-hand side of the engine is gained by turning the pump pulley until a hole lines up with the bolt.

### Refitting

**10** If necessary, the sealing ring on the high-pressure outlet should be renewed, using the same procedure as described in Section 30.

**11** Locate the steering pump on the mounting bracket and secure with the four bolts. Tighten the bolts to the specified torque.

**12** Check the condition of the drivebelt before refitting it – if there is any sign of deterioration, it makes sense to fit a new one. Slip the drivebelt over the pulleys, then rotate the drivebelt tensioner in a clockwise direction and locate the drivebelt around it. Release the tensioner to tension the drivebelt.

**13** Refit the lower belt cover.

**14** Refit the right-hand front wheel and lower the car to the ground. Tighten the wheel nuts to the specified torque.

**15** Reconnect the high-pressure line to the pump and tighten the union nut.

**16** Reconnect the fluid supply hose to the pump inlet and tighten the clip.

**17** Refit the hydraulic fluid line support to the pump mounting bracket and tighten the bolt.

**18** Refit the hydraulic fluid line support to the engine lifting bracket on the right-hand side of the engine and tighten the bolt.

**19** Fill and bleed the steering hydraulic system as described in Section 32.

## 34 Steering fluid cooler – removal and refitting

### Removal

**1** Apply the handbrake, then jack up the front of the car and support it on axle stands (see *Jacking and vehicle support*).

**2** The fluid hoses to and from the cooler must

**34.2 The fluid cooler hose connections are more easily reached with the front bumper removed**

**34.3a The cooler mounting bolts may be reached from above**

**34.3b Removing the steering fluid cooler from in front of the radiator**

now be disconnected. The connections at the cooler itself are inaccessible with the unit in place, so trace the hoses back from the cooler and disconnect them at the front of the subframe. Alternatively, remove the front bumper as described in Chapter 11 for access **(see illustration)**. Have a container ready to catch spilt fluid and plug the open hose ends quickly, to prevent fluid loss and dirt entry.

**3** If a long enough spanner is available, the cooler mounting bolts can be reached from above; take care not to damage the radiator (or the air conditioning condenser). Remove the two mounting bolts and slide the cooler (and where applicable, its hoses) out of position **(see illustrations)**. Handle the unit carefully, as the cooling fins are easily damaged.

### Refitting

**4** Refitting is a reversal of removal. It may be wise to update the spring-type hose clips with screw-type items when reconnecting the fluid hoses. On completion, fill and bleed the steering system as described in Section 32.

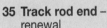

### 35 Track rod end –
renewal

### Removal

**1** Apply the handbrake and loosen the relevant front wheel nuts. Jack up the front of the car and support it on axle stands (see *Jacking and vehicle support*). Remove the front roadwheel.
**2** Using a suitable spanner, slacken by a quarter-turn the track rod locknut. Hold the track rod end stationary with another spanner engaged with the special flats while loosening the locknut **(see illustration)**.
**3** Extract the split pin, then unscrew the track rod end balljoint retaining nut.
**4** To release the tapered shank of the balljoint from the hub carrier steering arm, use a balljoint separator tool **(see illustration)**. If the balljoint is to be re-used, take care not to damage the dust cover when using the separator tool.
**5** Count the number of exposed threads visible on the inner section of the track rod and record this figure.

**6** Unscrew the track rod end from the track rod, counting the number of turns necessary to remove it. If necessary, hold the track rod stationary with grips.

### Refitting

**7** Screw the track rod end onto the track rod by the number of turns noted during removal, until it just contacts the locknut.
**8** Engage the shank of the balljoint with the hub carrier steering arm and refit the nut. Tighten the nut to the specified torque. If the balljoint shank turns while the nut is being tightened, press down on the balljoint. The tapered fit of the shank will lock it and prevent rotation as the nut is tightened.
**9** Check that the split pin holes in the nut and balljoint shank are aligned. If necessary turn the nut to the nearest alignment, making sure that the nut is still secure. Insert a new split pin and bend it back to secure.
**10** Now tighten the locknut, while holding the track rod end as before.
**11** Refit the roadwheel and lower the car to the ground. Tighten the wheel nuts to the specified torque.
**12** Finally check and if necessary adjust the front wheel alignment as described in Section 36.

### 36 Wheel alignment
and steering angles –
general information

**1** Accurate front wheel alignment is essential

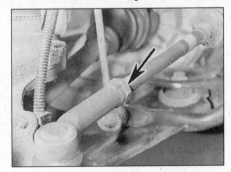

**35.2 Track rod end locknut**

to provide positive steering and to prevent excessive tyre wear. Before considering the steering/suspension geometry, check that the tyres are correctly inflated, that the front wheels are not buckled and that the steering linkage and suspension joints are in good order, without slackness or wear. Alignment of the front subframe is also critical to the front suspension geometry – refer to a Ford dealer for accurate setting-up.
**2** Wheel alignment consists of four factors **(see illustration overleaf)**:
**Camber** is the angle at which the front wheels are set from the vertical, when viewed from the front of the car. 'Positive camber' is the amount (in degrees) that the wheels are tilted outward at the top of the vertical.
**Castor** is the angle between the steering axis and a vertical line, when viewed from each side of the car. 'Positive castor' is when the steering axis is inclined rearward at the top.
**Steering axis inclination** is the angle (when viewed from the front of the car) between the vertical and an imaginary line drawn through the suspension strut upper mounting and the lower arm balljoint.
**Toe setting** is the amount by which the distance between the front inside edges of the roadwheels (measured at hub height) differs from the diametrically-opposite distance measured between the rear inside edges of the front roadwheels.
**3** With the exception of the toe setting, all other steering angles are set during manufacture and no adjustment is possible. It

**35.4 Using a balljoint separator tool to release the track rod end balljoint**

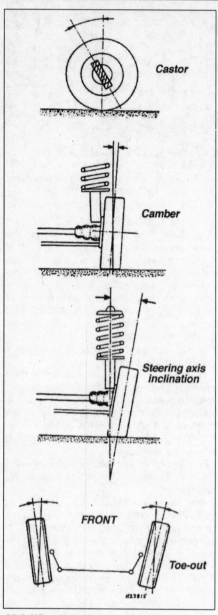

**36.2 Wheel alignment and steering angles**

can be assumed, therefore, that unless the car has suffered accident damage, all the pre-set steering angles will be correct. Should there be some doubt about their accuracy, it will be necessary to seek the help of a Ford dealer, as special gauges are needed to check the steering angles.

**4** Two methods are available to the home mechanic for checking the toe setting. One method is to use a gauge to measure the distance between the front and rear inside edges of the roadwheels. The other method is to use a scuff plate, in which each front wheel is rolled across a movable plate which records any deviation, or scuff, of the tyre from the straight-ahead position as it moves across the plate. Relatively-inexpensive equipment of both types is available from accessory outlets.

**5** If, after checking the toe setting using whichever method is preferable, it is found that adjustment is necessary, proceed as follows.

**6** Turn the steering wheel onto full-left lock and record the number of exposed threads on the right-hand track rod. Now turn the steering onto full-right lock and record the number of threads on the left-hand track rod. If there are the same number of threads visible on both sides, then subsequent adjustment can be made equally on both sides. If there are more threads visible on one side than the other, it will be necessary to compensate for this during adjustment. After adjustment, there must be the same number of threads visible on each track rod. This is most important.

**7** To alter the toe setting, slacken the locknut on the track rod and turn the track rod using self-locking pliers to achieve the desired setting. When viewed from the side of the car, turning the rod clockwise will increase the toe-in, turning it anti-clockwise will increase the toe-out. Only turn the track rods by a quarter of a turn each time and then recheck the setting.

**8** After adjustment, tighten the locknuts. Reposition the steering gear rubber gaiters, to remove any twist caused by turning the track rods.

**9** The rear wheel toe setting may also be checked and adjusted, but as this additionally requires alignment with the front wheels, it should be left to a Ford dealer or specialist having the required equipment.

# Chapter 11
# Bodywork and fittings

## Contents

| | Section number |
|---|---|
| Body side-trim mouldings and adhesive emblems – removal and refitting | 25 |
| Bonnet – removal, refitting and adjustment | 8 |
| Bonnet lock – removal, refitting and adjustment | 10 |
| Bonnet release cable and lever – removal and refitting | 9 |
| Boot lid – removal and refitting | 18 |
| Boot lid lock components – removal and refitting | 19 |
| Bumpers – removal and refitting | 6 |
| Central locking system components – testing, removal and refitting | 23 |
| Centre console – removal and refitting | 30 |
| Door – removal and refitting | 15 |
| Door handle and lock components – removal and refitting | 14 |
| Door inner trim panel – removal and refitting | 11 |
| Door window glass – removal and refitting | 12 |
| Door window regulator – removal and refitting | 13 |
| Exterior mirror and glass – removal and refitting | 16 |
| Facia – removal and refitting | 33 |
| Fuel filler flap and release cable – removal and refitting | 35 |

| | Section number |
|---|---|
| General information | 1 |
| Glovebox – removal and refitting | 32 |
| Interior mirror – removal and refitting | 17 |
| Interior trim panels – removal and refitting | 29 |
| Maintenance – bodywork and underframe | 2 |
| Maintenance – upholstery and carpets | 3 |
| Major body damage – repair | 5 |
| Minor body damage – repair | 4 |
| Overhead console – removal and refitting | 31 |
| Radiator grille – removal and refitting | 7 |
| Seat belts – removal and refitting | 28 |
| Seats – removal and refitting | 27 |
| Sunroof – general information and adjustment | 26 |
| Tailgate – removal and refitting | 20 |
| Tailgate lock components – removal and refitting | 22 |
| Tailgate support strut – removal and refitting | 21 |
| Wheel arch liner – removal and refitting | 34 |
| Windscreen and fixed windows – removal and refitting | 24 |

## Degrees of difficulty

| | | | | |
|---|---|---|---|---|
| **Easy,** suitable for novice with little experience  | **Fairly easy,** suitable for beginner with some experience | **Fairly difficult,** suitable for competent DIY mechanic | **Difficult,** suitable for experienced DIY mechanic | **Very difficult,** suitable for expert DIY or professional |

## Specifications

| Torque wrench settings | Nm | lbf ft |
|---|---|---|
| Bonnet and tailgate hinges | 24 | 18 |
| Boot lid | 10 | 7 |
| Bumper mounting nuts | 10 | 7 |
| Front seat mounting bolts | 28 | 21 |
| Rear seat backrest catch retaining bolts | 30 | 22 |
| Rear seat hinge pins | 20 | 15 |
| Seat belt mounting nuts and bolts | 38 | 28 |

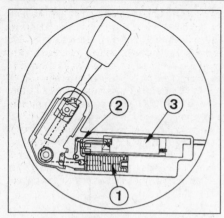

**1.5 Seat belt tensioner – models up to October 1996**

1 Coil spring
3 Spring mass sensor
2 Lever system

## 1 General information

The bodyshell and underframe on all models is of all-steel welded construction, incorporating progressive crumple zones at the front and rear, and a rigid centre safety cell.

In October 1996, the Mondeo was substantially facelifted – however, although the facelift models look very different to their pre-facelift counterparts, the underlying structure of the car (and most of the interior trim) was largely unchanged.

The bulkhead behind the engine compartment incorporates crash grooves which determine its energy-absorption characteristics, and special beams to prevent the intrusion of the front wheels into the passenger compartment during a serious accident. All passenger doors incorporate side impact bars.

All sheet metal surfaces which are prone to corrosion are galvanised. The painting process includes a base colour which closely matches the final topcoat, so that any stone damage is not as noticeable.

Automatic seat belts are fitted to all models, and the front seat belt stalks are mounted on automatic tensioners (also known as 'grabbers'). In the event of a serious front impact, the system is triggered and pulls the stalk buckle downwards to tension the seat belt. It is not possible to reset the tensioner once fired, and it must therefore be renewed. On models up to October 1996, the system utilises a spring mass sensor and a coil spring to fire the mechanism **(see illustration)**, and the tensioners can in theory operate independently of the airbag. From October 1996 onwards, the tensioners are fired by an explosive charge similar to that used in the airbag, and are triggered via the airbag control module.

Central locking is standard on all models, with later models having remote locking **(see illustration)**. All models also having a double-locking feature, where the lock mechanism is disconnected from the interior door handles, making it impossible to open any of the doors or the tailgate/boot lid from inside the car. This means that, even if a thief should break a side window, he will not be able to open the door using the interior handle. Models with the double-locking system are fitted with a control module located beneath the facia on the right-hand side. In the event of a serious accident, a crash sensor unlocks all doors if they were previously locked.

Many of the procedures in this Chapter require the battery to be disconnected. Refer to Chapter 5, Section 1 first.

## 2 Maintenance – bodywork and underframe

The general condition of the bodywork is the one thing that significantly affects a car's value. Maintenance is easy, but needs to be regular. Neglect, particularly after minor damage, can lead quickly to further deterioration and costly repair bills. It is important also to keep watch on those parts of the car not immediately visible, for instance the underside, inside all the wheel arches, and the lower part of the engine compartment.

The basic maintenance routine for the bodywork is washing – preferably with a lot of water, from a hose. This will remove all the loose solids which may have stuck to the car. It is important to flush these off in such a way as to prevent grit from scratching the finish. The wheel arches and underframe need washing in the same way, to remove any accumulated mud, which will retain moisture and tend to encourage rust. Paradoxically

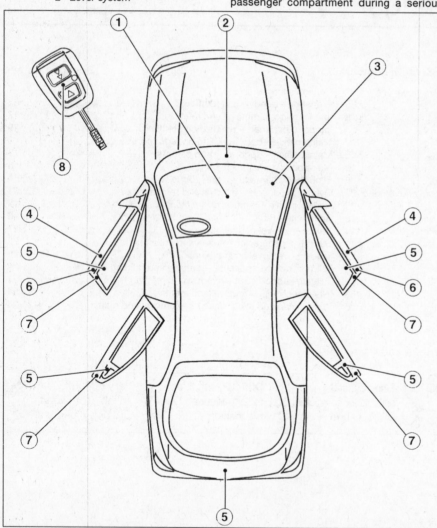

**1.6 Central locking component locations**

| | | |
|---|---|---|
| 1 Indicator light | 4 Infra-red receiver | 7 Ajar switch |
| 2 Buzzer | 5 Lock motor | 8 Infra-red transmitter |
| 3 Central locking module | 6 Set/reset switch | |

enough, the best time to clean the underframe and wheel arches is in wet weather, when the mud is thoroughly wet and soft. In very wet weather, the underframe is usually cleaned of large accumulations automatically, and this is a good time for inspection.

Periodically, except on cars with a wax-based underbody protective coating, it is a good idea to have the whole of the underframe of the car steam-cleaned, engine compartment included, so that a thorough inspection can be carried out to see what minor repairs and renovations are necessary. Steam-cleaning is available at many garages, and is necessary for the removal of the accumulation of oily grime, which sometimes is allowed to become thick in certain areas. If steam-cleaning facilities are not available, there are some excellent grease solvents available which can be brush-applied; the dirt can then be simply hosed off. Note that these methods should not be used on cars with wax-based underbody protective coating, or the coating will be removed. Such cars should be inspected annually, preferably just prior to Winter, when the underbody should be washed down, and any damage to the wax coating repaired. Ideally, a completely fresh coat should be applied. It would also be worth considering the use of such wax-based protection for injection into door panels, sills, box sections, etc, as an additional safeguard against rust damage, where such protection is not provided by the manufacturer.

After washing the paintwork, wipe off with a chamois leather to give an unspotted clear finish. A coat of clear protective wax polish will give added protection against chemical pollutants in the air. If the paintwork sheen has dulled or oxidised, use a cleaner/polisher combination to restore the brilliance of the shine. This requires a little effort, but such dulling is usually caused because regular washing has been neglected. Care needs to be taken with metallic paintwork, as special non-abrasive cleaner/polisher is required to avoid damage to the lacquer finish – also note that many 'solid' colours are in fact lacquered ('clear over base') these days. Always check that the door and ventilator opening drain holes and pipes are completely clear, so that water can be drained out. Brightwork should be treated in the same way as paintwork. Windscreens and windows can be kept clear of the smeary film which often appears, by the use of proprietary glass cleaner. Never use wax polish on the windscreen.

## 3 Maintenance –
### upholstery and carpets

Mats and carpets should be brushed or vacuum-cleaned regularly, to keep them free of grit. If they are badly stained, remove them from the car for scrubbing or sponging, and make quite sure they are dry before refitting.

Cloth or velour seats and interior trim panels can be kept clean by wiping with a damp cloth. If they do become stained (which can be more apparent on light-coloured cloth or velour upholstery), use a little liquid detergent and a soft nail brush to scour the grime out of the grain of the material. Keep the headlining clean in the same way as the upholstery

In the case of leather upholstery, a whole range of different products exist to clean, feed and generally restore the leather, and it is recommended that these are used exclusively. Ordinary detergents should be avoided, as they will prematurely dry out leather, causing it to crack and split.

When using liquid cleaners inside the car, do not over-wet the surfaces being cleaned. Excessive damp could get into the seams and padded interior, causing stains, offensive odours or even rot. If the inside of the car gets wet accidentally, it is worthwhile taking some trouble to dry it out properly, particularly where carpets are involved. *Do not leave oil or electric heaters inside the car for this purpose.*

## 4 Minor body damage –
### repair

### Minor scratches

If the scratch is very superficial, and does not penetrate to the metal of the bodywork, repair is very simple. Lightly rub the area of the scratch with a paintwork renovator, or a very fine cutting paste, to remove loose paint from the scratch, and to clear the surrounding bodywork of wax polish. Rinse the area with clean water.

In the case of metallic paint, the most commonly-found scratches are not in the paint, but in the lacquer top coat, and appear white. If care is taken, these can sometimes be rendered less obvious by very careful use of paintwork renovator (which would otherwise not be used on metallic paintwork); otherwise, repair of these scratches can be achieved by applying lacquer with a fine brush. Also note that damage to the lacquer coat will show up worse if (white) polish residue collects in the chip or scratch – clean any suspected area thoroughly.

Apply touch-up paint to the scratch using a fine paint brush; continue to apply fine layers of paint (allowing each one time to dry) until the surface of the paint in the scratch is level with the surrounding paintwork. Allow the new paint at least two weeks to harden, then blend it into the surrounding paintwork by rubbing the scratch area with a paintwork renovator or a very fine cutting paste. Finally, apply wax polish.

Where the scratch has penetrated right through to the metal of the bodywork, causing the metal to rust, a different repair technique is required. Remove any loose rust from the bottom of the scratch with a penknife,

then apply rust-inhibiting paint, to prevent the formation of rust in the future. Using a rubber or nylon applicator, fill the scratch with bodystopper paste. If required, this paste can be mixed with cellulose thinners, to provide a very thin paste which is ideal for filling narrow scratches. Before the stopper-paste in the scratch hardens, wrap a piece of smooth cotton rag around the top of a finger. Dip the finger in cellulose thinners, and quickly sweep it across the surface of the stopper-paste in the scratch; this will ensure that the surface of the stopper-paste is slightly hollowed. The scratch can now be painted over as described earlier in this Section.

### Dents

When deep denting of the bodywork has taken place, the first task is to pull the dent out, until the affected bodywork almost attains its original shape. There is little point in trying to restore the original shape completely, as the metal in the damaged area will have stretched on impact, and cannot be reshaped fully to its original contour. It is better to bring the level of the dent up to a point which is about 3 mm below the level of the surrounding bodywork. In cases where the dent is very shallow anyway, it is not worth trying to pull it out at all. If the underside of the dent is accessible, it can be hammered out gently from behind, using a mallet with a wooden or plastic head. Whilst doing this, hold a suitable block of wood firmly against the outside of the panel, to absorb the impact from the hammer blows and thus prevent a large area of the bodywork from being 'belled-out'.

Should the dent be in a section of the bodywork which has a double skin, or some other factor making it inaccessible from behind, a different technique is called for. Drill several small holes through the metal inside the area – particularly in the deeper section. Then screw long self-tapping screws into the holes, just sufficiently for them to gain a good purchase in the metal. Now the dent can be pulled out by pulling on the protruding heads of the screws with a pair of pliers.

The next stage of the repair is the removal of the paint from the damaged area, and from an inch or so of the surrounding 'sound' bodywork. This is accomplished most easily by using a wire brush or abrasive pad on a power drill, although it can be done just as effectively by hand, using sheets of abrasive paper. To complete the preparation for filling, score the surface of the bare metal with a screwdriver or the tang of a file, or alternatively, drill small holes in the affected area. This will provide a really good 'key' for the filler paste.

To complete the repair, see the Section on filling and respraying.

### Rust holes or gashes

Remove all paint from the affected area, and from an inch or so of the surrounding 'sound' bodywork, using an abrasive pad or a wire brush on a power drill. If these are not available, a few sheets of abrasive paper will do the job most effectively. With the paint removed, you will be able to judge the severity of the corrosion, and therefore decide whether to renew the whole panel (if this is possible) or to repair the affected area. New body panels are not as expensive as most people think, and it is often quicker and more satisfactory to fit a new panel than to attempt to repair large areas of corrosion.

Remove all fittings from the affected area, except those which will act as a guide to the original shape of the damaged bodywork. Then, using tin snips or a hacksaw blade, remove all loose metal and any other metal badly affected by corrosion. Hammer the edges of the hole inwards, in order to create a slight depression for the filler paste.

Wire-brush the affected area to remove the powdery rust from the surface of the remaining metal. Paint the affected area with rust-inhibiting paint, if the back of the rusted area is accessible, treat this also.

Before filling can take place, it will be necessary to block the hole in some way. This can be achieved by the use of aluminium or plastic mesh, or aluminium tape.

Aluminium or plastic mesh, or glass-fibre matting, is probably the best material to use for a large hole. Cut a piece to the approximate size and shape of the hole to be filled, then position it in the hole so that its edges are below the level of the surrounding bodywork. It can be retained in position by several blobs of filler paste around its periphery.

Aluminium tape should be used for small or very narrow holes. Pull a piece off the roll, trim it to the approximate size and shape required, then pull off the backing paper (if used) and stick the tape over the hole; it can be overlapped if the thickness of one piece is insufficient. Burnish down the edges of the tape with the handle of a screwdriver or similar, to ensure that the tape is securely attached to the metal underneath.

### Filling and respraying

Before using this Section, see the Sections on dent, deep scratch, rust holes and gash repairs.

Many types of bodyfiller are available, but generally speaking, those proprietary kits which contain a tin of filler paste and a tube of resin hardener are best for this type of repair. A wide, flexible plastic or nylon applicator will be found invaluable for imparting a smooth and well-contoured finish to the surface of the filler.

Mix up a little filler on a clean piece of card or board – measure the hardener carefully (follow the maker's instructions on the pack), otherwise the filler will set too rapidly or too slowly. Using the applicator, apply the filler paste to the prepared area; draw the applicator across the surface of the filler to achieve the correct contour and to level the surface. As soon as a contour that approximates to the correct one is achieved, stop working the

paste – if you carry on too long, the paste will become sticky and begin to 'pick-up' on the applicator. Continue to add thin layers of filler paste at 20-minute intervals, until the level of the filler is just proud of the surrounding bodywork.

Once the filler has hardened, the excess can be removed using a metal plane or file. From then on, progressively-finer grades of abrasive paper should be used, starting with a 40-grade production paper, and finishing with a 400-grade wet-and-dry paper. Always wrap the abrasive paper around a flat rubber, cork, or wooden block – otherwise the surface of the filler will not be completely flat. During the smoothing of the filler surface, the wet-and-dry paper should be periodically rinsed in water. This will ensure that a very smooth finish is imparted to the filler at the final stage.

At this stage, the 'dent' should be surrounded by a ring of bare metal, which in turn should be encircled by the finely 'feathered' edge of the good paintwork. Rinse the repair area with clean water, until all of the dust produced by the rubbing-down operation has gone.

Spray the whole area with a light coat of primer – this will show up any imperfections in the surface of the filler. Repair these imperfections with fresh filler paste or bodystopper, and once more smooth the surface with abrasive paper. Repeat this spray-and-repair procedure until you are satisfied that the surface of the filler, and the feathered edge of the paintwork, are perfect. Clean the repair area with clean water, and allow to dry fully.

The repair area is now ready for final spraying. Paint spraying must be carried out in a warm, dry, windless and dust-free atmosphere. This condition can be created artificially if you have access to a large indoor working area, but if you are forced to work in the open, you will have to pick your day very carefully. If you are working indoors, dousing the floor in the work area with water will help to settle the dust which would otherwise be in the atmosphere. If the repair area is confined to one body panel, mask off the surrounding panels; this will help to minimise the effects of a slight mis-match in paint colours. Bodywork fittings (eg chrome strips, door handles etc) will also need to be masked off. Use genuine masking tape, and several thicknesses of newspaper, for the masking operations.

Before commencing to spray, agitate the aerosol can thoroughly, then spray a test area (an old tin, or similar) until the technique is mastered. Cover the repair area with a thick coat of primer; the thickness should be built up using several thin layers of paint, rather than one thick one. Using 400-grade wet-and-dry paper, rub down the surface of the primer until it is really smooth. While doing this, the work area should be thoroughly doused with water, and the wet-and-dry paper periodically rinsed in water. Allow to dry before spraying on more paint.

Spray on the top coat, again building up the thickness by using several thin layers of paint.

Start spraying at one edge of the repair area, and then, using a side-to-side motion, work until the whole repair area and about 2 inches of the surrounding original paintwork is covered. Remove all masking material 10 to 15 minutes after spraying on the final coat of paint.

Allow the new paint at least two weeks to harden, then, using a paintwork renovator, or a very fine cutting paste, blend the edges of the paint into the existing paintwork. Finally, apply wax polish.

### Plastic components

With the use of more and more plastic body components by the car manufacturers (eg bumpers. spoilers, and in some cases major body panels), rectification of more serious damage to such items has become a matter of either entrusting repair work to a specialist in this field, or renewing complete components. Repair of such damage by the DIY owner is not really feasible, owing to the cost of the equipment and materials required for effecting such repairs. The basic technique involves making a groove along the line of the crack in the plastic, using a rotary burr in a power drill. The damaged part is then welded back together, using a hot-air gun to heat up and fuse a plastic filler rod into the groove. Any excess plastic is then removed, and the area rubbed down to a smooth finish. It is important that a filler rod of the correct plastic is used, as body components can be made of a variety of different types (eg polycarbonate, ABS, polypropylene).

Damage of a less serious nature (abrasions, minor cracks etc) can be repaired by the DIY owner using a two-part epoxy filler repair material. Once mixed in equal proportions, this is used in similar fashion to the bodywork filler used on metal panels. The filler is usually cured in twenty to thirty minutes, ready for sanding and painting.

If the owner is renewing a complete component himself, or if he has repaired it with epoxy filler, he will be left with the problem of finding a suitable paint for finishing which is compatible with the type of plastic used. At one time, the use of a universal paint was not possible, owing to the complex range of plastics encountered in body component applications. Standard paints, generally speaking, will not bond to plastic or rubber satisfactorily. However, it is now possible to obtain a plastic body parts finishing kit which consists of a pre-primer treatment, a primer and coloured top coat. Full instructions are normally supplied with a kit, but basically, the method of use is to first apply the pre-primer to the component concerned, and allow it to dry for up to 30 minutes. Then the primer is applied, and left to dry for about an hour before finally applying the special-coloured top coat. The result is a correctly-coloured component, where the paint will flex with the plastic or rubber, a property that standard paint does not normally possess.

**6.4 Screw securing the wheel arch liner to the front bumper**

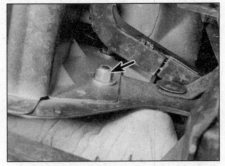

**6.5a Front bumper mounting bolt**

**6.5b Disconnecting the front bumper from the side guides**

## 5 Major body damage – repair

Where serious damage has occurred, or large areas need renewal due to neglect, it means that complete new panels will need welding-in; this is best left to professionals. If the damage is due to impact, it will also be necessary to check completely the alignment of the bodyshell; this can only be carried out accurately by a Ford dealer, using special jigs. If the body is left misaligned, it is primarily dangerous, as the car will not handle properly, and secondly, uneven stresses will be imposed on the steering, suspension and possibly transmission, causing abnormal wear or complete failure, particularly to items such as the tyres.

## 6 Bumpers – removal and refitting

### *Removal*

#### Front bumper – pre-facelift models

1 Apply the handbrake, jack up the front of the car and support it on axle stands (see *Jacking and vehicle support*).
2 Where applicable, disconnect the wiring plugs from the front foglights (Chapter 12).
3 Where applicable, disconnect the tubing from the headlight washer pump. Be prepared

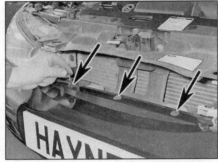

**6.6 Remove the three bumper retaining clips below the radiator grille**

for loss of fluid as this is done, and have ready a container to catch the spilt fluid.
4 Unscrew the screws securing the wheel arch liners to the front bumper **(see illustration)**.
5 Unscrew the bumper mounting nuts, and withdraw the bumper forwards from the car, at the same time disconnecting the guides from the side pins **(see illustrations)**. As the bumper is withdrawn, disconnect wiring from the low air temperature sensor, where applicable.

#### Front bumper – facelift models

6 Remove the radiator grille as described in Section 7, then prise out and remove the three clips beneath it **(see illustration)**.
7 Apply the handbrake, jack up the front of the car and support it on axle stands (see *Jacking and vehicle support*). Working under the front of the car, remove the clips and screws securing the radiator lower cover, and remove the cover.

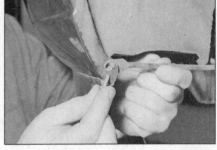

**6.10 Remove the bumper stay screw**

8 Where applicable, disconnect the wiring plugs from the front foglights (see Chapter 12).
9 Where applicable, disconnect the tubing from the headlight washer pump. Be prepared for loss of fluid as this is done, and have ready a container to catch the spilt fluid.
10 At each bumper end, remove the screw from each bumper stay bar **(see illustration)**.
11 Working from underneath, unscrew and remove the two mounting screws each side – if preferred, the rearmost screw can be reached from inside the wheel arch, once the wheel arch liner screws have been removed **(see illustrations)**. Have an assistant ready to support the bumper once the first pair of screws is removed.
12 Withdraw the bumper forwards from the front of the car, and remove it **(see illustration)**.

#### Rear bumper – pre-facelift models

13 Chock the front wheels, jack up the rear

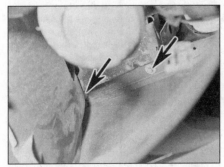

**6.11a Remove the two bumper mounting screws from underneath . . .**

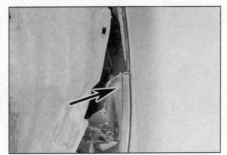

**6.11b . . . the rear screw can be reached once the front of the wheel arch liner has been pulled back**

**6.12 Removing the front bumper**

**6.16 Rear bumper mounting nuts**

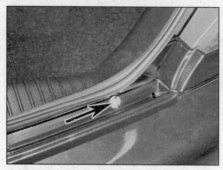

**6.17 One of the bumper top edge securing screws**

**6.19 Removing a bumper-to-wheel arch liner screw**

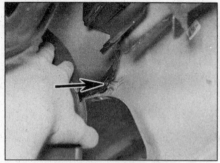

**6.20 Bumper-to-wing screw seen from below, with wheel arch liner held aside**

**6.21 Rear bumper lower securing screws**

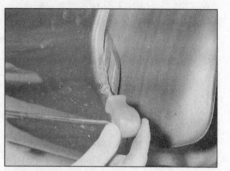

**6.25 Remove the bumper-to-wheel arch lower screw**

of the car and support it on axle stands (see *Jacking and vehicle support*).

**14** Disconnect the rear exhaust mounting rubber, and support the exhaust system on an axle stand.

**15** Remove the screws securing the wheel arch liners to the rear bumper.

**16** Unscrew the bumper mounting nuts **(see illustration)**, and withdraw the bumper rearwards from the car, at the same time

disconnecting the guides from the side pins.

### Rear bumper – facelift Saloon and Hatchback models

*Caution: Wear gloves when handling the rear bumper, as the bottom edge is sharp enough to cause injury.*

**17** Open the boot lid or tailgate, and remove the two screws securing the top edge of the bumper **(see illustration)**.

**18** Chock the front wheels, jack up the rear of the car and support it on axle stands.

**19** Remove the screw each side securing the bottom of the bumper end to the wheel arch liner **(see illustration)**.

**20** Remove the screws as necessary, and detach the rear edge of the wheel arch liner for access to the bumper upper screw **(see illustration)**.

**21** Remove the two screws on the underside of the bumper **(see illustration)**.

**22** With the help of an assistant, pull the bumper rearwards to disengage the side pegs.

**23** On models with the ultrasonic parking sensor, disconnect the wiring plugs from the sensors as they become accessible.

### Rear bumper – facelift Estate models

**24** Chock the front wheels, jack up the rear of the car and support it on axle stands.

**25** Remove the screw each side securing the bottom of the bumper end to the wheel arch liner **(see illustration)**.

**26** Remove the screws and clips securing the rear wheel arch liners, and remove the liners **(see illustrations)**.

**27** Remove the upper screw each side

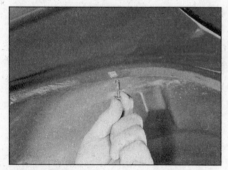

**6.26a Remove the screw and clip at the top . . .**

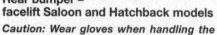
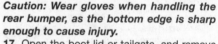

**6.26b . . . and the rest of the screws . . .**

**6.26c . . . and lower the wheel arch liner**

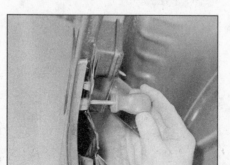

**6.27 Remove the upper screw from inside the wheel arch**

securing the top of the bumper end to the rear wing **(see illustration)**.

**28** Working underneath the rear of the car, remove the two nuts each side securing the bumper to the rear panel **(see illustration)**.

**29** With the help of an assistant to support one end of the bumper, slide the bumper to the rear, off the side locating pegs, and remove it **(see illustration)**. On models with the ultrasonic parking sensor, disconnect the wiring plugs from the sensors as they become accessible.

### Refitting

**30** Refitting is a reversal of the removal procedure. Make sure that, where applicable, the bumper guides are located correctly.

## 7 Radiator grille – removal and refitting

### Removal

**1** Support the bonnet in the open position.
**2** On later models, prise out the three securing clips and remove the cover panel around the bonnet lock **(see illustrations)**.
**3** Unscrew the two radiator grille upper mounting screws **(see illustrations)**.
**4** Release the clips at the base of the grille, and remove the radiator grille from the front panel **(see illustrations)**.

### Refitting

**5** Refitting is a reversal of the removal procedure.

## 8 Bonnet – removal, refitting and adjustment

### Removal

**1** Open the bonnet, and support it in the open position using the stay.
**2** Disconnect the battery negative (earth) lead (Chapter 5, Section 1).
**3** Prise out the clips from the insulator panel on the underside of the bonnet, for access to the windscreen washer hoses and engine

**7.4a Unclipping the radiator grille from the front panel – models up to October 1996 . . .**

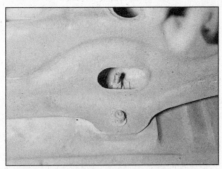

**6.28 Two of the rear bumper mounting nuts**

**7.2a Using a forked tool if available, prise out the three retaining clips . . .**

compartment light. It is not necessary to completely remove the insulator panel.
**4** Disconnect the wiring from the engine compartment light, and unclip the wiring from the bonnet.

**7.3a Removing a radiator grille mounting screw – models up to October 1996**

**7.4b . . . and removing the radiator grille – October 1996 and later models**

**6.29 Slide the bumper off the side locating pegs (one arrowed)**

**7.2b . . . and lift away the cover panel, disengaging it from the bonnet release lever**

**5** Unbolt the earth lead from the bonnet **(see illustration)**.
**6** Disconnect the windscreen washer hoses from the bottom of the jets, and unclip the hose from the bonnet.

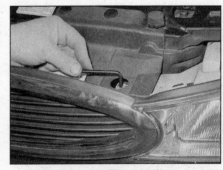

**7.3b Radiator grille mounting screw removal – October 1996 and later models**

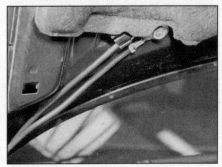

**8.5 Earth lead and washer hoses on the underside of the bonnet**

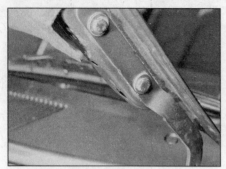

**8.7 Mark around the bonnet hinges with a soft pencil before removal**

**7** To assist in correctly realigning the bonnet when refitting it, mark the outline of the hinges with a soft pencil (see illustration). Loosen the two hinge retaining bolts on each side.

**8** With the help of an assistant, unscrew the four bolts, release the stay, and lift the bonnet from the car (see illustration).

### Refitting and adjustment

**9** Refitting is a reversal of the removal procedure, noting the following points:
  a) *Position the bonnet hinges within the outline marks made during removal, but if necessary alter its position to provide a uniform gap all round.*
  b) *Adjust the rear height of the bonnet by repositioning it on the hinges.*
  c) *Adjust the front height by repositioning the lock (see Section 10) and turning the rubber buffers on the engine compartment front cross panel up*

**9.3 Bonnet release lever**

**11.2a Prise out the plastic cover . . .**

**8.8 Removing the bonnet**

*or down to support the bonnet (see illustration).*

## 9 Bonnet release cable and lever – removal and refitting

### Removal

**1** With the bonnet open, disconnect the battery negative (earth) lead (Chapter 5, Section 1).

**2** Working inside the car, remove the trim from the B-pillar, and pull off the door weatherstrips from the bottom of the door apertures.

**3** Remove the clips and screws, and withdraw the lower side trim, to give access to the bonnet release lever (see illustration).

**4** Release the outer cable from the lever bracket.

**5** Unscrew and remove the lever mounting

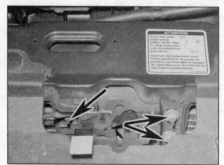

**10.3 Bonnet lock mounting nuts**

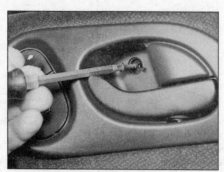

**11.2b . . . remove the screw . . .**

**8.9 Buffer for adjustment of the bonnet front height**

screws, and turn the lever clockwise through a quarter-turn to disconnect it from the cable.

**6** Remove the radiator grille (Section 7). Also remove the backing panel from the engine compartment front crossmember.

**7** Release the inner and outer cables from the lock.

**8** Withdraw the cable from the engine compartment, feeding it through the front crossmember, and removing the grommet from the bulkhead.

### Refitting

**9** Refitting is a reversal of the removal procedure.

## 10 Bonnet lock – removal, refitting and adjustment

### Removal

**1** Remove the radiator grille (Section 7).

**2** Release the inner and outer cables from the bonnet lock.

**3** Mark the position of the lock on the crossmember, then unscrew the mounting nuts and withdraw the lock (see illustration).

### Refitting and adjustment

**4** Refitting is a reversal of the removal procedure, starting by positioning the lock as noted before removal.

**5** If the front of the bonnet is not level with the front wings, the lock may be moved up or down within the mounting holes. After making an adjustment, raise or lower the rubber buffers to support the bonnet correctly.

## 11 Door inner trim panel – removal and refitting

### Removal

**1** Disconnect the battery negative (earth) lead (Chapter 5, Section 1).

**2** Carefully prise out the plastic cover with a small screwdriver. Remove the screw, and ease the bezel off the inner door handle (see illustrations).

**11.2c . . . and withdraw the bezel from the inner door handle**

**11.3a  Remove the window operating switch . . .**

**11.3b . . . and disconnect the multi-plug**

**3** Where applicable, remove the window operating switch and disconnect the multi-plug **(see illustrations)**.

### Front door

**4** Carefully prise out the cover, remove the screws and withdraw the door pull handle **(see illustrations)**.

**5** Prise off the plastic cap, remove the screw, and withdraw the quarter bezel from the front of the window opening **(see illustrations)**.

### Rear door

**6** Prise off the cap, then remove the screw and withdraw the door pull handle **(see illustrations)**.

### Front and rear doors

**7** On models fitted with manual (ie, non-electric) windows, fully shut the window, and note the position of the regulator handle.

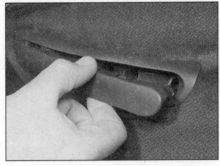

**11.4a  Remove the cover . . .**

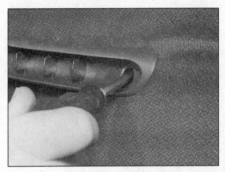

**11.4b . . . then remove the screws and withdraw the door pull handle**

Release the spring clip by inserting a clean cloth between the handle and the door trim. Using a 'sawing' action, pull the cloth against the open ends of the clip to release it, at the same time pulling the handle from the regulator shaft splines. Withdraw the handle (and where fitted, the spacer) and recover the clip **(see illustrations)**.

**8** Prise the caps from the trim panel retaining screws, then remove the screws and lift off

**11.5a  Remove the plastic cap and the screw . . .**

**11.5b . . . then withdraw the quarter bezel**

**11.6a  Remove the screw . . .**

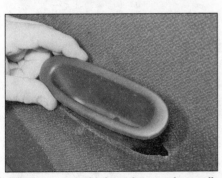

**11.6b . . . and withdraw the rear door pull handle**

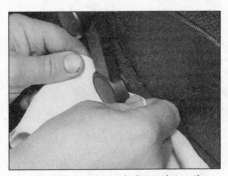

**11.7a  Using a clean cloth to release the spring clip from the window regulator handle**

**11.7b  Withdrawing the window regulator handle**

**11.7c Recover the spring clip from the window regulator handle**

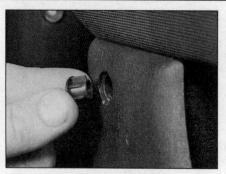

**11.8a Prise out the caps . . .**

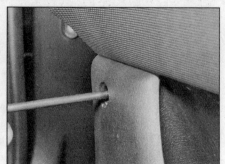

**11.8b . . . remove the inner-facing screws . . .**

**11.8c . . . and the side screws . . .**

**11.8d . . . then lift off the trim panel**

the panel **(see illustrations)**. Where a speaker is attached to the trim panel, disconnect the multi-plug.

**9** If necessary, the foam insulation may be removed from the door. First remove the speaker as described in Chapter 12.

**10** On models with manual windows, remove the foam spacer from the regulator spindle **(see illustration)**.

**11** On the rear door, unscrew the screws and remove the door pull bracket **(see illustration)**.

**12** Carefully slice along the bead of adhesive with a knife, and remove the foam insulation

**11.8e Door trim panel components**

| | | |
|---|---|---|
| 1 | Door | 4 | Top mounting |
| 2 | Foam seal | 5 | Centre |
| 3 | Trim panel | | mounting |

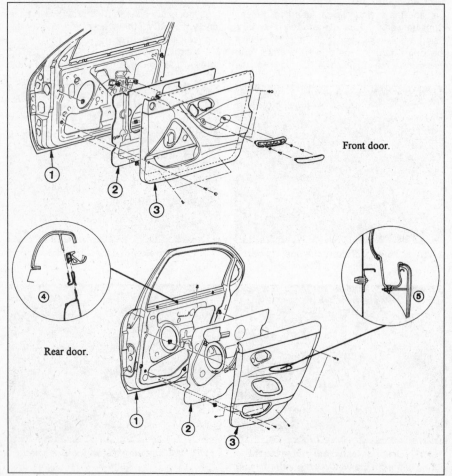

Front door.

Rear door.

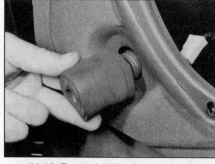

**11.10 Removing the foam spacer**

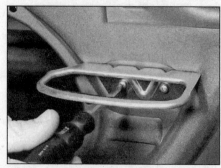

**11.11 Removing the door pull bracket from a rear door**

panel **(see illustration)**. By cutting along the bead of adhesive, the foam panel can easily be stuck back in place when refitting.

### Refitting

**13** Refitting is a reversal of the removal procedure.

### 12  Door window glass – removal and refitting

## Removal

### Front (manual/non-electric)

**1** Disconnect the battery negative (earth) lead (Chapter 5, Section 1).
**2** Remove the door inner trim panel as described in Section 11.
**3** Remove the door exterior mirror as described in Section 16.
**4** Temporarily refit the regulator handle on its splines.
**5** Lower the window until the glass support bracket is visible through the holes in the door inner panel. Remove the regulator handle.
**6** Carefully prise off the weatherstrip from the outside of the door.
**7** Support the glass, then unscrew the bolts from the support bracket.
**8** Lift the glass from the door while tilting it at the rear, and withdraw it from the outside.

### Front (electric)

**9** Disconnect the battery negative (earth) lead (Chapter 5, Section 1).

**11.12  Removing the foam insulation**

**10** Remove the door inner trim panel as described in Section 11.
**11** Remove the door exterior mirror as described in Section 16.
**12** Temporarily reconnect the battery and the window operating switch. Lower the window until the support bracket and bolts are visible through the holes in the door inner panel **(see illustration)**. Disconnect the battery lead and the operating switch again.
**13** Carefully prise off the weatherstrip from the outside of the door **(see illustration)**.
**14** Support the glass, then unscrew the bolts from the support bracket.
**15** Lift the glass from the door while tilting it at the rear, and withdraw it from the outside **(see illustration)**.

### Rear (manual/non-electric)

**16** Disconnect the battery negative (earth) lead (Chapter 5, Section 1).
**17** Remove the door inner trim panel as described in Section 11.

**18** Temporarily refit the regulator handle on its splines.
**19** Lower the window until the glass support bracket and bolts are visible through the holes in the door inner panel. Remove the regulator handle.
**20** Support the glass, then unscrew the bolts from the support bracket.
**21** Unscrew the screws, and remove the air vent grilles from the rear of the door **(see illustrations)**.
**22** Carefully prise off the weatherstrip from the outside of the door.
**23** Have an assistant raise the glass from the outside, and hold it near its shut position.
**24** Loosen (but do not remove) the three regulator mounting bolts, then slide the top bolts to the right, and push them out. Slide the bottom bolt upwards, and push it out. Lower the regulator assembly inside the door.
**25** Working inside the door, lower the glass until it is below the regulator position, and move the glass to the outer side of its channels.
**26** With the help of an assistant, lift the glass out of the door, and withdraw it from the outside **(see illustration)**.

### Rear (electric)

**27** The procedure is as just described for manual windows, making allowances for the difference in the regulator mechanism.

### Refitting

**28** Refitting is a reversal of the removal procedure, making sure that the glass is correctly located in the support bracket.

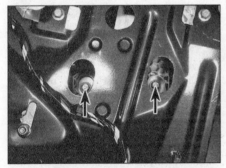

**12.12  Window support bracket bolts viewed through the holes in the door inner panel**

**12.13  Removing the weatherstrip from the outside of the door**

**12.15  Lifting the glass from the front door**

**12.21a  Unscrew the screws . . .**

**12.21b  . . . and remove the air vent grilles from the rear door**

**12.26  Lifting the glass from the rear door**

**13.2a Window regulator upper mounting bolts – front door**

**13.2b Electric window motor mounting bolts – front door**

**13.2c Window regulator mounting bolts – rear door**

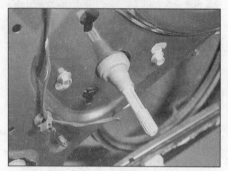

**13.2d Manual winder mounting bolts – rear door**

## 13 Door window regulator – removal and refitting

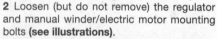
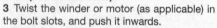

### Removal

1 Remove the window glass (Section 12).
2 Loosen (but do not remove) the regulator and manual winder/electric motor mounting bolts **(see illustrations)**.
3 Twist the winder or motor (as applicable) in the bolt slots, and push it inwards.
4 Slide the top bolts to the right, and push them out. Slide the bottom bolt upwards, and push it out.
5 On electric windows, disconnect the wiring multi-plug from the motor **(see illustration)**.
6 Withdraw the window regulator mechanism from inside the door, through the hole in the inner panel **(see illustrations)**.

### Refitting

7 Refitting is a reversal of the removal procedure.

## 14 Door handle and lock components – removal and refitting

### Removal

#### Front door exterior handle

1 Remove the door inner trim panel as described in Section 11.
2 Use a knife to cut through the adhesive

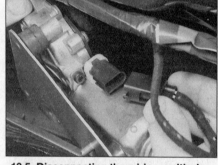

**13.5 Disconnecting the wiring multi-plug from an electrically-operated window**

strip, so that the foam insulator can be peeled back locally for access to the lock. Do not peel back the foam insulator without first cutting through the adhesive strip, otherwise the insulator will be damaged. To ensure a

**13.6b Front door window regulator removed from the car**

**13.6d Rear door window regulator removed from the car**

**13.6a Removing the window regulator mechanism from the front door**

good seal when the insulator is pressed back, do not touch the adhesive strip.
3 Unscrew and remove the two bolts for the exterior handle outer bezel, and remove the bezel **(see illustrations)**.

**13.6c Removing the window regulator mechanism from the rear door**

**14.3a Remove the two bolts . . .**

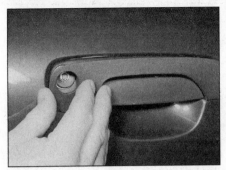

**14.3b . . . followed by the exterior handle bezel**

**14.4a  Unscrew the lock mounting bolts . . .**

**14.4b . . . and remove the plate**

**4** Unscrew and remove the lock mounting bolts on the inner rear edge of the door, and remove the plate. Also remove the additional support screw **(see illustrations)**.

**5** Unclip and disconnect the wiring multi-plugs for the central locking and alarm systems **(see illustration)**.

**6** Disconnect the wiring multi-plug from the door lock.

**7** Disconnect the inner handle illumination light. Undo the screws and remove the inner handle. Disconnect the operating cable from the inner handle, as described later in this Section **(see illustrations)**.

**8** Manipulate the lock and handle assembly as necessary, and disconnect the wiring multi-plugs for the alarm sensor and central locking. Withdraw the complete assembly from inside the door **(see illustrations)**.

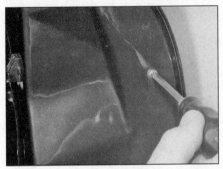

**14.4c  Removing the additional support screw**

**9** To disconnect the handle assembly from the lock bracket, slide the rubber posts inwards, and push out the assembly **(see illustration)**.

**10** To remove the handle itself, twist the door

**14.5  Disconnecting the central locking and alarm system wiring multi-plugs**

handle through a quarter-turn, and pull out the connecting rods **(see illustration)**.

**11** Remove the alarm sensor and the central locking 'set-reset' sensor **(see illustration)**.

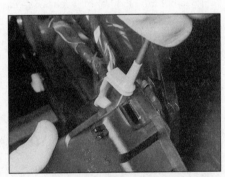

**14.7a  Removing the inner handle**

**14.7b  Disconnecting the operating cable from the inner handle**

**14.8a  Removing the lock and exterior handle assembly from inside the door**

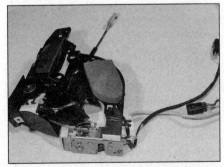

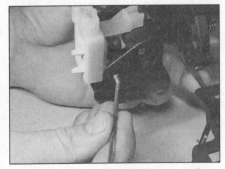

**14.8b  Front door lock and exterior handle assembly removed from the car**

**14.9  Disconnecting the handle assembly from the lock bracket**

**14.10  Pulling out the handle connecting rods**

14.11 Removing the central locking 'set-reset' sensor

14.14a Prise out the plug . . .

14.14b . . . and unscrew the handle mounting nuts

14.15 Disconnect the operating rod from the lock

### Rear door exterior handle

**12** Remove the door inner trim panel as described in Section 11.

**13** Use a knife to cut through the adhesive strip, so that the foam insulator can be peeled

14.16 Removing the rear door exterior handle

back for access to the lock. Do not peel back the foam insulator without first cutting through the adhesive strip. To ensure a good seal when the insulator is pressed back, do not touch the adhesive strip.

**14** Prise out the plug from the rear edge of

the door, then unscrew the handle mounting nuts **(see illustrations)**.

**15** Prise up the clip, and disconnect the operating rod from the lock **(see illustration)**.

**16** Withdraw the handle from the outside of the door **(see illustration)**.

### Interior handle

**17** Remove the door inner trim panel as described in Section 11.

**18** Use a knife to cut through the adhesive strip, so that the foam insulator can be peeled back for access to the lock. Do not peel back the foam insulator without first cutting through the adhesive strip. To ensure a good seal when the insulator is pressed back, do not touch the adhesive strip.

**19** Disconnect the interior handle illumination light.

**20** Undo the screws and remove the interior handle.

**21** To remove the cable, first pull back the plastic outer cable end and blanking piece. Apply light inward pressure to the control lever, with the lever in the locked position, until the inner cable is aligned with the release slot in the bottom of the cable holder.

**22** Push down on the cable ferrule, and disconnect the inner cable. Remove the handle assembly.

### Lock barrel

**23** Remove the exterior handle as described earlier in this Section.

**24** Prise out the barrel retaining tab from the handle body, using a small screwdriver **(see illustration)**.

**25** Insert the key, turn it so that it engages the barrel, then pull out the barrel **(see illustration)**.

### Lock motor – front door

**26** Remove the exterior handle as described earlier in this Section.

**27** Extract the clip, and pull out the operating rod.

**28** Remove the operating rod from the plastic bush, by turning it through a quarter-turn.

**29** Release the sensor wiring loom from the clip.

**30** Detach the mounting plate from the lock.

**31** Release the door-ajar sensor from the clip **(see illustration)**.

**32** Prise the plastic shield from the locating post **(see illustration)**.

14.24 Prise out the barrel retaining tab . . .

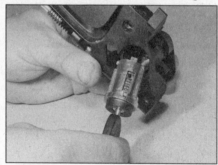

14.25 . . . and pull out the lock barrel

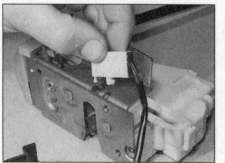

14.31 Unclipping the door-ajar sensor

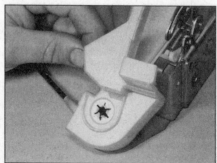

14.32 Removing the plastic shield from the locating post

**33** Slide the outer cable from the lock bracket, then turn the inner cable through a quarter-turn to remove it from the bell crank **(see illustration)**.

**34** Unscrew the mounting screws and remove the lock motor **(see illustration)**.

### Lock motor – rear door

**35** Remove the exterior handle as described earlier in this Section.

**36** Unscrew and remove the three lock mounting screws.

**37** Release the sensor wiring loom from the clip on the door.

**38** Disconnect the wiring multi-plug from the door lock.

**39** Disconnect the interior handle illumination light.

**40** Remove the screws, and remove the interior handle.

**41** Remove the lock assembly.

**42** Release the door-ajar sensor from the clip.

**43** Prise the plastic shield from the locating post.

**44** Slide the outer cable from the lock bracket, then turn the inner cable through a quarter-turn to remove it from the bell crank.

**45** Unscrew the mounting screws and remove the lock motor.

### Striker

**46** Using a pencil, mark the position of the striker.

**47** Undo the mounting screws using a Torx key, and remove the striker.

### Check strap

**48** Disconnect the battery negative (earth) lead (Chapter 5, Section 1).

**49** Using a Torx key, unscrew and remove the check strap mounting screw(s). On the front door, there are two screws; on the rear door, there is only one.

**50** Prise the rubber grommet from the door aperture, then unscrew the mounting nuts and withdraw the check strap from the door.

### *Refitting*

#### Handles

**51** Refitting is a reversal of the removal procedure.

#### Lock barrel

**52** Check that the retaining clip is fitted correctly.

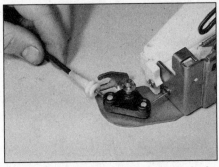

**14.33 Slide the outer cable from the lock bracket**

**53** Align the grooves on the barrel with the grooves on the body and operating lever, then carefully push the barrel into the handle until it engages the clip.

**54** The remaining refitting procedure is a reversal of removal.

### Lock motor

**55** Refitting is a reversal of the removal procedure.

### Striker

**56** Refitting is a reversal of the removal procedure, but check that the door lock passes over the striker centrally. If necessary, re-position the striker before fully tightening the mounting screws.

### Check strap

**57** Refitting is a reversal of the removal procedure.

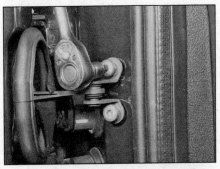

**15.2a Front door check strap mounting screw removal**

**14.34 Removing a lock motor**

## 15 Door – removal and refitting

### *Removal*

**1** Disconnect the battery negative (earth) lead (Chapter 5, Section 1).

**2** Using a Torx key, unscrew and remove the check strap mounting screw(s). On the front door, there are two screws; on the rear door, there is only one **(see illustrations)**.

**3** Disconnect the wiring connector(s) by twisting them anti-clockwise. On the front door, there are two connectors; on the rear door, there is only one **(see illustration)**.

**4** Extract the small circlips from the top of the upper and lower hinge pins **(see illustration)**.

**5** Have an assistant support the weight of the door, then drive the hinge pins down

**15.2b Front door check strap removed**

**15.3 Disconnecting a door wiring connector**

**15.4 Extract the small circlips . . .**

**15.5a . . . then drive out the hinge pins . . .**

15.5b . . . and remove them

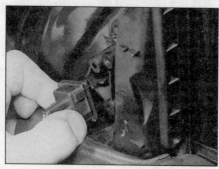

16.4 Disconnecting the wiring multi-plug from an electric exterior mirror

16.5a Unscrew the screws . . .

16.5b . . . and withdraw the mirror

through the hinges using a small drift (see illustrations).

6 Carefully withdraw the door from the hinges.

### Refitting

7 Refitting is a reversal of the removal procedure, but check that the door lock passes over the striker centrally. If necessary, re-position the striker.

## 16 Exterior mirror and glass – removal and refitting

### Removal

1 Where electric mirrors are fitted, disconnect the battery negative (earth) lead (Chapter 5, Section 1).

2 Prise off the cap, unscrew the screw, and remove the quarter bezel from the front of the window opening.

18.2 Unclip the trim cover, and prise out the wiring grommet

3 On manual mirrors, detach the adjustment lever by removing the two small screws and sliding off the lever.

4 On electric mirrors, disconnect the wiring multi-plug (see illustration).

5 On both types of mirror, use a Torx key to unscrew the mirror mounting screws, then withdraw the mirror from the outside of the door (see illustrations). Recover the gasket.

### Refitting

6 Refitting is a reversal of the removal procedure.

## 17 Interior mirror – removal and refitting

### Removal

1 Using a length of strong thin cord or fishing line, break the adhesive bond between the base

18.9 Boot lid hinge bolts

of the mirror and the glass. Have an assistant support and remove the mirror as it is released.

2 If the original mirror is to be refitted, thoroughly clean its base with methylated spirit and a lint-free cloth. Allow a period of one minute for the spirit to evaporate. Clean the windscreen black patch in a similar manner.

### Refitting

3 During the installation of the mirror, it is important that the mirror base, windscreen black patch and the adhesive patch are not touched or contaminated in any way, otherwise poor adhesion will result.

4 Prior to fitting the mirror, the car should ideally have been at an ambient temperature of at least 20°C.

5 With the contact surfaces thoroughly cleaned, remove the protective tape from one side of the adhesive patch, and press it firmly into contact with the mirror base.

6 If fitting the mirror to a new windscreen, the protective tape must also be removed from the windscreen black patch.

7 Using a hairdryer or a hot air gun, warm the mirror base and the adhesive patch for about 30 seconds to a temperature of 50 to 70°C. Peel back the protective tape from the other side of the adhesive patch on the mirror base. Align the mirror base and the windscreen patch, and press the mirror firmly into position. Hold the base of the mirror firmly against the windscreen for a minimum period of two minutes, to ensure full adhesion.

8 Wait at least thirty minutes before adjusting the mirror position.

## 18 Boot lid – removal and refitting

### Removal

1 Disconnect the battery negative (earth) lead (Chapter 5, Section 1), and open the boot lid.

2 On the right-hand hinge, pull off the trim covering, and release the wiring on the hinge arm. Prise out the grommet to free the wiring (see illustration).

3 Where fitted, remove the trim from inside the boot lid.

4 Disconnect the wiring at the connectors visible through the boot lid inner skin aperture.

5 Attach a length of strong cord to the end of the wires in the aperture, to act as an aid to guiding the wiring through the lid when it is refitted.

6 Withdraw the wiring loom through the boot lid apertures. Untie the cord, and leave it in the boot lid.

7 Mark the position of the hinge arms with a pencil.

8 Place rags beneath each corner of the boot lid, to prevent damage to the paintwork.

9 With the help of an assistant, unscrew the mounting bolts and lift the boot lid from the car (see illustration).

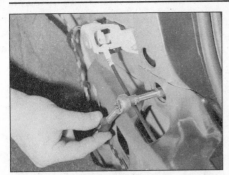

19.10a Remove the lock barrel trim panel mounting nuts from inside . . .

19.10b . . . and withdraw the panel from the outside

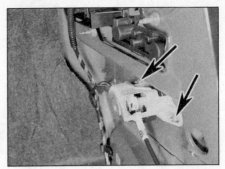

19.11a Remove the two nuts inside . . .

19.11b . . . then withdraw the lock barrel housing from outside

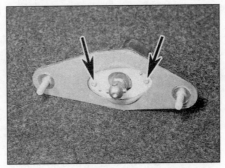

19.12 The lock barrel can be withdrawn after removing two small screws

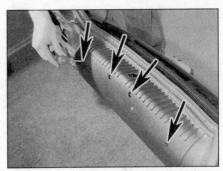

19.14 Remove the screws and lift off the centre trim panel

## Refitting

**10** Refitting is a reversal of the removal procedure, noting the following points:

a) *Check that the boot lid is correctly aligned with the surrounding bodywork, with an equal clearance around its edge.*

b) *Adjustment is made by loosening the hinge bolts, and moving the boot lid within the elongated mounting holes.*

c) *Check that the lock enters the striker centrally when the boot lid is closed.*

## 19 Boot lid lock components – removal and refitting

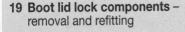

## Removal

### Lock barrel – pre-facelift models

**1** Disconnect the battery negative (earth) lead (Chapter 5, Section 1).

**2** With the boot lid open, remove the luggage space trim from the right-hand rear corner.

**3** Remove the screws, and prise out the rear light trim cover from the guides.

**4** Release the door-ajar sensor from the clip near the lock.

**5** Slide the outer cable from the lock bracket. Raise the inner cable until it is aligned with the slot in the barrel lever, and disconnect it.

**6** Pull out the lock locating spring clip.

**7** Detach the cable mounting bracket from the barrel, and remove the barrel.

### Lock barrel – facelift models

**8** Disconnect the battery negative (earth) lead (Chapter 5, Section 1).

**9** With the boot lid open, remove the luggage space trim from the right-hand rear corner.

**10** Remove the nuts below the light unit which retain the lock barrel trim panel, and withdraw the panel from the outside **(see illustrations)**.

**11** Working from the inside, remove the two nuts which secure the lock barrel housing, then lower the cable mounting bracket and withdraw the barrel and housing from the outside **(see illustrations)**.

**12** The lock barrel slides out of the housing for renewal, after removing two small screws **(see illustration)**.

### Lock

**13** Disconnect the battery negative (earth) lead (Chapter 5, Section 1).

**14** With the boot lid open, prise out the clips, remove the screws, and remove the side and centre trim panels around the lock **(see illustration)**.

**15** Release the door-ajar sensor from the clip near the lock, and (where applicable) disconnect the wiring plug for the alarm inhibitor switch. On later models, prise out the wiring harness from the bodywork, and disconnect the multi-plug for the door-ajar sensor **(see illustrations)**.

**16** Mark the position of the lock, for use when refitting. Using a Torx key, unscrew the lock mounting screws, and withdraw the lock **(see illustration)**.

**17** Early models have a cable-operated remote release, as well as the lock operating cable fitted to all models. Disconnect the cable(s) from the lock bracket. Where applicable, prise open the plastic lip, and

19.15a Unclip the door-ajar sensor/boot light switch from the lock . . .

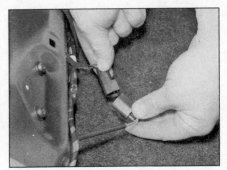

19.15b . . . and disconnect its wiring plug

**19.16 Remove the lock securing screws**

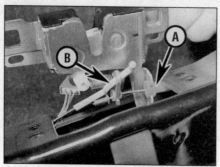

**19.17a Lock operating cable (A) and central locking motor rod (B)**

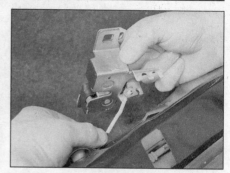

**19.17b Disconnect the central locking rod from the lock**

remove the central locking control rod **(see illustrations)**.

**18** Withdraw the lock assembly.

## Refitting

**19** Refitting is a reversal of the removal procedure. When refitting the lock, use the alignment marks made on removal to ensure that the lock is positioned accurately.

## 20 Tailgate – removal and refitting

## Removal

### Hatchback

**1** Disconnect the battery negative (earth) lead (Chapter 5, Section 1). Open the tailgate.

**20.7a Unclipping the upper trim panel from the tailgate**

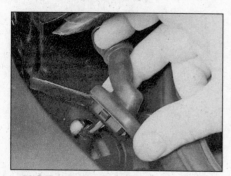

**20.8 Removing the wiring loom rubber grommet**

**2** The tailgate may be unbolted from the hinges and the hinges left in position, or the hinges may be detached from the roof panel by unscrewing the mounting nuts. In the latter case, carefully pull down the rear edge of the headlining for access to the nuts. Take care not to damage the headlining.

**3** Remove the parcel shelf left-hand support bracket as follows. Fold the rear seat forwards, and on pre-facelift models, disconnect the left-hand seat pull cable from the bracket and clips. Where necessary, pull up the rear seat side bolster (on low-series models, the bolster is retained with a screw), then unscrew the screws and remove the support bracket.

**4** Carefully remove the side trim from the left-hand side of the luggage area.

**5** Separate the tailgate wiring loom multi-plugs, located on the left-hand side of the luggage compartment, on top of the wheel arch.

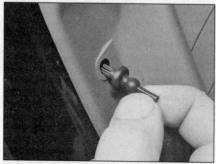

**20.7b Shelf cord post removal**

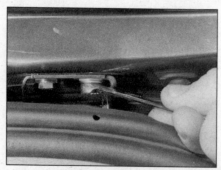

**20.13 Unscrewing the bolts securing the tailgate to the hinges**

**6** On models with a high-level rear brake light, remove the two light unit cover screws, and disconnect the bulbholder wiring.

**7** Unclip and remove the upper trim panel from the inside of the tailgate. Also remove the rear shelf cord plastic post **(see illustrations)**.

**8** Prise out the rubber grommet from the top of the tailgate aperture, and pull the wiring loom out through the hole in the body **(see illustration)**.

**9** Disconnect the rear window washer tube from the jet.

**10** Prise out the rubber grommet from the right-hand side of the tailgate aperture, and pull out the washer tube.

**11** Have an assistant support the tailgate in its open position.

**12** Using a small screwdriver, prise off the clips securing the struts to the tailgate. Pull the sockets from the ball-studs, and move the struts downwards.

**13** If the headlining has been pulled back, unscrew and remove the hinge nuts from the roof panel. Otherwise, unscrew the bolts securing the tailgate to the hinges **(see illustration)**.

**14** Withdraw the tailgate from the body aperture, taking care not to damage the paintwork.

### Estate

**15** Disconnect the battery negative (earth) lead (Chapter 5, Section 1).

**16** The tailgate may be unbolted from the hinges and the hinges left in position, or the hinges may be detached from the rear roof panel by unscrewing the mounting nuts. In the latter case, carefully pull down the rear edge of the headlining for access to the nuts. Take care not to damage the headlining.

**17** Unscrew the retaining screws, then unclip the D-pillar trim panels from both sides **(see illustration)**.

**18** Unclip and remove the upper trim panel from inside the tailgate.

**19** Carefully remove the side trim from the left-hand side of the luggage area, and separate the tailgate wiring loom multi-plugs in the rear light cluster housing.

**20** On models with a high-level rear brake light, remove the two light unit cover screws, and disconnect the bulbholder wiring.

**21** Attach a strong fine cord to the end of the wiring loom, to act as an aid to guiding the wiring through the tailgate when it is refitted.

**22** Prise the rubber grommet from the top left-hand side of the tailgate aperture, and pull out the wiring loom. Untie the cord, leaving it in position in the D-pillar.

**23** Disconnect the rear window washer tube from the jet. Pull out the rubber grommet, and remove the tube.

**24** Have an assistant support the tailgate in its open position.

**25** Using a small screwdriver, prise off the clip securing the struts to the tailgate. Pull the sockets from the ball-studs, and move the struts downwards.

**26** Unscrew and remove the hinge nuts from the roof panel, or the hinge bolts from the hinge, as desired **(see illustration)**. Withdraw the tailgate from the body aperture, taking care not to damage the paintwork.

### Refitting

**27** Refitting is a reversal of the removal procedure, but check that the tailgate is located centrally in the body aperture, and that the striker enters the lock centrally. If necessary, loosen the mounting nuts and re-position the tailgate as required.

## 21 Tailgate support strut – removal and refitting

### Removal

**1** Support the tailgate in its open position.

**2** Prise off the upper spring clip securing the strut to the tailgate, then pull the socket from the ball-stud **(see illustration)**.

**3** Similarly prise off the bottom clip, and pull the socket from the ball-stud **(see illustration)**. Withdraw the strut.

### Refitting

**4** Refitting is a reversal of removal, but make sure that the piston end of the strut is fitted on the body (ie, downwards).

## 22 Tailgate lock components – removal and refitting

### Removal

#### Lock barrel (Hatchback) – pre-facelift models

**1** Disconnect the battery negative (earth) lead (Chapter 5, Section 1).

**2** With the tailgate open, pull up the weatherstrip for access to the lock. Remove the screws and clips, and remove the trim panel from the rear of the luggage compartment.

**3** Unhook the parcel net, then remove the screws and clips, and remove the rear cross-member trim.

**4** Remove the screws, and prise out the rear light trim cover from the guides.

**5** Release the door-ajar sensor from the clip near the lock.

**6** Slide the outer cable from the lock bracket. Raise the inner cable until it is aligned with the slot in the barrel lever, and disconnect it **(see illustration)**.

**7** Pull out the lock barrel locating spring clip.

**8** Detach the cable mounting bracket from the barrel, and remove the barrel and cylinder **(see illustrations)**.

#### Lock barrel (Hatchback) – facelift models

**9** Refer to Section 19, paragraphs 8 to 12.

#### Lock barrel (Estate)

**10** Disconnect the battery negative (earth) lead (Chapter 5, Section 1).

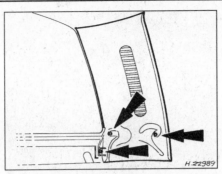

20.17 D-pillar trim panel retaining screws – Estate models

20.26 Tailgate hinge and bolts – Estate models

21.2 Prising the spring clip from the upper end of the strut

21.3 Prising the spring clip from the lower end of the strut

22.6 Tailgate lock barrel and bracket

22.8a Removing the lock barrel . . .

22.8b . . . and cylinder

22.11 Remove the four access plate retaining screws

22.12 Central locking and lock operating rods on lock barrel housing

22.13 Disconnect the door-ajar sensor/ boot light wiring plug

22.14 Removing the lock barrel housing – note one of the retaining tabs

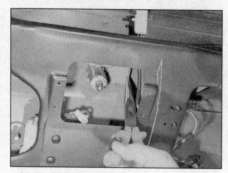

22.15 Slide out the lock barrel retaining clip . . .

22.16 . . . and withdraw the lock barrel from outside

11 Unclip and remove the tailgate trim panel, then undo the four retaining screws and remove the access plate (see illustration).
12 Noting their fitted positions, prise out the central locking and lock operating rods from the lock barrel housing (see illustration).

13 Disconnect the door-ajar sensor wiring plug (see illustration).
14 Prise up the plastic tabs either side, and remove the plastic housing from the lock barrel (see illustration).
15 Working through the aperture in the

tailgate inner panel, pull out the lock barrel locating clip (see illustration).
16 Withdraw the lock barrel from the outside of the tailgate (see illustration).

### Lock (Hatchback)

17 Disconnect the battery negative (earth) lead (Chapter 5, Section 1).
18 With the tailgate open, pull up the weather-strip for access to the lock. Remove the screws and clips, and remove the trim panel from the rear of the luggage compartment.
19 Release the door-ajar sensor from the clip near the lock (see illustration), and disconnect the wiring plug for the alarm inhibitor switch. On later models, prise out the wiring harness from the bodywork, and disconnect the multi-plug for the central locking motor.
20 Mark the position of the lock mounting screws, for use when refitting. Using a Torx key, unscrew the lock mounting screws, and withdraw the lock for access to the cable(s) (see illustration).
21 Early models have a cable-operated remote release, as well as the lock operating cable fitted to all models. Disconnect the cable(s) from the lock bracket (see illustration).
22 Prise open the plastic clip, and remove the central locking control rod.
23 Withdraw the lock assembly.

### Lock (Estate)

24 Disconnect the battery negative (earth) lead (Chapter 5, Section 1).
25 Open the tailgate. Undo the screws and remove the inner trim panel, releasing it from its various retaining clips (see illustrations).
26 Remove the four retaining screws and

22.19 Removing the door-ajar sensor from the lock

22.20 Removing a lock mounting screw

22.21 Disconnecting the cables from the lock

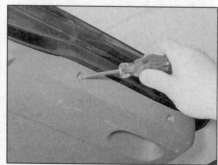

22.25a Remove the trim panel securing screws . . .

**22.25b ... then release the panel from its retaining clips, and remove it**

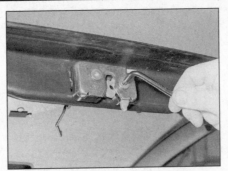

**22.27a Unscrew the lock securing screws ...**

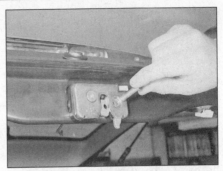

**22.27b ... and withdraw the lock assembly**

**22.28 Unclip the door-ajar sensor/boot light switch from the lock**

**22.29 Lock striker assembly – early Estate models**

take off the access plate, for access to the operating rod(s). Disconnect the rod from the lock barrel, and (where applicable) from the central locking motor, noting their fitted positions **(refer to illustration 22.12)**.

**27** Mark the position of the lock mounting screws, for use when refitting. Using a Torx key, unscrew the lock mounting screws, and carefully withdraw the lock **(see illustrations)**.

**28** Release the door-ajar sensor from the lock **(see illustration)**.

**29** If necessary, the lock striker assembly may be removed by disconnecting the release cable (early models) and unscrewing the mounting bolts **(see illustration)**.

### Refitting

**30** Refitting is a reversal of the removal procedure. When refitting the lock, use the alignment marks made on removal to ensure that the lock is positioned accurately.

## 23 Central locking system components – testing, removal and refitting

### Testing

**1** The central locking module incorporates a service-test mode, which is activated by operating one of the lock position switches 8 times within 10 seconds. A buzzer will sound, to indicate that the service-test mode is operating, and to indicate that no faults have been found in the system. If a fault has been found, the system should be checked by a Ford dealer or electrical specialist. The central locking module also incorporates the alarm system module.

### Removal

#### Central locking/alarm module

**2** To remove the module, first remove the lower right-hand facia panel (right-hand-drive models) or the glovebox (left-hand-drive models).

**3** Disconnect the battery negative (earth) lead (Chapter 5, Section 1).

**4** Unscrew the mounting bolts, and remove the module from the bracket beneath the facia.

**5** Disconnect the wiring multi-plug, and withdraw the module from inside the car.

**6** Note that a different module is used for models without an anti-theft alarm.

#### Set/reset switch (front doors)

**7** This procedure is covered in Section 14, under front door handle removal.

#### Door-ajar switch/sensor

**8** This procedure is covered in the relevant lock removal procedure – refer to Section 14, 19 or 22 as applicable.

#### Door motors

**9** This procedure is covered in Section 14.

#### Boot lid/tailgate motor

**10** Remove the lock as described in Section 19 or 22, as applicable.

**11** Remove the two motor securing screws, then manoeuvre the motor assembly out from the body, disconnecting the wiring plug **(see illustrations)**.

**23.11a Remove the two motor securing screws ...**

### Refitting

**12** In all cases, refitting is a reversal of the removal procedure.

## 24 Windscreen and fixed windows – removal and refitting

**1** The windscreen and rear window on all models are bonded in place with special mastic, as are the rear side windows on Estate models. Special tools are required to cut free the old units and fit new ones; special cleaning solutions and primer are also required. It is therefore recommended that this work is entrusted to a Ford dealer or windscreen specialist.

**2** Note that the windscreen contributes towards the structural strength of the car as a whole, so it is important that it is fitted correctly.

**23.11b ... remove the motor, and disconnect the wiring plug – Estate model shown, others similar**

## 25 Body side-trim mouldings and adhesive emblems – removal and refitting

### Removal

**1** Insert a length of strong cord (fishing line is ideal) behind the moulding or emblem concerned. With a sawing action, break the adhesive bond between the moulding or emblem and the panel **(see illustration)**.
**2** Thoroughly clean all traces of adhesive from the panel using methylated spirit, and allow the location to dry.

### Refitting

**3** Peel back the protective paper from the rear face of the new moulding or emblem. Carefully fit it into position on the panel concerned, but take care not to touch the adhesive. When in position, apply hand pressure to the moulding/emblem for a short period, to ensure maximum adhesion to the panel.

## 26 Sunroof – general information and adjustment

**1** The sunroof should operate freely, without sticking or binding, as it is opened and closed. It is worth periodically applying a little lubricant to the sunroof moving parts, to reduce the strain which would otherwise be placed on the opening handle (or motor).
**2** When in the closed position, check that the panel is flush with the surrounding roof panel.

**27.3a  Unscrew the Torx screws . . .**

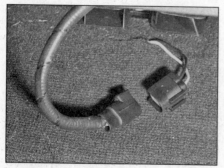

**27.5  Disconnecting an electric seat multi-plug**

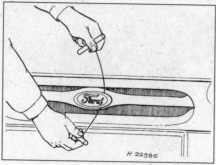

**25.1  Using a length of cord to remove the emblem from the radiator grille**

**3** If adjustment is required, open the sun blind, but leave the glass panel shut. Unscrew and remove the three lower frame-to-glass panel retaining screws. Slide the lower frame back into the roof.
**4** Loosen the central and front securing screws. Adjust the glass roof panel so that it is flush at its front edge with the roof panel, then retighten the securing screws.
**5** Pull the lower frame forwards, and insert and tighten its retaining screws to complete.

## 27 Seats – removal and refitting

### Removal

#### Front seat

**1** On models with electrically-operated or

**27.3b  . . . and remove the mounting trims for access to the front seat rear mounting bolts**

**27.7  Front seat front mounting bolt**

heated seats, or with side airbags, disconnect the battery negative lead, and position the lead away from the battery (see Chapter 5, Section 1). The same applies to facelift models from October 1996 onwards, which have pyrotechnic-type seat belt tensioners (see Section 28)

⚠ **Warning: On later models with pyrotechnic-type seat belt tensioners, wait 2 minutes before proceeding. Where side airbags are fitted, wait a minimum of 15 minutes, as a precaution against accidental firing of the airbag unit. This period ensures that any stored energy in the back-up capacitor is dissipated. Models with side airbags should have an AIRBAG or SRS label attached to the front seat's outermost side cushions.**

**2** Release the seat belt, and slide the seat fully forwards.
**3** Using a Torx key, undo the screws and remove the side and rear mounting trims, then unscrew the rear mounting bolts **(see illustrations)**.
**4** Slide the seat fully rearwards.
**5** On models with electrically-operated or heated seats, disconnect the various seat wiring multi-plugs from the seat base, noting their fitted positions **(see illustration)**.
**6** Where side airbags or pyrotechnic-type seat belt tensioners are fitted, remove the trim from the seat base to gain access to the airbag/tensioner wiring plug. Release the retaining clip and disconnect the plug. Note which way round the plug is fitted.
**7** Unscrew the front mounting bolts **(see illustration)**. Make a final check around and under the seat that nothing is till connected to it, and remove the seat from the car. On pre-facelift models with mechanical seat belt tensioners, note that the tensioners will deploy if the seat is roughly handled or dropped.

#### Rear seat cushion

**8** Fold the rear seat cushion forwards. (Note that, on some models, the seat cushion is held in place by screws which must be removed first.) Using a Torx key, unscrew and remove the mounting bolts from the hinges on each side **(see illustration)**.
**9** Withdraw the seat cushion from the car.

**27.8  Rear seat cushion hinge bolt**

### Rear seat backrest

**10** Fold the rear seat cushion and both backrests forwards.
**11** Unclip the backrest rear trims, where fitted, and raise them.
**12** Using a Torx key, unscrew the mounting bolts **(see illustration)**.
**13** Withdraw the backrest from inside the car.

### Rear seat side bolster

**14** Fold the rear seat backrest forwards.
**15** On low-series models, remove the screw and pull the bolster forwards to disengage the clips. On high-series models, simply pull the bolster upwards to disengage the clips.

### *Refitting*

**16** Refitting is a reversal of the removal procedure, but tighten the mounting bolts to the specified torque.

### 28 Seat belts –
removal and refitting

> ⚠ *Warning: Be careful when handling the seat belt tensioning device ('grabber'). On models up to October 1996, it contains a powerful spring; later models use a small explosive charge (pyrotechnic device) similar to the one used to deploy the airbag(s). Clearly, in either case, injury could be caused if these are released in an uncontrolled fashion. Once fired, the tensioner cannot be reset, and must be renewed. Note also that seat belts and associated components which have been subject to impact loads must be renewed.*

**27.12  Rear seat backrest mounting bolts**

**28.3a  Front seat belt guide and mounting bolt**

**28.2  Front seat belt reel unit lower mounting bolt**

**28.3b  Front seat belt shackle and mounting nut**

### *Removal*

#### Front seat belt – pre-facelift models

**Note:** *Before removing the seat belt stalk, ask a Ford dealer for one of the special plastic clips used to disarm the tensioner operating cable while it is disconnected.*

**1** Remove the trim from the B-pillar and the scuttle.

**2** Unscrew the mounting bolts and remove the seat belt reel unit **(see illustration)**.
**3** Unscrew the bolt securing the seat belt guide to the B-pillar, then unscrew the nut securing the seat belt upper shackle **(see illustrations)**.
**4** Where necessary, remove the screws and clips, and take off the seat lower side trim panel for access to the seat belt stalk.
**5** Pull down the tensioner inner cable, and slide the end fitting out of the bracket. Twist the outer cable through 90°, and remove it from the bracket. Fit the special plastic clip to the tensioner cable to disarm the tensioner **(see illustration)**.
**6** Undo the mounting nut, noting that on the right-hand seat, it has a **left-hand thread** (ie, unscrews clockwise), and remove the stalk and grabber assembly from the front seat **(see illustration)**.

> ⚠ *Warning: There is a potential risk of the grabber firing during (or after) removal, so it should be handled carefully – do not drop it.*

**28.6  Front seat stalk mounting nut**

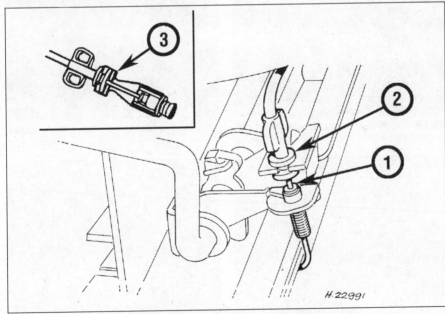
**28.5  Front seat belt stalk cable details**

1  Inner cable       2  Outer cable       3  Plastic clip

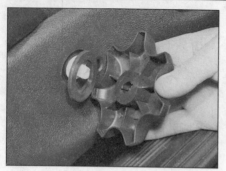

28.7a Remove the recline adjustment knob . . .

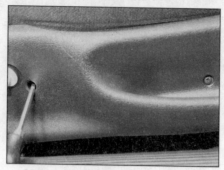

28.7b . . . unscrew the trim retaining screws . . .

28.7c . . . and unscrew the seat belt end retaining bolt

**7** Remove the recline adjustment knob and trim from the outer side of the front seat, then unscrew the bolt and remove the seat belt end from the seat **(see illustrations)**.

### Front seat belt – facelift models

**8** On models with the pyrotechnic type seat belt tensioner, disconnect the battery negative lead, and position the lead away from the battery (see Chapter 5, Section 1).

⚠️ *Warning: Before proceeding, wait a minimum of 2 minutes, as a precaution against accidental firing of the seat belt tensioner. This period ensures that any stored energy in the back-up capacitor is dissipated.*

**9** Remove the trim from the B-pillar and the scuttle.

**10** Unscrew the mounting bolt and remove the seat belt reel unit from the pillar.

**11** Unscrew the bolt securing the seat belt guide to the B-pillar, then unscrew the nut securing the seat belt upper shackle.

**12** Where necessary, remove the screws and clips, and take off the seat lower side trim panel for access to the seat belt stalk.

**13** Disconnect the wiring plug from the tensioner. Undo the mounting nut, and remove the stalk and grabber assembly from the front seat **(see illustrations)**.

⚠️ *Warning: There is a potential risk of the grabber firing during removal, so it should be handled carefully. Once removed, treat it with care – do not allow use chemicals on or near it, and do not expose it to high temperatures, or it may explode. Do not remove the tensioner mounting bolt from the unit – it is held captive by a paper washer.*

**14** Remove the recline adjustment knob and trim from the outer side of the front seat, then unscrew the bolt and remove the seat belt end from the seat.

### Rear side seat belt

**15** Unscrew the screws and remove the trim from the C-pillar. It will be necessary to detach the rear seat release cable, and remove the plastic cover from the rear seat lock **(see illustrations)**.

**16** Fold the rear seat cushions forward. Unscrew the mounting bolts from the seat belt shackle and reel **(see illustrations)**.

**17** Unscrew the mounting bolt securing the seat belt stalk, and withdraw the stalk. Also unscrew the mounting bolt from the lower anchorage, where applicable **(see illustration)**.

28.13a Disconnect the wiring connector . . .

28.13b . . . then unscrew the mounting nut and remove the tensioner assembly

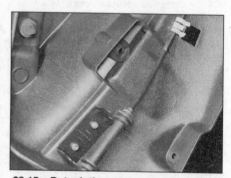

28.15a Detach the rear seat release cable

28.15b Removing the plastic cover from the rear seat lock

28.16a Rear seat belt shackle mounting bolt

28.16b Rear seat belt reel mounting bolt

### Rear centre seat belt

**18** The third, centre rear seat belt was offered as an option on facelift models. The belt reel is attached to the base of the seat backrest, but removal requires that the seat fabric be removed, so this operation should be referred to a Ford dealer or competent specialist. The belt stalks can be removed as described in paragraph 17.

### *Refitting*

**19** Refitting is a reversal of the removal procedure. Tighten the mounting nuts and bolts to the specified torque.

### 29 Interior trim panels – removal and refitting

### *Removal*

#### Sun visor

**1** Disconnect the wiring for the vanity mirror light, where fitted.
**2** Unscrew the mounting screws and remove the visor.
**3** Prise up the cover, unscrew the inner bracket mounting screws, and remove the bracket.

#### Passenger grab handle

**4** Prise up the covers, then unscrew the mounting screws and remove the grab handle.

#### A-pillar trim

**5** Pull away the door weatherstrip in the area of the trim.

**28.17 Rear seat belt lower anchorage**

**6** Release the alarm and aerial wiring from the upper and middle clips.
**7** Carefully press the trim away from the upper and middle clips, and pull the trim upwards. Recover the lower sealing strip.
**8** Remove the upper and middle clips from the pillar.

#### B-pillar and cowl side trim

**9** Pull away the door weatherstrip in the area of the trim.
**10** Undo the screws, release the fasteners and remove the lower trim **(see illustrations)**.
**11** Carefully separate the lower trim from the upper trim, using a screwdriver if necessary **(see illustration)**.
**12** Unscrew the seat belt mounting bolt from under the front seat, remove the remaining trim from the B-pillar, and feed the belt through the trim.

### C-pillar trim (Saloon and Hatchback)

**13** Pull away the door weatherstrip in the area of the trim.
**14** Fold the rear seat cushion forwards.
**15** On facelift Hatchback models, prise out the screw covers, and remove the two trim-to-parcel shelf support screws.
**16** Pull up the rear seat bolster, and release the upper hook **(see illustrations)**. Note that, on low-series models, the bolster is retained with a screw.
**17** Release the clips and locating tangs, and detach the upper trim. On models equipped with the ultrasonic parking sensor, release the warning light unit from the panel, or disconnect its wiring plug.
**18** Remove the rear seat belt lower mounting bolt, then remove the trim, and pass the seat belt through it.

### C-pillar trim (Estate)

**19** Prise off the caps, unscrew the screws, and remove the upper trim from the C-pillar **(see illustration)**.
**20** Unscrew the mounting bolt securing the rear seat belt upper shackle to the C-pillar.
**21** Unclip and remove the trim.
**22** On models equipped with the ultrasonic parking sensor, release the warning light unit from the panel, or disconnect its wiring plug.

### D-pillar trim (Estate)

**23** Remove the three mounting screws, then unclip the trim from the D-pillar.

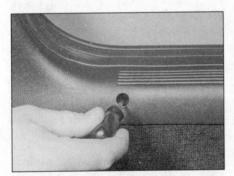

**29.10a Removing a middle screw from the lower trim**

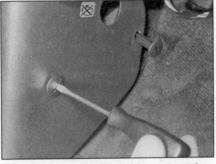

**29.10b Releasing the fasteners from the cowl side trim**

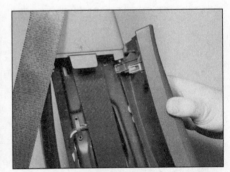

**29.11 Separating the B-pillar lower and upper trim**

**29.16a Pull up the rear seat bolster . . .**

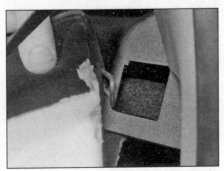

**29.16b . . . and release the upper hook**

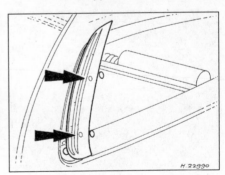

**29.19 Screw locations for the C-pillar upper trim – Estate models**

29.25a Unscrew the mounting screws from the upper corners . . .

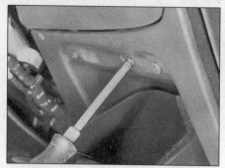

29.25b . . . and above the coin tray position . . .

29.25c . . . and withdraw the lower facia panel

29.26a Unscrew the screws (or release the clips) . . .

29.26b . . . and remove the lower centre panel

### Lower facia panel

24 Remove the steering column top and bottom shrouds.

25 Unscrew the mounting screws from the upper corners and above the coin tray position, and withdraw the lower facia panel from the facia **(see illustrations)**. Where applicable, detach the diagnostic plug connector from the panel.

### Lower centre panels

26 Release the two screws or clips each side, and withdraw the panels from the front of the centre console **(see illustrations)**.

### *Refitting*

27 Refitting is a reversal of the removal procedure. Where seat belt fastenings have been disturbed, make sure that they are tightened to the specified torque.

---

**30 Centre console –** removal and refitting

### *Removal*

1 Disconnect the battery negative (earth) lead (Chapter 5, Section 1).

2 Pull the ashtray from the facia, and prise off the cigar lighter surround **(see illustrations)**.

3 Unscrew the gear lever knob. Prise out the gear lever gaiter, and remove it over the top of the gear lever **(see illustrations)**.

4 Where applicable, lift out the rubber mat from the base of the rear storage compartment.

5 Prise out the coin storage tray (if fitted).

6 Prise off the plastic caps (where fitted), then unscrew the centre console mounting screws. These are located on each side, on the front top, and inside the cassette storage box **(see illustrations)**. The screws with the washers go on the side of the console; the front screws are smaller than the others, and black in colour.

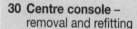

30.2a Remove the ashtray . . .

30.2b . . . then prise off the cigar lighter surround

30.3a Gear lever knob removal

30.3b Prising out the gear lever gaiter

30.6a Prise off the plastic caps . . .

30.6b ... and unscrew the mounting screws at the front top ...

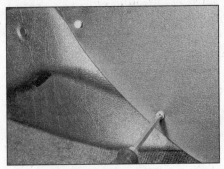

30.6c ... at the sides ...

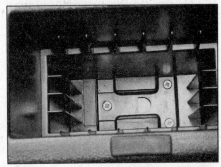

30.6d ... and inside the cassette storage box

30.8a Withdrawing the front of the console from the facia

30.8b Passing the gaiter over the handbrake lever

30.9 Disconnecting the cigar lighter wiring

**7** Fully apply the handbrake lever. On later models, it may be necessary to release the handbrake spring from the ratchet, in order to lift the lever high enough to remove the console.
**8** Withdraw the centre console, at the same time passing the gaiter over the handbrake lever **(see illustrations)**.
**9** Disconnect the cigar lighter wiring **(see illustration)**.

### Refitting

**10** Refitting is a reversal of the removal procedure.

---

### 31 Overhead console –
removal and refitting

### Removal

**1** Disconnect the battery negative (earth) lead (Chapter 5, Section 1).
**2** On models with an electrically-operated sunroof, remove the sunroof switch (Chapter 12, Section 4).
**3** On models with a manual sunroof, remove the sunroof handle, after undoing the securing screw **(see illustration)**.
**4** Push the console towards the windscreen, to disengage it from the clips.

### Refitting

**5** Refitting is a reversal of the removal procedure.

---

### 32 Glovebox –
removal and refitting

### Removal

**1** Open the glovebox. Using a screwdriver, carefully press in one side of the glovebox near the hinge, to release it from the plastic clip **(see illustration)**.
**2** Withdraw the glovebox and, where necessary, disconnect the wiring multi-plug for the light.
**3** If necessary, the lock may be removed by unscrewing the mounting screws and removing the lock plate and spring **(see illustration)**.
**4** To remove the lock barrel, depress the spring tabs.

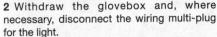

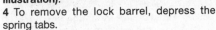

### Refitting

**5** Locate the barrel in the lock plate, making sure that the clips are fully engaged.
**6** Hold the latch pins together, and engage the right-hand pin of the lock plate.

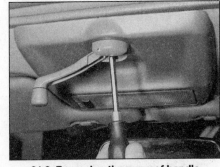

31.3 Removing the sunroof handle securing screw

32.1 Glovebox removal

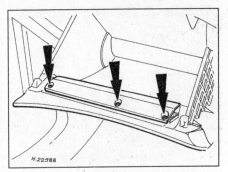

32.3 Glovebox lock mounting screws

**33.18a Prise off the covers . . .**

**33.18b . . . and pull away the weatherstrip to reveal the facia mounting bolts**

## 33 Facia –
### removal and refitting

### *Removal*

**1** Disconnect the battery negative (earth) lead (Chapter 5, Section 1).
**2** On pre-facelift models (up to October 1996), remove the windscreen wiper arms (Chapter 12), then remove the cowl from just in front of the windscreen. The cowl is in two sections, with retaining screws located along its front edge. With the cowl removed, disconnect the speedometer cable by pulling it from the intermediate inner cable extension.
**3** Remove the centre console (Section 30), then remove the lower centre panels as described in Section 29.
**4** Remove the steering column (Chapter 10).
**5** Remove the instrument panel (Chapter 12).
**6** Remove the radio and (if fitted) the CD player (Chapter 12).
**7** Remove the heater control panel (Chapter 3).
**8** Using a screwdriver, carefully prise out the headlight switch panel, and disconnect the wiring multi-plugs.
**9** Remove the glovebox (Section 32).
**10** Where applicable, remove the passenger airbag as described in Chapter 12.
**11** Remove the small piece of carpet from under the passenger side of the facia.
**12** Remove the side trim panels from the A- and B-pillars on each side of the car (Section 29). The upper panels on the B-pillars can be left in position.
**13** At the base of the right-hand A-pillar, disconnect the wiring multi-plugs, earth leads and aerial, noting their fitted positions.
**14** Identify the position of the wiring multi-plugs on the fusebox, then disconnect them.
**15** Disconnect the wiring from the footwell lights, where fitted.
**16** On pre-facelift models (up to October 1996), prise out the speedometer cable rubber grommet at the bulkhead near the pedal bracket, then release the cable from the clips.
**17** Remove the screws and withdraw the glovebox side trim, for access to the side facia mounting screw.
**18** Open the front doors. Prise off the trim covers, then pull away the door weatherstrip by the side mounting bolt positions on each side **(see illustrations)**.
**19** Unscrew the facia side mounting bolts.
**20** Unscrew the facia centre mounting bolts **(see illustrations)**.
**21** Withdraw the facia from the bulkhead, far enough to be able to reach in behind it.
**22** Disconnect the remaining multi-plugs and connections, noting their locations on the various components for correct refitting. It will also be necessary to release some wiring loom holders, clips and plastic ties, and the fresh air vent hoses **(see illustration)**.
**23** With the help of an assistant, withdraw the facia from one side of the car.

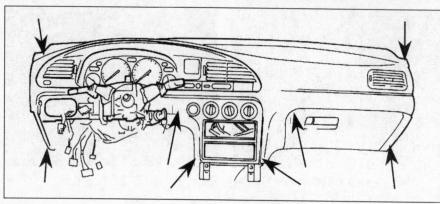

**33.20a Facia mounting bolt positions**

**7** Refit the spring, and engage the left-hand pin of the lock plate.
**8** Refit the lock plate, and tighten the screws.

**9** Reconnect the wiring multi-plug and refit the glovebox, making sure that it is fully inserted in the plastic clips.

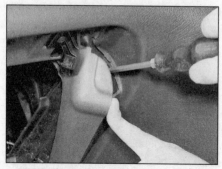

**33.20b Facia mounting bolt next to the glovebox**

**33.20c Facia centre mounting bolt next to the heater panel**

**33.20d Facia mounting bolt near the heater**

**33.22 Disconnecting the fresh air hoses**

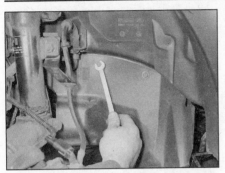

**34.2a Remove the auxiliary drivebelt cover panel screws . . .**

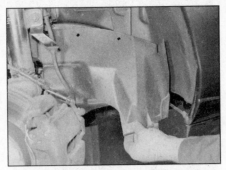

**34.2b . . . and remove the panel**

**34.2c On some models, there is a rear section which can be removed if required**

**34.5 Removing a front wheel arch liner**

**34.7a Remove the screw from the bottom of the liner . . .**

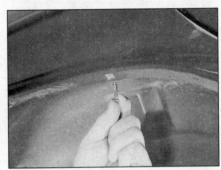

**34.7b . . . and the screw and clip from the top**

## Refitting

**24** Refitting is a reversal of the removal procedure. On completion, check the operation of all electrical components.

## 34 Wheel arch liner – removal and refitting

## Removal

### Front

**1** Apply the handbrake, then loosen the relevant front wheel nuts. Jack up the front of the car and support it on axle stands (see *Jacking and vehicle support*). Remove the front wheel.
**2** If the right-hand liner is being removed for access to other components, it might be enough to remove the auxiliary drivebelt cover panels from the inner side of the wheel arch, by removing the retaining screws. On some models, there are two panel sections (front and rear) – generally, only the front section need be removed for most work **(see illustrations)**.
**3** Prise out the stud clip on the front lower edge of the liner.
**4** Unscrew the screws securing the liner to the inner wheel arch panel.
**5** Remove the screws and clips securing the liner to the outer edge of the wheel arch and bumper. On later models, disconnect the bumper stay bar from the front of the wheel arch. Withdraw the liner from under the car **(see illustration)**.

### Rear

**6** Chock the front wheels, and engage 1st gear. Loosen the relevant rear wheel nuts, then jack up the rear of the car and support it on axle stands (see *Jacking and vehicle support*). Remove the rear wheel.
**7** Remove the screws and clips securing the liner to the outer edge of the wheel arch **(see illustrations)**.
**8** Unscrew and remove the screws securing the liner to the inner wheel arch, and withdraw the liner from under the car **(see illustrations)**.

## Refitting

**9** Refitting is a reversal of the removal procedure. If the wheels were removed, tighten the wheel nuts to the specified torque.

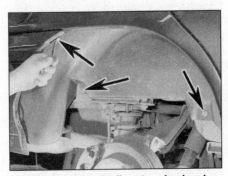

**34.8a Remove the liner-to-wheel arch screws . . .**

## 35 Fuel filler flap and release cable – removal and refitting

## Removal

### Filler flap

**1** Working in the luggage compartment, remove the trim clips and fold down the right-hand side trim panel. As the panel is lowered, feed the emergency release cable through.
**2** Unclip and remove the emergency filler flap release rod from the flap and the catch.
**3** Prise the spring clip off the lock, then working from outside, twist the catch anti-clockwise and withdraw it **(see illustration)**.

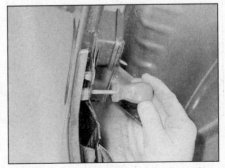

**34.8b . . . and remove the liner from the wheel arch**

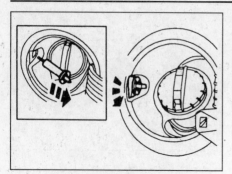

**35.3 Twist the fuel filler flap catch anti-clockwise, and withdraw it**

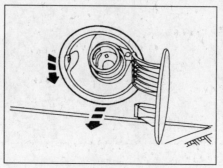

**35.4 Carefully twist the flap housing anti-clockwise to remove**

**35.7 Detach the cable end fitting and cable outer from the operating linkage**

**4** Completely remove the fuel filler cap. Remove the retaining screw to the rear of the filler neck, then carefully twist the filler flap housing approximately 30° anti-clockwise and pull it from the aperture in the rear wing **(see illustration)**.

**5** If required, the filler flap hinge locating pegs can be prised out of the housing – take care, as both the flap and housing are made of plastic.

### Release cable

**Note:** *If the release cable does not operate the flap, an emergency filler flap release cable is provided in the luggage compartment. Note that an inoperative cable may not have broken, but simply have come detached from the operating lever next to the driver's seat, as a result of the cable stretching in use.*

**6** Remove the luggage compartment right-hand side trim panel as described in paragraph 1.

**7** Detach the release cable from the filler flap operating linkage **(see illustration)**, then tie a piece of string to the cable end fitting.

**8** Moving to the front of the car, unclip the trim panels (refer to Section 29 if necessary) and pull back the carpet in the area around the operating lever next to the driver's seat.

**9** Unclip the cable end fitting from the operating lever, and unclip the cable outer from the floor. Gradually pull the cable through into the passenger compartment (it may be necessary to loosen further trim and carpeting to allow passage of the cable), then untie the string from the cable.

**10** When fitting the new cable, use the string to pull the cable through and into the correct position.

### Refitting

**11** Refitting is a reversal of removal.

# Chapter 12
# Body electrical system

## Contents

Section number

Airbag clock spring – removal and refitting ................... 31
Airbag control module – removal and refitting ................. 30
Airbag system – general information and precautions .......... 28
Airbag units – removal and refitting ......................... 29
Anti-theft alarm system – general information ................. 20
Auxiliary warning system – general information and component
   renewal ................................................... 19
Battery – check, maintenance and charging .......... See Chapter 1
Battery – removal and refitting ..................... See Chapter 5
Bulbs (exterior lights) – renewal ............................. 5
Bulbs (interior lights) – renewal ............................. 6
Clock – removal and refitting ................................ 13
Compact disc player – removal and refitting .................. 25
Cruise control system – general information and component renewal . . 21
Electric seat components – removal and refitting .............. 34
Electrical fault finding – general information ................. 2
Electrical system check ........................... See Chapter 1
Exterior light units – removal and refitting .................. 7
Fuses, relays and timer module – testing and renewal .......... 3
General information .......................................... 1
Headlight and front foglight beam alignment – checking and
   adjustment ............................................... 8

Section number

Headlight levelling motor – removal and refitting ............. 9
Horn – removal and refitting ................................ 14
Instrument panel – removal and refitting ..................... 10
Instrument panel components – removal and refitting .......... 11
Parking sensor system – general information .................. 32
Radio aerial – removal and refitting ......................... 27
Radio/cassette player – removal and refitting ................ 23
Radio/cassette player power amplifier – removal and refitting ..... 24
Satellite navigation system – general information ............. 33
Speakers – removal and refitting ............................ 26
Speedometer cable (pre-facelift models) – removal and refitting ... 12
Stop-light switch – removal and refitting ........... See Chapter 9
Switches – removal and refitting ............................. 4
Tailgate wiper motor assembly – removal and refitting ......... 17
Trip computer module – removal and refitting ................. 18
Windscreen wiper motor and linkage – removal and refitting ..... 16
Windscreen/tailgate washer system and wiper blade
   check ............................................ See Chapter 1
Windscreen/tailgate washer system components – removal and
   refitting ................................................. 22
Wiper arms – removal and refitting .......................... 15

## Degrees of difficulty

| **Easy,** suitable for novice with little experience | **Fairly easy,** suitable for beginner with some experience | **Fairly difficult,** suitable for competent DIY mechanic | **Difficult,** suitable for experienced DIY mechanic | **Very difficult,** suitable for expert DIY or professional |
|---|---|---|---|---|

## Specifications

### Fuses (and relays in fuseboxes)

**Note:** *Fuse ratings and circuits are liable to change from year to year. Consult the handbook supplied with the car, or consult a Ford dealer, for the latest information.*

### Auxiliary relays (not in the fuseboxes)

| Relay | Colour | Location | Circuit(s) protected |
|---|---|---|---|
| R17 | Black | Battery tray | Glow plugs |
| R18 | Black | Driver's door | Driver's window relay |
| R19 | Blue | Bracket below instruments | Cruise control cut-off |
| R20 | Blue | Bulb module bracket | Headlight washers |
| R21 | Orange | Bulb module bracket | Rear wiper interval |
| R22 | White | Interface module bracket | Foglights |
| R23 | Black | Steering column | Direction indicators |
| R24 | White | Door lock module bracket | Alarm (left side) |
| R25 | White | Door lock module bracket | Alarm (right side) |
| R26 | Black | Bracket below instruments | Heated seats |
| R27 | - | Bracket below instruments | Not used |
| R30 | - | Bracket below instruments | Not used |
| R34 | - | Bracket below instruments | Air conditioning |

## Bulbs

| | Wattage | Type |
|---|---|---|
| Direction indicator lights | 21 | Bayonet |
| Engine compartment | 10 | Wedge |
| Front foglight: | | |
| Pre-facelift models | 55 | H1 Halogen |
| Facelift models | 55 | H3 Halogen |
| Headlight dipped beam: | | |
| Pre-facelift models | 55 | H1 Halogen |
| Facelift models | 55 | H7LL Halogen |
| Headlight main beam: | | |
| Pre-facelift models | 55 | H1 Halogen |
| Facelift models | 55 | H7 Halogen |
| Interior light | 10 | Festoon |
| Luggage compartment: | | |
| Pre-facelift models | 10 | Festoon |
| Facelift models | 10 | Bayonet |
| Number plate lights | 5 | Festoon |
| Reading light | 5 | Wedge |
| Rear foglight (pre-facelift Hatchback and facelift Saloon) | 21 | Bayonet |
| Rear fog/tail lights (Estate, pre-facelift Saloon, and facelift Hatchback) | 21/5 | Bayonet |
| Rear tail light (Saloon and Hatchback) | 5 | Bayonet |
| Reversing lights | 21 | Bayonet |
| Side repeater lights | 5 | Wedge |
| Sidelights | 5 | Wedge |
| Stop-lights: | | |
| High-level | 5 | Wedge |
| In rear light cluster: | | |
| Facelift Saloon (stop- and tail light) | 21/5 | Bayonet |
| All other models | 21 | Bayonet |

## Torque wrench settings

| | Nm | lbf ft |
|---|---|---|
| Horn unit mounting bolt | 28 | 21 |
| Windscreen wiper motor bolts: | | |
| Into old motor (see text) | 8 | 6 |
| Into new motor (see text) | 12 | 9 |
| Wiper arm nuts | 25 | 18 |

## 1  General information

⚠ **Warning: Before carrying out any work on the electrical system, read through the precautions given in Safety first! at the beginning of this manual.**

The electrical system is of 12 volt negative-earth type. Power for the lights and all electrical accessories is supplied by a lead-acid battery which is charged by the alternator.

This Chapter covers repair and service procedures for the various electrical components not associated with the engine. Information on the battery, alternator, and starter motor can be found in Chapter 5.

All models have a driver's airbag built into the steering wheel, and some later models have a passenger airbag fitted to the facia panel – refer to Section 28.

All models are fitted with an alarm system incorporating a movement sensor and ignition immobiliser. On Saloon and Hatchback models, the alarm system horn is located on the left-hand side of the luggage compartment, but on Estate models, it is on the right-hand side.

Some models are fitted with a headlight levelling system, which is controlled by a knob on the facia. On position 0, the headlights are in their base position, and on position 5, the headlights are in their maximum inclined angle.

It should be noted that, when portions of the electrical system are serviced, the lead should be disconnected from the battery negative terminal, to prevent electrical shorts and fires.

In October 1996, the Mondeo was substantially facelifted – this mainly affects procedures relating to the front lights, though there are also detail differences to the interior switchgear.

*Caution: When disconnecting the battery for work described in the following Sections, refer to Chapter 5, Section 1.*

## 2  Electrical fault finding – general information

**Note:** *Refer to the precautions given in Safety first! and in Section 1 of this Chapter before starting work. The following tests relate to testing of the main electrical circuits, and should not be used to test delicate electronic circuits (such as engine management systems, anti-lock braking systems, etc), particularly where an electronic control module is used. Also refer to the precautions given in Chapter 5, Section 1.*

## General

**1** A typical electrical circuit consists of an electrical component, any switches, relays, motors, fuses, fusible links or circuit breakers related to that component, and the wiring and connectors which link the component to both the battery and the chassis. To help to pinpoint a problem in an electrical circuit, wiring diagrams are included at the end of this Chapter.

**2** Before attempting to diagnose an electrical fault, first study the appropriate wiring diagram, to obtain a complete understanding of the components included in the particular circuit concerned. The possible sources of a fault can be narrowed down by noting if other components related to the circuit are operating properly. If several components or circuits fail at one time, the problem is likely to be related to a shared fuse or earth connection.

**3** Electrical problems usually stem from simple causes, such as loose or corroded connections, a faulty earth connection, a blown fuse, a melted fusible link, or a faulty relay (refer to Section 3 for details of testing relays). Visually inspect the condition of all fuses, wires and connections in a problem circuit before testing the components. Use the wiring diagrams to determine which terminal connections will need to be checked in order to pinpoint the trouble-spot.

**4** The basic tools required for electrical fault finding include a circuit tester or voltmeter (a 12 volt bulb with a set of test leads can also be used for certain tests); an ohmmeter (to measure resistance and check for continuity); a battery and set of test leads; and a jumper wire, preferably with a circuit breaker or fuse incorporated, which can be used to bypass suspect wires or electrical components. Before attempting to locate a problem with test instruments, use the wiring diagram to determine where to make the connections.

**5** To find the source of an intermittent wiring fault (usually due to a poor or dirty connection, or damaged wiring insulation), a 'wiggle' test can be performed on the wiring. This involves wiggling the wiring by hand to see if the fault occurs as the wiring is moved. It should be possible to narrow down the source of the fault to a particular section of wiring. This method of testing can be used in conjunction with any of the tests described in the following sub-Sections.

**6** Apart from problems due to poor connections, two basic types of fault can occur in an electrical circuit – open-circuit, or short-circuit.

**7** Open-circuit faults are caused by a break somewhere in the circuit, which prevents current from flowing. An open-circuit fault will prevent a component from working.

**8** Short-circuit faults are caused by a 'short' somewhere in the circuit, which allows the current flowing in the circuit to 'escape' along an alternative route, usually to earth. Short-circuit faults are normally caused by a breakdown in wiring insulation, which allows a feed wire to touch either another wire, or an earthed component such as the bodyshell. A short-circuit fault will normally cause the relevant circuit fuse to blow.

## Finding an open-circuit

**9** To check for an open-circuit, connect one lead of a circuit tester or the negative lead of a voltmeter either to the battery negative terminal or to a known good earth.

**10** Connect the other lead to a connector in the circuit being tested, preferably nearest to the battery or fuse. At this point, battery voltage should be present, unless the lead from the battery or the fuse itself is faulty (bearing in mind that some circuits are live only when the ignition switch is moved to a particular position).

**11** Switch on the circuit, then connect the tester lead to the connector nearest the circuit switch on the component side.

**12** If voltage is present (indicated either by the tester bulb lighting or a voltmeter reading, as applicable), this means that the section of the circuit between the relevant connector and the switch is problem-free.

**13** Continue to check the remainder of the circuit in the same fashion.

**14** When a point is reached at which no voltage is present, the problem must lie between that point and the previous test point with voltage. Most problems can be traced to a broken, corroded or loose connection.

## Finding a short-circuit

**15** To check for a short-circuit, first disconnect the load(s) from the circuit (loads are the components which draw current from a circuit, such as bulbs, motors, heating elements, etc).

**16** Remove the relevant fuse from the circuit, and connect a circuit tester or voltmeter to the fuse connections.

**17** Switch on the circuit, bearing in mind that some circuits are live only when the ignition switch is moved to a particular position.

**18** If voltage is present (indicated either by the tester bulb lighting or a voltmeter reading, as applicable), this means that there is a short-circuit.

**19** If no voltage is present during this test, but the fuse still blows with the load(s) reconnected, this indicates an internal fault in the load(s).

## Finding an earth fault

**20** The battery negative terminal is connected to 'earth' – the metal of the engine/transmission unit and the bodywork – and many systems are wired so that they only receive a positive feed, the current returning via the metal of the car body. This means that the component mounting and the body form part of that circuit.

**21** Loose or corroded mountings can therefore cause a range of electrical faults, ranging from total failure of a circuit, to a puzzling partial failure. In particular, lights may shine dimly (especially when another circuit sharing the same earth point is in operation), motors (eg, wiper motors or the radiator cooling fan motor) may run slowly, and the operation of one circuit may have an apparently-unrelated effect on another.

**22** Note that on many cars, earth straps are used between certain components, such as the engine/transmission and the body, usually where there is no metal-to-metal contact between components, due to flexible rubber mountings, etc.

**23** To check whether a component is properly earthed, disconnect the battery (refer to Chapter 5, Section 1) and connect one lead of an ohmmeter to a known good earth point. Connect the other lead to the wire or earth connection being tested. The resistance reading should be zero; if not, check the connection as follows.

**24** If an earth connection is thought to be faulty, dismantle the connection, and clean both the bodyshell and the wire terminal (or the component earth connection mating surface) back to bare metal. Be careful to remove all traces of dirt and corrosion, then use a knife to trim away any paint, so that a clean metal-to-metal joint is made.

**25** On reassembly, tighten the joint fasteners securely; if a wire terminal is being refitted, use serrated washers between the terminal and the bodyshell, to ensure a clean and secure connection.

**26** When the connection is remade, prevent the onset of corrosion in the future by applying a coat of petroleum jelly or silicone-based grease, or by spraying on (at regular intervals) a maintenance spray such as WD-40.

---

## 3  Fuses, relays and timer module – testing and renewal

**Note:** *It is important to note that the ignition switch and the appropriate electrical circuit must always be switched off before any of the fuses (or relays) are removed and renewed. In the event of the fuse/relay unit having to be removed, the battery earth lead must be disconnected. When reconnecting the battery, reference should be made to Disconnecting the battery at the end of this manual.*

**1** Fuses are designed to break a circuit when a predetermined current is reached, in order to protect components and wiring which could be damaged by excessive current flow. Any excessive current flow will be due to a fault in the circuit, usually a short-circuit (see Section 2). The main fusebox, which also carries some relays, is located inside the car below the facia panel on the passenger's side, and is accessed by a lever behind the glovebox **(see illustration)**.

**2** A central timer module is located on the bottom of the main fusebox. This module contains the time control elements for the heated rear window, interior lights and

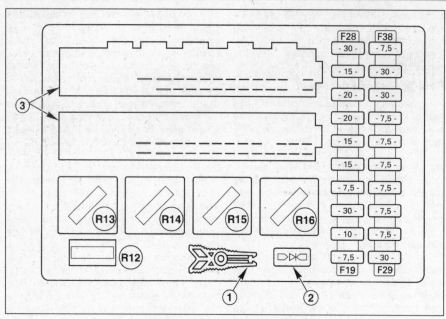

**3.1 Main fusebox layout – typical**

1 *Fuse/relay removal tweezers*

2 *Diode*
3 *Multi-plug connections*

intermittent wiper operation. The module also activates a warning buzzer/chime when the car is left with the lights switched on.

**3** The auxiliary fusebox is located in the engine compartment, next to the battery, and is accessed by unclipping and removing the cover. The auxiliary fusebox also contains some relays **(see illustration)**. Each circuit is identified by numbers on the main fusebox and on the inside of the auxiliary fusebox cover. Reference to the wiring diagrams at the end of this Chapter will indicate the circuits protected by each fuse. Plastic tweezers are attached to the main fusebox and to the inside face of the auxiliary fuse and block cover, to remove and fit the fuses and relays.

**4** To remove a fuse, use the tweezers provided to pull it out of the holder. Slide the fuse sideways from the tweezers. The wire within the fuse is clearly visible, and it will be broken if the fuse is blown **(see illustration)**.

**5** Always renew a fuse with one of an identical rating. Never substitute a fuse of a higher rating, or make temporary repairs using wire or a screw; more serious damage, or even fire, could result. The fuse rating is stamped on top of the fuse. Never renew a fuse more than once without tracing the source of the trouble.

**6** Spare fuses of various current ratings are provided in the cover of the auxiliary fusebox. Note that if the car is to be laid up for a long period, fuse 34 in the main fusebox should be removed, to prevent the ancillary electrical components from discharging the battery.

**7** Relays are electrically-operated switches, which are used in certain circuits. The various relays can be removed from their respective locations by carefully pulling them from the sockets. Each relay in the fuseboxes has a plastic bar on its upper surface to enable the use of the tweezers **(see illustration)**.

**8** If a component controlled by a relay becomes inoperative and the relay is suspect, listen to the relay as the circuit is operated. If the relay is functioning, it should be possible to hear it click as it is energised. If the relay proves satisfactory, the fault lies with the components or wiring of the system. If the relay is not being energised, then either the relay is not receiving a switching voltage, or the relay itself is faulty. (Do not overlook the relay

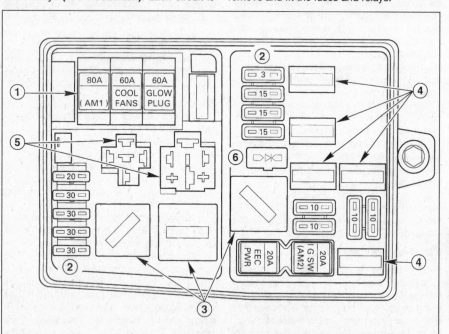

**3.3 Auxiliary fusebox layout – typical**

1 *Fuses 1 to 3*
2 *Fuses 4 to 8, 11 to 14*
3 *Relays R2, R5 and R6*

4 *Relays R7 to R11*
5 *Relay sockets for relays R1 and R4*
6 *Diode*

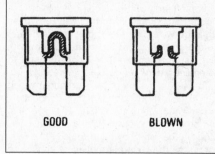

**3.4 The fuses can be checked visually to determine if they are blown**

**3.7 One-touch down window relay in the driver's door**

**4.3a On models with the PATS immobiliser, disconnect the wiring plug . . .**

**4.3b . . . then remove the mounting screw and remove the transceiver**

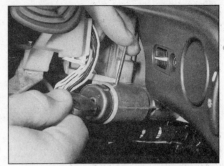

**4.4a Depress the locking plunger . . .**

**4.4b . . . and withdraw the ignition lock barrel**

**4.5a Release the retaining tab . . .**

**4.5b . . . and remove the ignition switch**

socket terminals when tracing faults.) Testing is by the substitution of a known good unit, but be careful; while some relays are identical in appearance and in operation, others look similar, but perform different functions.

**9** The central timer module located on the bottom of the main fusebox incorporates its own self-diagnosis function. Note that diagnosis cannot take place if the heated rear window is defective.

**10** To activate the system, press the heated rear window button while the ignition is being switched on, then release the button. Operate the light switch, washer pump switch and all of the door switches one after the other, and check that the buzzer confirms that the input signals are correct.

**11** Now move the wiper lever to the intermittent wipe position, and check the output signals by operating the same switches.

**12** The self-diagnosis function is turned off by switching the ignition off and on again.

### 4  Switches –
removal and refitting

#### Removal

**1** Before removing any switch, disconnect the battery negative (earth) lead (refer to Chapter 5, Section 1).

#### Ignition switch and lock barrel

**2** Remove the securing screws (two above, three below) and take off the steering column upper and lower shrouds.

**3** On models with the PATS (Safeguard) immobiliser, remove the immobiliser transceiver from the ignition switch by

disconnecting the wiring plug and removing the mounting screw **(see illustrations)**.

**4** Insert the ignition key, and turn it to the accessory position. Using a small screwdriver or twist drill through the hole in the side of the lock housing, depress the locking plunger and withdraw the lock barrel **(see illustrations)**.

**5** The switch may be removed from the steering column assembly by disconnecting the multi-plug, then using a screwdriver to release the switch retaining tab **(see illustrations)**.

#### Windscreen wiper switch

**6** Remove the two securing screws and take off the steering column upper shroud **(see illustration)**.

**7** Disconnect the switch multi-plug, then depress the plastic tab with a screwdriver, and lift the switch assembly from the steering column **(see illustrations)**.

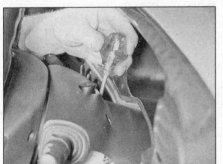

**4.6 Removing the steering column upper shroud screws**

**4.7a Disconnect the multi-plug . . .**

**4.7b . . . then depress the plastic tab with a screwdriver . . .**

4.7c . . . and remove the windscreen wiper switch

4.8 Prising out the light switch

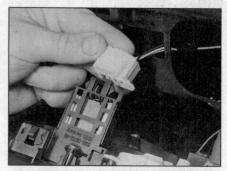

4.9 Disconnecting the multi-plugs from the light switch and rheostat

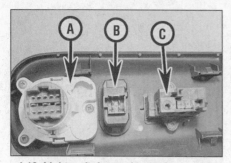

4.10 Light switch panel rear view – main switch (A), headlight aim control (B) and instrument dimmer (C)

4.18 Removing the mirror control switch

4.20 Removing the direction indicator multi-function switch and flasher unit

## Main light and foglight switch

**Note:** *From July 1994, a revised main light switch was introduced; this was fitted as standard in production. If the revised switch is to be fitted to a pre-July 1994 model, an adapter lead will also be required to prevent electrical damage occurring. Refer to your Ford dealer for further information.*

**8** Carefully prise the switch panel from the facia, using a screwdriver against a cloth pad to prevent damage to the facia **(see illustration)**.

**9** Disconnect the multi-plugs and withdraw the switch panel **(see illustration)**.

**10** Unscrew the mounting screws, and remove the switch from the panel **(see illustration)**.

**11** Pull off the switch control knob, and remove the blanking plug and retainer.

**12** Depress the plastic tabs, and remove the front cover and switch.

## Instrument light dimmer

**13** Carefully prise the light switch panel from the facia, using a screwdriver against a cloth pad to prevent damage to the facia.

**14** Disconnect the multi-plug from the rear of the switch, then remove the screws and withdraw the instrument light dimmer from the panel.

## Headlight aim adjustment control

**15** Carefully prise the light switch panel from the facia, using a screwdriver against a cloth pad to prevent damage to the facia.

**16** Disconnect the multi-plug from the rear of the control, then prise the control from the panel.

## Door mirror control switch

**17** Carefully prise the switch from the facia, using a screwdriver against a cloth pad to prevent damage to the facia.

**18** Disconnect the multi-plug and withdraw the switch **(see illustration)**.

## Indicator, dipped beam and hazard flasher switch

**19** Remove the two screws and take off the steering column upper shroud.

**20** Depress the retaining lug and withdraw the switch assembly, then disconnect the multi-plug **(see illustration)**.

**21** With the switch assembly removed, pull out the direction indicator relay (flasher unit) if required.

## Horn switch

**22** Remove the airbag unit from the steering wheel as described in Section 29.

**23** On models with cruise control, remove the switch components as described in Section 21.

**24** Disconnect the wiring connector, then (where applicable) remove the two securing screws and carefully prise out the switch assembly.

## Radio remote control switch

**25** Remove the two screws and take off the steering column upper shroud.

**26** Depress the retaining lug and withdraw the switch assembly, then disconnect the multi-plug.

## Cruise control switches

**27** Refer to Section 21.

## Electric window switch (single)

**28** Carefully prise out the switch from the door inner trim panel, using a cloth pad to prevent damage to the trim **(see illustration)**.

**29** Disconnect the multi-plug and remove the switch **(see illustration)**.

4.28 Prise the switch from the panel . . .

4.29 . . . and disconnect the wiring plug to remove the switch

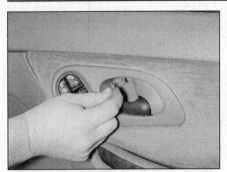

**4.30a  Prise off the trim cap . . .**

**4.30b  . . . and remove the screw beneath**

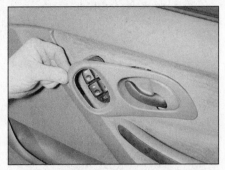

**4.31  Withdraw the bezel over the door handle**

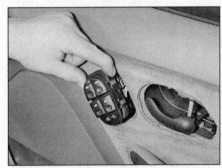

**4.32a  Remove the switch assembly . . .**

**4.32b  . . . and disconnect the wiring plugs**

**4.36  Disconnecting the multi-plug from the handbrake lever**

### Electric window switch (multiple)

**30**  Prise the blanking cap from inside the inner door handle cavity, and remove the screw (see illustrations).

**31**  Hold the inner door handle in its open position, then remove the bezel and withdraw it over the handle (see illustration).

**32**  Depress the retaining lug and remove the switch assembly, then disconnect the multi-plug (see illustrations).

### Electric sunroof switch

**33**  Carefully prise out the switch with a screwdriver, using a cloth pad to prevent damage to the trim.

**34**  Disconnect the multi-plug and remove the switch.

### Handbrake-on warning switch

**35**  Remove the centre console as described in Chapter 11.

**36**  Disconnect the multi-plug (see illustration), then remove the screw and withdraw the switch from the handbrake lever mounting bracket.

### Heated windscreen/rear window switch – pre-facelift models

**37**  Carefully prise out the switch, using a cloth pad to prevent damage to the trim (see illustration).

**38**  Disconnect the multi-plug and remove the switch (see illustration).

### Heated windscreen/rear window switch – facelift models

**39**  Carefully prise the main lighting switch panel from the facia, using a screwdriver

against a cloth pad to prevent damage to the facia. If necessary for access, disconnect the wiring plugs from the rear of the switches.

**40**  Reach in behind the switch panel, and push out the heated screen/rear window

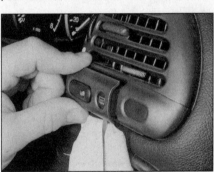

**4.37  Prising out the heated rear window switch**

**4.40  Reach in through the aperture and push the switches out from behind**

switch assembly from behind – do not prise from the front, or the switches may be damaged (see illustration).

**41**  Disconnect the multi-plugs and remove the switch assembly (see illustration).

**4.38  Disconnecting the multi-plug from the heated rear window switch**

**4.41  Disconnect the switch wiring plugs**

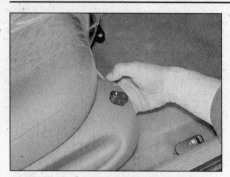

4.42 Push out the switch from below . . .

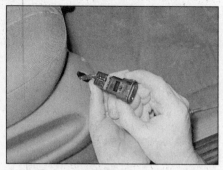

4.43 . . . and disconnect the switch multi-plug

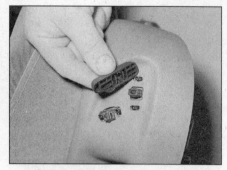

4.45 Pull off the switch control knobs

4.46a Working from below, remove the switch securing screws . . .

4.46b . . . then withdraw the switch from the seat and disconnect the wiring

4.56 Reach in through the radio aperture and push out the switch . . .

## Seat height adjustment switch (single switch)

42 Push the switch out from below (see illustration).

43 Disconnect the multi-plug and remove the switch (see illustration).

## Seat adjustment switches (two-part switch)

44 Remove the seat as described in Chapter 11.

45 Pull off the switch control knobs, noting their fitted position and orientation (see illustration).

46 Working from below the seat, unscrew and remove the two switch securing screws, and withdraw the switch (see illustrations).

47 Trace the switch wiring back to the connector plug, and disconnect the plug.

## Heated seat switch – pre-facelift models

48 Carefully prise out the switch with a screwdriver, using a cloth pad to prevent damage to the trim.

49 Disconnect the multi-plug and remove the switch.

## Heated seat switch – facelift models

50 Remove the radio/cassette unit as described in Section 23.

51 Reach in through the radio aperture, and push the switch out from behind.

52 Disconnect the multi-plug and remove the switch.

## Traction control switch – pre-facelift models

53 Carefully prise out the switch with a screw-driver, using a cloth pad to prevent damage to the trim.

54 Disconnect the multi-plug and remove the switch.

## Traction control switch – facelift models

55 Remove the radio/cassette unit as described in Section 23.

56 Reach in through the radio aperture, and push the switch out from behind (see illustration).

57 Disconnect the multi-plug and remove the switch (see illustration).

## Courtesy light door switch

58 Open the door, then unscrew the cross-head screw and carefully pull the switch from the pillar (see illustrations). Take care not to force the wire from the switch terminal, otherwise it will be difficult to retrieve it from the pillar.

4.57 . . . then disconnect its wiring plug

4.58a Unscrew the cross-head screw . . .

4.58b . . . and pull out the courtesy light switch

**59** Disconnect the wire, and tie it in a loose knot to prevent it dropping back into the pillar.

### Boot light switch

**60** Removing the switch will in most cases entail partially removing the lock components to gain access to the switch and its wiring plug – refer to the relevant Sections of Chapter 11 for lock removal details.

**61** The switch unclips from the lock body **(see illustration)**, and once the wiring plug has been disconnected, can be withdrawn from the lock.

### *Refitting*

**62** Refitting of all switches is a reversal of the removal procedure.

## 5  Bulbs (exterior lights) – renewal

**1** Whenever a bulb is renewed, note the following points:
a) *Switch off all exterior lights, and disconnect the battery negative lead before starting work (see Chapter 5, Section 1).*
b) *Remember that if the light has just been in use, the bulb may be extremely hot.*
c) *Always check the bulb contacts and holder, ensuring that there is clean metal-to-metal contact between the bulb and its live(s) and earth. Clean off any corrosion or dirt before fitting a new bulb.*
d) *Wherever bayonet-type bulbs are fitted,*

ensure that the live contact(s) bear firmly against the bulb contact.
e) *Always ensure that the new bulb is of the correct rating and that it is completely clean before fitting it; this applies particularly to headlight/foglight bulbs.*
f) *Do not touch the glass of halogen-type bulbs (headlights, front foglights) with the fingers, as this may lead to rapid blackening and failure of the new bulb; if the glass is accidentally touched, clean it with methylated spirit.*
g) *If renewing the bulb does not cure the problem, check the relevant fuse and relay with reference to the Specifications, and to the wiring diagrams at the end of this Chapter.*

### *Headlight (dipped beam)*

#### Pre-facelift models

**2** Working under the bonnet, depress the plastic clips and remove the cover from the rear of the headlight unit **(see illustration)**.
**3** Release the spring clip and withdraw the bulb, then disconnect the wiring plug **(see illustrations)**.
**4** Fit the new bulb using a reversal of the removal procedure. Do not touch the glass of the new headlight bulb with bare fingers. If the glass is accidentally touched, clean it with methylated spirit. Check the headlight beam alignment as described later in this Chapter.

#### Facelift models

**Note:** If the right-hand dipped beam has failed, it could be due to the dipped beam relay in the

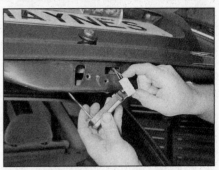

**4.61 Removing the boot light switch – Estate shown, others similar**

engine compartment fusebox having worked loose. Check that the relay is securely pushed into its socket before assuming the bulb has blown.

**5** Depending on model, and on which headlight is being worked on, it may be necessary to remove the headlight unit as described in Section 7, in order that the headlight rear cover can be removed.
**6** At the rear of the headlight, lift up the spring clip and fold down the rear cover for access to the bulb **(see illustration)**.
**7** Disconnect the wiring plug from the rear of the bulb **(see illustration)**.
**8** Release the wire clip securing the bulb, and remove the bulb. Note how the tabs fit in the slots on the rear of the headlight **(see illustrations)**.
**9** Fit the new bulb using a reversal of the removal procedure. Have the headlight beam alignment checked as described later in this Chapter.

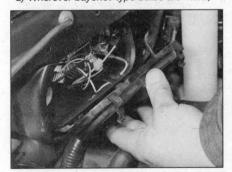

**5.2 Removing the cover from the rear of the headlight**

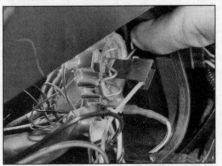

**5.3a Release the spring clip . . .**

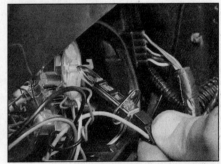

**5.3b . . . and withdraw the headlight bulb**

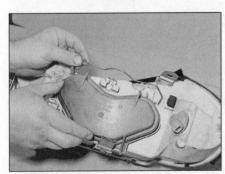

**5.6 Release the wire clip, and remove the headlight rear cover**

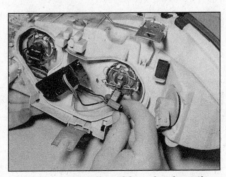

**5.7 Disconnect the wiring plug from the bulb**

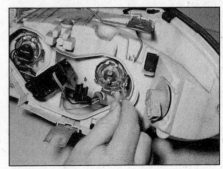

**5.8a Release the bulb retaining clip, pivot it aside . . .**

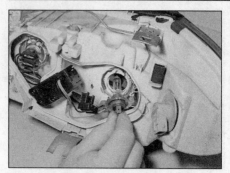

5.8b . . . and withdraw the bulb

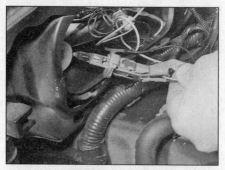

5.11 Removing the headlight (main beam) bulbholder

5.12 Removing the headlight (main beam) bulb from the bulbholder

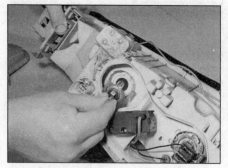

5.14 Removing the headlight main beam bulb

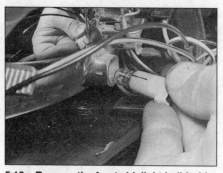

5.16a Remove the front sidelight bulbholder from the rear of the headlight unit . . .

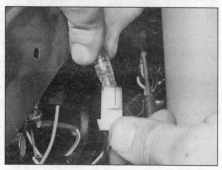

5.16b . . . and pull out the wedge-type bulb

## Headlight (main beam)

### Pre-facelift models

**10** Working under the bonnet, depress the plastic clips and remove the cover from the rear of the headlight unit.

**11** Turn the bulbholder anti-clockwise, and remove it from the rear of the headlight unit (**see illustration**).

**12** Pull out the bulb and disconnect the wiring plug (**see illustration**).

**13** Fit the new bulb using a reversal of the removal procedure, making sure that the bulbholder is correctly located in the headlight unit. Have the headlight beam alignment checked as described later in this Chapter.

### Facelift models

**14** Refer to paragraphs 5 to 9 inclusive (**see illustration**).

## Front sidelight

### Pre-facelift models

**15** Working under the bonnet, depress the plastic clips and remove the cover from the rear of the headlight unit.

**16** Pull the bulbholder from the rear of the headlight unit, and pull the wedge-type bulb from the bulbholder (**see illustrations**).

**17** Fit the new bulb using a reversal of the removal procedure.

### Facelift models

**18** The procedure is as described for pre-facelift models, except that it may be necessary to remove the headlight unit as described in Section 7, in order that the headlight rear cover can be removed (**see illustrations**).

## Front direction indicator

### Pre-facelift models

**19** Open the bonnet. Loosen (but do not remove) the screw located above the front direction indicator.

**20** Withdraw the front direction indicator light unit.

**21** Rotate the bulbholder anti-clockwise, and withdraw it from the light unit.

**22** Twist the bulb anti-clockwise, and remove it from the bulbholder (**see illustration**).

**23** Fit the new bulb using a reversal of the removal procedure, but before refitting the light unit, first insert the holding spring in its bore.

### Facelift models

**24** The front direction indicator bulbholder is mounted in the rear of the headlight unit.

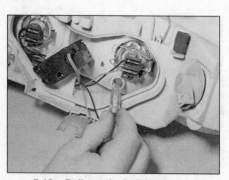

5.18a Pull out the bulbholder . . .

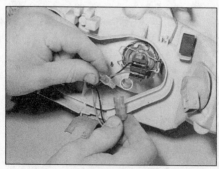

5.18b . . . then pull the bulb from the holder

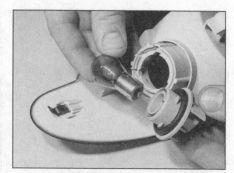

5.22 Removing the front direction indicator bulb

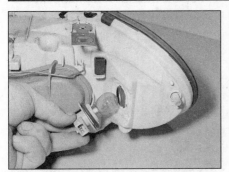

**5.25  Removing the direction indicator bulbholder from the rear of the headlight unit**

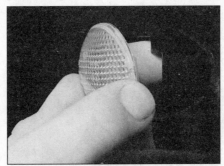

**5.28  Removing the side repeater from the front wing**

**5.29  Removing the bulbholder from the side repeater lens/bulbholder**

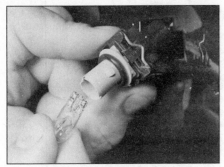

**5.30  Removing the wedge-type bulb from the side repeater bulbholder**

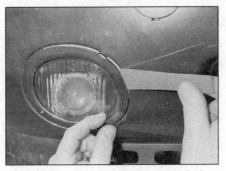

**5.36  Prise out the foglight surround trim**

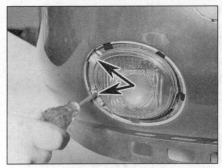

**5.37a  Undo the retaining screws . . .**

Depending on model, and on which light is being worked on, it may be necessary to remove the headlight unit as described in Section 7, to improve access.

**25** The procedure for bulb renewal is as described in paragraphs 21 and 22 **(see illustration)**.

**26** Refitting is a reversal of removal.

### Side repeaters

**27** The side repeater light is held in position by spring pressure.

**28** Depending on how the light unit was previously fitted, press it either forwards or rearwards, and remove it from the front wing **(see illustration)**.

**29** Turn the bulbholder anti-clockwise, and disconnect it from the housing **(see illustration)**.

**30** Pull the wedge-type bulb from the holder **(see illustration)**.

**31** Fit the new bulb using a reversal of the removal procedure.

### Front foglight

#### Pre-facelift models

**32** Unscrew the cross-head screws securing the front foglight unit to the valance, and withdraw the light unit.

**33** Prise open the plastic clips and remove the rear cover from the light unit.

**34** Release the spring clips and withdraw the bulb, then pull off the wiring connector.

**35** Fit the new bulb using a reversal of the removal procedure.

#### Facelift models

**36** Using a suitable flat-bladed screwdriver in

the recess at the bottom of the light, prise out the light surround trim **(see illustration)**.

**37** Unscrew the two cross-head screws, then press the side locking clip outwards and withdraw the light unit forwards. Disconnect

the square wiring plug from the rear of the unit **(see illustrations)**.

**38** Twist off the rear cover from the light unit, and disconnect the wiring from the rear cover **(see illustrations)**.

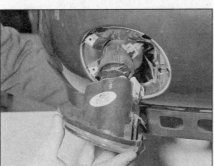

**5.37b  . . . withdraw the light unit . . .**

**5.37c  . . . and disconnect the wiring plug**

**5.38a  Twist off the light unit rear cover . . .**

**5.38b  . . . and disconnect the bulb wiring spade connector**

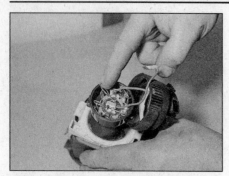

5.39a Release the bulb retaining clip . . .

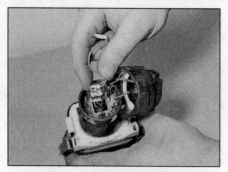

5.39b . . . and withdraw the bulb

5.41a Pull back the weatherstrip . . .

5.41b . . . and unclip the trim cover

**39** Release the legs of the wire clip, and take out the bulb, noting its direction of fitting **(see illustrations)**.
**40** Fit the new bulb using a reversal of the removal procedure.

5.42a Pressing the two plastic locking tabs together – Estate

### Rear light cluster

**41** With the tailgate or boot lid open, flip open the trim cover to reveal the bulbholder in the rear corner of the luggage compartment – the trim cover is secured by a number of turn-

fasteners. On Estate models, pull back the weatherstrip and release the trim cover clips **(see illustrations)**.
**42** Press the two plastic locking tabs together, and withdraw the rear light cluster bulbholder **(see illustrations)**.
**43** Depress and twist the appropriate bulb to remove it from the bulbholder **(see illustration)**.
**44** Fit the new bulb using a reversal of the removal procedure. Make sure that the rear light cluster is fully inserted.

### Number plate light

**45** Remove the cross-head screws from the number plate light, and remove the light unit **(see illustration)**.
**46** Release the festoon-type bulb from the contact springs **(see illustration)**.
**47** Fit the new bulb using a reversal of the removal procedure. Make sure that the tension

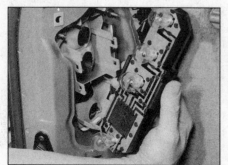

5.42b Removing the rear light cluster – Estate

5.42c Removing the rear light cluster – Saloon

5.43 Removing a bulb from the rear light cluster bulbholder

5.45 Remove the cross-head screws . . .

5.46 . . . for access to the festoon-type bulb

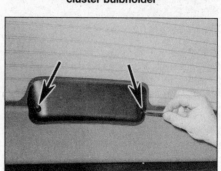

5.48 Remove the two light unit screws . . .

of the contact springs is sufficient to hold the bulb firmly.

### High-level stop-light

**48** Where applicable, open the tailgate. Remove the two light unit securing screws **(see illustration)**.
**49** Lower the light unit from the rear glass, and disconnect the wiring plug **(see illustration)**.
**50** Slide the light out of the housing, taking note of its fitted orientation, then unclip the red cover from the lens and bulbholder **(see illustrations)**.
**51** Pull out the relevant wedge-type bulb from the holder **(see illustration)**.
**52** Fit the new bulb, and refit the light unit using a reversal of the removal procedure.

## 6 Bulbs (interior lights) – renewal

**1** Whenever a bulb is renewed, note the following points:
 a) *Switch off all lights, and disconnect the battery negative lead before starting work (see Chapter 5, Section 1).*
 b) *Remember that if the light has just been in use, the bulb may be extremely hot.*
 c) *Always check the bulb contacts and holder, ensuring that there is clean metal-to-metal contact between the bulb and its live(s) and earth. Clean off any corrosion or dirt before fitting a new bulb.*
 d) *Wherever bayonet-type bulbs are fitted, ensure that the live contact(s) bear firmly against the bulb contact.*
 e) *Always ensure that the new bulb is of the correct rating and that it is completely clean before fitting it.*

### Engine compartment light

**2** With the bonnet open, pull the wedge-type bulb from the bulbholder.
**3** Fit the new bulb using a reversal of the removal procedure.

### Interior light

**4** Ensure that the interior light is switched off by locating the switch in its middle position. Using a small screwdriver, carefully prise out the light or bulb cover, as applicable **(see illustration)**.
**5** Lift up the reflector, then release the festoon-type bulb from the contact springs **(see illustration)**.
**6** Fit the new bulb using a reversal of the removal procedure. Make sure that the tension of the contact springs is sufficient to hold the bulb firmly.

### Map reading light

**7** With the reading light switched off, prise out the interior light using a small screwdriver.
**8** Swivel the contact plate upwards, and remove the bulb **(see illustrations)**.

**9** Fit the new bulb using a reversal of the removal procedure. Make sure that the tension of the contact springs is sufficient to hold the bulb firmly.

### Instrument panel illumination and warning lights

**10** Remove the instrument panel as described in Section 10.

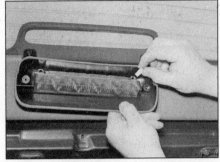
**5.49** . . . then lower the light unit and disconnect the wiring plug

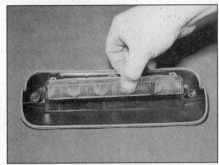
**5.50a** Slide the light out of the housing . . .

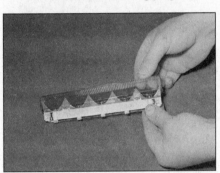
**5.50b** . . . and unclip the cover from the lens/bulbholder

**5.51** Pull out the relevant wedge-type bulb

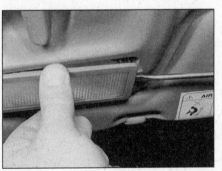
**6.4** Prise out the interior light with a screwdriver

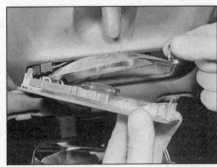
**6.5** Lifting the reflector from the interior light

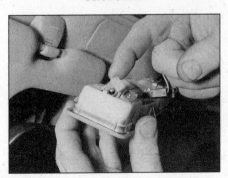
**6.8a** Swivel the contact plate upwards . . .

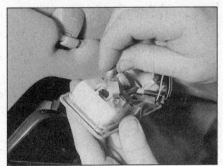
**6.8b** . . . and remove the reading light bulb

**6.11 Removing a bulb from the rear of the instrument panel**

**11** Twist the bulbholder anti-clockwise to remove it **(see illustration)**.

**12** Fit the new bulbholder using a reversal of the removal procedure.

### Foglight warning indicator (pre-facelift models)

**13** Using a screwdriver, prise out the indicator from the facia, and disconnect the multi-plug.

**14** Twist the bulbholder anti-clockwise with the screwdriver, and remove it **(see illustration)**.

**15** Fit the new bulb using a reversal of the removal procedure.

### Hazard warning light

**16** Pull the cover directly up from the switch, then remove the bulb **(see illustrations)**.

**17** Fit the new bulb using a reversal of the removal procedure.

### Glovebox light

**18** Open the glovebox, then pull out the

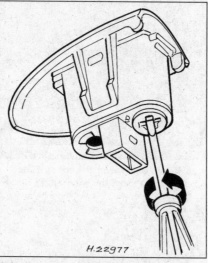

**6.14 Removing the bulb from the foglight warning indicator**

wedge-type bulb from the light located under the upper edge.

### Main light switch illumination

**19** Carefully prise the switch panel from the facia, using a screwdriver against a cloth pad to prevent damage to the facia.

**20** Disconnect the multi-plugs as necessary, and withdraw the switch panel.

**21** Twist the bulbholder to release it from the light switch, and pull out the wedge-type bulb **(see illustration)**.

**22** Fit the new bulb using a reversal of the removal procedure.

### Heater fan switch illumination

**23** Pull off the switch knob, then depress and twist the bulb to remove it.

### Interior door handle illumination

**24** Disconnect the battery negative (earth) lead (refer to Chapter 5, Section 1).

**25** Remove the door interior trim panel (and the foam insulation panel) as described in Chapter 11.

**26** The bulbholder is on the back of the interior door handle – pull out the bulbholder and remove the bulb.

**27** Fit the new bulb using a reversal of the removal procedure.

### Clock illumination

**Note:** *On later models, the clock illumination bulb is not readily renewable. The clock may have to be removed and taken to a Ford dealer or automotive electrician for bulb renewal.*

**28** Disconnect the battery negative (earth) lead (refer to Chapter 5, Section 1).

**29** Remove the clock as described in Section 13.

**30** Twist the bulbholder anti-clockwise using a screwdriver, then remove the bulbholder from the rear of the clock **(see illustrations)**.

**31** Fit the new bulb using a reversal of the removal procedure.

### Heater control illumination

**32** Remove the heater control panel (Chapter 3), then twist the bulbholder anti-clockwise and remove the bulb from the rear of the panel **(see illustration)**.

**6.16a Pull off the hazard warning light cover . . .**

**6.16b . . . and remove the bulb**

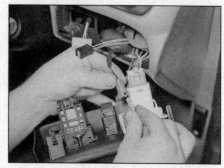

**6.21 Removing the main light switch illumination bulb**

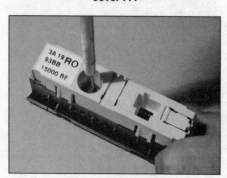

**6.30a Twist the bulbholder anti-clockwise . . .**

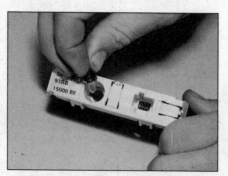

**6.30b . . . and remove it from the rear of the clock – early model shown**

**6.32 Heater control panel removed – bulbholders arrowed**

## Luggage compartment light

**33** With the light switched off (disconnect the battery negative lead), prise out the light using a small screwdriver.
**34** On pre-facelift models, hinge back the contact plate, and release the festoon-type bulb from the contact springs.
**35** On facelift models, twist the bulb anti-clockwise to remove it.
**36** Fit the new bulb using a reversal of the removal procedure. On models with a festoon-type bulb, make sure that the tension of the contact springs is sufficient to hold the bulb firmly.

## Footwell illumination light

**37** Disconnect the battery negative (earth) lead (refer to Chapter 5, Section 1).
**38** Remove the screws securing the driver's side lower facia panel, and remove the panel for access to the bulb **(see illustration)**.
**39** Pull the bulb out of its holder to remove.
**40** Fit the new bulb using a reversal of the removal procedure.

| 7 | Exterior light units – removal and refitting |
|---|---|

**1** Before removing any light unit, note the following points:
  a) Ensure that the light is switched off, and disconnect the battery negative lead before starting work (see Chapter 5, Section 1).

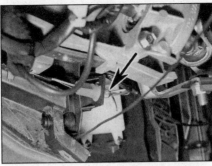

**6.38  Driver's footwell illumination bulb**

  b) Remember that if the light has just been in use, the bulb and lens may be extremely hot.

## Headlight unit

### Pre-facelift models

**Note:** From December 1995, certain Mondeos had more powerful headlight units (with H7 bulbs) fitted in production, and the wiring loom was modified. To fit a later light unit to an earlier car, an adapter lead must also be obtained from your Ford dealer; in this case, find and quote the engine wiring loom part number, which appears on the battery positive lead.
**2** With the bonnet supported in its open position, loosen (but do not remove) the screw located above the front direction indicator.
**3** Withdraw the front direction indicator unit forwards, and disconnect the wiring multi-plug. Place the unit to one side.
**4** Disconnect the wiring multi-plug for the headlight unit **(see illustration)**.

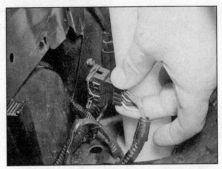

**7.4  Disconnecting the headlight unit wiring multi-plug**

**5** Remove the radiator grille as described in Chapter 11.
**6** Remove the front bumper as described in Chapter 11.
**7** The headlights fitted from new are a single unit, joined by a plastic back-piece running across the front of the car. However, if it is required to renew a headlight unit on one side only, the back-piece must first be removed complete, then cut in half on the bench.
**8** Unscrew the mounting bolts from each side of the headlight unit, and withdraw the unit from the front of the car. Use a hacksaw to cut through the centre of the headlight unit (ie, between the two headlights), and obtain a connecting kit from a Ford dealer to attach the new unit **(see illustrations)**.
**9** If necessary, the lens may be removed separately by releasing the clips. To remove the diffuser, release the clips, then remove the rubber seal **(see illustrations)**.

**7.8a  Unscrew the outer mounting screws . . .**

**7.8b  . . . and inner mounting screws . . .**

**7.8c  . . . and withdraw the headlight unit assembly**

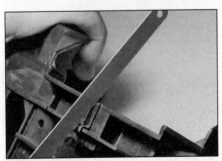

**7.8d  Using a hacksaw to cut through the middle of the headlight back-piece, in order to fit a new unit**

**7.9a  Release the clips . . .**

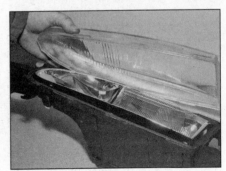

**7.9b  . . . and remove the headlight lens**

7.12a Remove the inner screw . . .

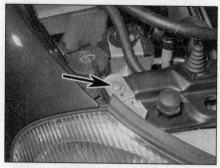

7.12b . . . and the upper screw (arrowed) on the cross panel

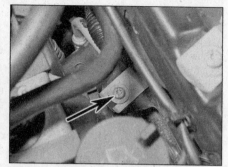

7.13 Loosen, but do not remove, the screw behind the headlight

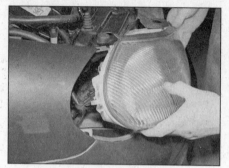

7.14a Withdraw the headlight . . .

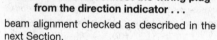

7.14b . . . and disconnect the wiring plug from the direction indicator . . .

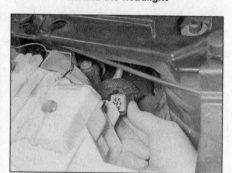

7.14c . . . and from the rear of the headlight

**10** Refitting is a reversal of removal, noting the following points:

a) *When refitting the rubber seal on the head- light unit, note that it has a tapered seat.*

b) *Have the beam alignment checked as described in the next Section.*

### Facelift models

**11** Remove the radiator grille (Chapter 11).
**12** Supporting the headlight, remove the retaining screw from the inner side of the headlight, and the screw securing the outer side to the cross panel **(see illustrations)**.
**13** Loosen, but do not remove, the remaining screw behind the headlight **(see illustration)**.
**14** Withdraw the headlight from the front of the car, and disconnect the wiring plugs from the direction indicator bulbholder, and from the rear of the headlight itself **(see illustrations)**.
**15** Refitting is a reversal of removal. Have the

beam alignment checked as described in the next Section.

## Front direction indicator

### Pre-facelift models

**16** With the bonnet supported in its open position, loosen (but do not remove) the screw located above the front direction indicator **(see illustration)**.
**17** Withdraw the front direction indicator light unit.
**18** Rotate the bulbholder anti-clockwise, and withdraw it from the light unit. Alternatively, the wiring plug can be disconnected from the bulbholder, leaving the bulb in position **(see illustration)**. Remove the light unit.
**19** Refitting is a reversal of removal.

### Facelift models

**20** On these models, the front direction indicator is incorporated into the headlight unit, and is not available separately.

## Front foglight

### Pre-facelift models

**21** Unscrew the cross-head screws securing the front foglight unit to the valance, and withdraw the light unit from the valance.
**22** Prise open the plastic clips, and remove the rear cover from the light unit.
**23** Release the spring clips and withdraw the bulb, then pull off the wiring connector. Remove the foglight unit.
**24** Refitting is a reversal of removal. Have the beam alignment checked as described in the next Section.

### Facelift models

**25** To improve access to the rear of the light unit, remove the screws and clips, and lower the radiator lower cover.
**26** Removal of the foglight is covered in Section 5, paragraphs 36 and 37.
**27** Refitting is a reversal of removal. Have the beam alignment checked as described in the next Section.

## Rear light cluster

**28** With the tailgate or boot lid open, unhook the parcel net (where fitted) from the rear of the luggage compartment.
**29** On pre-facelift Saloon and Hatchback models, remove the screws, release the clips, and remove the trim panel from the rear cross panel.
**30** Release the turn-fasteners, and remove the trim cover from the rear of the light unit **(see illustrations)**.

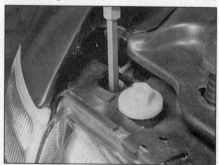

7.16 Loosen the front direction indicator retaining screw

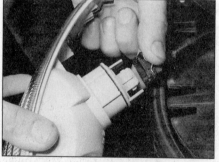

7.18 Disconnecting the wiring plug from the indicator bulbholder

7.30a Turn and remove the fasteners . . .

7.30b . . . and remove the trim cover from behind the light unit

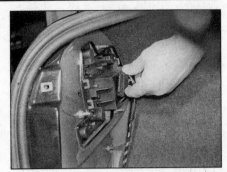

7.31a Disconnect the wiring plug from the bulbholder . . .

7.31b . . . and if required, unclip the bulbholder from the light unit

7.32a Depending on model, there will be either three or four mounting nuts (arrowed)

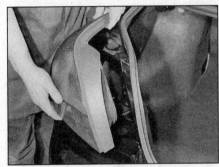

7.32b Removing the rear light cluster (facelift Saloon model shown)

**31** Disconnect the wiring multi-plug from the bulbholder. If a new light unit is being fitted, unclip the bulbholder from the rear of the light unit **(see illustrations)**.

**32** Support the light unit, then unscrew the mounting nuts, and withdraw the light unit from the outside of the car **(see illustrations)**.

**33** Refitting is a reversal of removal. On pre-facelift models, check the condition of the sealer on the body panel, and if necessary renew it.

### Rear number plate light assembly

**34** Remove both number plate light bulbs as described in Section 5.

**35** With the tailgate or boot lid open, remove the screws and withdraw the inner trim panel, releasing it from its various clips.

**36** Unscrew the nuts, and remove the outer cover and number plate base from the tailgate.

**37** Disconnect the multi-plug and remove the light assembly.

**38** Refitting is a reversal of removal.

**8  Headlight and front foglight beam alignment –** checking and adjustment

**1** Accurate adjustment of the headlight or front foglight beams is only possible using optical beam-setting equipment. This work should therefore be carried out by a Ford dealer, or other service station with the necessary facilities.

**2** Temporary adjustment can be made after renewal of a bulb or light unit, or as an emergency measure if the alignment is incorrect following accident damage.

**3** To adjust the headlight aim, turn the adjustment screws on the top of the headlight unit to make the adjustment **(see illustration)**.

**4** Adjustment of the front foglight beam is carried out using the small Allen screw visible through the surround trim **(see illustration)**.

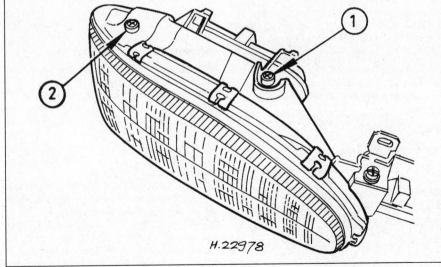

H.22978

8.3 Headlight beam setting adjustment screws – typical

1   Vertical alignment screw                    2   Horizontal alignment screw

8.4 Adjusting the front foglight beam

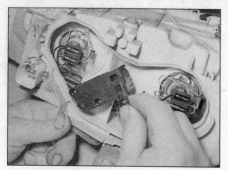

**9.3 Disconnect the motor wiring plug**

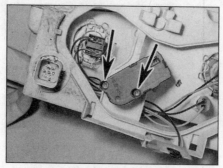

**9.6a Remove the motor screws . . .**

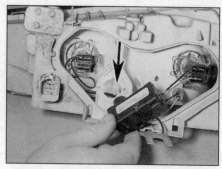

**9.6b . . . then separate the motor linkage balljoint**

**5** Before making any adjustments to the settings, it is important that the tyre pressures are correct, and that the car is standing on level ground.

**6** Bounce the front of the car a few times to settle the suspension. Ideally, somebody of

**10.4 Removing the foglight warning indicator**

**10.5 Removing a switch blanking cover**

**10.6b . . . and the remaining screws . . .**

average size should sit in the driver's seat during the adjustment, and the car should have a full tank of fuel.

**7** Where a car is fitted with a headlight beam levelling system, set the switch to the 0 position before making any adjustments.

**8** Whenever temporary adjustments are made, the settings must be checked and if necessary reset by a Ford dealer or other qualified person as soon as possible.

### 9 Headlight levelling motor – removal and refitting

#### Removal

**1** Make sure the beam adjustment switch is in the 0 position.

**2** Remove the headlight unit as described in Section 7, then remove the rear cover.

**10.6a With the blanking covers removed, unscrew the concealed screws . . .**

**10.6c . . . and lift out the instrument panel surround**

**3** Disconnect the wiring multi-plug from the motor **(see illustration)**.

#### Pre-facelift models

**4** Rotate the motor upwards approximately 60°, then pull it forwards slightly.

**5** Disconnect the adjustment spindle by pressing the ball coupling to one side, away from the socket on the reflector.

#### Facelift models

**6** Unscrew the motor securing screws from the rear of the headlight, and separate the operating linkage balljoint fitting **(see illustrations)**.

#### All models

**7** Withdraw the motor from the headlight unit.

#### Refitting

**8** Refitting is a reversal of the removal procedure, noting the following points:

a) Make sure the beam adjustment switch is still in the 0 position.

b) Refit the motor, then engage the adjuster.

c) On completion, test the operation of the system, and have the beam alignment checked as described in Section 8.

### 10 Instrument panel – removal and refitting

#### Removal

**1** Disconnect the battery negative (earth) lead (refer to Chapter 5, Section 1).

**2** Remove the clock as described in Section 13.

**3** Remove the heated rear window and heated windscreen switches, as applicable, as described in Section 4.

**4** On pre-facelift models, where fitted, remove the display indicator for the foglights **(see illustration)**.

**5** Where applicable on pre-facelift models, remove any blanking covers from the unused switch positions **(see illustration)**.

**6** Prise out the blanking covers, then unscrew the retaining screws and remove the instrument panel surround **(see illustrations)**.

**7** On later models with air conditioning, as the surround is withdrawn, remove the O-ring from the cabin temperature sensor, and detach the sensor from the surround.

**8** Unscrew the mounting screws, and withdraw the instrument panel a little way from the facia **(see illustration)**.

**9** Disconnect the multi-plugs from the rear of the instrument panel **(see illustration)**.

**10** Withdraw the instrument panel from the facia. On pre-facelift models, release the speedometer intermediate cable as the panel is withdrawn.

### Refitting

**11** Refitting is a reversal of the removal procedure.

## 11 Instrument panel components – removal and refitting

### Removal

**1** Remove the warning light and illumination bulbs by twisting them anti-clockwise **(see illustration)**.

**2** Carefully prise off the glass and bezel from the front of the instrument panel, noting the positions of the retaining lugs **(see illustration)**.

**3** Note the positions of the diffusers, then remove them from the instrument panel.

**4** To remove the speedometer head, unscrew the Torx mounting screws and withdraw the head from the housing.

**5** To remove the tachometer, unscrew the single Torx screw and withdraw it from the housing.

**6** Similarly remove the fuel gauge and temperature gauge by unscrewing the single screws.

**7** Remove all the pin contacts.

**8** Using a small punch, push in the main multi-plug securing pins, and remove the multi-plugs. The connectors for each gauge should be pressed back through the panel as far as possible without actually removing them.

**9** Carefully lift the printed circuit from the location dowels on the housing, taking care not to damage it.

### Refitting

**10** Refitting is a reversal of the removal procedure.

**10.8  Three of the instrument panel mounting screws (arrowed)**

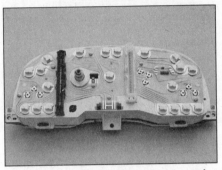

**11.1  Rear view of the instrument panel, showing bulbholders**

## 12 Speedometer cable (pre-facelift models) – removal and refitting

**Note:** *On facelift models, the speedometer drive cable was discontinued, and an electronic speedometer driven by a signal from the vehicle speed sensor is fitted. Refer to Chapter 4A for details on the vehicle speed sensor.*

### Removal

**1** Remove the windscreen wiper arms as described in Section 15.

**2** With the bonnet closed, release the grille panel upper edge from just in front of the windscreen, by prising off the caps and unscrewing the upper retaining screws.

**3** Open the bonnet, and support with the stay.

**4** Pull off the sealing strip from the cross panel at the rear of the engine compartment.

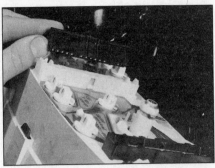

**10.9  Disconnecting the multi-plugs from the rear of the instrument panel**

**11.2  Bezel retaining lug on the instrument panel**

**5** Unscrew the lower screws, and remove the grille panel halves from in front of the windscreen, withdrawing first one side and then the other.

**6** Disconnect the battery negative (earth) lead (refer to Chapter 5, Section 1).

**7** Reach in behind the bulkhead. Squeeze the collar on the upper end of the speedometer cable, where it is attached to the intermediate cable from the rear of the speedometer head. Disconnect the cable, and withdraw it from the bulkhead inner panel, together with the rubber grommet **(see illustrations)**.

**8** Apply the handbrake, jack up the front of the car and support it on axle stands (see *Jacking and vehicle support*).

**9** Unscrew the nut and disconnect the speedometer cable from the vehicle speed sensor on the transmission, then withdraw the cable from within the engine compartment **(see illustrations)**. Use two spanners to loosen the

**12.7a  Squeeze the collar . . .**

**12.7b  . . . and disconnect the speedometer main cable from the intermediate cable**

**12.9a  Unscrew the cable nut . . .**

**12.9b . . . and disconnect the speedometer cable from the vehicle speed sensor**

nut – one to counterhold the sensor, and the other to unscrew the cable nut.

## Refitting

**10** Refitting is a reversal of the removal procedure.

### 13 Clock – removal and refitting

## Removal

**1** Disconnect the battery negative (earth) lead (refer to Chapter 5, Section 1).
**2** Using a small screwdriver, prise the clock out of the facia **(see illustration)**, starting at the lower left corner. To prevent damage to the facia, place a cloth pad beneath the screwdriver.

**13.2 Prising the clock out of the facia – early model shown, others similar**

**14.4 Horn and mounting bracket (arrowed)**

**3** Disconnect the multi-plug(s) from the rear of the clock, and withdraw the clock **(see illustration)**.
**4** On some models, the bulb can be removed by twisting it anti-clockwise; on others, the clock should be taken to a Ford dealer or automotive electrical specialist for bulb renewal.

## Refitting

**5** Refitting is a reversal of the removal procedure. Reset the clock on completion.

### 14 Horn – removal and refitting

## Removal

**1** Apply the handbrake, jack up the front of the car and support it on axle stands (see *Jacking and vehicle support*).
**2** Unscrew the bolts, and release the clips securing the radiator lower cover to the front of the car.
**3** Disconnect the wiring from the horn terminal.
**4** Unscrew the mounting bolt, and withdraw the horn with its mounting bracket from under the car **(see illustration)**.

## Refitting

**5** Refitting is a reversal of the removal procedure. Tighten the horn unit mounting bolt to the specified torque.

**13.3 Disconnecting the multi-plug from the rear of the clock**

**15.3 Loosening the wiper arm retaining nut**

### 15 Wiper arms – removal and refitting

## Removal

**1** Disconnect the battery negative (earth) lead (refer to Chapter 5, Section 1). If the windscreen wiper arms are to be removed, close the bonnet.
**2** With the wiper(s) 'parked' (ie, in the normal at-rest position), mark the positions of the blade(s) on the screen, using a wax crayon or strips of masking tape.
**3** Lift up the plastic cap from the bottom of the wiper arm, and loosen the nut one or two turns **(see illustration)**.
**4** Lift the wiper arm, and release it from the taper on the spindle by moving it to one side.
**5** Completely remove the nut, and withdraw wiper arm from the spindle **(see illustration)**.

## Refitting

**6** Refitting is a reversal of the removal procedure. Make sure that the arm is fitted in the previously-noted position before tightening its nut to the specified torque.

### 16 Windscreen wiper motor and linkage – removal and refitting

## Removal

**1** Disconnect the battery negative (earth) lead (refer to Chapter 5, Section 1).
**2** Remove the wiper arms as described in Section 15.
**3** With the bonnet closed, release the grille panel upper edge from just in front of the windscreen, by prising off the caps and unscrewing the upper retaining screws **(see illustrations)**.
**4** Open the bonnet, and support it with the stay.
**5** Pull off the bonnet sealing strip from the cross panel at the rear of the engine compartment **(see illustration)**.
**6** Unscrew the lower screws, and remove the grille panel halves from in front of the

**15.5 Removing the wiper arm from the spindle**

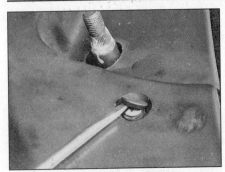

**16.3a Prise off the cap . . .**

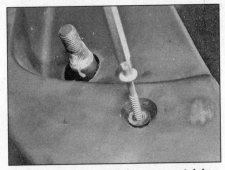

**16.3b . . . and remove the upper retaining screws**

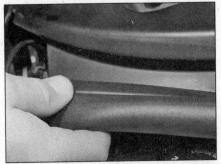

**16.5 Removing the bonnet sealing strip**

**16.6a Unscrew the lower screws . . .**

**16.6b . . . and remove the grille panel from in front of the windscreen**

**16.7 Wiper motor mounting bolt locations (right-hand-drive)**

windscreen, withdrawing one side then the other side **(see illustrations)**.

7 Unscrew the mounting bolts securing the wiper motor and linkage to the bulkhead **(see illustration)**. The linkage is on the right-hand side of the bulkhead.

8 Disconnect the wiper motor multi-plug.

9 Withdraw the wiper motor, complete with the linkage, from the bulkhead **(see illustration)**.

10 Mark the position of the motor arm on the mounting plate, then unscrew the centre nut **(see illustration)**.

11 Unscrew the motor mounting bolts, and separate the motor from the linkage assembly.

### Refitting

12 Refitting is a reversal of the removal procedure, noting the following points:
 a) *There are two tightening torques for the motor mounting bolts – the lower one for bolts that are being re-inserted into an old motor, and the higher ones for bolts that are being inserted into a new motor.*
 b) *Make sure that the wiper motor is in its 'parked' position before fitting the motor arm, and check that the wiper linkage is in line with the motor arm.*

**16.9 Removing the wiper motor and linkage**

**16.10 Wiper motor arm and mounting plate located on the motor**

## 17 Tailgate wiper motor assembly – removal and refitting
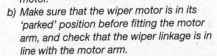

### Removal

1 Disconnect the battery negative (earth) lead (refer to Chapter 5, Section 1).

2 Remove the tailgate wiper arm as described in Section 15.

3 Remove the tailgate inner trim panel by unscrewing the retaining screws.

4 Release the wiper motor multi-plug from the clip, then disconnect it **(see illustration)**.

5 Disconnect the wiper motor earth lead.

6 Unscrew the mounting bolts, and remove the wiper motor from inside the tailgate **(see illustrations)**.

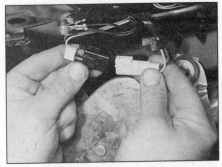

**17.4 Disconnecting the tailgate wiper motor multi-plug**

**17.6a Unscrew the mounting bolts . . .**

**17.6b  . . . and remove the tailgate wiper motor assembly (Hatchback shown – Estate similar)**

**17.7a  Tailgate wiper motor assembly and mounting plate**

**17.7b  A mounting rubber removed from the mounting plate**

**7** Unbolt and remove the mounting plate. If necessary, remove the mounting rubbers for renewal **(see illustrations)**.

### Refitting

**8** Refitting is a reversal of the removal procedure. Make sure that the wiper motor is in its 'parked' position before fitting the wiper arm.

## 18  Trip computer module – removal and refitting

The trip computer is incorporated in the clock. Refer to Section 13.

## 19  Auxiliary warning system – general information and component renewal

**1** Most models are fitted with an auxiliary warning system, which monitors brake lights, sidelights, dipped beam and tail lights, external temperature, door/tailgate/boot lid opening, brake pad wear, and coolant and washer levels. Some models have an engine oil level sensor as part of the system, which works in conjunction with the oil pressure warning light on the instrument panel.

**2** The auxiliary warning system module and graphic warning display are combined into one unit.

### Service interval reminder

**3** The system also includes a service interval reminder warning light, which is illuminated if the specified mileage (or time) since the last service has been reached.

**4** To reset the service interval system and turn off the light on pre-facelift models, a switch inside the glovebox must be depressed for a minimum of 4 seconds with the ignition switched on. On facelift models, the switch is behind the arrow-shaped symbol in the display panel, and is depressed using a thin probe, again for 4 seconds with the ignition switched on (see Chapter 1, Section 1). In either case, this should be carried out by a Ford dealer if the car is still in the warranty period.

### Component renewal

**5** The following paragraphs describe brief removal procedures for the auxiliary warning system components. Disconnect the battery negative (earth) lead before commencing work (refer to Chapter 5, Section 1). Refitting procedures are a reversal of removal.

#### Display module

**6** Remove the instrument panel surround, referring to Section 10.

**7** Unscrew the mounting screws, disconnect the multi-plugs and remove the assembly.

#### Display module warning bulb

**8** Remove the display module as described above.

**9** Prise off the cover, and pull out the relevant bulb and bulbholder.

#### Bulb failure module

**10** Remove the lower facia panel from under the steering wheel.

**11** Unclip the bulb failure module and disconnect the multi-plug.

#### Service indicator reset switch – pre-facelift models

**12** Remove the glove compartment lid as described in Chapter 11, Section 32.

**13** Carefully lever out the switch using a small screwdriver.

**14** Remove the rear cover and disconnect the wiring **(see illustration)**.

#### Low air temperature warning sender unit

**15** Remove the front bumper.

**16** Unclip the sender unit and disconnect the multi-plug **(see illustration)**.

#### Engine oil level sensor

**17** Apply the handbrake, jack up the front of the car and support it on axle stands.

**18** Place a container beneath the oil level sensor in the sump, to catch any spilt oil.

**19** Unscrew the screws and remove the cover from the sensor.

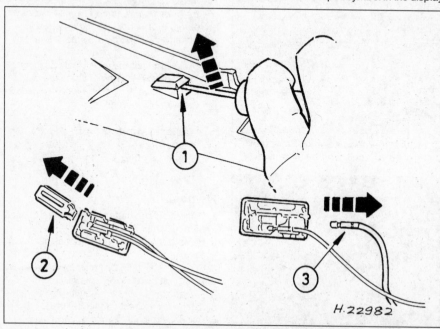

**19.14  Service indicator switch removal**

1  *Lever out the switch*  2  *Cover*  3  *Wiring*

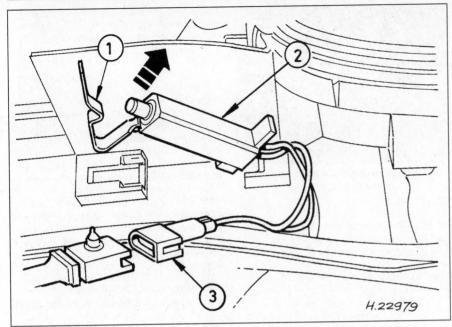

**19.16 Low air temperature sender unit removal**

1 *Clip*  2 *Sender unit*  3 *Multi-plug*

**20** Disconnect the multi-plug.
**21** Unscrew and remove the sensor, and remove the seal **(see illustration)**.
**22** After refitting the sensor, top-up the engine oil as described in *Weekly checks*.

### Door ajar sensor

**23** Remove the door lock as described in Chapter 11, Section 14.
**24** Unclip the sensor and disconnect the multi-plug.

### Low coolant warning switch

**25** Refer to Chapter 3, Section 6.

### Low washer fluid switch

**26** Disconnect the multi-plug from the washer fluid reservoir.
**27** Drain or syphon out the fluid from the reservoir.
**28** Using a screwdriver, lever out the switch from the reservoir **(see illustration)**.
**29** After refitting the switch, refill the reservoir with reference to *Weekly checks*.

### Brake pad wear sensors

**30** The sensor wires are built into the brake pad friction material. When the friction material wears down sufficiently that pad

renewal is required, the sensor wire is exposed, and makes contact with the brake disc. This completes the warning light circuit, and the warning light will come on. Note that, if the sensor wire insulation is damaged, this might result in the warning light giving a false indication of pad wear.

### 20 Anti-theft alarm system – general information

**1** All models are fitted with a perimetric anti-theft alarm system, incorporating an ignition immobiliser. The system protects all doors, including the bonnet and boot lid/ tailgate, and is activated when the car is locked. A volumetric alarm, which protects the interior with ultrasonic detection, is available as an option – on later Estate models with this feature, additional glass breakage detection is incorporated into the rear glass.
**2** The system includes a start inhibitor circuit, which makes it impossible to start the engine with the system armed. On later models with the passive anti-theft system (or PATS), the immobiliser is deactivated by a transponder chip built into the ignition key. The PATS (or Safeguard) circuit is separate from the alarm, meaning that the car is immobilised even if the alarm is not set.
**3** On later models, the radio/cassette unit is incorporated into the alarm system – if an attempt is made to remove the unit while the alarm is active, the alarm will sound.
**4** The PATS transceiver unit is fitted around the ignition switch, and it 'reads' the code from a microchip in the ignition key. This means that any new or duplicate keys must be obtained through a Ford dealer – any cut locally may not contain the microchip, and will therefore not disarm the immobiliser.

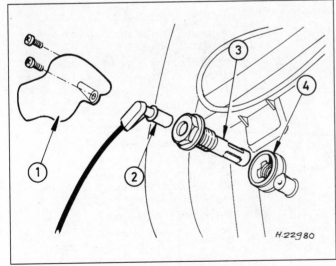

**19.21 Engine oil level sensor removal**

1 *Cover*  2 *Multi-plug*  3 *Sensor*  4 *Seal*

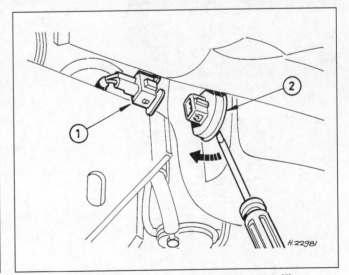

**19.28 Removing the low washer fluid switch (2)**

1 *Multi-plug*

**20.5a Disconnecting a movement sensor multi-plug**

**20.5b Removing a movement sensor**

check that the echo frequency matches the original frequency. If there is any significant difference, the system triggers the alarm.

**6** The alarm module is incorporated into the central locking module, on a bracket beneath the right-hand side of the facia, together with the PATS module on later models. The set and reset switches are located in a housing by the lock barrel holder in the front doors.

**7** To allow temporary opening of the tailgate or boot lid, an inhibit switch is fitted to the lock. This suppresses the alarm system until the tailgate or boot lid is closed again.

**8** Where remote central locking is fitted, an infra-red receiver is located on the exterior door handle **(see illustration)**. Note that excessive heat can destroy this receiver; therefore, it should be covered with aluminium tape if (for instance) a paint-drying heat process is to be used.

**9** The alarm system is fitted with its own horn. On Hatchback and Saloon models, it is located on the left-hand side of the luggage compartment; on Estate models, it is located on the right-hand side of the luggage compartment **(see illustrations)**.

**10** The alarm system incorporates a self-test function, which can be activated by operating the bonnet switch or one of the lock position switches eight times within 10 seconds. During the check, the horn or buzzer issues acoustic signals which should occur every time a door, bonnet or tailgate is opened. If the doors are double-locked, the signal will occur when something is moved within the passenger compartment. A more comprehensive test can be made using the Ford FDS 2000 diagnostic tester.

**11** The door lock switches associated with the alarm system are located behind the door trim panels **(see illustration)**.

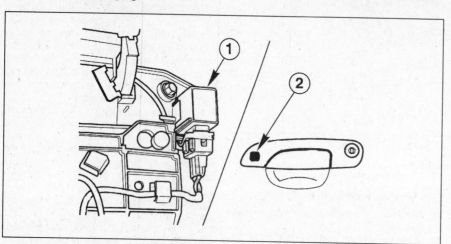

**20.8 Infra-red receiver location on the door handle**

*1  Receiver*

*2  Infra-red eye on the door handle*

**5** The movement sensors on the volumetric system consist of two ultrasonic units, located in the B-pillars, incorporating transmitters and receivers **(see illustrations)**. The receivers

**20.9a Alarm system horn location on Hatchback and Saloon models . . .**

**20.9b . . . and on Estate models**

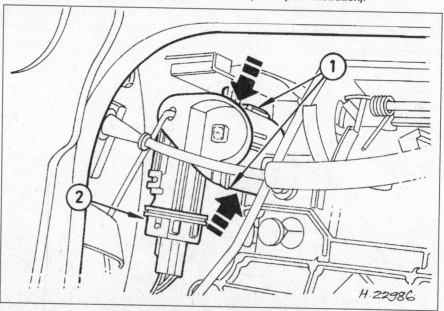

**20.11 Alarm system door lock switch removal**

*1  Clips (arrowed)*

*2  Multi-plug*

## 21 Cruise control system – general information and component renewal

**1** Cruise control is available as an option on some models.

**2** The cruise control system components are shown in the accompanying illustration **(see illustration)**. The system is active at road speeds between 25 mph and 125 mph.

**3** The system consists of an electronic speed control unit with integral actuator and switches mounted in the engine compartment with a control cable connected to the throttle lever, driver-operated switches, brake and clutch pedal switches, an indicator light, and the vehicle speed sensor.

**4** The driver-operated switches are mounted on the steering wheel, and allow the driver to control the various functions.

**5** The vehicle speed sensor is mounted on the transmission, and generates pulses which are fed to the speed control unit. On early models, the speedometer drive cable is attached to the vehicle speed sensor – on later models, an electronic speedometer uses the speed sensor signal directly.

**6** The stop-light switch, brake pedal switch and (when applicable) clutch pedal switch are used to disable the cruise control system. The stop-light switch is activated when the brake pedal is applied gently, and the brake pedal switch is activated when the brake pedal is applied forcibly.

**7** An indicator light on the instrument panel is illuminated when the system is in operation.

**8** The following paragraphs describe brief removal procedures for the cruise control system components. The battery negative (earth) lead should be disconnected before commencing work (refer to Chapter 5, Section 1). Refitting is a reversal of removal.

### Steering wheel switches

**9** Remove the airbag unit from the steering wheel as described in Section 29.

**10** Disconnect the wiring plugs, noting the location of each plug and how the wiring is routed for refitting **(see illustrations)**.

**11** Remove the two screws each side securing the operating switches, and remove

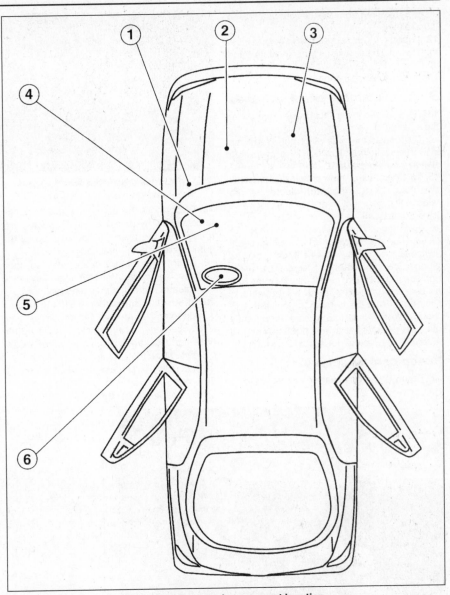

**21.2 Cruise control component location**

1 Speed control unit
2 Vehicle speed sensor
3 Throttle valve actuator
4 Interrupt relay (vehicles with traction control system only)
5 Stop-light switch, brake and clutch pedal-operated disable switches
6 Driver's controls (buttons on steering wheel)

**21.10a Disconnect the spade connectors . . .**

**21.10b . . . including the earth wire from the contact plate . . .**

**21.10c . . . and the main multi-plug connector**

them as required from the steering wheel **(see illustration)**.

**12** If required (for access to the horn switch, for example), the switch contact plates and springs can be removed, after unscrewing the two retaining screws each side.

### Brake and clutch pedal switches

**13** Remove the lower facia panel from under the steering column.

**14** Disconnect the multi-plugs from the clutch switch, brake pedal switch and stop-light switch **(see illustration)**.

**15** To remove the clutch and brake pedal switches, twist them anti-clockwise. To remove the stop-light switch, twist it clockwise **(see illustration)**.

**16** Refitting is the reverse of removal. To ensure correct operation of the brake pedal switches, reset the switch by fully extending its plunger **(see illustration)**. Depress the pedal until the distance between it and the mounting bracket is as shown for the stop-light switch in Chapter 9. Hold the pedal in this position, clip the switch securely into position and gently raise the pedal to the at-rest position. This will automatically set the position of the switch.

### Speed control actuator

**17** Remove the air cleaner as described in Chapter 4A.

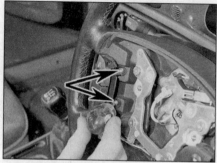

**21.11 Remove the switch securing screws and take out the switch**

**18** Disconnect the actuator cable from the throttle lever, by releasing the inner cable end fitting from the segment and unclipping the outer cable from the bracket.

**19** Disconnect the actuator multi-plug, then unscrew the actuator mounting bolt, and slide the actuator out of the mounting pin holes.

**20** Remove the actuator from the engine compartment. On models with air conditioning, it may be necessary to unclip and lift up the right-hand section of the windscreen cowl panel, to allow the actuator to be removed.

**21** Depress the actuating cable cap locking arm, and remove the cap by turning it anti-clockwise **(see illustration)**.

**22** Gently raise the cable retaining lug by a maximum of 0.5 mm, and push the cable end out of the slot in the pulley.

**23** When refitting, make sure that the cable end locks into the slot in the pulley.

**24** To locate the cable cap onto the actuator pulley, keep the cable taut and in the pulley groove, and pull the throttle lever end of the cable to draw the cable cap onto the pulley.

**25** To refit the cable cap, keep the cable taut and the pulley still, then refit the cable cap tabs into the actuator slots; turn the cap clockwise until the locking arm locates on the locking stop. **Note:** *Incorrect assembly of the cable onto the pulley may result in a high idle speed. Check that the throttle lever is in its idle position after refitting the actuator.*

### 22 Windscreen/tailgate washer system components – removal and refitting

### Removal

#### Washer reservoir and pump

**1** Apply the handbrake and loosen the right-hand front wheel nuts. Jack up the front of the car and support on axle stands (see *Jacking and vehicle support*). Remove the front wheel.

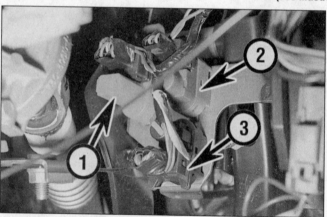

**21.14 Cruise control switches on the pedal bracket**

1  *Clutch pedal position switch*
2  *Brake pedal de-activator switch*
3  *Stop-light switch*

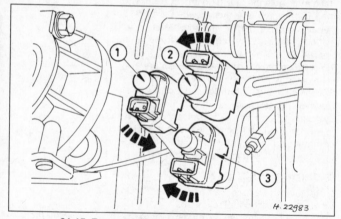

**21.15 Removal of the cruise control switches**

1  *Clutch switch*
2  *Brake pedal switch*
3  *Stop-light switch*

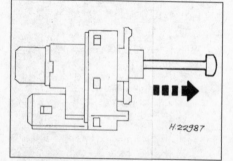

**21.16 Resetting the brake pedal and stop-light switches**

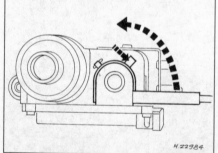

**21.21 Removing the actuator cable locking arm**

**22.3 Washer reservoir mounting bolts**

**22.4  Disconnecting the washer pump and level sensor multi-plugs**

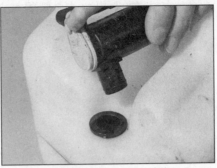

**22.7  Pulling the windscreen washer pump from the reservoir**

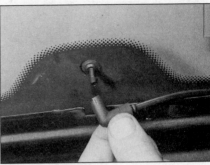

**22.12  Pull the washer tube from the bottom of the nozzle**

**2** Unscrew the bolts, and release the clips to remove the radiator lower cover. Release the wheel arch liner fasteners as necessary for access to the reservoir.
**3** Unscrew the mounting bolts, and pull the reservoir forwards slightly **(see illustration)**. For better access, it may be necessary to remove the front bumper.
**4** Disconnect the multi-plugs for the windscreen washer pump and fluid level sensor **(see illustration)**.
**5** Disconnect the hoses from the windscreen washer pump and (where applicable) from the headlight washer pump. Anticipate some loss of fluid by placing a container beneath the reservoir.
**6** Withdraw the reservoir from the car.
**7** Pull the level sensor, the windscreen washer pump, and (where applicable) the headlight washer pump, from the reservoir **(see illustration)**.
**8** Remove the rubber seals.

### Washer nozzle (windscreen)

**9** With the bonnet supported in its open position, carefully disconnect the washer tube from the bottom of the nozzle.
**10** Using a screwdriver and working from under the bonnet, carefully prise out the nozzle. Where necessary, disconnect the wiring for the nozzle heater.

### Washer nozzle (rear window)

**11** With the tailgate open, carefully pull off the inner trim panel from the top of the tailgate.
**12** Pull the washer tube from the bottom of the nozzle **(see illustration)**.
**13** Carefully prise the nozzle out of the tailgate glass, then prise out the rubber grommet **(see illustrations)**. Where necessary, disconnect the wiring for the nozzle heater.

### Washer nozzle (headlight)

**14** Remove the front bumper as described in Chapter 11.
**15** Disconnect the washer tube from the base of the nozzle.
**16** Pull off the nozzle retaining clip and withdraw the nozzle from the bumper.

### *Refitting*

**17** Refitting is a reversal of the removal procedure, noting the following points:

**22.13a  Remove the nozzle from the tailgate glass . . .**

a) In the case of the screen washer nozzles, press them in until they are fully engaged.
b) The rear window washer nozzle must rest against the rubber seal.
c) After refitting the headlight washer nozzle, refit the front bumper as described in Chapter 11.

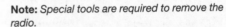

**23  Radio/cassette player –** removal and refitting

**Note:** *Special tools are required to remove the radio.*
**1** If a Ford 'Keycode' unit is fitted, and the unit and/or the battery is disconnected, the unit will not function again on reconnection until the correct security code is entered. Details of this procedure are given in the 'Ford Audio Systems Operating Guide' supplied with the

**23.6a  Using the special U-shaped rods to remove the radio – early type . . .**

**22.13b  . . . and prise out the rubber grommet**

car when new, with the code itself being given in a 'Radio Passport' and/or a 'Keycode Label' at the same time.
**2** For obvious security reasons, the re-coding procedure is not given in this manual – if you do not have the code or details of the correct procedure, but can supply proof of ownership and a legitimate reason for wanting this information, the car's selling dealer may be able to help.
**3** Note that these units will allow only ten attempts at entering the code – any further attempts will render the unit permanently inoperative until it has been reprogrammed by Ford themselves. At first, three consecutive attempts are allowed; if all three are incorrect, a 30-minute delay is required before another attempt can be made. Each of any subsequent attempts (up to the maximum of ten) can be made only after a similar delay.

### *Removal*

**4** Disconnect the battery negative (earth) lead.
**5** Where fitted, prise the cover/surround from the front of the radio/cassette player. Note that the cover is not fitted to all models.
**6** On models without the satellite navigation system, in order to release the radio retaining clips, two U-shaped rods must be inserted into the special holes on each side of the radio **(see illustrations)**. If possible, it is preferable to obtain purpose-made rods from an audio specialist, as these have cut-outs which snap firmly into the clips so that the radio can be pulled out.
**7** On models with the satellite navigation

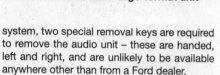

23.6b ... and later large-format unit

23.9a Disconnect the aerial lead ...

23.9b ... and the remaining wiring plugs, noting their locations

system, two special removal keys are required to remove the audio unit – these are handed, left and right, and are unlikely to be available anywhere other than from a Ford dealer.

8 Pull the unit squarely from its aperture, or it may jam. If the unit proves difficult to withdraw, remove the cassette tray (or where applicable, the CD player) from beneath the unit, then reach through the aperture and ease it out from behind.

9 With the radio partly withdrawn, disconnect the feed, earth, aerial and speaker leads **(see illustrations)**. Where applicable, also detach and remove the plastic support bracket from the rear of the unit.

## *Refitting*

10 Refitting is a reversal of removal. With the leads reconnected to the rear of the unit, press it into position until the retaining clips are felt to engage. Reactivate the unit by entering the correct code in accordance with the maker's instructions.

## 24 Radio/cassette player power amplifier – removal and refitting

### *Removal*

1 Disconnect the battery negative (earth) lead. See Chapter 5, Section 1.
2 Unscrew the screws and remove the lower facia panel.
3 The radio/cassette player power amplifier is located beneath the facia.

25.10a Remove the mounting bolts each side ...

4 Unscrew the cross-head screws, disconnect the wiring and remove the amplifier.

## *Refitting*

5 Refitting is a reversal of the removal procedure.

## 25 Compact disc player – removal and refitting

1 A compact disc (CD) player is available as an optional extra on most models. On some models, an autochanger version is available, which can hold a number of discs at a time.

## *Removal*

2 The battery negative (earth) lead should be disconnected before commencing work.

### CD player, or autochanger control unit

3 The procedure is identical to that for the radio/cassette player described in Section 23.

### CD player autochanger – pre-facelift models

4 On pre-facelift models, the CD player autochanger unit is mounted on the right-hand side of the luggage compartment. The wiring loom passes up the C-pillar, across to the left-hand side A-pillar, then to the centre console area.
5 Remove the trim cover from the autochanger unit.
6 Unscrew the mounting screws, and remove the autochanger unit from its mounting bracket.

25.10b ... then disconnect the wiring plug and remove the unit

7 Disconnect the multi-plug and remove the unit from the luggage compartment.

### CD player autochanger – facelift models

8 The CD autochanger unit is mounted in a bracket below the front passenger's seat.
9 Refer to Chapter 11 and remove the front passenger's seat.
10 Remove the unit mounting bolts either side, and disconnect the wiring plug **(see illustrations)**. Slide the player out of the brackets below the seat, and remove it from the car.

## *Refitting*

11 Refitting is a reversal of the removal procedure.

## 26 Speakers – removal and refitting

**Note:** *If the speakers work intermittently, this can be due to the wiring multi-plug overheating – a revised plug is available from your Ford dealer.*

### *Removal*

1 Remove the door trim panel as described in Chapter 11.
2 Unscrew the cross-head screws, and withdraw the speaker from the door inner panel.
3 Disconnect the wiring and remove the speaker.

## *Refitting*

4 Refitting is a reversal of the removal procedure.

## 27 Radio aerial – removal and refitting

## *Removal*

1 If just the aerial mast is to be removed, this can be unscrewed from the base, from outside.
2 To remove the aerial base, prise out the trim

cover from the headlining immediately below the base of the aerial **(see illustration)**.

**3** Unscrew the cross-head or Torx screw from the base of the aerial **(see illustration)**, disconnect the wiring, and remove the base and gasket from outside.

## Refitting

**4** Refitting is a reversal of the removal procedure.

## 28 Airbag system – general information and precautions

All models are fitted with a driver's airbag, which is designed to prevent serious chest and head injuries to the driver during an accident. A similar bag for the front seat passenger is also available. The sensor and electronic unit for the airbag is located next to the steering column inside the car, and contains a back-up capacitor, crash sensor, decelerometer, safety sensor, integrated circuit and microprocessor. The airbag is inflated by a gas generator, which forces the bag out of the module cover in the centre of the steering wheel. A rotary contact (known as the 'clock spring') ensures that a good electrical connection is maintained with the airbag at all times – as the steering wheel is turned in each direction, the spring winds and unwinds **(see illustration)**.

Later models equipped with both driver's and passenger's airbags can also be specified with side airbags, which are built into the sides of the front seats. The intention of the side airbags is principally to offer greater passenger protection in a side impact. Although the side airbags are linked to the front airbags, a separate sensor for the side airbags (below the driver's side carpet) is used to detect lateral movement.

⚠ *Warning: When working on the airbag system, always wait at least 15 minutes after disconnecting the battery, as a precaution against accidental deployment of the airbag unit. This period ensures that any stored energy in the back-up capacitor is dissipated. Do not use battery-operated radio key code savers, as this may cause the airbag to be deployed, with the possibility of personal injury.*

## Precautions

⚠ *Warning: The following precautions must be observed when working on cars equipped with an airbag system, to prevent the possibility of personal injury.*

### General precautions

The following precautions must be observed when carrying out work on a car equipped with an airbag:

a) *Do not disconnect the battery with the engine running.*

b) *Before carrying out any work in the vicinity of the airbag, removal of any of*

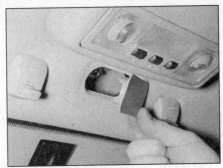

**27.2 Remove the trim cover from the headlining . . .**

the airbag components, or any welding work on the car, de-activate the system as described in the following sub-Section.

c) *Do not attempt to test any of the airbag system circuits using test meters or any other test equipment.*

d) *If the airbag warning light comes on, or any fault in the system is suspected, consult a Ford dealer without delay. Do not attempt to carry out fault diagnosis,*

**27.3 . . . for access to the aerial mounting screw**

or any dismantling of the components. Note that, on some Mondeos, the airbag warning light will come on when the car reaches 10 years old – the airbag was supposed to be renewed after this period.

### Precautions handling an airbag

a) *Transport the airbag by itself, bag upward.*

b) *Do not put your arms around the airbag.*

c) *Carry the airbag close to the body, bag outward.*

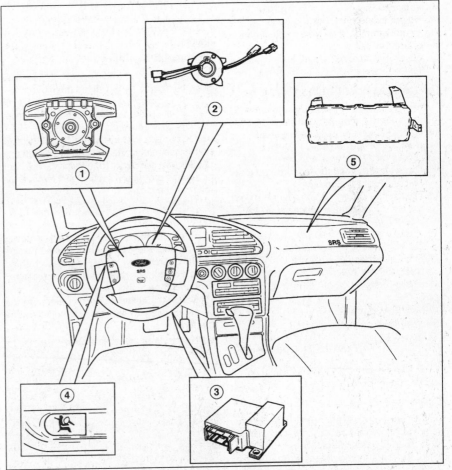

**28.1 Airbag system components**

1  Airbag module (driver's)
2  Clock spring
3  Diagnostic and sensor unit
4  Airbag indicator light
5  Airbag module (passenger's)

**29.3 Unscrewing an airbag mounting bolt**

d) *Do not drop the airbag or expose it to impacts.*
e) *Do not attempt to dismantle the airbag unit.*
f) *Do not connect any form of electrical equipment to any part of the airbag circuit.*

### Precautions storing an airbag unit

a) *Store the unit in a cupboard with the airbag upward.*
b) *Do not expose the airbag to temperatures above 80°C.*
c) *Do not expose the airbag to flames.*
d) *Do not attempt to dispose of the airbag – consult a Ford dealer.*
e) *Never refit an airbag which is known to be faulty or damaged.*

### De-activation of airbag system

The system must be de-activated as follows, before carrying out any work on the airbag components or surrounding area.
a) *Remove the ignition key.*
b) *Switch off all electrical equipment.*
c) *Disconnect the battery negative lead (see Disconnecting the battery).*
d) *Insulate the battery negative terminal and the end of the battery negative lead to prevent any possibility of contact.*
e) ***Wait for at least 15 minutes** before carrying out any further work.*
f) *Ensure that the battery is still disconnected, before reconnecting any airbag wiring.*

### 29 Airbag units – removal and refitting

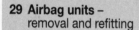

**Note:** *Refer to the precautions in Section 28 before starting work.*

### Driver's airbag

**1** Disconnect the battery negative (earth) lead (refer to Chapter 5, Section 1). Wait a minimum of 15 minutes before proceeding.
**2** Rotate the steering wheel so that one of the airbag mounting bolt holes (at the rear of the steering wheel boss) is visible above the steering column upper shroud.
**3** Unscrew and remove the first mounting bolt, then turn the steering wheel through 180°

**29.4 Disconnecting the airbag wiring multi-plug**

and remove the remaining mounting bolt **(see illustration)**.
**4** Carefully withdraw the airbag unit from the steering wheel far enough to disconnect the wiring multi-plug, then remove it from inside the car **(see illustration)**.
**5** Refitting is a reversal of the removal procedure.

### Passenger's airbag

**6** Disconnect the battery negative (earth) lead (refer to Chapter 5, Section 1). Wait a minimum of 15 minutes before proceeding.
**7** Remove the glovebox as described in Chapter 11.

#### Pre-facelift models

**8** Remove the three retaining screws and withdraw the closing panel behind the glovebox.
**9** Remove the screw securing the inner end of the ventilation duct, and disconnect the duct from the facia end vent.
**10** Disconnect the two airbag inflator multi-plugs, noting their locations for refitting.
**11** Support the unit, then remove the four airbag unit mounting screws, and remove the unit from the facia.
**12** Refitting is a reversal of removal.

#### Facelift models

**13** Remove the three retaining screws, then release the clip at the right-hand side and withdraw the closing panel behind the glovebox. As the panel is withdrawn, disconnect the bulbholder.
**14** Carefully cut the cable-ties securing the wiring harness to the top of the glovebox aperture.

**30.3 Airbag control module multi-plug**

**15** Remove the radio/cassette unit as described in Section 23.
**16** Working through the radio aperture, remove the screws securing the passenger side ventilation duct for the facia end vent.
**17** Detach the ventilation duct from the facia end vent, and remove the duct from the facia.
**18** Disconnect the wiring multi-plug from the end of the airbag unit.
**19** Support the unit, then remove the four airbag unit mounting screws, and remove the unit from the facia.
**20** Refitting is a reversal of removal.

### Side airbag

**21** The side airbag units are built into the front seats, and their removal requires that the seat fabric be removed. This is not considered to be a DIY operation, and should be referred to a Ford dealer.

### 30 Airbag control module – removal and refitting

**Note:** *Refer to the precautions in Section 28 before starting work.*

### Removal

**1** Disconnect the battery negative (earth) lead (refer to Chapter 5, Section 1). Wait a minimum of 15 minutes before proceeding.
**2** Remove the complete facia panel (see Chapter 11).
**3** Disconnect the multi-plug from the module **(see illustration)**, by pressing the two-stage locking handle to the side – the first stage disconnects the multi-plug, and the second releases the connector from the module.
**4** Unscrew the mounting bolts and remove the module from the car.

### Refitting

**5** Refitting is a reversal of the removal procedure.

### 31 Airbag clock spring – removal and refitting

### Removal

**1** Remove the driver's airbag unit as described in Section 29.
**2** Disconnect the horn switch multi-plug.
**3** If fitted, disconnect the multi-plugs for the cruise control switches.
**4** Remove the steering wheel and column shrouds as described in Chapter 10.
**5** Disconnect the clock spring wiring plug from the underside of the steering column.
**6** Detach the steering column multi-function switches by depressing the plastic retaining tabs with a flat-bladed screwdriver.
**7** Using a small screwdriver, release the three retaining tabs, then remove the clock spring from the steering column, feeding the wiring through.

## Refitting

**8** Refitting is a reversal of the removal procedure, noting the following points:

a) *Make sure that the front wheels are still pointing straight-ahead.*

b) *The clock spring must be fitted in its central position, with the special alignment marks aligned and the TOP mark uppermost. To check for this position, turn the clock spring housing anti-clockwise until it is tight, then turn in the opposite direction by two-and-three-quarter turns.*

## 32 Parking sensor system – general information

Offered as an option on facelift models, the park reverse aid is an ultrasonic proximity detection system, intended to help avoid rear collisions when reversing.

The system consists of four ultrasonic sensors mounted in the rear bumper, a display/buzzer unit mounted in the C-pillar trim panel, and an ECU mounted behind the left-hand side trim panel in the luggage compartment.

The system is only operational when reverse gear is engaged; changing audible and visual signals warn the driver of impending contact as the car reverses towards an object in its path.

The sensors in the bumper can be unclipped and disconnected once the rear bumper is removed as described in Chapter 11.

To remove the display/buzzer unit, remove the C-pillar trim panel as described in Chapter 11, Section 29.

The system ECU can be disconnected once the luggage area left-hand trim panel is removed.

## 33 Satellite navigation system – general information

This system was optional on later models, and uses Global Positioning System (GPS)

**34.7  Front seat removed, showing three seat adjustment motors and associated wiring plugs**

satellites to track the car against a digital map stored on CD. The system antenna gathers positional information from the satellites. The ABS rear wheel sensors provide the system with data on how far the car has travelled, and a compass is fitted. The CD autochanger is the communication link from the navigation module to the display panel on the radio/cassette unit. The digital map is stored on a CD, which is read by the navigation module. The navigation module is the heart of the system, processing all data received from the antenna, wheel sensors, compass and map CD, and providing instructions which are displayed on the radio/cassette display panel.

Two generations of the system were offered (RNS 1 and 2), and component locations vary according to which system is fitted. Any problems with the system should be referred to a Ford dealer for diagnosis.

## 34 Electric seat components – removal and refitting

### Heated seats

**1** If heated seats are fitted, both driver's and front passenger seats have heating elements built into the seat cushion and backrest.

**2** No repairs can be made to the heating elements without dismantling the seat and removing the seat fabric – therefore this

**34.8  Typical seat motor mounting frame bolt**

work should be left to a Ford dealer or other specialist.

**3** The heated seat switches are removed as described in Section 4.

**4** For further diagnosis of any problems with the system, refer to Sections 2 and 3, and to the wiring diagrams at the end of this Chapter.

### Seat adjustment components

**5** Only the driver's seat is equipped with motors, and only the highest specification models have anything other than a height adjustment motor.

**6** To gain access to the motors, remove the driver's seat as described in Chapter 11.

**7** The motors are bolted to a mounting frame, which in turn is bolted to the seat base. Before removing a motor, trace its wiring back from the motor to its wiring plug, and disconnect it **(see illustration)**.

**8** Remove the mounting frame bolts **(see illustration)** or the motor mounting bolts, as applicable, and remove the components from the seat base.

**9** Refitting is a reversal of removal. It is worth periodically greasing the worm-drive components and seat runners, to ensure trouble-free operation.

**10** The seat adjustment switches are removed as described in Section 4.

**11** For further diagnosis of any problems with the system, refer to Sections 2 and 3, and to the wiring diagrams at the end of this Chapter.

## KEY TO SYMBOLS

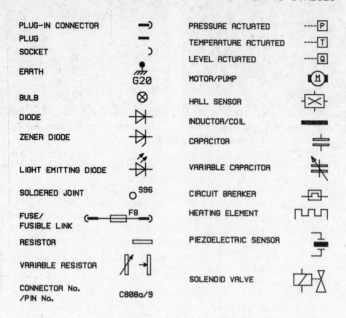

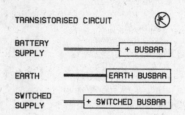

| | |
|---|---|
| PLUG-IN CONNECTOR | |
| PLUG | |
| SOCKET | |
| EARTH | G20 |
| BULB | ⊗ |
| DIODE | |
| ZENER DIODE | |
| LIGHT EMITTING DIODE | |
| SOLDERED JOINT | S96 |
| FUSE/ FUSIBLE LINK | F8 |
| RESISTOR | |
| VARIABLE RESISTOR | |
| CONNECTOR No. /PIN No. | C808a/9 |

| | |
|---|---|
| PRESSURE ACTUATED | P |
| TEMPERATURE ACTUATED | T |
| LEVEL ACTUATED | Q |
| MOTOR/PUMP | M |
| HALL SENSOR | |
| INDUCTOR/COIL | |
| CAPACITOR | |
| VARIABLE CAPACITOR | |
| CIRCUIT BREAKER | |
| HEATING ELEMENT | |
| PIEZOELECTRIC SENSOR | |
| SOLENOID VALVE | |

| | |
|---|---|
| TRANSISTORISED CIRCUIT | |
| BATTERY SUPPLY | + BUSBAR |
| EARTH | EARTH BUSBAR |
| SWITCHED SUPPLY | + SWITCHED BUSBAR |

### NOTES:

1. All diagrams are divided into numbered circuits depending on function e.g. Diagram 11 : Exterior lighting.
2. Items are arranged in relation to a plan view of the vehicle.
3. Wires may interconnect between diagrams and are located by using a grid reference e.g. 2/A1 denotes a position on diagram 2 grid location A1.
4. Complex items appear on the diagrams in sections and are shown in full on the internal connections page (see below).
5. Brackets show how the circuit may be connected in more than one way.
6. Items with a broken border have other connections shown elsewhere.
7. Not all items are fitted to all models.

## INTERNAL CONNECTION DETAILS

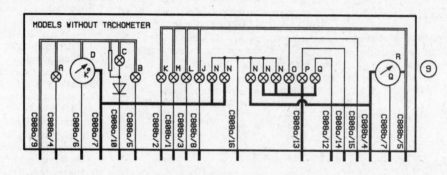

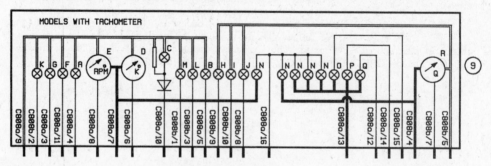

### KEY TO INSTRUMENT CLUSTER (ITEM 9)

A = Traction Control Warning Light
B = Airbag Warning Light
C = No Charge Warning Light
D = Temperature Gauge
E = Tachometer
F = Cruse Control Warning Light
G = Low Oil Level Warning Light
H = Overdrive Off Warning Light
I = Sport Warning Light
J = Adaptive Damping Warning Light
K = Anti-lock Braking Warning Light
L = Low Brake Fluid Level/ Handbrake-on Warning Light
M = Low Oil Pressure Warning Light
N = Instrument Illumination
O = Direction Indicator Warning Light LH
P = Direction Indicator Warning Light RH
Q = High Beam Warning Light
R = Fuel Gauge

H24540

T.M.MARKE

**Notes, internal connection details and key to symbols**

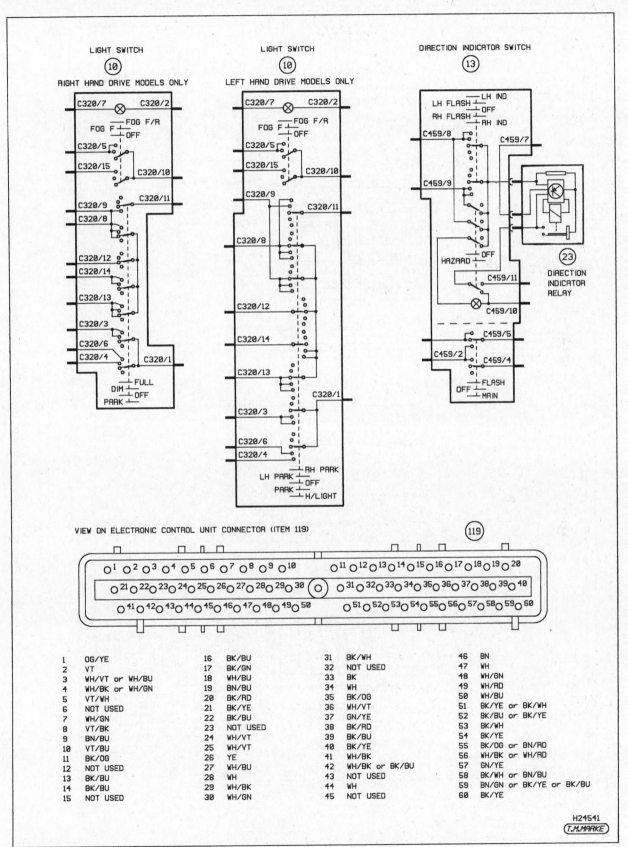

**VIEW ON ELECTRONIC CONTROL UNIT CONNECTOR (ITEM 119)**

| | | | |
|---|---|---|---|
| 1 OG/YE | 16 BK/BU | 31 BK/WH | 46 BN |
| 2 VT | 17 BK/GN | 32 NOT USED | 47 WH |
| 3 WH/VT or WH/BU | 18 WH/BU | 33 BK | 48 WH/GN |
| 4 WH/BK or WH/GN | 19 BN/BU | 34 WH | 49 WH/RD |
| 5 VT/WH | 20 BK/RD | 35 BK/OG | 50 WH/BU |
| 6 NOT USED | 21 BK/YE | 36 WH/VT | 51 BK/YE or BK/WH |
| 7 WH/GN | 22 BK/BU | 37 GN/YE | 52 BK/BU or BK/YE |
| 8 VT/BK | 23 NOT USED | 38 BK/RD | 53 BK/WH |
| 9 BN/BU | 24 WH/VT | 39 BK/BU | 54 BK/YE |
| 10 VT/BU | 25 WH/VT | 40 BK/YE | 55 BK/OG or BN/RD |
| 11 BK/OG | 26 YE | 41 WH/BK | 56 WH/BK or WH/RD |
| 12 NOT USED | 27 WH/BU | 42 WH/BK or BK/BU | 57 GN/YE |
| 13 BK/BU | 28 WH | 43 NOT USED | 58 BK/WH or BN/BU |
| 14 BK/BU | 29 WH/BK | 44 WH | 59 BN/GN or BK/YE or BK/BU |
| 15 NOT USED | 30 WH/GN | 45 NOT USED | 60 BK/YE |

H24541

**Internal connection details continued**

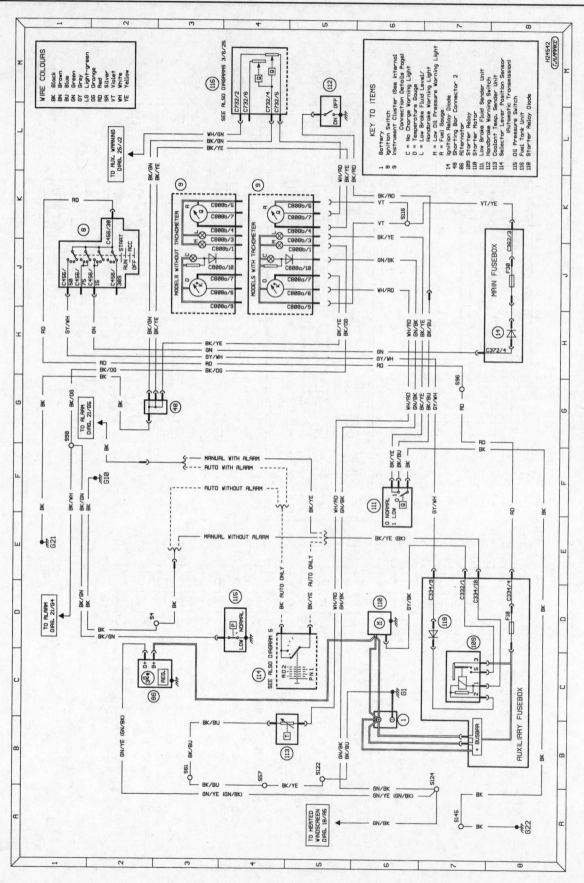

Diagram 1: Starting, charging, warning lights and gauges

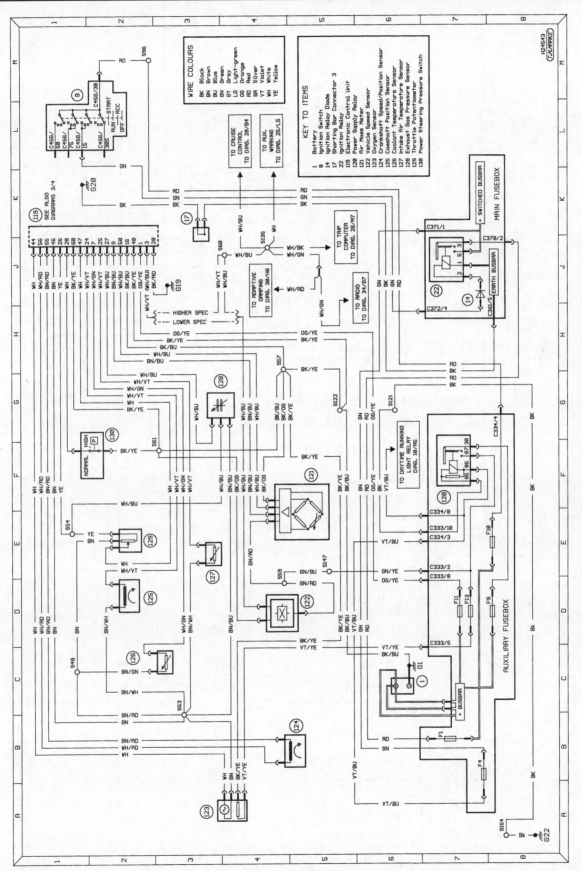

H24543

**WIRE COLOURS**

| BK | Black |
|---|---|
| BN | Brown |
| BU | Blue |
| GN | Green |
| GY | Grey |
| LG | Light-green |
| OG | Orange |
| RD | Red |
| SR | Silver |
| VT | Violet |
| WH | White |
| YE | Yellow |

**KEY TO ITEMS**

| 1 | Battery |
|---|---|
| 8 | Ignition Switch |
| 14 | Ignition Relay Diode |
| 17 | Shorting Bar Connector 3 |
| 22 | Ignition Relay |
| 119 | Electronic Control Unit |
| 120 | Power Supply Relay |
| 121 | Air Mass Meter |
| 122 | Vehicle Speed Sensor |
| 123 | Oxygen Sensor |
| 124 | Crankshaft Speed/Position Sensor |
| 125 | Camshaft Position Sensor |
| 126 | Coolant Temperature Sensor |
| 127 | Intake Air Temperature Sensor |
| 128 | Exhaust Gas Pressure Sensor |
| 129 | Throttle Potentiometer |
| 130 | Power Steering Pressure Switch |

Diagram 2: Engine management – sensor inputs (manual transmission models)

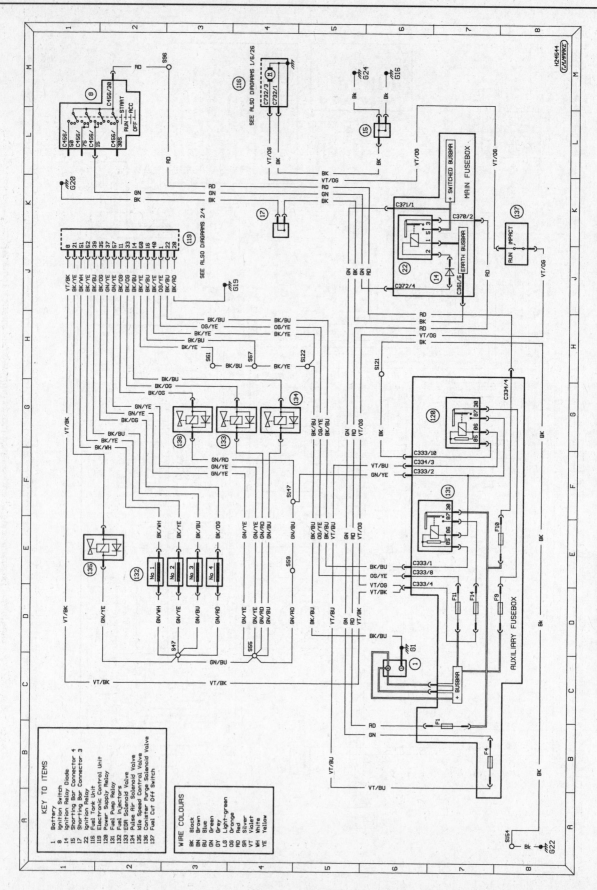

**Diagram 3: Engine management – solenoid outputs and fuel pump (manual transmission models)**

KEY TO ITEMS

1 Battery
8 Ignition Switch
14 Ignition Relay Diode
15 Shorting Bar Connector 4
17 Shorting Bar Connector 3
22 Ignition Relay
116 Fuel Tank Unit
119 Electronic Control Unit
128 Power Supply Relay
131 Fuel Pump Relay
132 Fuel Injectors
133 EGR Solenoid Valve
134 Pulse Air Solenoid Valve
135 Idle Speed Control Valve
136 Canister Purge Solenoid Valve
137 Fuel Cut Off Switch

WIRE COLOURS

BK Black
BN Brown
BU Blue
GN Green
GY Grey
LG Light-green
OG Orange
RD Red
SR Silver
VT Violet
WH White
YE Yellow

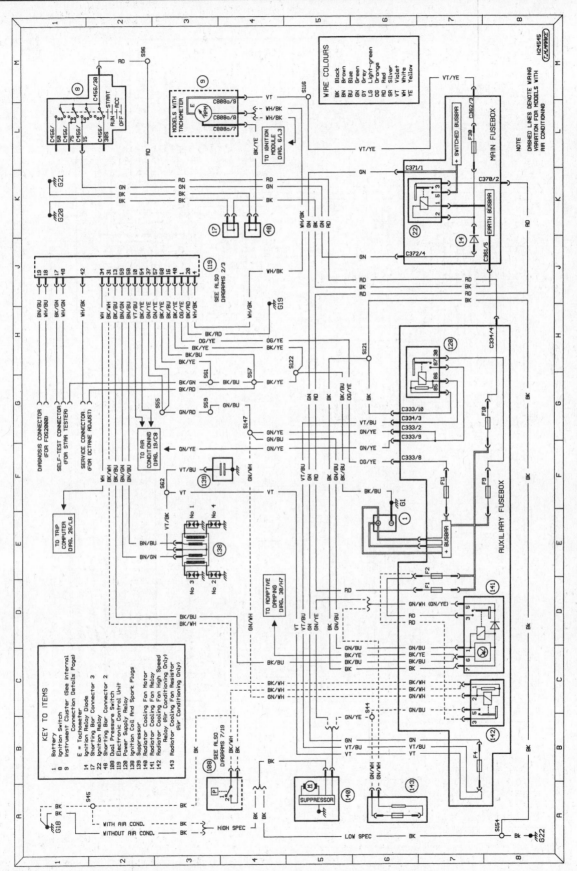

**Diagram 4: Engine management – ignition, tachometer, cooling fan and diagnostic connectors (manual transmission models)**

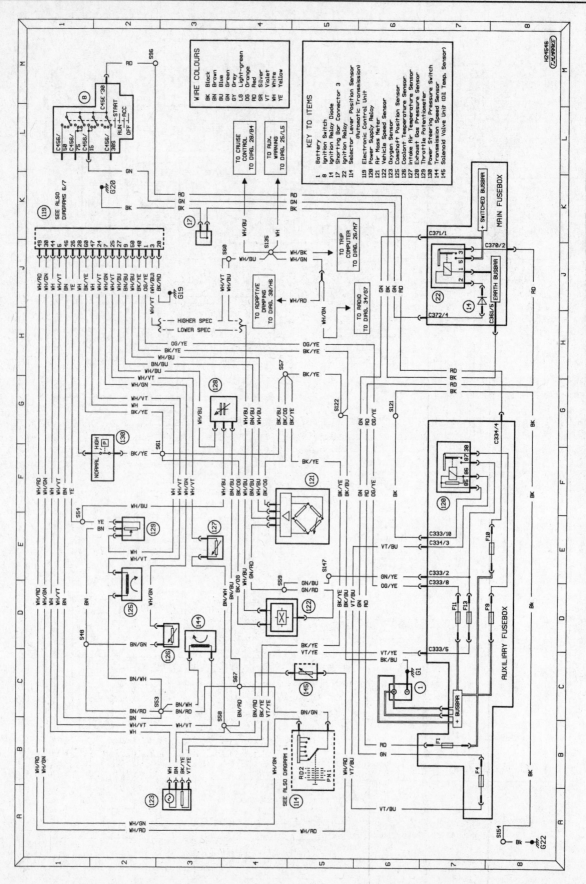

**Diagram 5: Engine management – sensor inputs (automatic transmission models)**

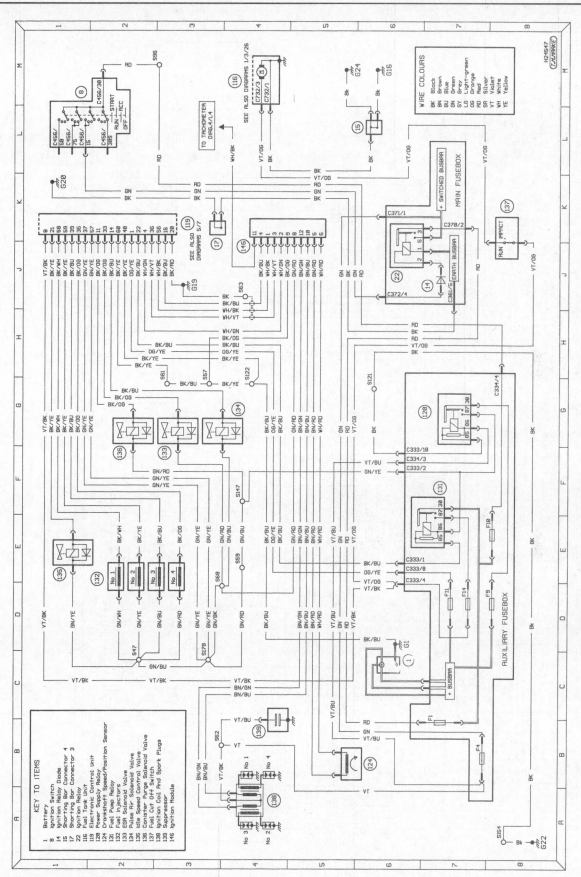

Diagram 6: Engine management – solenoid outputs, ignition and fuel pump (automatic transmission models)

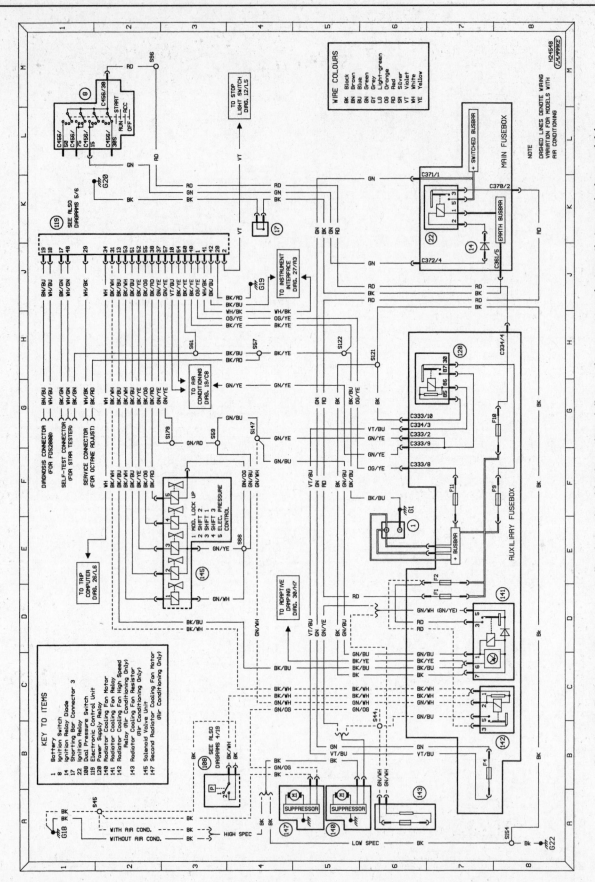

Diagram 7: Engine management – cooling fan, solenoid valve unit and diagnostic connectors (automatic transmission models)

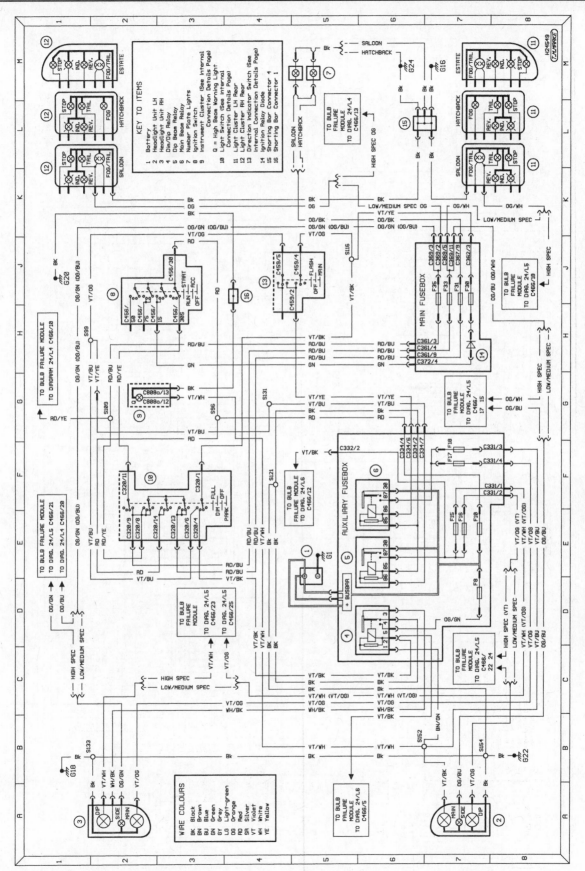

Diagram 8: Exterior lighting – side and headlights (right-hand drive models): dim-dip

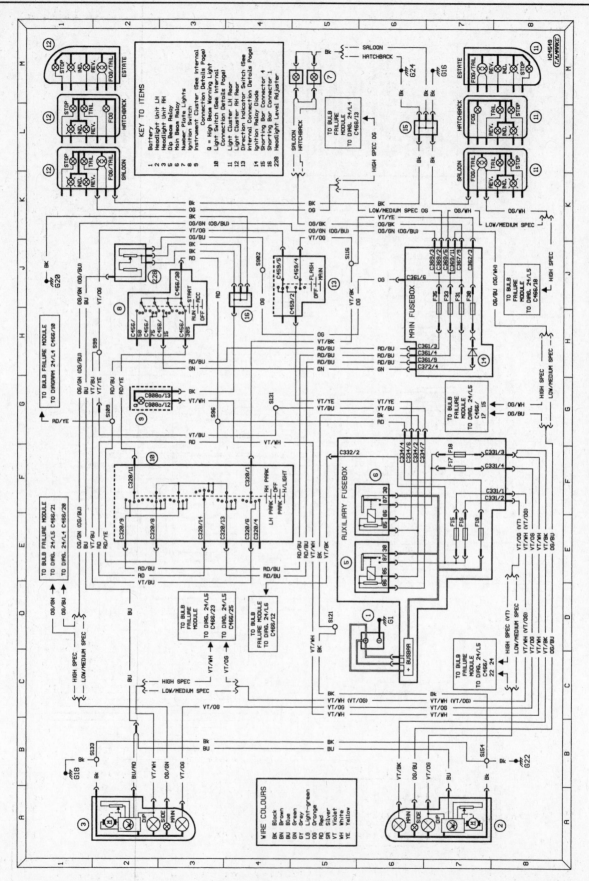

**Diagram 9: Exterior lighting – side and headlights (left-hand drive models): non dim-dip)**

KEY TO ITEMS

1 Battery
2 Headlight Unit LH
3 Headlight Unit RH
4 Dip Beam Relay
5 Main Beam Relay
6 Number Plate Lights
7 Ignition Switch
8 Instrument Cluster (See Internal Connection Details Page)
9 = Light Switch (See Internal Connection Details Page)
10 Light Switch (See Internal Connection Details Page)
11 Light Cluster LH Rear
12 Light Cluster RH Rear
13 Direction Indicator Switch (See Internal Connection Details Page)
14 Ignition Relay Diode
15 Shorting Bar Connector 4
16 Shorting Bar Connector 1
22B Headlight Level Adjuster

WIRE COLOURS

BK Black
BN Brown
BU Blue
GN Green
GY Grey
LG Light-green
OG Orange
RD Red
SR Silver
VT Violet
WH White
YE Yellow

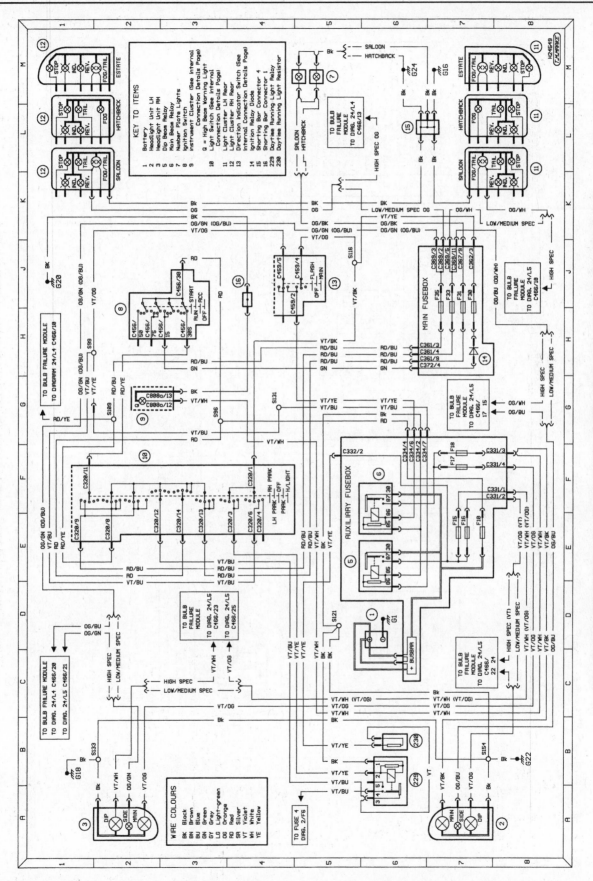

**Diagram 10: Exterior lighting – side and headlights (left-hand drive models): daytime running lights**

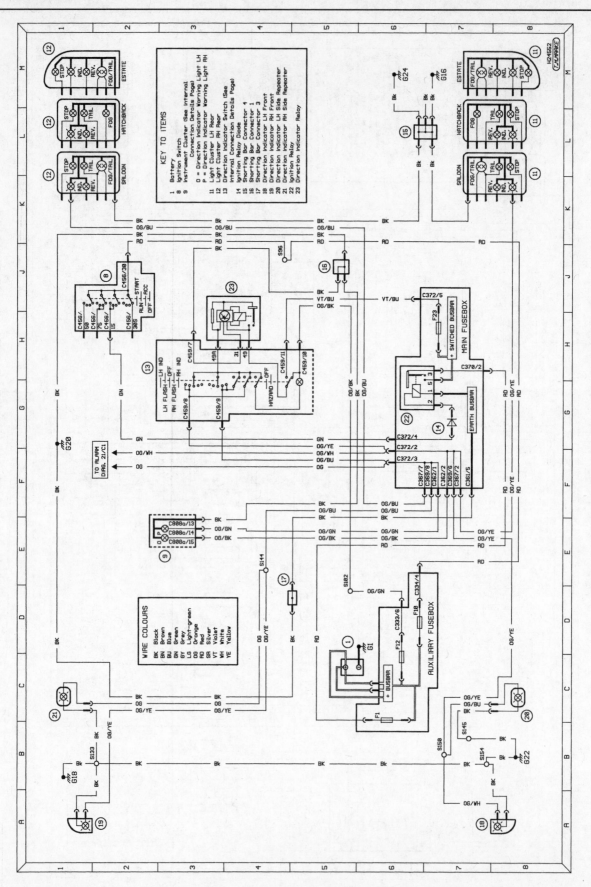

**Diagram 11: Exterior lighting – hazard flasher and direction indicators**

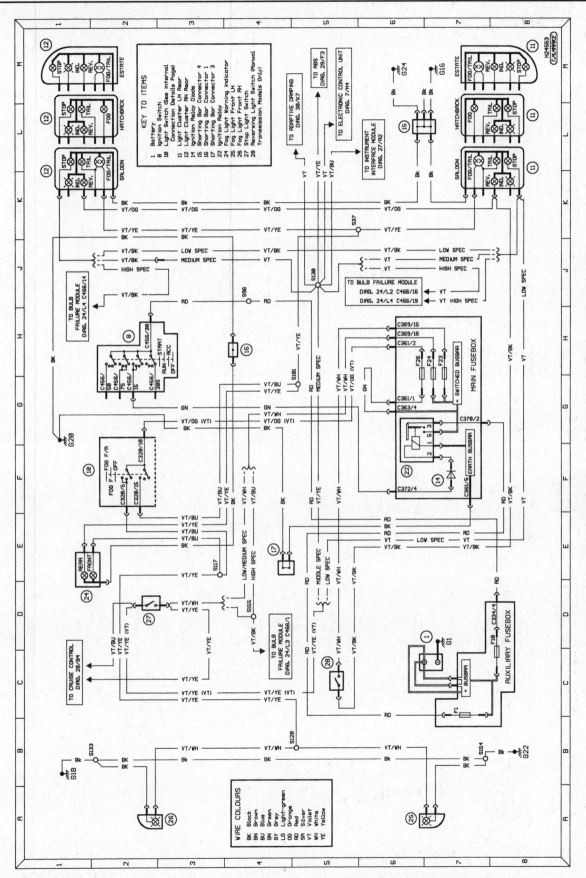

KEY TO ITEMS

1 Battery
8 Ignition Switch (See internal Connection Details Page)
10 Light Switch
11 Light Cluster LH Rear
12 Light Cluster RH Rear
14 Ignition Relay Diode
15 Shorting Bar Connector 4
16 Shorting Bar Connector 1
17 Shorting Bar Connector 3
22 Ignition Relay
24 Fog Light Warning Indicator
25 Fog Light Front LH
26 Fog Light Front RH
27 Stop Light Switch
28 Reversing Light Switch (Manual Transmission Models Only)

WIRE COLOURS

BK  Black
BN  Brown
BU  Blue
GN  Green
GY  Grey
LG  Light-green
OG  Orange
RD  Red
SR  Silver
VT  Violet
WH  White
YE  Yellow

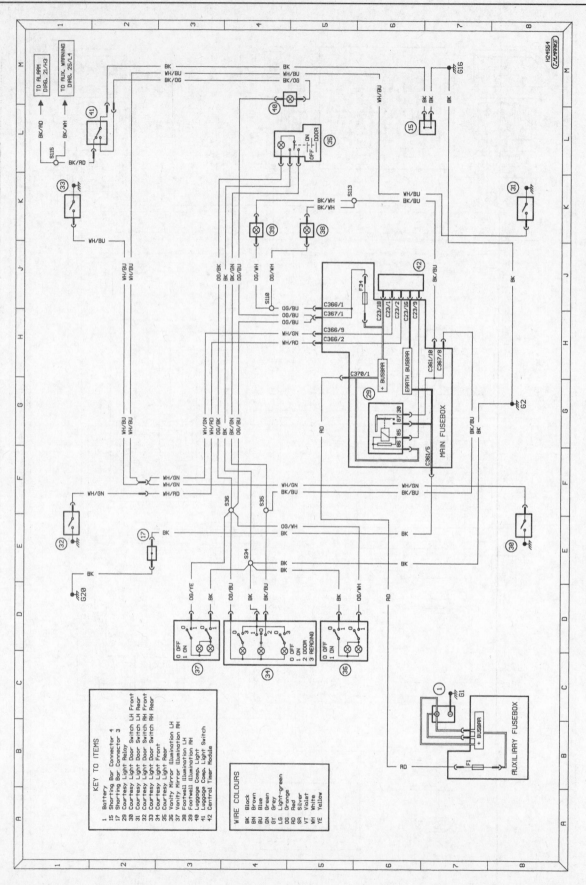

**Diagram 13: Interior lighting – front and rear courtesy, footwell and luggage compartment lights**

KEY TO ITEMS

1   Battery
15  Shorting Bar Connector 4
17  Shorting Bar Connector 3
29  Courtesy Light Relay
30  Courtesy Light Switch LH Front
31  Courtesy Light Switch LH Rear
32  Courtesy Light Switch RH Front
33  Courtesy Light Switch RH Rear
34  Courtesy Light Front
35  Courtesy Light Rear
36  Vanity Mirror Illumination LH
37  Vanity Mirror Illumination RH
38  Footwell Illumination LH
39  Footwell Illumination RH
40  Luggage Comp. Light
41  Luggage Comp. Light Switch
42  Central Timer Module

WIRE COLOURS

BK  Black
BN  Brown
BU  Blue
GN  Green
GY  Grey
LG  Light-green
OG  Orange
RD  Red
SR  Silver
VT  Violet
WH  White
YE  Yellow

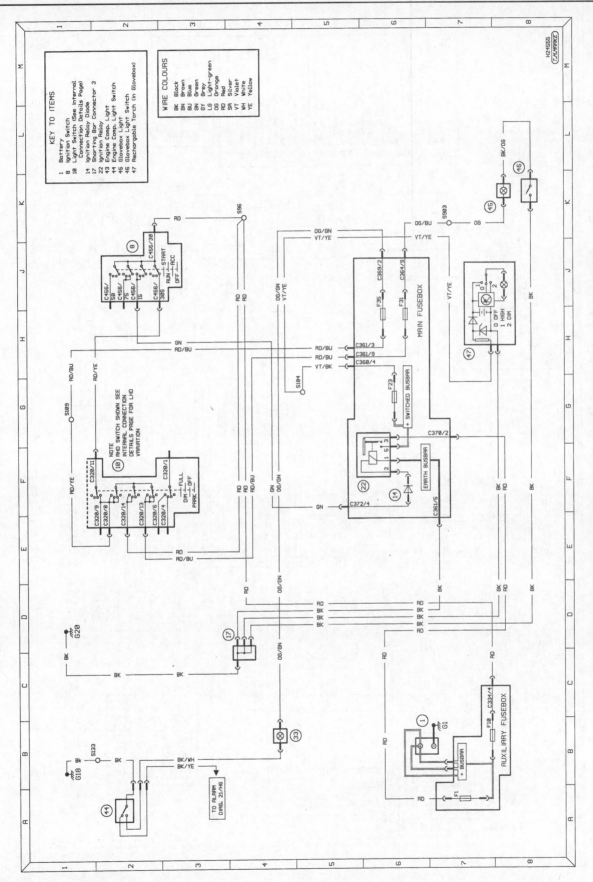

**Diagram 14: Interior lighting – torch, glovebox and engine compartment lights**

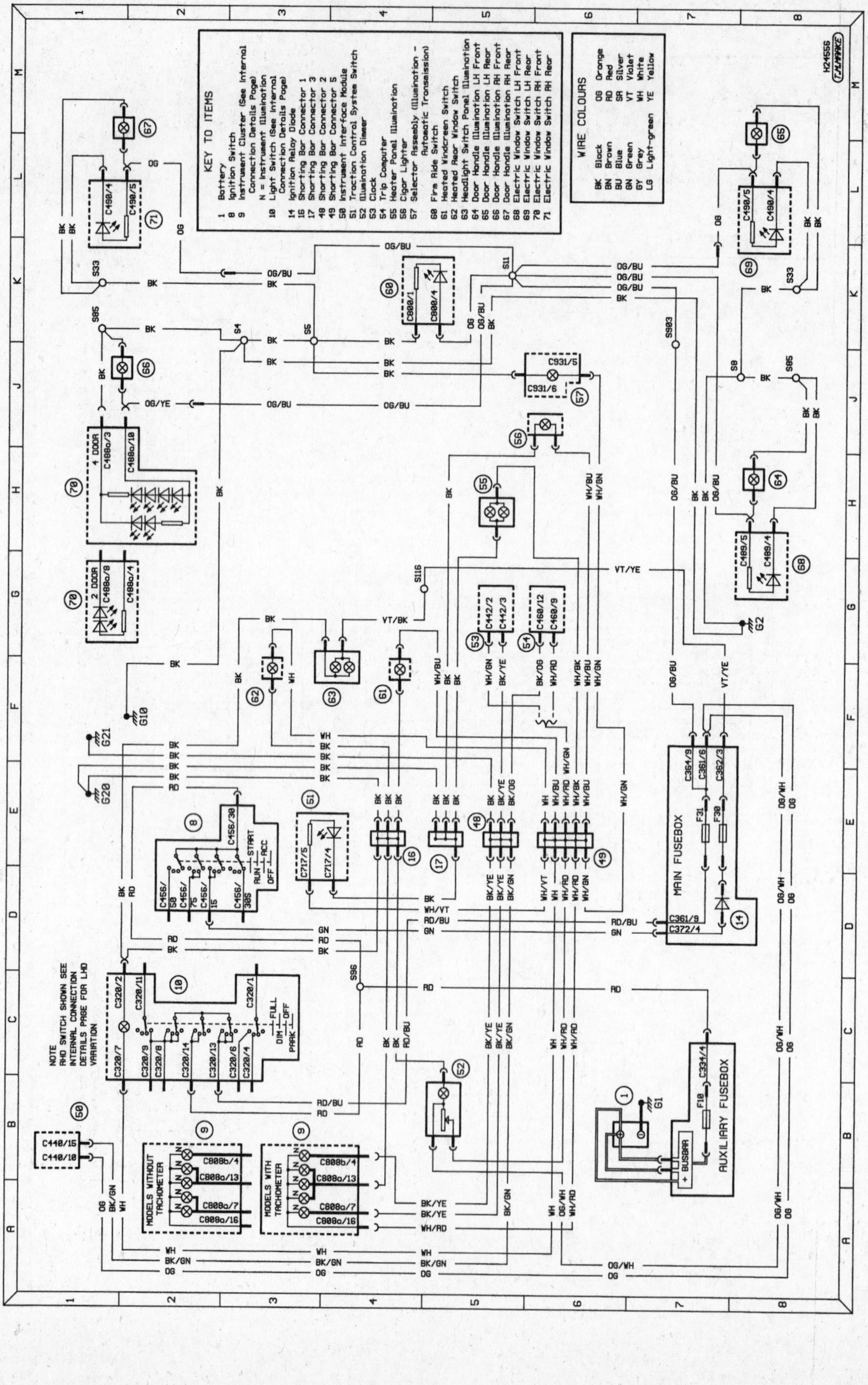

**KEY TO ITEMS**

1. Battery
8. Ignition Switch
9. Instrument Cluster (See Internal Connection Details Page)
   N = Instrument Illumination (See Internal Connection Details Page)
14. Ignition Relay Diode
16. Shorting Bar Connector 1
17. Shorting Bar Connector 2
18. Shorting Bar Connector 3
49. Shorting Bar Connector 5
50. Instrument Interface Module
51. Traction Control System Switch
52. Illumination Dimmer
53. Clock
54. Trip Computer
55. Heater Panel Illumination
56. Cigar Lighter
57. Selector Assembly (Illumination – Automatic Transmission)
58. Fire Ride Switch
61. Heated Windscreen Switch
62. Heated Rear Window Switch
63. Headlight Switch Panel Illumination
64. Door Handle Illumination LH Front
65. Door Handle Illumination LH Rear
66. Door Handle Illumination RH Front
67. Door Handle Illumination RH Rear
68. Electric Window Switch LH Front
69. Electric Window Switch LH Rear
70. Electric Window Switch RH Front
71. Electric Window Switch RH Rear

**WIRE COLOURS**

| | | | |
|---|---|---|---|
| BK | Black | OG | Orange |
| BN | Brown | RD | Red |
| BU | Blue | SR | Silver |
| GN | Green | VT | Violet |
| GY | Grey | WH | White |
| LG | Light-green | YE | Yellow |

**NOTE**
RHD SWITCH SHOWN SEE INTERNAL CONNECTION DETAILS PAGE FOR LHD VARIATION

MAIN FUSEBOX

AUXILIARY FUSEBOX

MODELS WITHOUT TACHOMETER

MODELS WITH TACHOMETER

**Diagram 15: Interior illumination**

H245GG

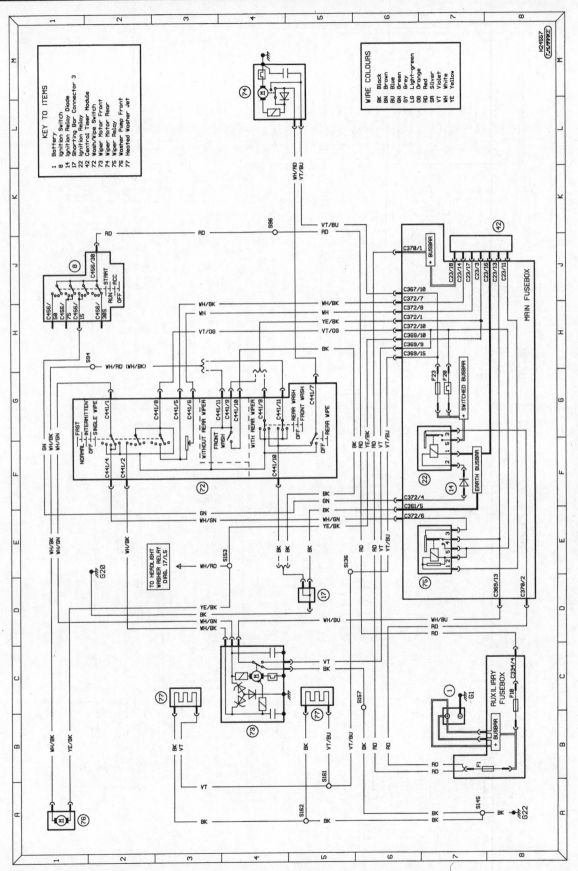

Diagram 16: Wash/wipe and heated washer jets

KEY TO ITEMS

| | |
|---|---|
| 1 | Battery |
| 8 | Ignition Switch |
| 14 | Ignition Relay Diode |
| 17 | Shorting Bar Connector 3 |
| 22 | Ignition Relay |
| 42 | Central Timer Module |
| 72 | Wash/Wipe Switch |
| 73 | Wiper Motor Front |
| 74 | Wiper Motor Rear |
| 75 | Wiper Relay |
| 76 | Washer Pump Front |
| 77 | Heated Washer Jet |

WIRE COLOURS

| | |
|---|---|
| BK | Black |
| BN | Brown |
| BU | Blue |
| GN | Green |
| GY | Grey |
| LG | Light-green |
| OG | Orange |
| RD | Red |
| SR | Silver |
| VT | Violet |
| WH | White |
| YE | Yellow |

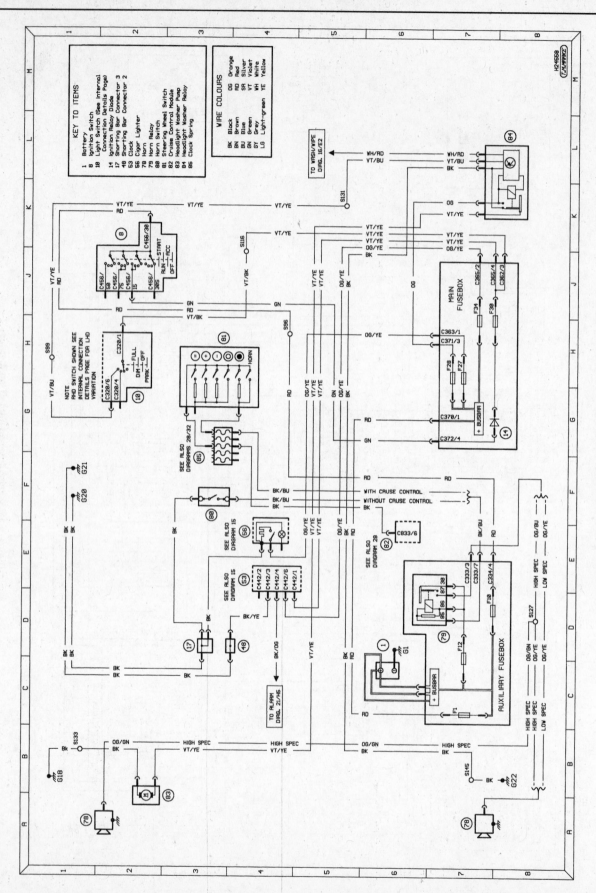

Diagram 17 Headlight washer, horn, clock and cigar lighter

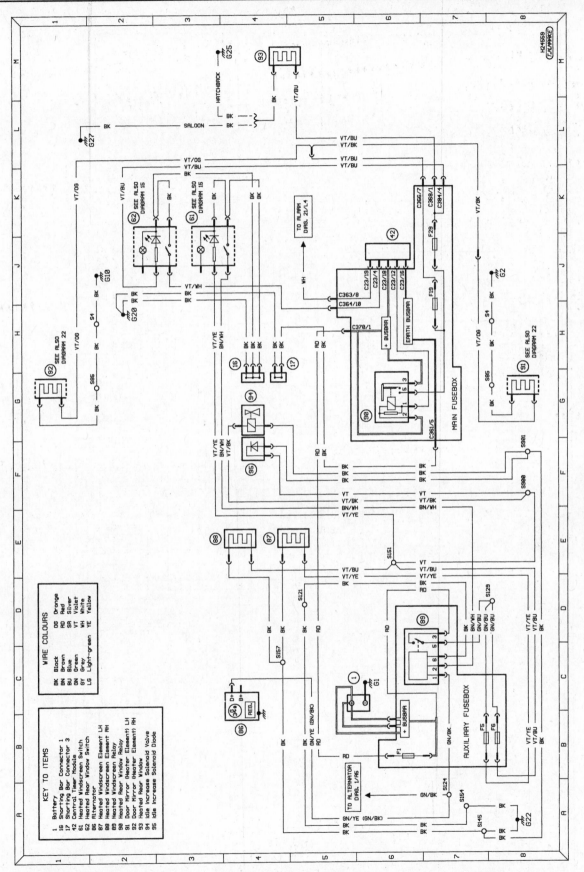

H24659

T/ALMAKE

## KEY TO ITEMS

1    Battery
16   Shorting Bar Connector 1
17   Shorting Bar Connector 3
42   Central Timer Module
61   Heated Windscreen Switch
62   Heated Rear Window Switch
86   Alternator
87   Heated Windscreen Element LH
88   Heated Windscreen Element RH
89   Heated Windscreen Relay
90   Heated Rear Window Relay
91   Heated Rear Window
92   Door Mirror (Heater) Element LH
93   Door Mirror (Heater) Element RH
94   Heated Rear Window
94   Idle Increase Solenoid Valve
95   Idle Increase Solenoid Diode

## WIRE COLOURS

BK   Black
BN   Brown
BU   Blue
GN   Green
GY   Grey
LG   Light-green
OG   Orange
RD   Red
SR   Silver
VT   Violet
WH   White
YE   Yellow

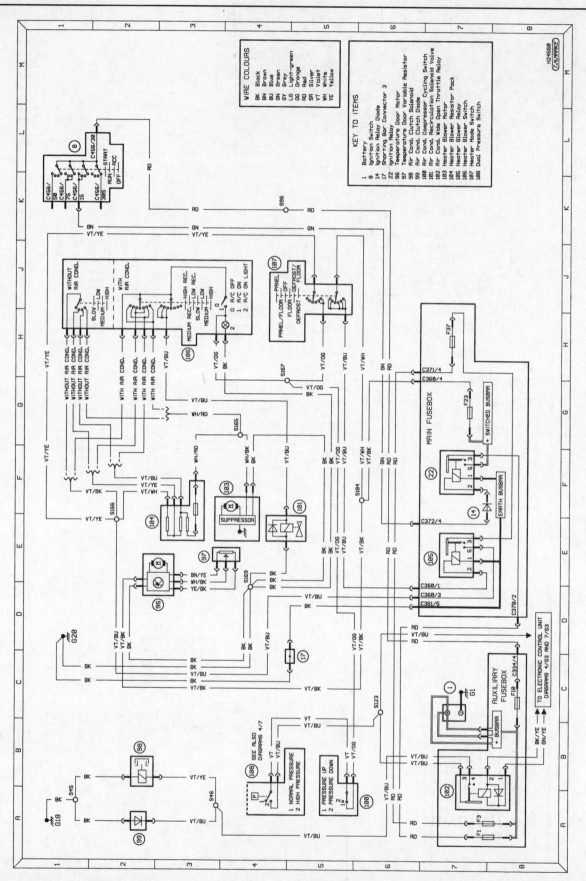

**Diagram 19: Air conditioning and heater blower**

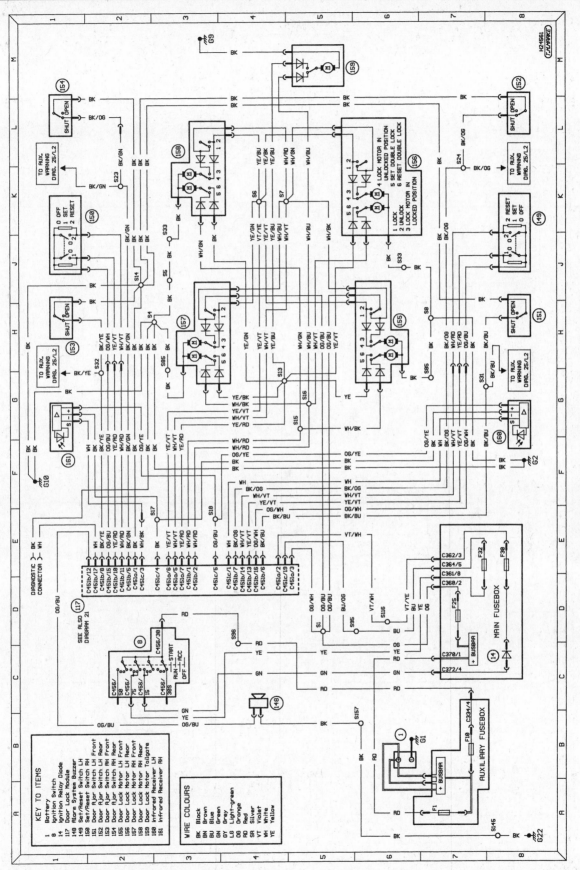

Diagram 20: Central door locking (with double locking)

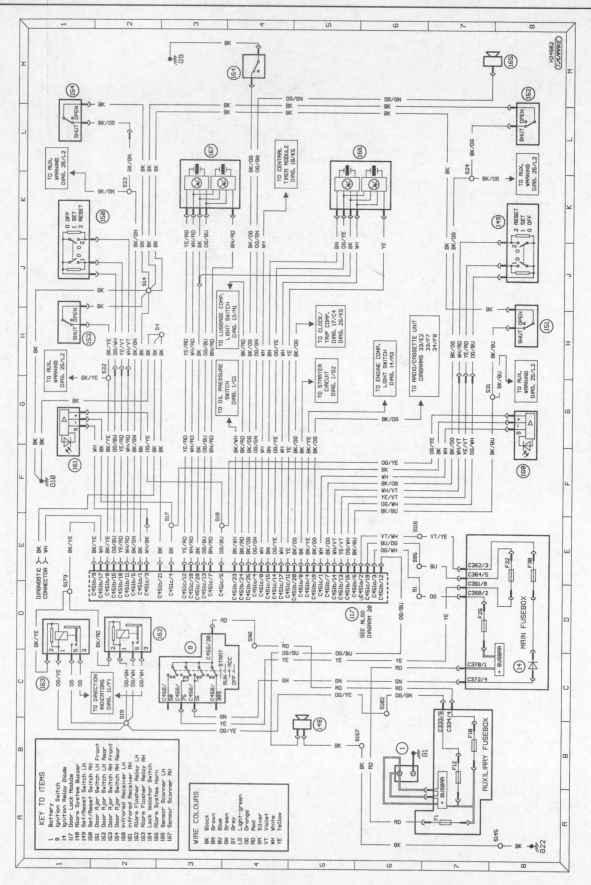

**Diagram 21: Anti-theft alarm**

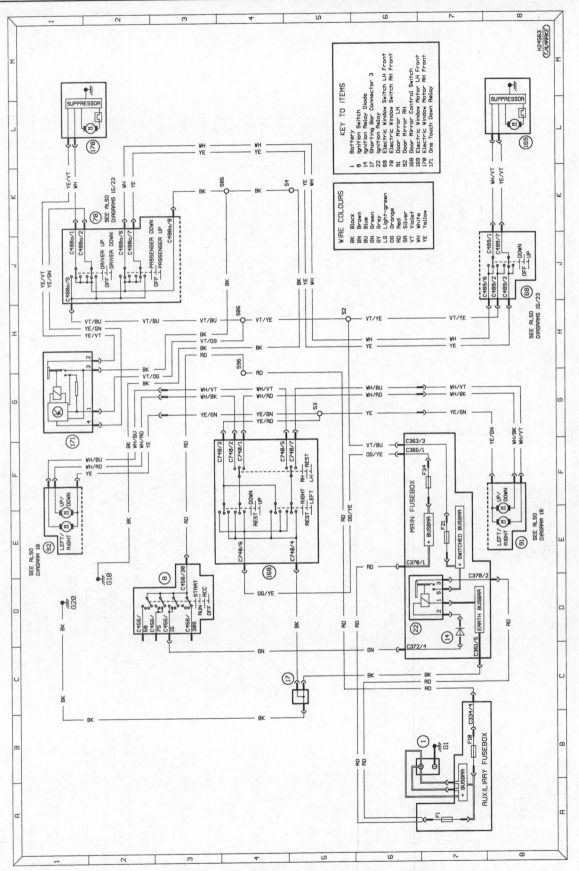

Diagram 22: Electric mirrors and (front) electric window

KEY TO ITEMS

| | |
|---|---|
| 1 | Battery |
| 8 | Ignition Switch |
| 14 | Ignition Relay Diode |
| 17 | Shorting Bar Connector 3 |
| 22 | Ignition Relay |
| 68 | Electric Window Switch LH Front |
| 78 | Electric Window Switch RH Front |
| 91 | Door Mirror LH |
| 92 | Door Mirror RH |
| 168 | Door Mirror Control Switch |
| 169 | Electric Window Motor LH Front |
| 170 | Electric Window Motor RH Front |
| 171 | One Touch Down Relay |

WIRE COLOURS

| | |
|---|---|
| BK | Black |
| BN | Brown |
| BU | Blue |
| GN | Green |
| GY | Grey |
| LG | Light-green |
| OG | Orange |
| RD | Red |
| SR | Silver |
| VT | Violet |
| WH | White |
| YE | Yellow |

H24563

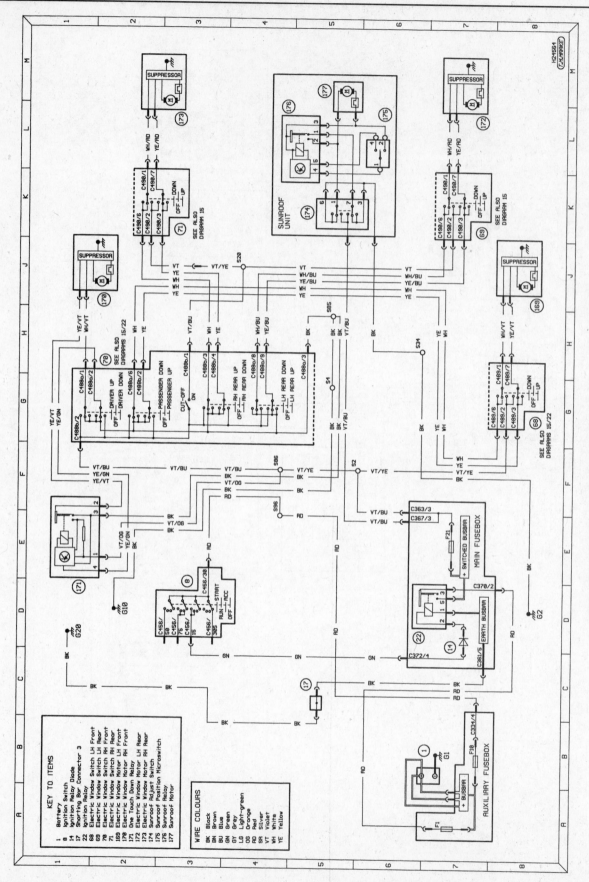

**Diagram 23: Electric sunroof and (front and rear) electric windows**

KEY TO ITEMS

| | |
|---|---|
| 1 | Battery |
| 8 | Ignition Switch |
| 14 | Ignition Relay Diode |
| 17 | Shorting Relay Connector 3 |
| 22 | Ignition Relay |
| 68 | Electric Window Switch LH Front |
| 69 | Electric Window Switch LH Rear |
| 70 | Electric Window Switch RH Rear |
| 71 | Electric Window Switch RH Front |
| 169 | Electric Window Motor LH Front |
| 170 | Electric Window Motor LH Rear |
| 171 | One Touch Down Relay |
| 172 | Electric Window Motor RH Rear |
| 173 | Electric Window Motor RH Front |
| 174 | Sunroof Adjust Switch |
| 175 | Sunroof Position Microswitch |
| 176 | Sunroof Relay |
| 177 | Sunroof Motor |

WIRE COLOURS

| | |
|---|---|
| BK | Black |
| BN | Brown |
| BU | Blue |
| GN | Green |
| GY | Gray |
| LG | Light-green |
| OG | Orange |
| RD | Red |
| SR | Silver |
| VT | Violet |
| WH | White |
| YE | Yellow |

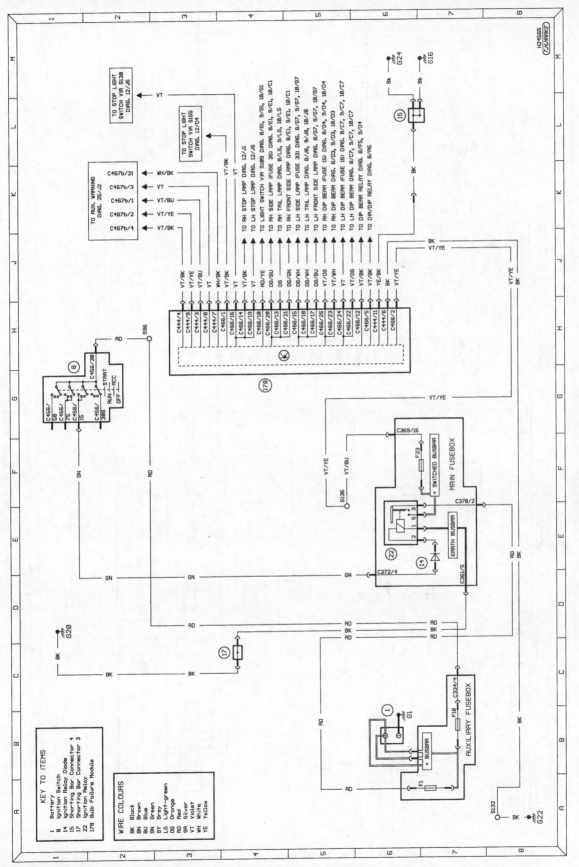

Diagram 24: Bulb failure warning system

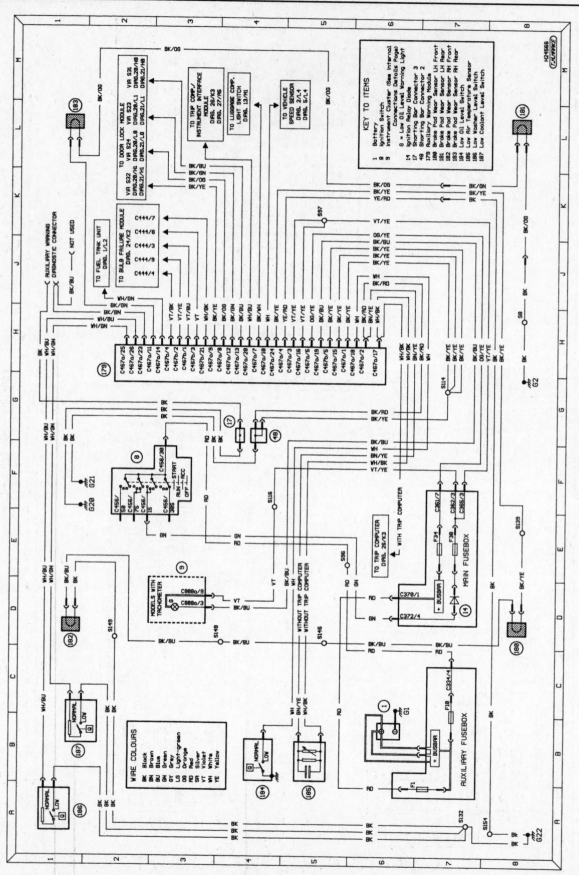

**Diagram 25: Auxiliary warning system**

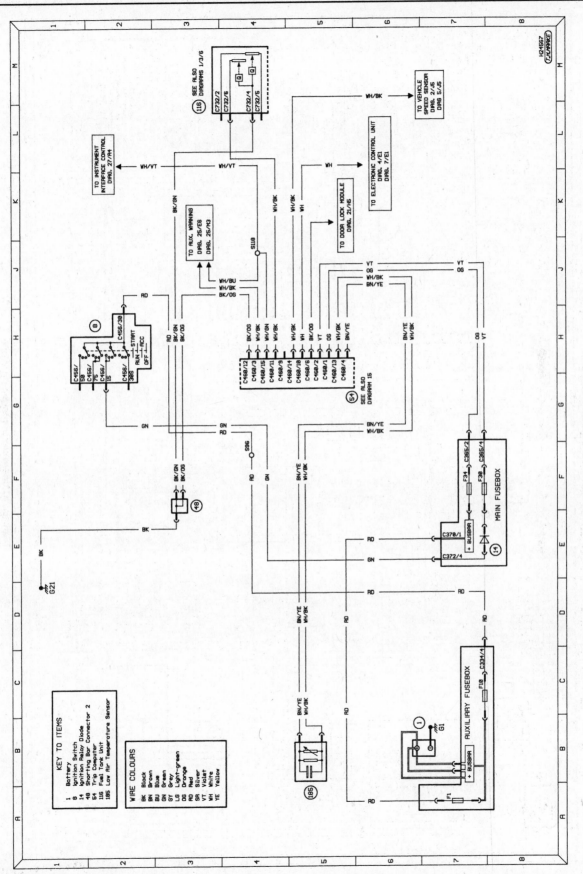

Diagram 26: Trip computer

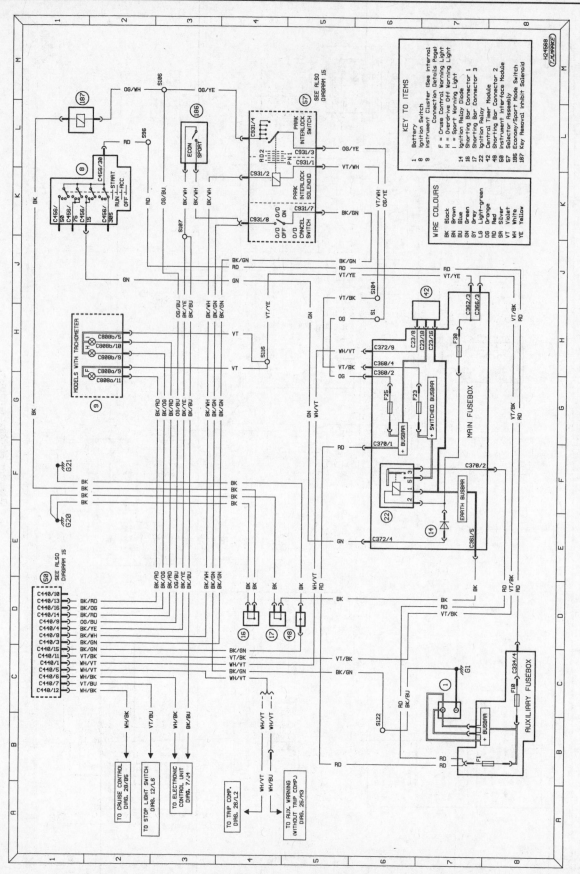

**Diagram 27: Instrument interface control**

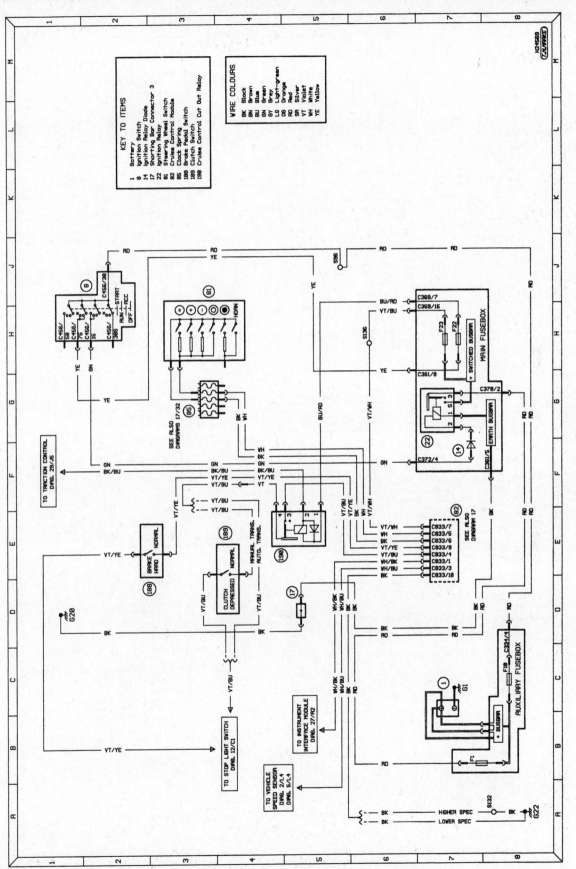

KEY TO ITEMS

1  Battery
8  Ignition Switch
14  Ignition Relay Diode
17  Shorting Bar Connector 3
22  Ignition Relay
81  Steering Wheel Switch
82  Cruise Control Module
85  Clock Spring
188  Brake Pedal Switch
189  Clutch Switch
198  Cruise Control Cut Out Relay

WIRE COLOURS

BK  Black
BN  Brown
BU  Blue
GN  Green
GY  Grey
LG  Light-green
OG  Orange
RD  Red
SR  Silver
VT  Violet
WH  White
YE  Yellow

Diagram 28: Cruise control

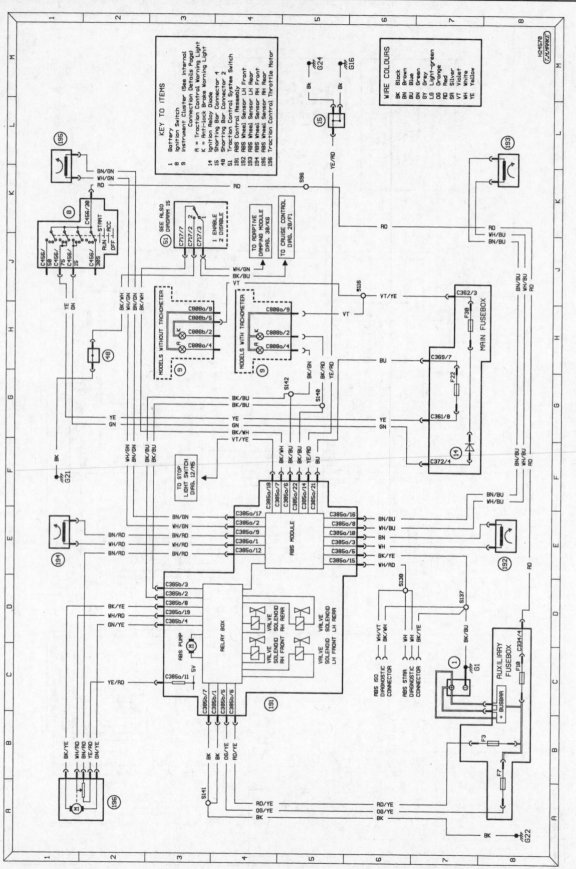

**Diagram 29: ABS with traction control**

KEY TO ITEMS

1 Battery
8 Ignition Switch
9 Instrument Cluster (See internal Connection Details Page)
A = Traction Control Warning Light
K = Anti-lock Brake Warning Light
14 Ignition Relay Diode
15 Shorting Bar Connector 1
48 Shorting Bar Connector 2
51 Traction Control System Switch
191 ABS Control Assembly
192 ABS Wheel Sensor LH Front
193 ABS Wheel Sensor LH Rear
194 ABS Wheel Sensor RH Front
195 ABS Wheel Sensor RH Rear
196 Traction Control Throttle Motor

WIRE COLOURS

BK Black
BN Brown
BU Blue
GN Green
GY Grey
LG Light-green
OG Orange
RD Red
SR Silver
VT Violet
WH White
YE Yellow

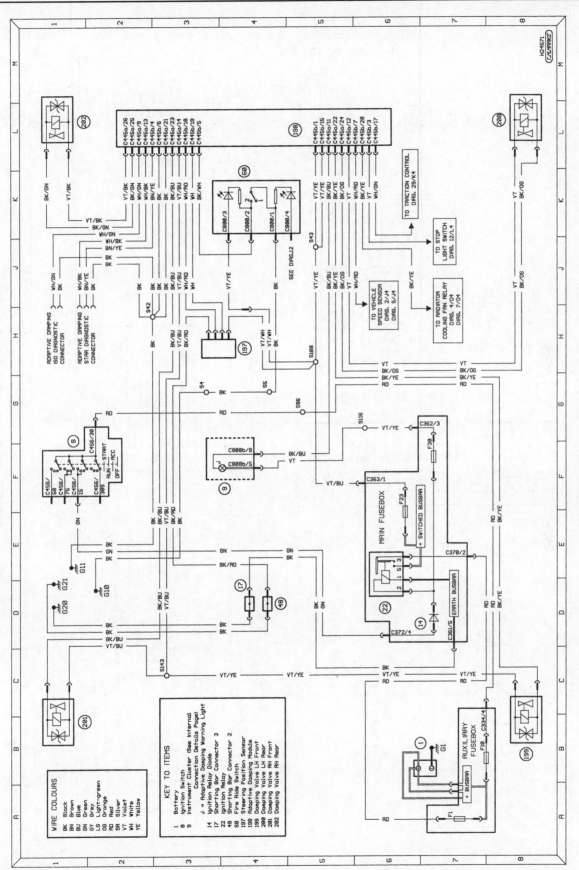

Diagram 30: Adaptive damping system

**WIRE COLOURS**

BK Black
BN Brown
BU Blue
GN Green
GY Grey
LG Light-green
OG Orange
RD Red
SR Silver
VT Violet
WH White
YE Yellow

**KEY TO ITEMS**

1 Battery
8 Ignition Switch
9 Instrument Cluster (See Internal Connection Details Page)

J = Adaptive Damping Warning Light
14 Ignition Relay Diode
17 Shorting Bar Connector 3
22 Ignition Relay
48 Shorting Bar Connector 2
68 Fire Ride Switch
197 Steering Position Sensor
198 Adaptive Damping Module
199 Damping Valve LH Front
201 Damping Valve LH Rear
201 Damping Valve RH Front
202 Damping Valve RH Rear

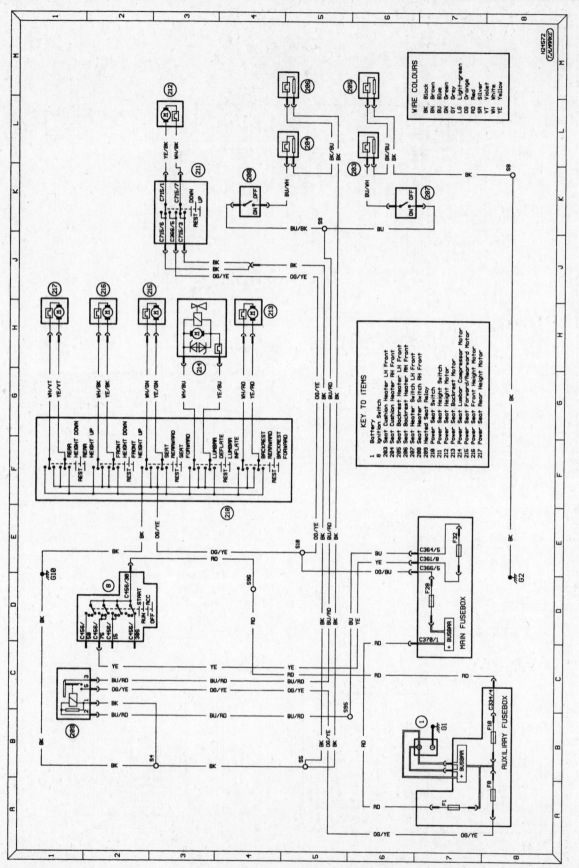

**Diagram 31: Heated seats and driver's seat electric adjustment**

WIRE COLOURS
BK Black
BN Brown
BU Blue
GN Green
GY Grey
LG Light-green
OG Orange
RD Red
SR Silver
VT Violet
WH White
YE Yellow

KEY TO ITEMS

1 Battery
8 Ignition Switch
203 Seat Cushion Heater LH Front
204 Seat Cushion Heater RH Front
205 Seat Backrest Heater LH Front
206 Seat Backrest Heater RH Front
207 Seat Heater Switch LH Front
208 Seat Heater Switch RH Front
209 Heated Seat Relay
210 Power Seat Switch
211 Power Seat Height Switch
212 Power Seat Height Motor
213 Power Seat Backrest Motor
214 Power Seat Lumbar Compressor Motor
215 Power Seat Forward/Rearward Motor
216 Power Seat Front Height Motor
217 Power Seat Rear Height Motor

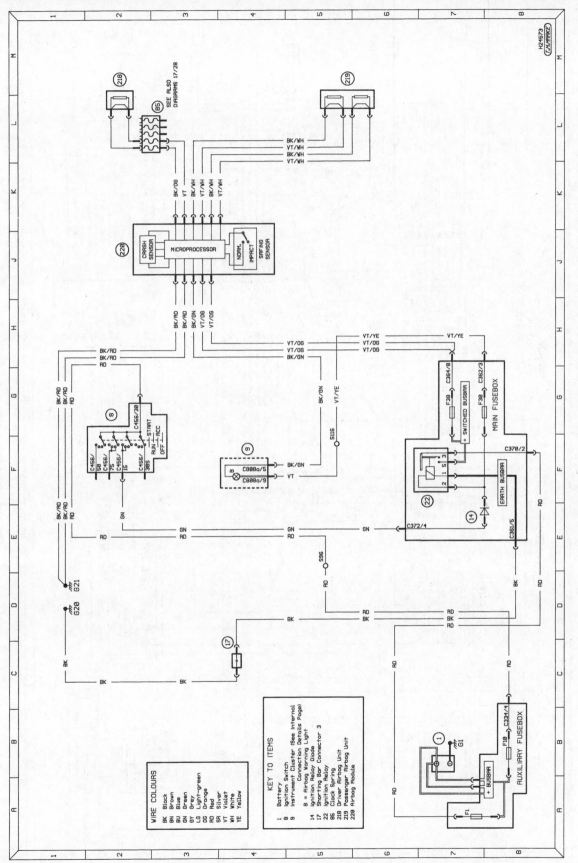

**Diagram 32: Driver and passenger air bags**

WIRE COLOURS

BK Black
BN Brown
BU Blue
GN Green
GY Grey
LG Light-green
OG Orange
RD Red
SR Silver
VT Violet
WH White
YE Yellow

KEY TO ITEMS

1 Battery
8 Ignition Switch
9 Instrument Cluster (See Internal
    Connection Details Page)
B = Airbag Warning Light
14 Ignition Relay Diode
17 Ignition Bar Connector 3
22 Ignition Relay
86 Clock Spring
218 Driver Airbag Unit
219 Passenger Airbag Unit
220 Airbag Module

SEE ALSO
DIAGRAMS 17/28

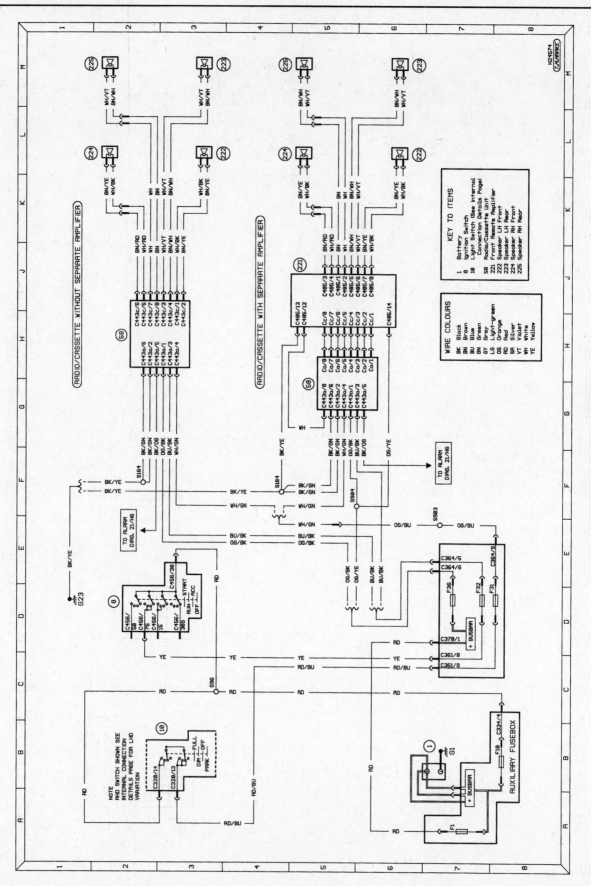

**Diagram 33: Radio/cassette (with amplifier)**

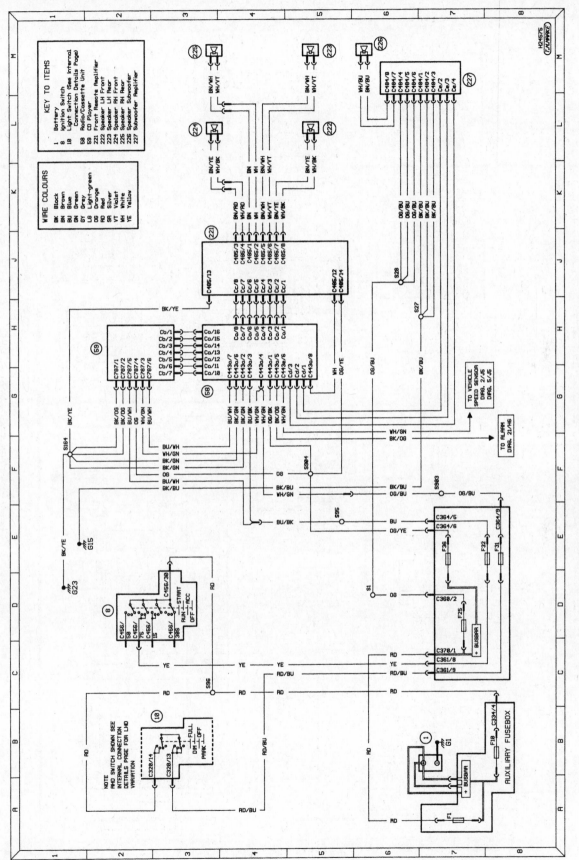

**Diagram 34: Radio/cassette and CD player (with subwoofer)**

KEY TO ITEMS
1 Battery
8 Ignition Switch (See Internal
10 Light Switch (See Internal
   Connection Details Page)
58 Radio/Cassette Unit
59 CD Player
221 Front Remote Amplifier
222 Speaker LH Front
223 Speaker LH Rear
224 Speaker RH Front
225 Speaker RH Rear
226 Speaker Subwoofer
227 Subwoofer Amplifier

WIRE COLOURS
BK  Black
BN  Brown
BU  Blue
GN  Green
GY  Grey
LG  Light-green
OG  Orange
RD  Red
SR  Silver
VT  Violet
WH  White
YE  Yellow

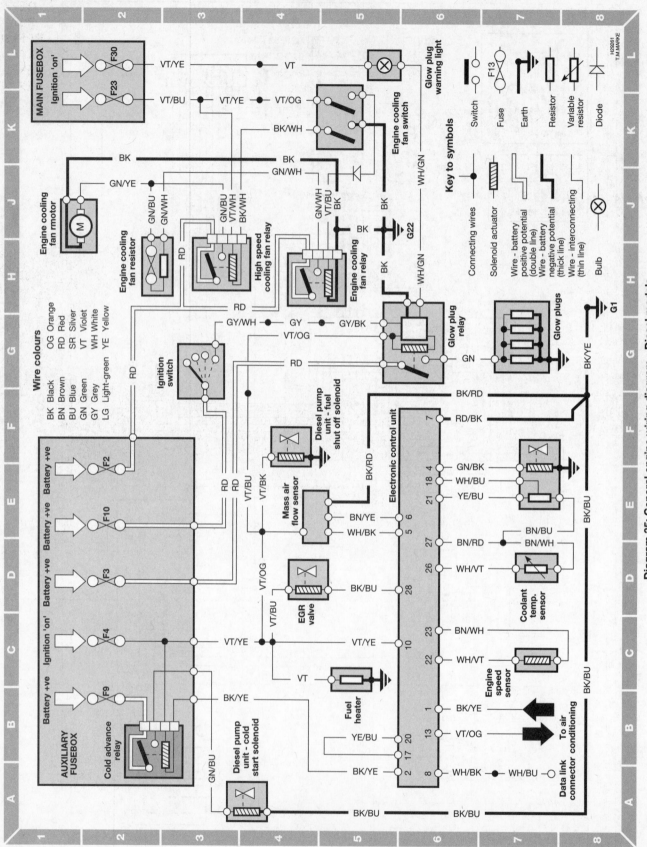

Diagram 35: General engine wiring diagram - Diesel models

# Reference

Dimensions and weights . . . . . . . . . . . . . . . . . . **REF•1**
Conversion factors . . . . . . . . . . . . . . . . . . . . . . . **REF•2**
Buying spare parts . . . . . . . . . . . . . . . . . . . . . . . **REF•3**
Vehicle identification . . . . . . . . . . . . . . . . . . . . . **REF•4**
General repair procedures . . . . . . . . . . . . . . . . **REF•5**
Jacking and vehicle support . . . . . . . . . . . . . . . **REF•6**

Disconnecting the battery . . . . . . . . . . . . . . . . . **REF•7**
Tools and working facilities . . . . . . . . . . . . . . . **REF•8**
MOT test checks . . . . . . . . . . . . . . . . . . . . . . . **REF•10**
Fault finding . . . . . . . . . . . . . . . . . . . . . . . . . . . **REF•14**
Glossary of technical terms . . . . . . . . . . . . . . **REF•23**
Index . . . . . . . . . . . . . . . . . . . . . . . . . . . . . . . . . **REF•28**

# Dimensions and weights

**Note:** *All figures are approximate, and may vary according to model. Refer to manufacturer's data for exact figures.*

## Dimensions

| | Pre-facelift models | Facelift models |
|---|---|---|
| Overall length: | | |
| Saloon and Hatchback | 4481 mm | 4556 mm |
| Estate | 4631 mm | 4671 mm |
| Overall width – including mirrors | 1925 mm | 1925 mm |
| Overall height – at kerb weight: | | |
| Saloon and Hatchback | 1403 to 1435 mm | 1327 to 1427 mm |
| Estate | 1416 to 1501 mm | 1405 to 1510 mm |

## Weights

| | Pre-facelift models | Facelift models |
|---|---|---|
| Kerb weight: | | |
| Saloon and Hatchback models | 1337 kg | 1359 to 1505 kg |
| Estate models | 1382 kg | 1415 to 1568 kg |
| Maximum roof rack load: | | |
| Estate with integral roof rack | 100 kg | 100 kg |
| All others | 75 kg | 75 kg |
| Maximum towing weight | 1500 kg | 1500 kg |
| Trailer nose weight limit | 75 kg | 75 kg |

## Length (distance)

| | | | | | |
|---|---|---|---|---|---|
| Inches (in) | x 25.4 | = Millimetres (mm) | x 0.0394 | = | Inches (in) |
| Feet (ft) | x 0.305 | = Metres (m) | x 3.281 | = | Feet (ft) |
| Miles | x 1.609 | = Kilometres (km) | x 0.621 | = | Miles |

## Volume (capacity)

| | | | | | |
|---|---|---|---|---|---|
| Cubic inches (cu in; in³) | x 16.387 | = Cubic centimetres (cc; cm³) | x 0.061 | = | Cubic inches (cu in; in³) |
| Imperial pints (Imp pt) | x 0.568 | = Litres (l) | x 1.76 | = | Imperial pints (Imp pt) |
| Imperial quarts (Imp qt) | x 1.137 | = Litres (l) | x 0.88 | = | Imperial quarts (Imp qt) |
| Imperial quarts (Imp qt) | x 1.201 | = US quarts (US qt) | x 0.833 | = | Imperial quarts (Imp qt) |
| US quarts (US qt) | x 0.946 | = Litres (l) | x 1.057 | = | US quarts (US qt) |
| Imperial gallons (Imp gal) | x 4.546 | = Litres (l) | x 0.22 | = | Imperial gallons (Imp gal) |
| Imperial gallons (Imp gal) | x 1.201 | = US gallons (US gal) | x 0.833 | = | Imperial gallons (Imp gal) |
| US gallons (US gal) | x 3.785 | = Litres (l) | x 0.264 | = | US gallons (US gal) |

## Mass (weight)

| | | | | | |
|---|---|---|---|---|---|
| Ounces (oz) | x 28.35 | = Grams (g) | x 0.035 | = | Ounces (oz) |
| Pounds (lb) | x 0.454 | = Kilograms (kg) | x 2.205 | = | Pounds (lb) |

## Force

| | | | | | |
|---|---|---|---|---|---|
| Ounces-force (ozf; oz) | x 0.278 | = Newtons (N) | x 3.6 | = | Ounces-force (ozf; oz) |
| Pounds-force (lbf; lb) | x 4.448 | = Newtons (N) | x 0.225 | = | Pounds-force (lbf; lb) |
| Newtons (N) | x 0.1 | = Kilograms-force (kgf; kg) | x 9.81 | = | Newtons (N) |

## Pressure

| | | | | | |
|---|---|---|---|---|---|
| Pounds-force per square inch (psi; lbf/in²; lb/in²) | x 0.070 | = Kilograms-force per square centimetre (kgf/cm²; kg/cm²) | x 14.223 | = | Pounds-force per square inch (psi; lbf/in²; lb/in²) |
| Pounds-force per square inch (psi; lbf/in²; lb/in²) | x 0.068 | = Atmospheres (atm) | x 14.696 | = | Pounds-force per square inch (psi; lbf/in²; lb/in²) |
| Pounds-force per square inch (psi; lbf/in²; lb/in²) | x 0.069 | = Bars | x 14.5 | = | Pounds-force per square inch (psi; lbf/in²; lb/in²) |
| Pounds-force per square inch (psi; lbf/in²; lb/in²) | x 6.895 | = Kilopascals (kPa) | x 0.145 | = | Pounds-force per square inch (psi; lbf/in²; lb/in²) |
| Kilopascals (kPa) | x 0.01 | = Kilograms-force per square centimetre (kgf/cm²; kg/cm²) | x 98.1 | = | Kilopascals (kPa) |
| Millibar (mbar) | x 100 | = Pascals (Pa) | x 0.01 | = | Millibar (mbar) |
| Millibar (mbar) | x 0.0145 | = Pounds-force per square inch (psi; lbf/in²; lb/in²) | x 68.947 | = | Millibar (mbar) |
| Millibar (mbar) | x 0.75 | = Millimetres of mercury (mmHg) | x 1.333 | = | Millibar (mbar) |
| Millibar (mbar) | x 0.401 | = Inches of water (inH₂O) | x 2.491 | = | Millibar (mbar) |
| Millimetres of mercury (mmHg) | x 0.535 | = Inches of water (inH₂O) | x 1.868 | = | Millimetres of mercury (mmHg) |
| Inches of water (inH₂O) | x 0.036 | = Pounds-force per square inch (psi; lbf/in²; lb/in²) | x 27.68 | = | Inches of water (inH₂O) |

## Torque (moment of force)

| | | | | | |
|---|---|---|---|---|---|
| Pounds-force inches (lbf in; lb in) | x 1.152 | = Kilograms-force centimetre (kgf cm; kg cm) | x 0.868 | = | Pounds-force inches (lbf in; lb in) |
| Pounds-force inches (lbf in; lb in) | x 0.113 | = Newton metres (Nm) | x 8.85 | = | Pounds-force inches (lbf in; lb in) |
| Pounds-force inches (lbf in; lb in) | x 0.083 | = Pounds-force feet (lbf ft; lb ft) | x 12 | = | Pounds-force inches (lbf in; lb in) |
| Pounds-force feet (lbf ft; lb ft) | x 0.138 | = Kilograms-force metres (kgf m; kg m) | x 7.233 | = | Pounds-force feet (lbf ft; lb ft) |
| Pounds-force feet (lbf ft; lb ft) | x 1.356 | = Newton metres (Nm) | x 0.738 | = | Pounds-force feet (lbf ft; lb ft) |
| Newton metres (Nm) | x 0.102 | = Kilograms-force metres (kgf m; kg m) | x 9.804 | = | Newton metres (Nm) |

## Power

| | | | | | |
|---|---|---|---|---|---|
| Horsepower (hp) | x 745.7 | = Watts (W) | x 0.0013 | = | Horsepower (hp) |

## Velocity (speed)

| | | | | | |
|---|---|---|---|---|---|
| Miles per hour (miles/hr; mph) | x 1.609 | = Kilometres per hour (km/hr; kph) | x 0.621 | = | Miles per hour (miles/hr; mph) |

## Fuel consumption*

| | | | | | |
|---|---|---|---|---|---|
| Miles per gallon, Imperial (mpg) | x 0.354 | = Kilometres per litre (km/l) | x 2.825 | = | Miles per gallon, Imperial (mpg) |
| Miles per gallon, US (mpg) | x 0.425 | = Kilometres per litre (km/l) | x 2.352 | = | Miles per gallon, US (mpg) |

## Temperature

Degrees Fahrenheit = (°C x 1.8) + 32          Degrees Celsius (Degrees Centigrade; °C) = (°F - 32) x 0.56

*It is common practice to convert from miles per gallon (mpg) to litres/100 kilometres (l/100km), where mpg x l/100 km = 282*

Spare parts are available from many sources, including maker's appointed garages, accessory shops, and motor factors. To be sure of obtaining the correct parts, it will sometimes be necessary to quote the vehicle identification number (see *Vehicle identification*). If possible, it can also be useful to take the old parts along for positive identification. Items such as starter motors and alternators may be available under a service exchange scheme – any parts returned should always be clean.

Our advice regarding spare part sources is as follows.

## Officially-appointed garages

This is the best source of parts which are peculiar to your car, and which are not otherwise generally available (e.g., badges, interior trim, certain body panels, etc). It is also the only place at which you should buy parts if the car is still under warranty.

## Accessory shops

These are very good places to buy materials and components needed for the maintenance of your car (oil, air and fuel filters, light bulbs, drivebelts, greases, brake pads, touch-up paint, etc). Components of this nature sold by a reputable shop are of the same standard as those used by the car manufacturer.

Besides components, these shops also sell tools and general accessories, usually have convenient opening hours, charge lower prices, and can often be found close to home. Some accessory shops have parts counters where components needed for almost any repair job can be purchased or ordered.

## Motor factors

Good factors will stock all the more important components which wear out comparatively quickly, and can sometimes supply individual components needed for the overhaul of a larger assembly (e.g., brake seals and hydraulic parts, bearing shells, pistons, valves). They may also handle work such as cylinder block reboring, crankshaft regrinding, etc.

## Tyre and exhaust specialists

These outlets may be independent, or members of a local or national chain. They frequently offer competitive prices when compared with a main dealer or local garage, but it will pay to obtain several quotes before making a decision. When researching prices, also ask what 'extras' may be added – for instance fitting a new valve and balancing the wheel are both commonly charged on top of the price of a new tyre.

## Other sources

Beware of parts or materials obtained from market stalls, car boot sales or similar outlets. Such items are not invariably sub-standard, but there is little chance of compensation if they do prove unsatisfactory. In the case of safety-critical components such as brake pads, there is the risk not only of financial loss, but also of an accident causing injury or death.

Second-hand components or assemblies obtained from a car breaker can be a good buy in some circumstances, but his sort of purchase is best made by the experienced DIY mechanic.

When ordering spare parts, always give as much information as possible. Quote the car model, year of manufacture, body and engine numbers as appropriate.

The *vehicle identification plate* is located on the engine compartment front crossmember **(see illustration)**. In addition to many other details, it carries the Vehicle Identification Number, maximum vehicle weight information, and codes for interior trim and body colours.

The *Vehicle Identification Number* is given on the vehicle identification plate. It is also stamped on the engine compartment bulkhead, and into the body, so that it can be seen through the bottom left-hand corner of the windscreen **(see illustrations)**.

The *engine number* is stamped onto the cylinder block/crankcase, below and in front of the fuel filter **(see illustration)**.

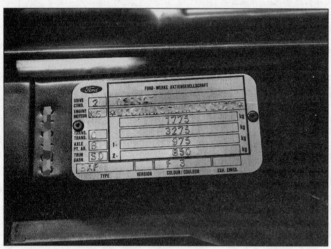

Vehicle identification plate on engine compartment front crossmember

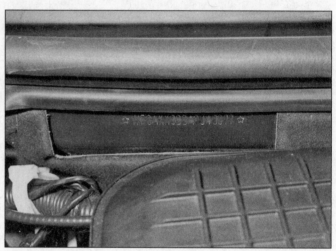

Vehicle identification number on engine compartment bulkhead

Vehicle identification number in body, visible through bottom left-hand corner of windscreen

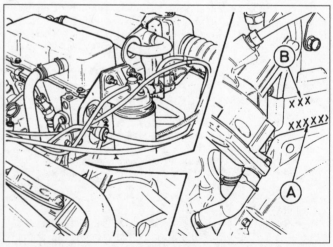

Engine number (A) and code (B) on the transmission end of the block

Whenever servicing, repair or overhaul work is carried out on the car or its components, observe the following procedures and instructions. This will assist in carrying out the operation efficiently and to a professional standard of workmanship.

## Joint mating faces and gaskets

When separating components at their mating faces, never insert screwdrivers or similar implements into the joint between the faces in order to prise them apart. This can cause severe damage which results in oil leaks, coolant leaks, etc upon reassembly. Separation is usually achieved by tapping along the joint with a soft-faced hammer in order to break the seal. However, note that this method may not be suitable where dowels are used for component location.

Where a gasket is used between the mating faces of two components, a new one must be fitted on reassembly; fit it dry unless otherwise stated in the repair procedure. Make sure that the mating faces are clean and dry, with all traces of old gasket removed. When cleaning a joint face, use a tool which is unlikely to score or damage the face, and remove any burrs or nicks with an oilstone or fine file.

Make sure that tapped holes are cleaned with a pipe cleaner, and keep them free of jointing compound, if this is being used, unless specifically instructed otherwise.

Ensure that all orifices, channels or pipes are clear, and blow through them, preferably using compressed air.

## Oil seals

Oil seals can be removed by levering them out with a wide flat-bladed screwdriver or similar implement. Alternatively, a number of self-tapping screws may be screwed into the seal, and these used as a purchase for pliers or some similar device in order to pull the seal free.

Whenever an oil seal is removed from its working location, either individually or as part of an assembly, it should be renewed.

The very fine sealing lip of the seal is easily damaged, and will not seal if the surface it contacts is not completely clean and free from scratches, nicks or grooves. If the original sealing surface of the component cannot be restored, and the manufacturer has not made provision for slight relocation of the seal relative to the sealing surface, the component should be renewed.

Protect the lips of the seal from any surface which may damage them in the course of fitting. Use tape or a conical sleeve where possible. Lubricate the seal lips with oil before fitting and, on dual-lipped seals, fill the space between the lips with grease.

Unless otherwise stated, oil seals must be fitted with their sealing lips toward the lubricant to be sealed.

Use a tubular drift or block of wood of the appropriate size to install the seal and, if the seal housing is shouldered, drive the seal down to the shoulder. If the seal housing is unshouldered, the seal should be fitted with its face flush with the housing top face (unless otherwise instructed).

## Screw threads and fastenings

Seized nuts, bolts and screws are quite a common occurrence where corrosion has set in, and the use of penetrating oil or releasing fluid will often overcome this problem if the offending item is soaked for a while before attempting to release it. The use of an impact driver may also provide a means of releasing such stubborn fastening devices, when used in conjunction with the appropriate screwdriver bit or socket. If none of these methods works, it may be necessary to resort to the careful application of heat, or the use of a hacksaw or nut splitter device.

Studs are usually removed by locking two nuts together on the threaded part, and then using a spanner on the lower nut to unscrew the stud. Studs or bolts which have broken off below the surface of the component in which they are mounted can sometimes be removed using a stud extractor. Always ensure that a blind tapped hole is completely free from oil, grease, water or other fluid before installing the bolt or stud. Failure to do this could cause the housing to crack due to the hydraulic action of the bolt or stud as it is screwed in.

When tightening a castellated nut to accept a split pin, tighten the nut to the specified torque, where applicable, and then tighten further to the next split pin hole. Never slacken the nut to align the split pin hole, unless stated in the repair procedure.

When checking or retightening a nut or bolt to a specified torque setting, slacken the nut or bolt by a quarter of a turn, and then retighten to the specified setting. However, this should not be attempted where angular tightening has been used.

For some screw fastenings, notably cylinder head bolts or nuts, torque wrench settings are no longer specified for the latter stages of tightening, "angle-tightening" being called up instead. Typically, a fairly low torque wrench setting will be applied to the bolts/nuts in the correct sequence, followed by one or more stages of tightening through specified angles.

## Locknuts, locktabs and washers

Any fastening which will rotate against a component or housing during tightening should always have a washer between it and the relevant component or housing.

Spring or split washers should always be renewed when they are used to lock a critical component such as a big-end bearing retaining bolt or nut. Locktabs which are folded over to retain a nut or bolt should always be renewed.

Self-locking nuts can be re-used in non-critical areas, providing resistance can be felt when the locking portion passes over the bolt or stud thread. However, it should be noted that self-locking stiffnuts tend to lose their effectiveness after long periods of use, and should then be renewed as a matter of course.

Split pins must always be replaced with new ones of the correct size for the hole.

When thread-locking compound is found on the threads of a fastener which is to be re-used, it should be cleaned off with a wire brush and solvent, and fresh compound applied on reassembly.

## Special tools

Some repair procedures in this manual entail the use of special tools such as a press, two or three-legged pullers, spring compressors, etc. Wherever possible, suitable readily-available alternatives to the manufacturer's special tools are described, and are shown in use. In some instances, where no alternative is possible, it has been necessary to resort to the use of a manufacturer's tool, and this has been done for reasons of safety as well as the efficient completion of the repair operation. Unless you are highly-skilled and have a thorough understanding of the procedures described, never attempt to bypass the use of any special tool when the procedure described specifies its use. Not only is there a very great risk of personal injury, but expensive damage could be caused to the components involved.

## Environmental considerations

When disposing of used engine oil, brake fluid, antifreeze, etc, give due consideration to any detrimental environmental effects. Do not, for instance, pour any of the above liquids down drains into the general sewage system, or onto the ground to soak away. Many local council refuse tips provide a facility for waste oil disposal, as do some garages. If none of these facilities are available, consult your local Environmental Health Department, or the National Rivers Authority, for further advice.

With the universal tightening-up of legislation regarding the emission of environmentally-harmful substances from motor vehicles, most vehicles have tamperproof devices fitted to the main adjustment points of the fuel system. These devices are primarily designed to prevent unqualified persons from adjusting the fuel/air mixture, with the chance of a consequent increase in toxic emissions. If such devices are found during servicing or overhaul, they should, wherever possible, be renewed or refitted in accordance with the manufacturer's requirements or current legislation.

**OIL CARE** · FOLLOW THE CODE

OIL BANK LINE
**0800 66 33 66**
www.oilbankline.org.uk

*Note: It is antisocial and illegal to dump oil down the drain. To find the location of your local oil recycling bank, call this number free.*

# Jacking and vehicle support

The jack supplied with the vehicle tool kit should only be used for changing the roadwheels – see *Wheel changing* at the front of this book. When carrying out any other kind of work, raise the car using a hydraulic (or 'trolley') jack, and always supplement the jack with axle stands positioned under the jacking points. If the roadwheels do not have to be removed, consider using wheel ramps – if wished, these can be placed under the wheels once the car has been raised using a hydraulic jack, and the car lowered onto the ramps so that it is effectively resting on its wheels, on the ramps.

When jacking up the car to carry out repair or maintenance tasks, bear in mind the following points:

**Do not** jack up the car on anything other than firm, level ground. If the area to be used has even a slight slope, take this into account, and be sure to chock the wheels remaining on the ground. Jacking up the car on a soft surface is not advisable, as the car may sink while being worked on. Jacking up on a gravel surface is particularly dangerous, as the jack or axle stands can tilt sufficiently to slip off the jacking point.

**Always** apply the handbrake, and use wheel chocks on the wheels remaining on the ground. If the handbrake must be released for the work being carried out, engage a gear, and ensure that the wheel chocks are in place before releasing the brake.

**Do not** jack the car under any other part of the sill, sump, floor pan, or any of the steering or suspension components. With the car raised, an axle stand should be positioned beneath the jack location point on the sill.

**Never** work under, around or near a raised vehicle unless it is adequately supported in at least two places with axle stands. Remember – a hydraulic (trolley) jack may 'creep' down in use, and may even lose all hydraulic pressure without warning.

**Do not** run the engine while the car is raised. If this cannot be avoided, make sure the transmission is not in gear.

If the front of the car is to be raised, first apply the handbrake, and/or place chocks behind the rear wheels. Either place the jack head under the front jacking points on the door sill, with a block of wood to prevent damage, or use the two front support points shown in the accompanying illustration, and lift the car evenly **(see illustrations)**.

To raise the rear of the car, chock the front wheels and engage a gear. Use the jacking point at the rear of each door sill, with a block of wood to prevent damage **(see illustration)**.

To raise the side of the car, prepare the car as described for front AND rear lifting. Place the jack head under the appropriate point indicated in the accompanying illustration. If a trolley jack or similar is used on the sill jacking points, make up a wooden spacer with a groove cut in it to accept the underbody flange, so that there is no risk of the jack slipping or buckling the flange.

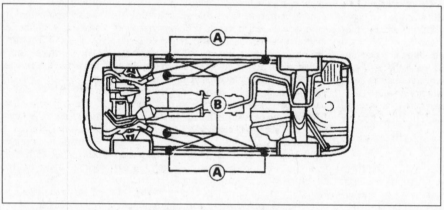

**Jacking and supporting points**

A  *Jacking points for vehicle jack in roadside use. May also be used as support points with axle stands*

B  *Jacking points for trolley jack. May be used as additional support points with axle stands*

**Using the front jacking point and support point (with wooden blocks) to raise the front of the car**

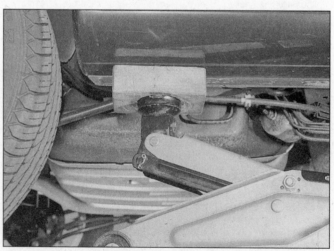

**Using the rear jacking point to raise the rear of the car**

Several systems fitted to the car require battery power to be available at all times, either to ensure their continued operation (such as the clock), or to maintain electronic memory settings which would otherwise be erased. Whenever the battery is to be disconnected, first note the following points, to ensure there are no unforeseen consequences:

a) First, on any car with central door locking, it is a wise precaution to remove the key from the ignition, and to keep it with you, so that it does not get locked in if the central locking engages when the battery is reconnected.

b) During normal operation, the car's engine management ECU learns and stores idling and other engine operating values in its memory. Whenever the battery is disconnected, this information is lost, and has to be re-learned. The ECU does this by itself, but until then, there may be surging, hesitation, erratic idle and a generally inferior level of performance. To allow the ECU to re-learn these values, start the engine and let it run as close to idle speed as possible until it reaches its normal operating temperature, then run it for approximately two minutes at 1200 rpm. Next, drive the car as far as necessary – approximately 5 miles of varied driving conditions is usually sufficient – to complete the re-learning process.

c) If the battery is disconnected while the alarm system is armed or activated, the alarm will remain in the same state when the battery is reconnected. The same applies to the engine immobiliser system. In some cases, the alarm may sound on reconnecting the battery – have the remote control ready to disarm the system.

d) If work is being carried out on the car's airbag or seat belt tensioner systems, the battery should be reconnected last – ie, **after** all the airbag and belt tensioner wiring has been reconnected.

e) Where electric windows with 'one-touch' operation are fitted, this function may not work correctly until each window has been reset. This is done by fully opening the window, keeping the button pressed for a few seconds after opening so the system can 'learn' the fully-open position. Close the window, again keeping the button pressed for a second or two.

f) If a Ford 'Keycode' audio unit is fitted, and the unit and/or the battery is disconnected, the unit will not function again on reconnection until the correct security code is entered. Details of this procedure, which varies according to the unit and model year, are given in the 'Ford Audio Systems Operating Guide' supplied with the car when new, with the code itself being given in a 'Radio Passport' and/or a 'Keycode Label' at the same time. Ensure you have the correct code before you disconnect the battery. For obvious security reasons, the procedure is not given in this manual. If you do not have the code or details of the correct procedure, but can supply proof of ownership and a legitimate reason for wanting this information, the car's selling dealer may be able to help.

Devices known as 'memory-savers' or 'code-savers' can be used to avoid some of the above problems. Precise details of use vary according to the device used. Typically, it is plugged into the cigar lighter socket, and is connected by its own wiring to a spare battery; the car's battery is then disconnected from the electrical system, leaving the memory-saver to pass sufficient current to maintain audio unit security codes and other memory values, and also to run permanently-live circuits such as the clock.

⚠️ **Warning: Some of these devices allow a considerable amount of current to pass, which can mean that many of the car's systems are still operational when the main battery is disconnected. If a 'memory-saver' is used, ensure that the circuit concerned is actually 'dead' before carrying out any work on it.**

## Introduction

A selection of good tools is a fundamental requirement for anyone contemplating the maintenance and repair of a motor vehicle. For the owner who does not possess any, their purchase will prove a considerable expense, offsetting some of the savings made by doing-it-yourself. However, provided that the tools purchased meet the relevant national safety standards and are of good quality, they will last for many years and prove an extremely worthwhile investment.

To help the average owner to decide which tools are needed to carry out the various tasks detailed in this manual, we have compiled three lists of tools under the following headings: *Maintenance and minor repair, Repair and overhaul*, and *Special*. Newcomers to practical mechanics should start off with the *Maintenance and minor repair* tool kit, and confine themselves to the simpler jobs around the vehicle. Then, as confidence and experience grow, more difficult tasks can be undertaken, with extra tools being purchased as, and when, they are needed. In this way, a *Maintenance and minor repair* tool kit can be built up into a *Repair and overhaul* tool kit over a considerable period of time, without any major cash outlays. The experienced do-it-yourselfer will have a tool kit good enough for most repair and overhaul procedures, and will add tools from the *Special* category when it is felt that the expense is justified by the amount of use to which these tools will be put.

## Maintenance and minor repair tool kit

The tools given in this list should be considered as a minimum requirement if routine maintenance, servicing and minor repair operations are to be undertaken. We recommend the purchase of combination spanners (ring one end, open-ended the other); although more expensive than open-ended ones, they do give the advantages of both types of spanner.

☐ *Combination spanners:*
  *Metric - 8 to 19 mm inclusive*
☐ *Adjustable spanner - 35 mm jaw (approx.)*
☐ *Spark plug spanner (with rubber insert) - petrol models*
☐ *Spark plug gap adjustment tool - petrol models*
☐ *Set of feeler gauges*
☐ *Brake bleed nipple spanner*
☐ *Screwdrivers:*
  *Flat blade - 100 mm long x 6 mm dia*
  *Cross blade - 100 mm long x 6 mm dia*
  *Torx - various sizes (not all vehicles)*
☐ *Combination pliers*
☐ *Hacksaw (junior)*
☐ *Tyre pump*
☐ *Tyre pressure gauge*
☐ *Oil can*
☐ *Oil filter removal tool*
☐ *Fine emery cloth*
☐ *Wire brush (small)*
☐ *Funnel (medium size)*
☐ *Sump drain plug key (not all vehicles)*

## Repair and overhaul tool kit

These tools are virtually essential for anyone undertaking any major repairs to a motor vehicle, and are additional to those given in the *Maintenance and minor repair* list. Included in this list is a comprehensive set of sockets. Although these are expensive, they will be found invaluable as they are so versatile - particularly if various drives are included in the set. We recommend the half-inch square-drive type, as this can be used with most proprietary torque wrenches.

The tools in this list will sometimes need to be supplemented by tools from the *Special* list:

☐ *Sockets (or box spanners) to cover range in previous list (including Torx sockets)*
☐ *Reversible ratchet drive (for use with sockets)*
☐ *Extension piece, 250 mm (for use with sockets)*
☐ *Universal joint (for use with sockets)*
☐ *Flexible handle or sliding T "breaker bar" (for use with sockets)*
☐ *Torque wrench (for use with sockets)*
☐ *Self-locking grips*
☐ *Ball pein hammer*
☐ *Soft-faced mallet (plastic or rubber)*
☐ *Screwdrivers:*
  *Flat blade - long & sturdy, short (chubby), and narrow (electrician's) types*
  *Cross blade - long & sturdy, and short (chubby) types*
☐ *Pliers:*
  *Long-nosed*
  *Side cutters (electrician's)*
  *Circlip (internal and external)*
☐ *Cold chisel - 25 mm*
☐ *Scriber*
☐ *Scraper*
☐ *Centre-punch*
☐ *Pin punch*
☐ *Hacksaw*
☐ *Brake hose clamp*
☐ *Brake/clutch bleeding kit*
☐ *Selection of twist drills*
☐ *Steel rule/straight-edge*
☐ *Allen keys (inc. splined/Torx type)*
☐ *Selection of files*
☐ *Wire brush*
☐ *Axle stands*
☐ *Jack (strong trolley or hydraulic type)*
☐ *Light with extension lead*
☐ *Universal electrical multi-meter*

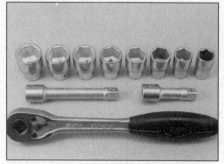
Sockets and reversible ratchet drive

Brake bleeding kit

Torx key, socket and bit

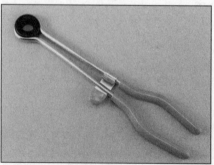
Hose clamp

Angular-tightening gauge

## Special tools

The tools in this list are those which are not used regularly, are expensive to buy, or which need to be used in accordance with their manufacturers' instructions. Unless relatively difficult mechanical jobs are undertaken frequently, it will not be economic to buy many of these tools. Where this is the case, you could consider clubbing together with friends (or joining a motorists' club) to make a joint purchase, or borrowing the tools against a deposit from a local garage or tool hire specialist. It is worth noting that many of the larger DIY superstores now carry a large range of special tools for hire at modest rates.

The following list contains only those tools and instruments freely available to the public, and not those special tools produced by the vehicle manufacturer specifically for its dealer network. You will find occasional references to these manufacturers' special tools in the text of this manual. Generally, an alternative method of doing the job without the vehicle manufacturers' special tool is given. However, sometimes there is no alternative to using them. Where this is the case and the relevant tool cannot be bought or borrowed, you will have to entrust the work to a dealer.

- [ ] Angular-tightening gauge
- [ ] Valve spring compressor
- [ ] Valve grinding tool
- [ ] Piston ring compressor
- [ ] Piston ring removal/installation tool
- [ ] Cylinder bore hone
- [ ] Balljoint separator
- [ ] Coil spring compressors (where applicable)
- [ ] Two/three-legged hub and bearing puller
- [ ] Impact screwdriver
- [ ] Micrometer and/or vernier calipers
- [ ] Dial gauge
- [ ] Stroboscopic timing light
- [ ] Dwell angle meter/tachometer
- [ ] Fault code reader
- [ ] Cylinder compression gauge
- [ ] Hand-operated vacuum pump and gauge
- [ ] Clutch plate alignment set
- [ ] Brake shoe steady spring cup removal tool
- [ ] Bush and bearing removal/installation set
- [ ] Stud extractors
- [ ] Tap and die set
- [ ] Lifting tackle
- [ ] Trolley jack

## Buying tools

Reputable motor accessory shops and superstores often offer excellent quality tools at discount prices, so it pays to shop around.

Remember, you don't have to buy the most expensive items on the shelf, but it is always advisable to steer clear of the very cheap tools. Beware of 'bargains' offered on market stalls or at car boot sales. There are plenty of good tools around at reasonable prices, but always aim to purchase items which meet the relevant national safety standards. If in doubt, ask the proprietor or manager of the shop for advice before making a purchase.

## Care and maintenance of tools

Having purchased a reasonable tool kit, it is necessary to keep the tools in a clean and serviceable condition. After use, always wipe off any dirt, grease and metal particles using a clean, dry cloth, before putting the tools away. Never leave them lying around after they have been used. A simple tool rack on the garage or workshop wall for items such as screwdrivers and pliers is a good idea. Store all normal spanners and sockets in a metal box. Any measuring instruments, gauges, meters, etc, must be carefully stored where they cannot be damaged or become rusty.

Take a little care when tools are used. Hammer heads inevitably become marked, and screwdrivers lose the keen edge on their blades from time to time. A little timely attention with emery cloth or a file will soon restore items like this to a good finish.

## Working facilities

Not to be forgotten when discussing tools is the workshop itself. If anything more than routine maintenance is to be carried out, a suitable working area becomes essential.

It is appreciated that many an owner-mechanic is forced by circumstances to remove an engine or similar item without the benefit of a garage or workshop. Having done this, any repairs should always be done under the cover of a roof.

Wherever possible, any dismantling should be done on a clean, flat workbench or table at a suitable working height.

Any workbench needs a vice; one with a jaw opening of 100 mm is suitable for most jobs. As mentioned previously, some clean dry storage space is also required for tools, as well as for any lubricants, cleaning fluids, touch-up paints etc, which become necessary.

Another item which may be required, and which has a much more general usage, is an electric drill with a chuck capacity of at least 8 mm. This, together with a good range of twist drills, is virtually essential for fitting accessories.

Last, but not least, always keep a supply of old newspapers and clean, lint-free rags available, and try to keep any working area as clean as possible.

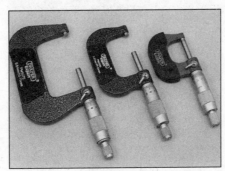

**Micrometers**

**Dial test indicator ("dial gauge")**

**Strap wrench**

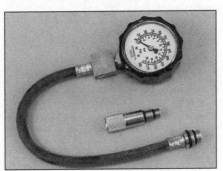

**Compression tester**

**Fault code reader**

This is a guide to getting your vehicle through the MOT test. Obviously it will not be possible to examine the vehicle to the same standard as the professional MOT tester. However, working through the following checks will enable you to identify any problem areas before submitting the vehicle for the test.

It has only been possible to summarise the test requirements here, based on the regulations in force at the time of printing. Test standards are becoming increasingly stringent, although there are some exemptions for older vehicles.

An assistant will be needed to help carry out some of these checks.

*The checks have been sub-divided into four categories, as follows:*

**1** Checks carried out **FROM THE DRIVER'S SEAT**

**2** Checks carried out **WITH THE VEHICLE ON THE GROUND**

**3** Checks carried out **WITH THE VEHICLE RAISED AND THE WHEELS FREE TO TURN**

**4** Checks carried out on **YOUR VEHICLE'S EXHAUST EMISSION SYSTEM**

---

**1** Checks carried out **FROM THE DRIVER'S SEAT**

### Handbrake

☐ Test the operation of the handbrake. Excessive travel (too many clicks) indicates incorrect brake or cable adjustment.
☐ Check that the handbrake cannot be released by tapping the lever sideways. Check the security of the lever mountings.

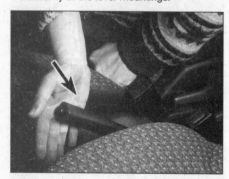

☐ Check that the brake pedal is secure and in good condition. Check also for signs of fluid leaks on the pedal, floor or carpets, which would indicate failed seals in the brake master cylinder.
☐ Check the servo unit (when applicable) by operating the brake pedal several times, then keeping the pedal depressed and starting the engine. As the engine starts, the pedal will move down slightly. If not, the vacuum hose or the servo itself may be faulty.

### Steering wheel and column

☐ Examine the steering wheel for fractures or looseness of the hub, spokes or rim.
☐ Move the steering wheel from side to side and then up and down. Check that the steering wheel is not loose on the column, indicating wear or a loose retaining nut. Continue moving the steering wheel as before, but also turn it slightly from left to right.
☐ Check that the steering wheel is not loose on the column, and that there is no abnormal

### Footbrake

☐ Depress the brake pedal and check that it does not creep down to the floor, indicating a master cylinder fault. Release the pedal, wait a few seconds, then depress it again. If the pedal travels nearly to the floor before firm resistance is felt, brake adjustment or repair is necessary. If the pedal feels spongy, there is air in the hydraulic system which must be removed by bleeding.

movement of the steering wheel, indicating wear in the column support bearings or couplings.

### Windscreen, mirrors and sunvisor

☐ The windscreen must be free of cracks or other significant damage within the driver's field of view. (Small stone chips are acceptable.) Rear view mirrors must be secure, intact, and capable of being adjusted.

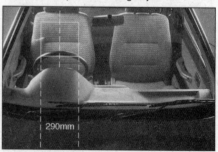

290mm

☐ The driver's sunvisor must be capable of being stored in the "up" position.

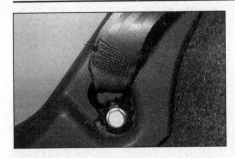

## Seat belts and seats

**Note:** *The following checks are applicable to all seat belts, front and rear.*

☐ Examine the webbing of all the belts (including rear belts if fitted) for cuts, serious fraying or deterioration. Fasten and unfasten each belt to check the buckles. If applicable, check the retracting mechanism. Check the security of all seat belt mountings accessible from inside the vehicle.

☐ Seat belts with pre-tensioners, once activated, have a "flag" or similar showing on the seat belt stalk. This, in itself, is not a reason for test failure.

☐ The front seats themselves must be securely attached and the backrests must lock in the upright position.

## Doors

☐ Both front doors must be able to be opened and closed from outside and inside, and must latch securely when closed.

## 2 Checks carried out WITH THE VEHICLE ON THE GROUND

## Vehicle identification

☐ Number plates must be in good condition, secure and legible, with letters and numbers correctly spaced – spacing at (A) should be at least twice that at (B).

☐ The VIN plate and/or homologation plate must be legible.

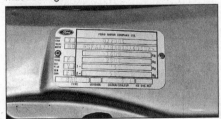

## Electrical equipment

☐ Switch on the ignition and check the operation of the horn.

☐ Check the windscreen washers and wipers, examining the wiper blades; renew damaged or perished blades. Also check the operation of the stop-lights.

☐ Check the operation of the sidelights and number plate lights. The lenses and reflectors must be secure, clean and undamaged.

☐ Check the operation and alignment of the headlights. The headlight reflectors must not be tarnished and the lenses must be undamaged.

☐ Switch on the ignition and check the operation of the direction indicators (including the instrument panel tell-tale) and the hazard warning lights. Operation of the sidelights and stop-lights must not affect the indicators - if it does, the cause is usually a bad earth at the rear light cluster.

☐ Check the operation of the rear foglight(s), including the warning light on the instrument panel or in the switch.

☐ The ABS warning light must illuminate in accordance with the manufacturers' design. For most vehicles, the ABS warning light should illuminate when the ignition is switched on, and (if the system is operating properly) extinguish after a few seconds. Refer to the owner's handbook.

## Footbrake

☐ Examine the master cylinder, brake pipes and servo unit for leaks, loose mountings, corrosion or other damage.

☐ The fluid reservoir must be secure and the fluid level must be between the upper (A) and lower (B) markings.

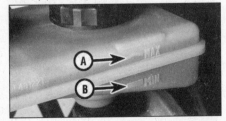

☐ Inspect both front brake flexible hoses for cracks or deterioration of the rubber. Turn the steering from lock to lock, and ensure that the hoses do not contact the wheel, tyre, or any part of the steering or suspension mechanism. With the brake pedal firmly depressed, check the hoses for bulges or leaks under pressure.

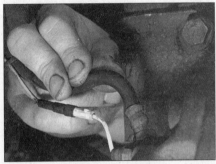

## Steering and suspension

☐ Have your assistant turn the steering wheel from side to side slightly, up to the point where the steering gear just begins to transmit this movement to the roadwheels. Check for excessive free play between the steering wheel and the steering gear, indicating wear or insecurity of the steering column joints, the column-to-steering gear coupling, or the steering gear itself.

☐ Have your assistant turn the steering wheel more vigorously in each direction, so that the roadwheels just begin to turn. As this is done, examine all the steering joints, linkages, fittings and attachments. Renew any component that shows signs of wear or damage. On vehicles with power steering, check the security and condition of the steering pump, drivebelt and hoses.

☐ Check that the vehicle is standing level, and at approximately the correct ride height.

## Shock absorbers

☐ Depress each corner of the vehicle in turn, then release it. The vehicle should rise and then settle in its normal position. If the vehicle continues to rise and fall, the shock absorber is defective. A shock absorber which has seized will also cause the vehicle to fail.

## Exhaust system

☐ Start the engine. With your assistant holding a rag over the tailpipe, check the entire system for leaks. Repair or renew leaking sections.

**3** Checks carried out **WITH THE VEHICLE RAISED AND THE WHEELS FREE TO TURN**

*Jack up the front and rear of the vehicle, and securely support it on axle stands. Position the stands clear of the suspension assemblies. Ensure that the wheels are clear of the ground and that the steering can be turned from lock to lock.*

## Steering mechanism

☐ Have your assistant turn the steering from lock to lock. Check that the steering turns smoothly, and that no part of the steering mechanism, including a wheel or tyre, fouls any brake hose or pipe or any part of the body structure.
☐ Examine the steering rack rubber gaiters for damage or insecurity of the retaining clips. If power steering is fitted, check for signs of damage or leakage of the fluid hoses, pipes or connections. Also check for excessive stiffness or binding of the steering, a missing split pin or locking device, or severe corrosion of the body structure within 30 cm of any steering component attachment point.

## Front and rear suspension and wheel bearings

☐ Starting at the front right-hand side, grasp the roadwheel at the 3 o'clock and 9 o'clock positions and rock gently but firmly. Check for free play or insecurity at the wheel bearings, suspension balljoints, or suspension mountings, pivots and attachments.
☐ Now grasp the wheel at the 12 o'clock and 6 o'clock positions and repeat the previous inspection. Spin the wheel, and check for roughness or tightness of the front wheel bearing.

☐ If excess free play is suspected at a component pivot point, this can be confirmed by using a large screwdriver or similar tool and levering between the mounting and the component attachment. This will confirm whether the wear is in the pivot bush, its retaining bolt, or in the mounting itself (the bolt holes can often become elongated).

☐ Carry out all the above checks at the other front wheel, and then at both rear wheels.

## Springs and shock absorbers

☐ Examine the suspension struts (when applicable) for serious fluid leakage, corrosion, or damage to the casing. Also check the security of the mounting points.
☐ If coil springs are fitted, check that the spring ends locate in their seats, and that the spring is not corroded, cracked or broken.
☐ If leaf springs are fitted, check that all leaves are intact, that the axle is securely attached to each spring, and that there is no deterioration of the spring eye mountings, bushes, and shackles.

☐ The same general checks apply to vehicles fitted with other suspension types, such as torsion bars, hydraulic displacer units, etc. Ensure that all mountings and attachments are secure, that there are no signs of excessive wear, corrosion or damage, and (on hydraulic types) that there are no fluid leaks or damaged pipes.
☐ Inspect the shock absorbers for signs of serious fluid leakage. Check for wear of the mounting bushes or attachments, or damage to the body of the unit.

## Driveshafts (fwd vehicles only)

☐ Rotate each front wheel in turn and inspect the constant velocity joint gaiters for splits or damage. Also check that each driveshaft is straight and undamaged.

## Braking system

☐ If possible without dismantling, check brake pad wear and disc condition. Ensure that the friction lining material has not worn excessively, (A) and that the discs are not fractured, pitted, scored or badly worn (B).

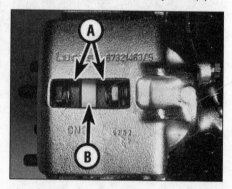

☐ Examine all the rigid brake pipes underneath the vehicle, and the flexible hose(s) at the rear. Look for corrosion, chafing or insecurity of the pipes, and for signs of bulging under pressure, chafing, splits or deterioration of the flexible hoses.
☐ Look for signs of fluid leaks at the brake calipers or on the brake backplates. Repair or renew leaking components.
☐ Slowly spin each wheel, while your assistant depresses and releases the footbrake. Ensure that each brake is operating and does not bind when the pedal is released.

☐ Examine the handbrake mechanism, checking for frayed or broken cables, excessive corrosion, or wear or insecurity of the linkage. Check that the mechanism works on each relevant wheel, and releases fully, without binding.

☐ It is not possible to test brake efficiency without special equipment, but a road test can be carried out later to check that the vehicle pulls up in a straight line.

## Fuel and exhaust systems

☐ Inspect the fuel tank (including the filler cap), fuel pipes, hoses and unions. All components must be secure and free from leaks.

☐ Examine the exhaust system over its entire length, checking for any damaged, broken or missing mountings, security of the retaining clamps and rust or corrosion.

## Wheels and tyres

☐ Examine the sidewalls and tread area of each tyre in turn. Check for cuts, tears, lumps, bulges, separation of the tread, and exposure of the ply or cord due to wear or damage. Check that the tyre bead is correctly seated on the wheel rim, that the valve is sound and properly seated, and that the wheel is not distorted or damaged.

☐ Check that the tyres are of the correct size for the vehicle, that they are of the same size

and type on each axle, and that the pressures are correct.

☐ Check the tyre tread depth. The legal minimum at the time of writing is 1.6 mm over at least three-quarters of the tread width. Abnormal tread wear may indicate incorrect front wheel alignment.

## Body corrosion

☐ Check the condition of the entire vehicle structure for signs of corrosion in load-bearing areas. (These include chassis box sections, side sills, cross-members, pillars, and all suspension, steering, braking system and seat belt mountings and anchorages.) Any corrosion which has seriously reduced the thickness of a load-bearing area is likely to cause the vehicle to fail. In this case professional repairs are likely to be needed.

☐ Damage or corrosion which causes sharp or otherwise dangerous edges to be exposed will also cause the vehicle to fail.

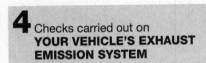

**4** Checks carried out on **YOUR VEHICLE'S EXHAUST EMISSION SYSTEM**

## Petrol models

☐ The engine should be warmed up, and running well (ignition system in good order, air filter element clean, etc).

☐ Before testing, run the engine at around 2500 rpm for 20 seconds. Let the engine drop to idle, and watch for smoke from the exhaust. If the idle speed is too high, or if dense blue or black smoke emerges for more than 5 seconds, the vehicle will fail. Typically, blue smoke signifies oil burning (engine wear); black smoke means unburnt fuel (dirty air cleaner element, or other fuel system fault).

☐ An exhaust gas analyser for measuring carbon monoxide (CO) and hydrocarbons (HC) is now needed. If one cannot be hired or borrowed, have a local garage perform the check.

## CO emissions (mixture)

☐ The MOT tester has access to the CO limits for all vehicles. The CO level is measured at idle speed, and at 'fast idle' (2500 to 3000 rpm). The following limits are given as a general guide:

*At idle speed* – Less than 0.5% CO
*At 'fast idle'* – Less than 0.3% CO
*Lambda reading* – 0.97 to 1.03

☐ If the CO level is too high, this may point to poor maintenance, a fuel injection system problem, faulty lambda (oxygen) sensor or catalytic converter. Try an injector cleaning treatment, and check the vehicle's ECU for fault codes.

## HC emissions

☐ The MOT tester has access to HC limits for all vehicles. The HC level is measured at 'fast idle' (2500 to 3000 rpm). The following limits are given as a general guide:

*At 'fast idle'* – Less then 200 ppm

☐ Excessive HC emissions are typically caused by oil being burnt (worn engine), or by a blocked crankcase ventilation system ('breather'). If the engine oil is old and thin, an oil change may help. If the engine is running badly, check the vehicle's ECU for fault codes.

## Diesel models

☐ The only emission test for diesel engines is measuring exhaust smoke density, using a calibrated smoke meter. The test involves accelerating the engine at least 3 times to its maximum unloaded speed.

**Note:** *On engines with a timing belt, it is VITAL that the belt is in good condition before the test is carried out.*

☐ With the engine warmed up, it is first purged by running at around 2500 rpm for 20 seconds. A governor check is then carried out, by slowly accelerating the engine to its maximum speed. After this, the smoke meter is connected, and the engine is accelerated quickly to maximum speed three times. If the smoke density is less than the limits given below, the vehicle will pass:

*Non-turbo vehicles*: 2.5m-1
*Turbocharged vehicles*: 3.0m-1

☐ If excess smoke is produced, try fitting a new air cleaner element, or using an injector cleaning treatment. If the engine is running badly, where applicable, check the vehicle's ECU for fault codes. Also check the vehicle's EGR system, where applicable. At high mileages, the injectors may require professional attention.

## Engine

- [ ] Engine fails to rotate when attempting to start
- [ ] Engine rotates, but will not start
- [ ] Engine difficult to start when cold
- [ ] Engine difficult to start when hot
- [ ] Starter motor noisy or excessively-rough in engagement
- [ ] Engine starts, but stops immediately
- [ ] Engine idles erratically
- [ ] Engine misfires at idle speed
- [ ] Engine misfires throughout the driving speed range
- [ ] Engine hesitates on acceleration
- [ ] Engine stalls
- [ ] Engine lacks power
- [ ] Engine backfires
- [ ] Oil pressure warning light illuminated with engine running
- [ ] Engine runs-on after switching off
- [ ] Engine noises

## Cooling system

- [ ] Overheating
- [ ] Overcooling
- [ ] External coolant leakage
- [ ] Internal coolant leakage
- [ ] Corrosion

## Fuel and exhaust systems

- [ ] Excessive fuel consumption
- [ ] Fuel leakage and/or fuel odour
- [ ] Excessive noise from exhaust system
- [ ] Excessive smoke

## Clutch

- [ ] Pedal travels to floor – no pressure or very little resistance
- [ ] Clutch fails to disengage (unable to select gears)
- [ ] Clutch slips (engine speed increases, with no increase in vehicle speed)
- [ ] Judder as clutch is engaged
- [ ] Noise when depressing or releasing clutch pedal

## Manual transmission

- [ ] Noisy in neutral with engine running
- [ ] Noisy in one particular gear
- [ ] Difficulty engaging gears
- [ ] Jumps out of gear
- [ ] Vibration
- [ ] Lubricant leaks

## Driveshafts

- [ ] Clicking or knocking noise on turns (at slow speed on full-lock)
- [ ] Vibration when accelerating or decelerating

## Braking system

- [ ] Car pulls to one side under braking
- [ ] Noise (grinding or high-pitched squeal) when brakes applied
- [ ] Excessive brake pedal travel
- [ ] Brake pedal feels spongy when pressed
- [ ] Brake pedal feels hard when pressed
- [ ] Excessive brake pedal effort required to stop car
- [ ] Judder felt through brake pedal or steering wheel when braking
- [ ] Brakes binding
- [ ] Rear wheels locking under normal braking

## Suspension and steering systems

- [ ] Car pulls to one side
- [ ] Wheel wobble and vibration
- [ ] Excessive pitching and/or rolling around corners, or during braking
- [ ] Wandering or general instability
- [ ] Excessively-stiff steering
- [ ] Excessive play in steering
- [ ] Lack of power assistance
- [ ] Noises from power steering system
- [ ] Tyre wear excessive

## Electrical system

- [ ] Battery will not hold a charge for more than a few days
- [ ] Ignition/no-charge warning light remains illuminated with engine running
- [ ] Ignition/no-charge warning light fails to come on
- [ ] Lights inoperative
- [ ] Instrument readings inaccurate or erratic
- [ ] Horn inoperative, or unsatisfactory in operation
- [ ] Windscreen/tailgate wipers inoperative, or unsatisfactory in operation
- [ ] Windscreen/tailgate washers inoperative, or unsatisfactory in operation
- [ ] Electric windows inoperative, or unsatisfactory in operation
- [ ] Central locking system inoperative, or unsatisfactory in operation

# Introduction

The car owner who does his or her own maintenance according to the recommended service schedules should not have to use this section of the manual very often. Modern component reliability is such that, provided those items subject to wear or deterioration are inspected or renewed at the specified intervals, sudden failure is comparatively rare. Faults do not usually just happen as a result of sudden failure, but develop over a period of time. Major mechanical failures in particular are usually preceded by characteristic symptoms over hundreds or even thousands of miles. Those components which do occasionally fail without warning are often small and easily carried in the car.

With any fault-finding, the first step is to decide where to begin investigations. Sometimes this is obvious, but on other occasions, a little detective work will be necessary. The owner who makes half a dozen haphazard adjustments or replacements may be successful in curing a fault (or its symptoms), but will be none the wiser if the fault recurs, and ultimately may have spent more time and money than was necessary. A calm and logical approach will be found to be more satisfactory in the long run. Always take into account any warning signs or abnormalities that may have been noticed in the period preceding the fault – power loss, high or low gauge readings, unusual smells, etc – and remember that failure of components such as fuses or glow plugs may only be pointers to some underlying fault.

The pages which follow provide an easy-reference guide to the more common problems which may occur during the operation of the vehicle. These problems and their possible causes are grouped under headings denoting various components or systems, such as Engine, Cooling system, etc. The general Chapter which deals with the problem is also shown in brackets; refer to the relevant part of that Chapter for system-specific information. Whatever the fault, certain basic principles apply. These are as follows:

*Verify the fault.* This is simply a matter of being sure you know exactly what the symptoms are before starting work. This is particularly important if you are investigating a fault for someone else, who may not have described it very accurately.

*Don't overlook the obvious.* For example, if it won't start, is there fuel in the tank? (Don't take anyone else's word on this particular point, and don't trust the fuel gauge either!) If an electrical fault is indicated, look for loose or broken wires before digging out the test gear.

*Cure the disease, not the symptom.* Substituting a flat battery with a fully-charged one will get you off the hard shoulder, but if the underlying cause is not attended to, the new battery will go the same way. Similarly, cranking the engine for ages to bleed out air may get the car going, but the reason for the air in the fuel system will have to be established and corrected.

*Don't take anything for granted.* Particularly, don't forget that a 'new' component may itself be defective (especially if it's been rattling around in the boot for months), and don't leave components out of a fault diagnosis sequence just because they are new or recently-fitted. When you do finally diagnose a difficult fault, you'll probably realise that all the evidence was there from the start.

*Consider what work, if any, has recently been carried out.* Many faults arise through careless or hurried work. For instance, if any work has been performed under the bonnet, could some of the wiring have been dislodged or incorrectly routed, or a hose trapped? Have all the fasteners been properly tightened? Were new, genuine parts and new gaskets used? There is often a certain amount of detective work to be done in this case, as an apparently-unrelated task can have far-reaching consequences.

### Diesel fault diagnosis

The majority of starting problems on small diesel engines are electrical in origin. The mechanic who is familiar with petrol engines but less so with diesel may be inclined to view the diesel's injectors and pump in the same light as the spark plugs and distributor, but this is generally a mistake.

When investigating complaints of difficult starting for someone else, make sure that the correct starting procedure is understood and is being followed. Some drivers are unaware of the significance of the preheating warning light – many modern engines are sufficiently forgiving for this not to matter in mild weather, but with the onset of winter, problems begin.

As a rule of thumb, if the engine is difficult to start but runs well when it has finally got going, the problem is electrical (battery, starter motor or preheating system). If poor performance is combined with difficult starting, the problem is likely to be in the fuel system. The low-pressure (supply) side of the fuel system should be checked before suspecting the injectors and high-pressure pump. The most common fuel supply problem is air getting into the system, and any pipe from the fuel tank forwards must be scrutinised if air leakage is suspected. Normally the pump is the last item to suspect, since unless it has been tampered with, there is no reason for it to be at fault.

# Engine

### Engine fails to rotate when attempting to start

- ☐ Battery terminal connections loose or corroded (*Weekly checks*).
- ☐ Battery discharged or faulty (Chapter 5).
- ☐ Broken, loose or disconnected wiring in the starting circuit (Chapter 5).
- ☐ Defective starter solenoid or switch (Chapter 5).
- ☐ Defective starter motor (Chapter 5).
- ☐ Starter pinion or flywheel ring gear teeth loose or broken (Chapter 2A or 5).
- ☐ Engine earth strap broken or disconnected (Chapter 5).
- ☐ Engine full of water (after driving in flood conditions) – remove glow plugs and expel water (Chapter 5).

### Engine rotates, but will not start

- ☐ Fuel tank empty.
- ☐ Battery discharged (engine rotates slowly) (Chapter 5).
- ☐ Battery terminal connections loose or corroded (*Weekly checks*).
- ☐ Alarm or immobiliser fault (Chapter 12).
- ☐ Air in the fuel system – bleed, and check fuel lines for leaks (Chapter 4A).
- ☐ Injection pump stop solenoid faulty (Chapter 4A).
- ☐ Broken, loose or disconnected wiring in the engine management circuit (Chapter 4A).
- ☐ Fuel injection system fault (Chapter 4A).
- ☐ Major mechanical failure (eg camshaft drivebelt snapped) (Chapter 2A).

# Engine (continued)

## Engine difficult to start when cold

☐ Battery discharged (Chapter 5).
☐ Battery terminal connections loose or corroded (*Weekly checks*).
☐ Damaged or faulty glow plugs, or glow plug electrical supply fault (Chapter 5).
☐ Cold start valve/relay fault (Chapter 4A).
☐ Air in the fuel system – bleed, and check fuel lines for leaks (Chapter 4A).
☐ Fuel injection system fault (Chapter 4A).
☐ Low cylinder compressions (Chapter 2A).

## Engine difficult to start when hot

☐ Air filter element dirty or clogged (Chapter 1).
☐ Fuel injection system fault (Chapter 4A).
☐ Low cylinder compressions (Chapter 2A).
☐ Air in the fuel system – bleed, and check fuel lines for leaks (Chapter 4A).

## Starter motor noisy or excessively-rough in engagement

☐ Starter pinion or flywheel ring gear teeth loose or broken (Chapter 2 or 5).
☐ Starter motor mounting bolts loose or missing (Chapter 5).
☐ Starter motor internal components worn or damaged (Chapter 5).

## Engine starts, but stops immediately

☐ Blocked injector/fuel injection system fault (Chapter 4A or 4B).
☐ Injection pump stop solenoid faulty (Chapter 4A).
☐ Faulty EGR valve or associated pipework (Chapter 4B).

## Engine idles erratically

☐ Valve clearances incorrect (Chapter 2A).
☐ Air filter element clogged (Chapter 1).
☐ Air in the fuel system – bleed, and check fuel lines for leaks (Chapter 4A).
☐ Faulty EGR valve or associated pipework (Chapter 4B).
☐ Uneven or low cylinder compressions (Chapter 2A).
☐ Camshaft lobes worn (Chapter 2A).
☐ Timing belts incorrectly fitted (Chapter 2A).
☐ Blocked injector/fuel injection system fault (Chapter 4A).

## Engine misfires at idle speed

☐ Air in the fuel system – bleed, and check fuel lines for leaks (Chapter 4A).
☐ Blocked injector/fuel injection system fault (Chapter 4A).
☐ Uneven or low cylinder compressions (Chapter 2A).
☐ Disconnected, leaking, or perished crankcase ventilation hoses (Chapter 4B).

## Engine misfires throughout the driving speed range

☐ Fuel filter choked (Chapter 1).
☐ Fuel tank vent blocked, or fuel pipes restricted (Chapter 4A).
☐ Uneven or low cylinder compressions (Chapter 2A).
☐ Blocked injector/fuel injection system fault (Chapter 4A).

## Engine hesitates on acceleration

☐ Blocked injector/fuel injection system fault (Chapter 4A).

## Engine stalls

☐ Fuel filter choked (Chapter 1).
☐ Fuel tank vent blocked, or fuel pipes restricted (Chapter 4A).
☐ Blocked injector/fuel injection system fault (Chapter 4A).
☐ Injection pump badly adjusted, or anti-stall system fault (Chapter 4A).
☐ Faulty EGR valve or associated pipework (Chapter 4B).

## Engine lacks power

☐ Valve clearances incorrect (Chapter 2A).
☐ Timing belts incorrectly fitted or tensioned (Chapter 2A).
☐ Fuel filter choked (Chapter 1).
☐ Turbocharger wastegate vacuum pipe split (Chapter 4A).
☐ Uneven or low cylinder compressions (Chapter 2A or 2B).
☐ Blocked injector/fuel injection system fault (Chapter 4A).
☐ Brakes binding (Chapter 1 or 9).
☐ Clutch slipping (Chapter 6).

## Engine backfires

☐ Timing belts incorrectly fitted or tensioned (Chapter 2A).
☐ Blocked injector/fuel injection system fault (Chapter 4A).

## Oil pressure warning light illuminated with engine running

☐ Low oil level, or incorrect oil grade (*Weekly checks*).
☐ Worn engine bearings and/or oil pump (Chapter 2B).
☐ High engine operating temperature (Chapter 3).
☐ Oil pump pressure relief valve defective (Chapter 2A).
☐ Oil pump pick-up strainer clogged – remove sump and inspect (Chapter 2A).

## Engine runs-on after switching off

☐ Excessive carbon build-up in engine – overhaul required (Chapter 2B).
☐ High engine operating temperature (Chapter 3).
☐ Injection pump stop solenoid faulty (Chapter 4A).

## Engine noises

### Pre-ignition (pinking) or knocking during acceleration or under load

☐ Excessive carbon build-up in engine – overhaul required (Chapter 2B).
☐ Blocked injector/fuel injection system fault (Chapter 4A).

### Whistling or wheezing noises

☐ Leaking inlet manifold gasket (Chapter 4A).
☐ Leaking exhaust manifold gasket, pipe-to-manifold joint, or turbocharger/intercooler joints (Chapter 4A).
☐ Leaking vacuum hose (Chapter 4A or 9).
☐ Blowing cylinder head gasket (Chapter 2A).

### Tapping or rattling noises

☐ Valve clearances incorrect (Chapter 2A).
☐ Worn camshaft (Chapter 2A).
☐ Ancillary component fault (water pump, alternator, etc) (Chapter 3, 5, etc).

### Knocking or thumping noises

☐ Worn big-end bearings (regular heavy knocking, perhaps less under load) (Chapter 2B).
☐ Worn main bearings (rumbling and knocking, perhaps worsening under load) (Chapter 2B).
☐ Piston slap (most noticeable when cold) – engine worn (Chapter 2B).
☐ Ancillary component fault (water pump, alternator, etc) (Chapter 3, 5, etc).

# Cooling system

## Overheating

- ☐ Insufficient coolant in system (*Weekly checks*).
- ☐ Thermostat faulty (Chapter 3).
- ☐ Radiator core blocked, or grille restricted (Chapter 3).
- ☐ Radiator cooling fan or fan switch faulty (Chapter 3).
- ☐ Pressure cap faulty (Chapter 3).
- ☐ Inaccurate temperature gauge sender unit (Chapter 3).
- ☐ Airlock in cooling system (Chapter 1).

## Overcooling

- ☐ Thermostat faulty (Chapter 3).
- ☐ Inaccurate temperature gauge sender unit (Chapter 3).

## External coolant leakage

- ☐ Deteriorated or damaged hoses or hose clips (Chapter 1).
- ☐ Radiator core or heater matrix leaking (Chapter 3).
- ☐ Pressure cap faulty (Chapter 3).
- ☐ Water pump leaking (Chapter 3).
- ☐ Boiling due to overheating (Chapter 3).
- ☐ Cylinder block core plug leaking (Chapter 2B).

## Internal coolant leakage

- ☐ Leaking cylinder head gasket (Chapter 2A).
- ☐ Cracked cylinder head or cylinder bore (Chapter 2A or 2B).

## Corrosion

- ☐ Infrequent draining and flushing (Chapter 1).
- ☐ Incorrect coolant mixture or inappropriate coolant type (*Weekly checks*).

# Fuel and exhaust systems

## Excessive fuel consumption

- ☐ Air filter element dirty or clogged (Chapter 1).
- ☐ Injectors need recalibrating/servicing – after high mileage (Chapter 4A)
- ☐ Fuel injection pump fault (Chapter 4A).
- ☐ Tyres under-inflated (*Weekly checks*).
- ☐ Brakes binding (Chapter 1 or 9).

## Fuel leakage and/or fuel odour

- ☐ Damaged or corroded fuel tank, pipes or connections (Chapter 4A or 4B).

## Excessive noise from exhaust system

- ☐ Leaking exhaust system or manifold joints (Chapter 1 or 4A).
- ☐ Leaking, corroded or damaged silencers or pipe (Chapter 1 or 4A).
- ☐ Broken mountings causing body or suspension contact (Chapter 1 or 4A).

## Excessive smoke

- ☐ Injectors need recalibrating/servicing – after high mileage (Chapter 4A)
- ☐ Fuel injection pump fault (Chapter 4A).

# Clutch

## Pedal travels to floor – no pressure or very little resistance

- ☐ Broken clutch cable – cable-operated clutch (Chapter 6).
- ☐ Clutch out of adjustment (Chapter 6).
- ☐ Clutch master cylinder failure – hydraulic clutch (Chapter 6).
- ☐ Clutch fluid leak – hydraulic clutch (Chapter 6).
- ☐ Broken clutch release bearing or fork, as applicable (Chapter 6).
- ☐ Broken diaphragm spring in clutch pressure plate (Chapter 6).

## Clutch fails to disengage (unable to select gears)

- ☐ Clutch out of adjustment (Chapter 6).
- ☐ Air in clutch hydraulic system – bleeding required – hydraulic clutch (Chapter 6).
- ☐ Clutch master or slave cylinder fault – hydraulic clutch (Chapter 6).
- ☐ Clutch disc sticking on gearbox input shaft splines (Chapter 6).
- ☐ Clutch disc sticking to flywheel or pressure plate (Chapter 6).
- ☐ Faulty pressure plate assembly (Chapter 6).
- ☐ Clutch release mechanism worn or incorrectly assembled – cable-operated clutch (Chapter 6).

## Clutch slips (engine speed increases, with no increase in vehicle speed)

- ☐ Clutch out of adjustment (Chapter 6).
- ☐ Clutch disc linings excessively worn (Chapter 6).
- ☐ Clutch disc linings contaminated with oil or grease (Chapter 6).
- ☐ Faulty pressure plate or weak diaphragm spring (Chapter 6).

## Judder as clutch is engaged

- ☐ Clutch disc linings contaminated with oil or grease (Chapter 6).
- ☐ Clutch disc linings excessively worn (Chapter 6).
- ☐ Clutch cable sticking or frayed – cable-operated clutch (Chapter 6).
- ☐ Faulty or distorted pressure plate or diaphragm spring (Chapter 6).
- ☐ Worn or loose engine or gearbox mountings (Chapter 2A or 2B).
- ☐ Clutch disc hub or gearbox input shaft splines worn (Chapter 6).

## Noise when depressing or releasing clutch pedal

- ☐ Worn clutch release bearing (Chapter 6).
- ☐ Worn or dry clutch pedal bushes (Chapter 6).
- ☐ Clutch cable sticking or frayed – cable-operated clutch (Chapter 6).
- ☐ Clutch master cylinder fault – hydraulic clutch (Chapter 6).
- ☐ Faulty pressure plate assembly (Chapter 6).
- ☐ Pressure plate diaphragm spring broken (Chapter 6).
- ☐ Broken clutch disc cushioning springs (Chapter 6).

# Manual transmission

### Noisy in neutral with engine running

☐ Input shaft bearings worn (noise apparent with clutch pedal released, but not when depressed) (Chapter 7).*
☐ Clutch release bearing worn (noise apparent with clutch pedal depressed, possibly less when released) (Chapter 6).

### Noisy in one particular gear

☐ Worn, damaged or chipped gear teeth (Chapter 7).*

### Difficulty engaging gears

☐ Clutch fault (Chapter 6).
☐ Worn or damaged gearchange linkage (Chapter 7).
☐ Incorrectly-adjusted gearchange linkage (Chapter 7).
☐ Worn synchroniser units (Chapter 7).*

### Jumps out of gear

☐ Worn or damaged gearchange linkage (Chapter 7).
☐ Incorrectly-adjusted gearchange linkage (Chapter 7).
☐ Worn synchroniser units (Chapter 7).*
☐ Worn selector forks (Chapter 7).*

### Vibration

☐ Lack of oil (Chapter 1).
☐ Worn bearings (Chapter 7).*

### Lubricant leaks

☐ Leaking differential output oil seal (Chapter 7).
☐ Leaking housing joint (Chapter 7).*
☐ Leaking input shaft oil seal (Chapter 7).*

*Although the corrective action necessary to remedy the symptoms described is beyond the scope of the home mechanic, the above information should be helpful in isolating the cause of the condition, so that the owner can communicate clearly with a professional mechanic.*

# Driveshafts

### Clicking or knocking noise on turns (at slow speed on full-lock)

☐ Lack of constant velocity joint lubricant, possibly due to damaged gaiter (Chapter 8).
☐ Worn outer constant velocity joint (Chapter 8).

### Vibration when accelerating or decelerating

☐ Worn inner constant velocity joint (Chapter 8).
☐ Worn right-hand driveshaft support bearing (Chapter 8).
☐ Bent or distorted driveshaft (Chapter 8).

# Braking system

**Note:** *Before assuming that a brake problem exists, make sure that the tyres are in good condition and correctly inflated, that the front wheel alignment is correct, the front wheels are balanced, and that the car is not loaded with weight in an unequal manner. The alignment of the front subframe is also important – if the car pulls to one side, it may be worth having the subframe alignment checked and adjusted by a Ford dealer, in addition to the more usual checks. Apart from checking the condition of all wiring and hose connections, any faults occurring on the anti-lock braking system should be referred to a Ford dealer for diagnosis.*

### Car pulls to one side under braking

☐ Worn, defective, damaged or contaminated brake pads/shoes on one side (Chapter 1 or 9).
☐ Seized or partially-seized front brake caliper/wheel cylinder piston (Chapter 1 or 9).
☐ A mixture of brake pad/shoe lining materials fitted between sides (Chapter 1 or 9).
☐ Brake caliper or backplate mounting bolts loose (Chapter 9).
☐ Worn or damaged steering or suspension components (Chapter 1 or 10).

### Noise (grinding or high-pitched squeal) when brakes applied

☐ Brake pad or shoe friction lining material worn down to metal backing (Chapter 1 or 9).
☐ Excessive corrosion of brake disc or drum. may be apparent after the car has been standing for some time (Chapter 1 or 9).
☐ Foreign object (stone chipping, etc) trapped between brake disc and shield (Chapter 1 or 9).

### Excessive brake pedal travel

☐ Inoperative rear brake self-adjust mechanism – drum brakes (Chapter 1 or 9).
☐ Faulty master cylinder (Chapter 9).
☐ Air in hydraulic system – bleeding required (Chapter 9).
☐ Brake fluid contaminated – change fluid (Chapter 1).
☐ Faulty vacuum servo unit (Chapter 9).

### Brake pedal feels spongy when pressed

☐ Air in hydraulic system – bleeding required (Chapter 9).
☐ Brake fluid contaminated – change fluid (Chapter 1).
☐ Deteriorated flexible rubber brake hoses (Chapter 1 or 9).
☐ Master cylinder mounting nuts loose (Chapter 9).
☐ Faulty master cylinder (Chapter 9).

### Brake pedal feels hard when pressed

☐ Faulty vacuum pump, or leaking vacuum pipe (Chapter 9).
☐ Faulty vacuum servo unit (Chapter 9).

### Excessive brake pedal effort required to stop car

☐ Faulty vacuum pump, or leaking vacuum pipe (Chapter 9).
☐ Faulty vacuum servo unit (Chapter 9).
☐ Primary or secondary hydraulic circuit failure (Chapter 9).
☐ Seized brake caliper or wheel cylinder piston(s) (Chapter 9).
☐ Brake pads or brake shoes incorrectly fitted (Chapter 1 or 9).
☐ Incorrect grade of brake pads or brake shoes fitted (Chapter 1 or 9).
☐ Brake pads or brake shoe linings contaminated (Chapter 1 or 9).

### Judder felt through brake pedal or steering wheel when braking

☐ Excessive run-out or distortion of discs/drums (Chapter 9).
☐ Brake pad or brake shoe linings worn (Chapter 1 or 9).
☐ Brake caliper or brake backplate mounting bolts loose (Chapter 9).
☐ Wear in suspension or steering components or mountings (Chapter 1 or 10).
☐ Vibration through pedal under heavy braking – ABS in operation – no fault (models with ABS).

### Brakes binding

☐ Seized brake caliper or wheel cylinder piston(s) (Chapter 9).
☐ Incorrectly-adjusted handbrake mechanism (Chapter 9).
☐ Faulty master cylinder (Chapter 9).

### Rear wheels locking under normal braking

☐ Rear brake shoe linings contaminated (Chapter 1 or 9).
☐ Faulty brake pressure regulator (Chapter 9).

# Suspension and steering

**Note:** *Before diagnosing suspension or steering faults, be sure that the trouble is not due to incorrect tyre pressures, mixtures of tyre types, worn tyres, or binding brakes. The alignment of the front subframe is also important – if the car pulls to one side or exhibits abnormal front tyre wear, it may be worth having the subframe alignment checked and adjusted by a Ford dealer, in addition to the more usual checks.*

## Car pulls to one side

☐ Defective or worn tyre (*Weekly checks*).
☐ Tyre pressure low on one side of the car (*Weekly checks*).
☐ Excessive wear in suspension or steering components (Chapter 1 or 10).
☐ Incorrect front wheel alignment (Chapter 10).
☐ Front subframe out of alignment – see note above.
☐ Accident damage to steering or suspension components (Chapter 1).

## Wheel wobble and vibration

☐ Front roadwheels out of balance (vibration felt mainly through the steering wheel) (*Weekly checks* and Chapter 1).
☐ Rear roadwheels out of balance (vibration felt throughout the car) (*Weekly checks* and Chapter 1).
☐ Roadwheels damaged or distorted (*Weekly checks*).
☐ Faulty, worn or damaged tyre (*Weekly checks*).
☐ Worn steering or suspension joints, bushes or components (Chapter 1 or 10).
☐ Wheel bolts loose (Chapter 1).

## Excessive pitching and/or rolling around corners, or during braking

☐ Defective shock absorbers (Chapter 1 or 10).
☐ Broken or weak spring and/or suspension component (Chapter 1 or 10).
☐ Worn or damaged anti-roll bar or mountings (Chapter 10).

## Wandering or general instability

☐ Incorrect front wheel alignment (Chapter 10).
☐ Front subframe out of alignment – see note at the start of this Section.
☐ Worn steering or suspension joints, bushes or components (Chapter 1 or 10).
☐ Roadwheels out of balance (*Weekly checks* and Chapter 1).
☐ Faulty or damaged tyre (*Weekly checks*).
☐ Wheel bolts loose (Chapter 1).
☐ Defective shock absorbers (Chapter 1 or 10).
☐ Excessively-stiff steering
☐ Incorrect power steering fluid level (*Weekly checks*).
☐ Lack of steering gear lubricant (Chapter 10).
☐ Seized track rod end balljoint or suspension balljoint (Chapter 1 or 10).
☐ Broken auxiliary drivebelt or drivebelt tensioner fault – power steering (Chapter 1).
☐ Incorrect front wheel alignment (Chapter 10).
☐ Steering rack or column bent or damaged (Chapter 10).

## Excessive play in steering

☐ Worn steering column flexible coupling (Chapter 10).
☐ Worn steering track rod end balljoints (Chapter 1 or 10).
☐ Worn rack-and-pinion steering gear (Chapter 10).
☐ Worn steering or suspension joints, bushes or components (Chapter 1 or 10).

## Lack of power assistance

☐ Broken or incorrectly-adjusted auxiliary drivebelt (Chapter 1).
☐ Incorrect power steering fluid level (*Weekly checks*).
☐ Restriction in power steering fluid hoses (Chapter 1).
☐ Faulty power steering pump (Chapter 10).
☐ Faulty rack-and-pinion steering gear (Chapter 10).

## Noises from power steering system

☐ Air in hydraulic system – bleeding required (Chapter 10).
☐ Faulty power steering pump (Chapter 10).
☐ High-pressure pipes poorly routed (Chapter 10).

## Tyre wear excessive

### Tyres worn on inside or outside edges

☐ Tyres under-inflated (wear on both edges) (*Weekly checks*).
☐ Incorrect camber or castor angles (wear on one edge only) (Chapter 10).
☐ Worn steering or suspension joints, bushes or components (Chapter 1 or 10).
☐ Front subframe out of alignment – see note at the start of this Section.
☐ Excessively-hard cornering.
☐ Accident damage.

### Tyre treads exhibit feathered edges

☐ Incorrect toe setting (Chapter 10).

### Tyres worn in centre of tread

☐ Tyres over-inflated (*Weekly checks*).

### Tyres worn on inside and outside edges

☐ Tyres under-inflated (*Weekly checks*).

### Tyres worn unevenly

☐ Tyres/wheels out of balance (*Weekly checks* and Chapter 1).
☐ Excessive wheel or tyre run-out (*Weekly checks*).
☐ Worn shock absorbers (Chapter 1 or 10).
☐ Faulty tyre (*Weekly checks*).

# Electrical system

**Note:** *For problems associated with the starting system, refer to the faults listed under 'Engine' earlier in this Section.*

## Battery will not hold a charge for more than a few days

- ☐ Battery defective internally (Chapter 5).
- ☐ Battery terminal connections loose or corroded (*Weekly checks*).
- ☐ Auxiliary drivebelt worn or incorrectly adjusted (Chapter 1).
- ☐ Alternator not charging at correct output (Chapter 5).
- ☐ Alternator or voltage regulator faulty (Chapter 5).
- ☐ Short-circuit causing continual battery drain (Chapters 5 and 12).

## Ignition/no-charge warning light remains illuminated with engine running

- ☐ Auxiliary drivebelt broken, worn, or incorrectly adjusted (Chapter 1).
- ☐ Alternator brushes worn, sticking, or dirty (Chapter 5).
- ☐ Alternator brush springs weak or broken (Chapter 5).
- ☐ Internal fault in alternator or voltage regulator (Chapter 5).
- ☐ Broken, disconnected, or loose wiring in charging circuit (Chapter 5).

## Ignition/no-charge warning light fails to come on

- ☐ Warning light bulb blown (Chapter 12).
- ☐ Broken, disconnected, or loose wiring in warning light circuit (Chapter 12).
- ☐ Alternator faulty (Chapter 5).

## Lights inoperative

- ☐ Bulb blown (Chapter 12).
- ☐ Corrosion of bulb or bulbholder contacts (Chapter 12).
- ☐ Blown fuse (Chapter 12).
- ☐ Faulty relay (Chapter 12).
- ☐ Broken, loose, or disconnected wiring (Chapter 12).
- ☐ Faulty switch (Chapter 12).

## Instrument readings inaccurate or erratic

### Instrument readings increase with engine speed

- ☐ Faulty voltage stabiliser (Chapter 12).

### Fuel or temperature gauges give no reading

- ☐ Faulty gauge sender unit (Chapter 3 or 4A).
- ☐ Wiring open-circuit (Chapter 12).
- ☐ Faulty gauge (Chapter 12).

### Fuel or temperature gauges give continuous maximum reading

- ☐ Faulty gauge sender unit (Chapter 3 or 4A).
- ☐ Wiring short-circuit (Chapter 12).
- ☐ Faulty gauge (Chapter 12).

## Horn inoperative, or unsatisfactory in operation

### Horn operates all the time

- ☐ Horn push either earthed or stuck down (Chapter 12).
- ☐ Horn cable-to-horn push earthed (Chapter 12).

### Horn fails to operate

- ☐ Blown fuse (Chapter 12).
- ☐ Cable or cable connections loose, broken or disconnected (Chapter 12).
- ☐ Faulty horn (Chapter 12).

### Horn emits intermittent or unsatisfactory sound

- ☐ Cable connections loose (Chapter 12).
- ☐ Horn mountings loose (Chapter 12).
- ☐ Faulty horn (Chapter 12).

## Windscreen/tailgate wipers inoperative, or unsatisfactory in operation

### Wipers fail to operate, or operate very slowly

- ☐ Wiper blades stuck to screen, or linkage seized or binding (*Weekly checks* or Chapter 12).
- ☐ Blown fuse (*Weekly checks* or Chapter 12).
- ☐ Cable or cable connections loose, broken or disconnected (Chapter 12).
- ☐ Faulty relay (Chapter 12).
- ☐ Faulty wiper motor (Chapter 12).

### Wiper blades sweep over too large or too small an area of the glass

- ☐ Wiper arms incorrectly positioned on spindles (Chapter 12).
- ☐ Excessive wear of wiper linkage (Chapter 12).
- ☐ Wiper motor or linkage mountings loose or insecure (Chapter 12).

### Wiper blades fail to clean the glass effectively

- ☐ Wiper blade rubbers worn or perished (*Weekly checks*).
- ☐ Wiper arm tension springs broken, or arm pivots seized (Chapter 12).
- ☐ Insufficient windscreen washer additive to adequately remove road film (*Weekly checks*).

## Windscreen/tailgate washers inoperative, or unsatisfactory in operation

### One or more washer jets inoperative

- ☐ Blocked washer jet.
- ☐ Disconnected, kinked or restricted fluid hose (Chapter 12).
- ☐ Insufficient fluid in washer reservoir (*Weekly checks*).

### Washer pump fails to operate

- ☐ Broken or disconnected wiring or connections (Chapter 12).
- ☐ Blown fuse (*Weekly checks* or Chapter 12).
- ☐ Faulty washer switch (Chapter 12).
- ☐ Faulty washer pump (Chapter 12).

### Washer pump runs for some time before fluid is emitted from jets

- ☐ Faulty one-way valve in fluid supply hose (Chapter 12).

# Electrical system (continued)

## Electric windows inoperative, or unsatisfactory in operation

### Window glass will only move in one direction

☐ Faulty switch (Chapter 12).

### Window glass slow to move

☐ Regulator seized or damaged, or in need of lubrication (Chapter 11).
☐ Door internal components or trim fouling regulator (Chapter 11).
☐ Faulty motor (Chapter 11).

### Window glass fails to move

☐ Blown fuse (Chapter 12).
☐ Faulty relay (Chapter 12).
☐ Broken or disconnected wiring or connections (Chapter 12).
☐ Faulty motor (Chapter 11).

## Central locking system inoperative, or unsatisfactory in operation

### Complete system failure

☐ Blown fuse (*Weekly checks* or Chapter 12).
☐ Faulty relay (Chapter 12).
☐ Faulty control module (Chapter 11).
☐ Broken or disconnected wiring or connections (Chapter 12).

### Latch locks but will not unlock, or unlocks but will not lock

☐ Broken or disconnected latch operating rods or levers (Chapter 11).
☐ Faulty relay (Chapter 12).
☐ Faulty control module (Chapter 11).

### One solenoid/motor fails to operate

☐ Broken or disconnected wiring or connections (Chapter 12).
☐ Faulty operating assembly (Chapter 11).
☐ Broken, binding or disconnected latch operating rods or levers (Chapter 11).
☐ Fault in door latch (Chapter 11).

## A

**ABS (Anti-lock brake system)** A system, usually electronically controlled, that senses incipient wheel lockup during braking and relieves hydraulic pressure at wheels that are about to skid.

**Air bag** An inflatable bag hidden in the steering wheel (driver's side) or the dash or glovebox (passenger side). In a head-on collision, the bags inflate, preventing the driver and front passenger from being thrown forward into the steering wheel or windscreen.

**Air cleaner** A metal or plastic housing, containing a filter element, which removes dust and dirt from the air being drawn into the engine.

**Air filter element** The actual filter in an air cleaner system, usually manufactured from pleated paper and requiring renewal at regular intervals.

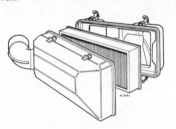

*Air filter*

**Allen key** A hexagonal wrench which fits into a recessed hexagonal hole.

**Alligator clip** A long-nosed spring-loaded metal clip with meshing teeth. Used to make temporary electrical connections.

**Alternator** A component in the electrical system which converts mechanical energy from a drivebelt into electrical energy to charge the battery and to operate the starting system, ignition system and electrical accessories.

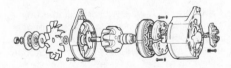

*Alternator (exploded view)*

**Ampere (amp)** A unit of measurement for the flow of electric current. One amp is the amount of current produced by one volt acting through a resistance of one ohm.

**Anaerobic sealer** A substance used to prevent bolts and screws from loosening. Anaerobic means that it does not require oxygen for activation. The Loctite brand is widely used.

**Antifreeze** A substance (usually ethylene glycol) mixed with water, and added to a vehicle's cooling system, to prevent freezing of the coolant in winter. Antifreeze also contains chemicals to inhibit corrosion and the formation of rust and other deposits that would tend to clog the radiator and coolant passages and reduce cooling efficiency.

**Anti-seize compound** A coating that reduces the risk of seizing on fasteners that are subjected to high temperatures, such as exhaust manifold bolts and nuts.

*Anti-seize compound*

**Asbestos** A natural fibrous mineral with great heat resistance, commonly used in the composition of brake friction materials. Asbestos is a health hazard and the dust created by brake systems should never be inhaled or ingested.

**Axle** A shaft on which a wheel revolves, or which revolves with a wheel. Also, a solid beam that connects the two wheels at one end of the vehicle. An axle which also transmits power to the wheels is known as a live axle.

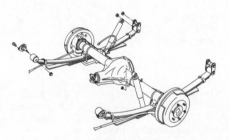

*Axle assembly*

**Axleshaft** A single rotating shaft, on either side of the differential, which delivers power from the final drive assembly to the drive wheels. Also called a driveshaft or a halfshaft.

## B

**Ball bearing** An anti-friction bearing consisting of a hardened inner and outer race with hardened steel balls between two races.

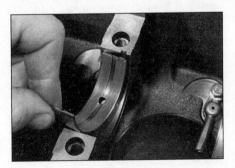

*Bearing*

**Bearing** The curved surface on a shaft or in a bore, or the part assembled into either, that permits relative motion between them with minimum wear and friction.

**Big-end bearing** The bearing in the end of the connecting rod that's attached to the crankshaft.

**Bleed nipple** A valve on a brake wheel cylinder, caliper or other hydraulic component that is opened to purge the hydraulic system of air. Also called a bleed screw.

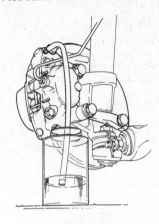

*Brake bleeding*

**Brake bleeding** Procedure for removing air from lines of a hydraulic brake system.

**Brake disc** The component of a disc brake that rotates with the wheels.

**Brake drum** The component of a drum brake that rotates with the wheels.

**Brake linings** The friction material which contacts the brake disc or drum to retard the vehicle's speed. The linings are bonded or riveted to the brake pads or shoes.

**Brake pads** The replaceable friction pads that pinch the brake disc when the brakes are applied. Brake pads consist of a friction material bonded or riveted to a rigid backing plate.

**Brake shoe** The crescent-shaped carrier to which the brake linings are mounted and which forces the lining against the rotating drum during braking.

**Braking systems** For more information on braking systems, consult the *Haynes Automotive Brake Manual*.

**Breaker bar** A long socket wrench handle providing greater leverage.

**Bulkhead** The insulated partition between the engine and the passenger compartment.

## C

**Caliper** The non-rotating part of a disc-brake assembly that straddles the disc and carries the brake pads. The caliper also contains the hydraulic components that cause the pads to pinch the disc when the brakes are applied. A caliper is also a measuring tool that can be set to measure inside or outside dimensions of an object.

**Camshaft** A rotating shaft on which a series of cam lobes operate the valve mechanisms. The camshaft may be driven by gears, by sprockets and chain or by sprockets and a belt.

**Canister** A container in an evaporative emission control system; contains activated charcoal granules to trap vapours from the fuel system.

*Canister*

**Carburettor** A device which mixes fuel with air in the proper proportions to provide a desired power output from a spark ignition internal combustion engine.

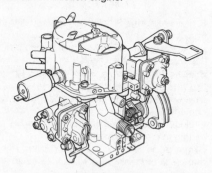

*Carburettor*

**Castellated** Resembling the parapets along the top of a castle wall. For example, a castellated balljoint stud nut.

*Castellated nut*

**Castor** In wheel alignment, the backward or forward tilt of the steering axis. Castor is positive when the steering axis is inclined rearward at the top.

**Catalytic converter** A silencer-like device in the exhaust system which converts certain pollutants in the exhaust gases into less harmful substances.

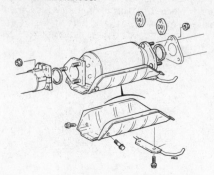

*Catalytic converter*

**Circlip** A ring-shaped clip used to prevent endwise movement of cylindrical parts and shafts. An internal circlip is installed in a groove in a housing; an external circlip fits into a groove on the outside of a cylindrical piece such as a shaft.

**Clearance** The amount of space between two parts. For example, between a piston and a cylinder, between a bearing and a journal, etc.

**Coil spring** A spiral of elastic steel found in various sizes throughout a vehicle, for example as a springing medium in the suspension and in the valve train.

**Compression** Reduction in volume, and increase in pressure and temperature, of a gas, caused by squeezing it into a smaller space.

**Compression ratio** The relationship between cylinder volume when the piston is at top dead centre and cylinder volume when the piston is at bottom dead centre.

**Constant velocity (CV) joint** A type of universal joint that cancels out vibrations caused by driving power being transmitted through an angle.

**Core plug** A disc or cup-shaped metal device inserted in a hole in a casting through which core was removed when the casting was formed. Also known as a freeze plug or expansion plug.

**Crankcase** The lower part of the engine block in which the crankshaft rotates.

**Crankshaft** The main rotating member, or shaft, running the length of the crankcase, with offset "throws" to which the connecting rods are attached.

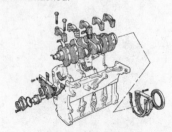

*Crankshaft assembly*

**Crocodile clip** See Alligator clip

# D

**Diagnostic code** Code numbers obtained by accessing the diagnostic mode of an engine management computer. This code can be used to determine the area in the system where a malfunction may be located.

**Disc brake** A brake design incorporating a rotating disc onto which brake pads are squeezed. The resulting friction converts the energy of a moving vehicle into heat.

**Double-overhead cam (DOHC)** An engine that uses two overhead camshafts, usually one for the intake valves and one for the exhaust valves.

**Drivebelt(s)** The belt(s) used to drive accessories such as the alternator, water pump, power steering pump, air conditioning compressor, etc. off the crankshaft pulley.

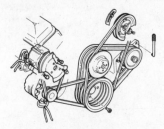

*Accessory drivebelts*

**Driveshaft** Any shaft used to transmit motion. Commonly used when referring to the axleshafts on a front wheel drive vehicle.

*Driveshaft*

**Drum brake** A type of brake using a drum-shaped metal cylinder attached to the inner surface of the wheel. When the brake pedal is pressed, curved brake shoes with friction linings press against the inside of the drum to slow or stop the vehicle.

*Drum brake assembly*

## E

**EGR valve** A valve used to introduce exhaust gases into the intake air stream.

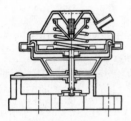

*EGR valve*

**Electronic control unit (ECU)** A computer which controls (for instance) ignition and fuel injection systems, or an anti-lock braking system. For more information refer to the *Haynes Automotive Electrical and Electronic Systems Manual*.

**Electronic Fuel Injection (EFI)** A computer controlled fuel system that distributes fuel through an injector located in each intake port of the engine.

**Emergency brake** A braking system, independent of the main hydraulic system, that can be used to slow or stop the vehicle if the primary brakes fail, or to hold the vehicle stationary even though the brake pedal isn't depressed. It usually consists of a hand lever that actuates either front or rear brakes mechanically through a series of cables and linkages. Also known as a handbrake or parking brake.

**Endfloat** The amount of lengthwise movement between two parts. As applied to a crankshaft, the distance that the crankshaft can move forward and back in the cylinder block.

**Engine management system (EMS)** A computer controlled system which manages the fuel injection and the ignition systems in an integrated fashion.

**Exhaust manifold** A part with several passages through which exhaust gases leave the engine combustion chambers and enter the exhaust pipe.

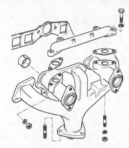

*Exhaust manifold*

## F

**Fan clutch** A viscous (fluid) drive coupling device which permits variable engine fan speeds in relation to engine speeds.

**Feeler blade** A thin strip or blade of hardened steel, ground to an exact thickness, used to check or measure clearances between parts.

*Feeler blade*

**Firing order** The order in which the engine cylinders fire, or deliver their power strokes, beginning with the number one cylinder.

**Flywheel** A heavy spinning wheel in which energy is absorbed and stored by means of momentum. On cars, the flywheel is attached to the crankshaft to smooth out firing impulses.

**Free play** The amount of travel before any action takes place. The "looseness" in a linkage, or an assembly of parts, between the initial application of force and actual movement. For example, the distance the brake pedal moves before the pistons in the master cylinder are actuated.

**Fuse** An electrical device which protects a circuit against accidental overload. The typical fuse contains a soft piece of metal which is calibrated to melt at a predetermined current flow (expressed as amps) and break the circuit.

**Fusible link** A circuit protection device consisting of a conductor surrounded by heat-resistant insulation. The conductor is smaller than the wire it protects, so it acts as the weakest link in the circuit. Unlike a blown fuse, a failed fusible link must frequently be cut from the wire for replacement.

## G

**Gap** The distance the spark must travel in jumping from the centre electrode to the side

*Adjusting spark plug gap*

electrode in a spark plug. Also refers to the spacing between the points in a contact breaker assembly in a conventional points-type ignition, or to the distance between the reluctor or rotor and the pickup coil in an electronic ignition.

**Gasket** Any thin, soft material - usually cork, cardboard, asbestos or soft metal - installed between two metal surfaces to ensure a good seal. For instance, the cylinder head gasket seals the joint between the block and the cylinder head.

*Gasket*

**Gauge** An instrument panel display used to monitor engine conditions. A gauge with a movable pointer on a dial or a fixed scale is an analogue gauge. A gauge with a numerical readout is called a digital gauge.

## H

**Halfshaft** A rotating shaft that transmits power from the final drive unit to a drive wheel, usually when referring to a live rear axle.

**Harmonic balancer** A device designed to reduce torsion or twisting vibration in the crankshaft. May be incorporated in the crankshaft pulley. Also known as a vibration damper.

**Hone** An abrasive tool for correcting small irregularities or differences in diameter in an engine cylinder, brake cylinder, etc.

**Hydraulic tappet** A tappet that utilises hydraulic pressure from the engine's lubrication system to maintain zero clearance (constant contact with both camshaft and valve stem). Automatically adjusts to variation in valve stem length. Hydraulic tappets also reduce valve noise.

## I

**Ignition timing** The moment at which the spark plug fires, usually expressed in the number of crankshaft degrees before the piston reaches the top of its stroke.

**Inlet manifold** A tube or housing with passages through which flows the air-fuel mixture (carburettor vehicles and vehicles with throttle body injection) or air only (port fuel-injected vehicles) to the port openings in the cylinder head.

## J

**Jump start** Starting the engine of a vehicle with a discharged or weak battery by attaching jump leads from the weak battery to a charged or helper battery.

## L

**Load Sensing Proportioning Valve (LSPV)** A brake hydraulic system control valve that works like a proportioning valve, but also takes into consideration the amount of weight carried by the rear axle.

**Locknut** A nut used to lock an adjustment nut, or other threaded component, in place. For example, a locknut is employed to keep the adjusting nut on the rocker arm in position.

**Lockwasher** A form of washer designed to prevent an attaching nut from working loose.

## M

**MacPherson strut** A type of front suspension system devised by Earle MacPherson at Ford of England. In its original form, a simple lateral link with the anti-roll bar creates the lower control arm. A long strut - an integral coil spring and shock absorber - is mounted between the body and the steering knuckle. Many modern so-called MacPherson strut systems use a conventional lower A-arm and don't rely on the anti-roll bar for location.

**Multimeter** An electrical test instrument with the capability to measure voltage, current and resistance.

## N

**NOx** Oxides of Nitrogen. A common toxic pollutant emitted by petrol and diesel engines at higher temperatures.

## O

**Ohm** The unit of electrical resistance. One volt applied to a resistance of one ohm will produce a current of one amp.

**Ohmmeter** An instrument for measuring electrical resistance.

**O-ring** A type of sealing ring made of a special rubber-like material; in use, the O-ring is compressed into a groove to provide the sealing action.

*O-ring*

**Overhead cam (ohc) engine** An engine with the camshaft(s) located on top of the cylinder head(s).

**Overhead valve (ohv) engine** An engine with the valves located in the cylinder head, but with the camshaft located in the engine block.

**Oxygen sensor** A device installed in the engine exhaust manifold, which senses the oxygen content in the exhaust and converts this information into an electric current. Also called a Lambda sensor.

## P

**Phillips screw** A type of screw head having a cross instead of a slot for a corresponding type of screwdriver.

**Plastigage** A thin strip of plastic thread, available in different sizes, used for measuring clearances. For example, a strip of Plastigage is laid across a bearing journal. The parts are assembled and dismantled; the width of the crushed strip indicates the clearance between journal and bearing.

*Plastigage*

**Propeller shaft** The long hollow tube with universal joints at both ends that carries power from the transmission to the differential on front-engined rear wheel drive vehicles.

**Proportioning valve** A hydraulic control valve which limits the amount of pressure to the rear brakes during panic stops to prevent wheel lock-up.

## R

**Rack-and-pinion steering** A steering system with a pinion gear on the end of the steering shaft that mates with a rack (think of a geared wheel opened up and laid flat). When the steering wheel is turned, the pinion turns, moving the rack to the left or right. This movement is transmitted through the track rods to the steering arms at the wheels.

**Radiator** A liquid-to-air heat transfer device designed to reduce the temperature of the coolant in an internal combustion engine cooling system.

**Refrigerant** Any substance used as a heat transfer agent in an air-conditioning system. R-12 has been the principle refrigerant for many years; recently, however, manufacturers have begun using R-134a, a non-CFC substance that is considered less harmful to the ozone in the upper atmosphere.

**Rocker arm** A lever arm that rocks on a shaft or pivots on a stud. In an overhead valve engine, the rocker arm converts the upward movement of the pushrod into a downward movement to open a valve.

**Rotor** In a distributor, the rotating device inside the cap that connects the centre electrode and the outer terminals as it turns, distributing the high voltage from the coil secondary winding to the proper spark plug. Also, that part of an alternator which rotates inside the stator. Also, the rotating assembly of a turbocharger, including the compressor wheel, shaft and turbine wheel.

**Runout** The amount of wobble (in-and-out movement) of a gear or wheel as it's rotated. The amount a shaft rotates "out-of-true." The out-of-round condition of a rotating part.

## S

**Sealant** A liquid or paste used to prevent leakage at a joint. Sometimes used in conjunction with a gasket.

**Sealed beam lamp** An older headlight design which integrates the reflector, lens and filaments into a hermetically-sealed one-piece unit. When a filament burns out or the lens cracks, the entire unit is simply replaced.

**Serpentine drivebelt** A single, long, wide accessory drivebelt that's used on some newer vehicles to drive all the accessories, instead of a series of smaller, shorter belts. Serpentine drivebelts are usually tensioned by an automatic tensioner.

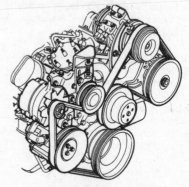
*Serpentine drivebelt*

**Shim** Thin spacer, commonly used to adjust the clearance or relative positions between two parts. For example, shims inserted into or under bucket tappets control valve clearances. Clearance is adjusted by changing the thickness of the shim.

**Slide hammer** A special puller that screws into or hooks onto a component such as a shaft or bearing; a heavy sliding handle on the shaft bottoms against the end of the shaft to knock the component free.

**Sprocket** A tooth or projection on the periphery of a wheel, shaped to engage with a chain or drivebelt. Commonly used to refer to the sprocket wheel itself.

**Starter inhibitor switch** On vehicles with an automatic transmission, a switch that prevents starting if the vehicle is not in Neutral or Park.

**Strut** See MacPherson strut.

# T

**Tappet** A cylindrical component which transmits motion from the cam to the valve stem, either directly or via a pushrod and rocker arm. Also called a cam follower.

**Thermostat** A heat-controlled valve that regulates the flow of coolant between the cylinder block and the radiator, so maintaining optimum engine operating temperature. A thermostat is also used in some air cleaners in which the temperature is regulated.

**Thrust bearing** The bearing in the clutch assembly that is moved in to the release levers by clutch pedal action to disengage the clutch. Also referred to as a release bearing.

**Timing belt** A toothed belt which drives the camshaft. Serious engine damage may result if it breaks in service.

**Timing chain** A chain which drives the camshaft.

**Toe-in** The amount the front wheels are closer together at the front than at the rear. On rear wheel drive vehicles, a slight amount of toe-in is usually specified to keep the front wheels running parallel on the road by offsetting other forces that tend to spread the wheels apart.

**Toe-out** The amount the front wheels are closer together at the rear than at the front. On front wheel drive vehicles, a slight amount of toe-out is usually specified.

**Tools** For full information on choosing and using tools, refer to the *Haynes Automotive Tools Manual.*

**Tracer** A stripe of a second colour applied to a wire insulator to distinguish that wire from another one with the same colour insulator.

**Tune-up** A process of accurate and careful adjustments and parts replacement to obtain the best possible engine performance.

**Turbocharger** A centrifugal device, driven by exhaust gases, that pressurises the intake air. Normally used to increase the power output from a given engine displacement, but can also be used primarily to reduce exhaust emissions (as on VW's "Umwelt" Diesel engine).

# U

**Universal joint or U-joint** A double-pivoted connection for transmitting power from a driving to a driven shaft through an angle. A U-joint consists of two Y-shaped yokes and a cross-shaped member called the spider.

# V

**Valve** A device through which the flow of liquid, gas, vacuum, or loose material in bulk may be started, stopped, or regulated by a movable part that opens, shuts, or partially obstructs one or more ports or passageways. A valve is also the movable part of such a device.

**Valve clearance** The clearance between the valve tip (the end of the valve stem) and the rocker arm or tappet. The valve clearance is measured when the valve is closed.

**Vernier caliper** A precision measuring instrument that measures inside and outside dimensions. Not quite as accurate as a micrometer, but more convenient.

**Viscosity** The thickness of a liquid or its resistance to flow.

**Volt** A unit for expressing electrical "pressure" in a circuit. One volt that will produce a current of one ampere through a resistance of one ohm.

# W

**Welding** Various processes used to join metal items by heating the areas to be joined to a molten state and fusing them together. For more information refer to the *Haynes Automotive Welding Manual.*

**Wiring diagram** A drawing portraying the components and wires in a vehicle's electrical system, using standardised symbols. For more information refer to the *Haynes Automotive Electrical and Electronic Systems Manual.*

**Note:** *References throughout this index are in the form* **"Chapter number"** • **"Page number"**. *So, for example, 2C•15 refers to page 15 of Chapter 2C.*

# A

**A-pillar trim** – 11•25
**ABS**
    hydraulic unit – 9•16
    relay box – 9•17
    wheel sensor – 9•17
**Accelerator cable** – 4A•4
**Accelerator pedal** – 4A•4
**Accessory shops** – REF•3
**Accumulator/dehydrator** – 3•11
**Acknowledgements** – 0•6
**Adhesive emblems** – 11•22
**Advance solenoid**
    cold start – 4A•14
    turbo boost – 4A•11, 4A•13
**Aerial** – 12•28
**Air conditioning system** – 1•12, 3•10, 3•11
    compressor drivebelt – 1•10
    control – 3•9
**Air distribution control** – 3•10
**Air filter** – 1•19, 4A•3
**Air temperature warning sender unit** – 12•22
**Airbags** – 0•5, 12•29,12•30
**Airflow sensor** – 4A•11
**Airlocks** – 1•22
**Alarm system** – 12•23
    central locking – 11•21
**Alternator** – 5•3, 5•4
    drivebelt – 1•10
**Amplifier** – 12•28
**Antifreeze** – 0•13, 0•17, 1•21, 3•2
**Anti-roll bar and links** – 10•8, 10•13, 10•16
**Anti-stall speed** – 4A•5
**Anti-theft alarm system** – 12•23
**Asbestos** – 0•5
**Auxiliary drivebelts** – 1•9
**Auxiliary shaft** – 2B•10
    oil seal – 2A•15
    toothed pulley – 2A•14
**Auxiliary warning system** – 12•22

# B

**B-pillar and cowl side trim** – 11•25
**Battery** – 0•5, 0•15, 5•2, REF•7
    leads – 5•3
    maintenance and charging – 1•8
**Big-end bearings** – 2B•15
**Bleeding**
    brakes – 9•14
    clutch – 6•8
    fuel system – 4A•3
    steering system – 10•22
**Blower motor** – 3•7
    control – 3•9
**Body corrosion** – REF•13
*Body electrical system* – 12•1 et seq
*Bodywork and fittings* – 11•1 et seq
**Bonnet** – 11•7, 11•8
    check and lubrication – 1•16

**Boot lid** – 11•16, 11•17
    lock – 11•21
**Boot light switch** – 12•9
**Brake fluid** – 0•13, 0•17, 1•20
**Brake line** – 1•15
*Braking system* – 1•15, 1•16, 9•1 et seq, REF•10, REF•11, REF•12
    fault finding – REF•19
    pad wear sensors – 12•23
    pedal switch (cruise control system) – 12•26
**Bulbs** – 12•9, 12•13
    failure module – 12•22
**Bumpers** – 11•5
**Burning** – 0•5
**Buying spare parts** – REF•3

# C

**C-pillar trim** – 11•25
**Cables**
    accelerator – 4A•4
    bonnet release – 11•8
    clutch – 6•3
    cold start – 4A•9
    fuel filler flap release – 11•29
    handbrake – 9•20
    speedometer – 12•19
**Calipers** – 9•4, 9•10
**Camshaft** – 2A•15
    oil seal – 2A•15
    toothed pulley – 2A•13
**Carpets** – 11•3
**Cassette player** – 12•27, 12•28
**Catalytic converter** – 4B•1, 4B•2
**CD player** – 12•28
**Central locking system** – 11•21
**Centre console** – 11•26
**Centre panels** – 11•26
**Charging** – 1•8, 5•2, 5•3
**Check strap** – 11•15
**Clock** – 12•20
    illumination – 12•14
*Clutch* – 1•17, 6•1 et seq
    fault finding – REF•17
    fluid – 0•13, 0•17
    pedal switch (cruise control system) – 12•26
**Coil spring** – 10•16
**Cold start system** – 4A•11
    cable – 4A•9
**Compression test** – 2A•5
**Compressor** – 3•11
**Condenser** – 3•11
**Connecting rods** – 2B•11, 2B•14, 2B•16
**Consoles** – 11•26, 11•27
**Conversion factors** – REF•2
**Coolant** – 0•13, 0•17, 1•20
    level warning switch – 12•23
    low level switch – 3•5
    temperature sensor – 3•5, 4A•11
**Cooling fan(s)** – 3•4

*Cooling, heating & ventilation systems* – 3•1 et seq
    fault finding – REF•17
**Courtesy light** – 12•13
    switch – 12•8
**Crankcase** – 2B•12
**Crankcase emission control** – 4B•1
**Crankshaft** – 2B•12, 2B•15, 2B•16
    oil seals – 2A•23
    position sensor – 4A•11, 4A•13
    pulley – 2A•10
    toothed pulleys – 2A•13
**Crossmember** – 10•14, 10•18
**Cruise control system** – 12•25
**Crushing** – 0•5
**CV joint** – 1•14, 8•3, 8•5
**Cylinder block** – 2B•12
**Cylinder head** – 2A•18, 2B•8, 2B•9, 2B•10
    cover – 2A•7

# D

**D-pillar trim** – 11•25
**Dehydrator** – 3•11
**Dents** – 11•3
**Diesel injection equipment** – 0•5
    fault finding – REF•15
**Dimensions** – REF•1
**Dipped beam switch** – 12•6
**Direction indicator** – 12•10, 12•11, 12•16
**Disc brakes** – 1•15, 1•16, 9•4, 9•11
**Disconnecting the battery** – REF•7
**Display module** – 12•22
**Door ajar sensor** – 12•23
**Doors** – REF•11
    check and lubrication – 1•16
    handle illumination – 12•14
    mirror control switch – 12•6
**Drivebelts** – 1•9
**Driveshafts** – 8•1 et seq, REF•12
    fault finding – REF•18
    rubber gaiter and CV joint – 1•14
**Drivetrain** – 1•17
**Drum brakes** – 1•16, 9•5

# E

**Earth fault** – 12•3
**ECU engine management** – 4A•13
**Electric seat components** – 12•31
**Electric shock** – 0•5
**Electric window switch** – 12•6, 12•7
**Electrical equipment** – 0•15, 1•17, REF•11
    check – 1•11
    fault finding – 12•2, REF•21, REF•22
**Electrolyte** – 1•8
**Emblems** – 11•22
*Emission control systems* – 4B•1 et seq, REF•13
**Engine compartment**
    light – 12•13
    wiring – 1•12

**Note:** *References throughout this index are in the form* "**Chapter number**" • "**Page number**". *So, for example, 2C•15 refers to page 15 of Chapter 2C.*

*Engine electrical systems* – 5•1 et seq
*Engine in-car repair procedures* –
2A•1 et seq
  fault finding – REF•15, REF•16
**Engine management system** – 4A•11
  ECU – 4A•13
**Engine oil** – 0•12, 0•17, 1•7
  level sensor – 12•22
*Engine removal and overhaul procedures* –
2B•1 et seq
**Environmental considerations** – REF•5
**Evaporator** – 3•11
**Exhaust emission control** – 4B•1
**Exhaust gas recirculation system** – 4B•1
  EGR pipe – 4B•2
  EGR valve – 4B•2
**Exhaust manifold** – 1•13, 2A•8
**Exhaust specialists** – REF•3
**Exhaust system** – 1•15, 4A•11, REF•12,
  REF•13
**Expansion tank** – 3•7
  pressure cap – 1•22

## F

**Facia** – 11•28
  panel – 11•26
  vents – 3•8
**Fan(s)** – 3•4
  switch – 3•5
*Fault finding* – REF•14 et seq
  braking system – REF•19
  clutch – ref•17
  cooling system – REF•17
  diesel systems – REF•15
  driveshafts – REF•18
  electrical system – 12•2, REF•21, REF•22
  engine – REF•15, REF•16
  fuel and exhaust systems – REF•17
  manual transmission – REF•18
  suspension and steering systems –
  REF•20
**Filling** – 11•4
**Filter**
  air – 1•19, 4A•3
  fuel – 1•11, 1•18
  oil – 1•7
  pollen – 1•17
**Fire** – 0•5
**Fixed windows** – 11•21
**Fluids** – 0•17
  leaks – 1•11
**Flywheel** – 2A•24
**Foglight** – 12•11, 12•16
  beam alignment – 12•17
  switch – 12•6
  warning indicator – 12•14
**Footwell illumination light** – 12•15
**Ford Mondeo manual** – 0•6
*Fuel and exhaust systems* – 4A•1 et seq
  fault finding – REF•17
**Fuel filler flap** – 11•29

**Fuel filter** – 1•11, 1•18
**Fuel gauge sender unit** – 4A•9
**Fuel heater** – 4A•8
**Fuel hoses** – 1•12
**Fuel injection pump** – 4A•5, 4A•6
  drivebelt tensioner – 2A•13
  timing – 4A•6
  toothed pulley – 2A•14
**Fuel injectors** – 4A•7
**Fuel line** – 1•15
**Fuel shut-off (stop) solenoid** – 4A•8
**Fuel system** – REF•13
**Fuel tank** – 4A•10
**Fume or gas intoxication** – 0•5
**Fuses** – 12•3

## G

**Gaiters**
  driveshaft – 1•14, 8•3, 8•5
  steering gear – 10•22
**Garages** – REF•3
**Gashes** – 11•3
**Gaskets** – REF•5
**Gearchange**
  linkage – 7•2, 7•3
  selector shaft oil seal – 7•5
**General repair procedures** – REF•5
**Glass** – 11•11
*Glossary of technical terms* – REF•23 et seq
**Glovebox** – 11•27
  light – 12•14
**Glow plugs** – 5•6
**Grab handle** – 11•25
**Grille** – 11•7

## H

**Handbrake** – 9•19, 9•20, REF•10
  warning switch – 12•7
**Handles**
  door illumination – 12•14
  doors – 11•12, 11•15
  grab – 11•25
**Hazard warning light** – 12•14
  switch – 12•6
**Headlight** – 12•15
  aim adjustment control – 12•6
  beam alignment – 12•17
  dipped beam – 12•9
  levelling motor – 12•18
  main beam – 12•10
  washer nozzle – 12•27
**Heated rear window switch** – 12•7
**Heated seats** – 12•31
  switch – 12•8
**Heated windscreen switch** – 12•7
**Heating/ventilation system** – 3•2, 3•7
  blower motor – 3•7
  control illumination – 12•14
  controls – 3•9

fan switch illumination – 12•14
  matrix – 3•8
**High-level stop-light** – 12•13
**Horn** – 12•20
  switch – 12•6
**Hoses** – 1•11, 3•3, 9•13
**Hub and bearings** – 10•4, 10•5, 10•10,
  10•11, •15
**Hydraulic unit (ABS)** – 9•16
**Hydrofluoric acid** – 0•5

## I

**Identifying leaks** – 0•10
**Idle speed** – 4A•5
**Idler pulley** – 2A•14
**Idle-up control system** – 4A•8
**Ignition switch** – 12•5
**Indicators** – 12•10, 12•11, 12•16
  switch – 12•6
**Injection pump** – 4A•5, 4A•6
  drivebelt – 2A•10,
  drivebelt tensioner – 2A•13
  timing – 4A•6
  toothed pulley – 2A•14
**Injectors** – 4A•7
**Inlet manifold** – 2A•7
**Instrument panel** – 1•17, 12•18, 12•19
  illumination – 12•14
  light dimmer – 12•6
**Intercooler** – 4A•9
**Interior light** – 12•13
  door switch – 12•8

## J

**Jacking and vehicle support** – REF•6
**Joint mating faces** – REF•5
**Jump starting** – 0•8

## L

**Leakdown test** – 2A•5
**Leaks** – 0•10, 1•11
**Lights** – 12•13, 12•15
**Locknuts, locktabs and washers** – REF•5
**Locks**
  bonnet – 11•8
  boot lid – 11•17, 11•21
  central locking – 11•21
  doors – 11•12, 11•15
  steering – 12•5
  tailgate – 11•19, 11•21
**Low air temperature warning sender unit** –
  12•22
**Low coolant warning switch** – 12•23
**Low washer fluid switch** – 12•23
**Lower arms** – 10•8, 10•10, 10•14, 10•17
**Lubricants and fluids** – 0•17
**Luggage compartment light** – 12•15

**Note:** *References throughout this index are in the form* **"Chapter number"** • **"Page number"**. *So, for example, 2C•15 refers to page 15 of Chapter 2C.*

# M

**Main bearings** – 2B•15
**Main light switch** – 12•6
  illumination – 12•14
**Manifolds**
  exhaust – 1•13, 2A•8
  inlet – 2A•7
*Manual transmission* – 7•1 et seq
  fault finding – REF•18
  oil – 0•17, 1•13
**Map reading light** – 12•13
**Mass airflow sensor** – 4A•11
**Master cylinder**
  brakes – 9•11
  clutch – 6•4
**Matrix** – 3•8
**Maximum speed** – 4A•5
**Metal lines** – 1•12
**Mirrors** – 11•16, REF•10
  control switch – 12•6
*MOT test checks* – REF•10 et seq
**Motor factors** – REF•3
**Mountings** – 2A•24

# N

**Needle lift sensor** – 4A•11, 4A•14
**Number plate light** – 12•12, 12•17

# O

**Oil**
  engine – 0•12, 0•17, 1•7
  manual transmission – 0•17, 1•13
**Oil cooler** – 2A•23
**Oil filter** – 1•7
**Oil level sensor** – 12•22
**Oil pressure warning light switch** – 2A•23
**Oil pump** – 2A•22
**Oil seals** – REF•5
  auxiliary shaft – 2A•15
  camshaft – 2A•15
  crankshaft – 2A•23
  gearchange selector shaft – 7•5
  speedometer drive pinion – 7•5
  transmission – 7•4
**Open-circuit** – 12•3
**Overhead console** – 11•27

# P

**Pads** – 9•3, 9•8
  wear sensors – 12•23
**Parking sensor system** – 12•31
**Parts** – REF•3
**Pedals**
  accelerator – 4A•4
  brake – 9•12, 9•13
  clutch – 6•5
**Pipes** – 9•13
**Pistons** – 2B•11, 2B•14, 2B•16
**Plastic components** – 11•4
**Poisonous or irritant substances** – 0•5
**Pollen filter** – 1•17
**Power amplifier** – 12•28
**Power steering**
  fluid – 0•12, 0•17
  pressure switch – 4A•13, 4A•14
  pump drivebelt – 1•10
**Preheating system** – 5•6
**Pressure cap** – 1•22
**Pressure-control relief valve** – 9•15
**Pressure-cycling and pressure-regulating
  switches** – 3•12
**Puncture repair** – 0•9

# R

**Radiator** – 3•6
  electric cooling fan(s) – 3•4
  fan switch – 3•5
  grille – 11•7
**Radio** – 12•27, 12•28
  aerial – 12•28
  remote control switch – 12•6
**Rear light cluster** – 12•12, 12•16
**Rear window**
  switch – 12•7
  washer nozzle – 12•27
**Regulator**
  door window – 11•12
  voltage – 5•4
**Relays** – 12•3
  ABS – 9•17
**Release bearing** – 6•6
**Release shaft and bush** – 6•7
**Repair procedures** – REF•5

**Respraying** – 11•4
**Reversing light switch** – 7•5
**Road test** – 1•16
*Roadside repairs* – 0•7 et seq
**Roadwheels**
  check and balancing – 1•14
  nut tightness check – 1•16
*Routine maintenance and servicing* –
  1•1 et seq
  bodywork and underframe – 11•2
  upholstery and carpets – 11•3
**Rust holes** – 11•3

# S

**Safety first!** – 0•5, 0•12, 0•13
**Satellite navigation system** – 12•31
**Scalding** – 0•5
**Scratches** – 11•3
**Screw threads and fastenings** – REF•5
**Seat belts** – 1•13, 11•23
**Seats** – 11•22, 12•31
  heater switch – 12•8
  height adjustment switch – 12•8
**Service interval display** – 1•6, 12•22
  reset switch – 12•22
**Shock absorbers** – 10•16, REF•11, REF•12
**Shoes** – 9•6
**Short-circuit** – 12•3
**Shut-off (stop) solenoid** – 4A•8
**Side airbag** – 12•30
**Side repeaters** – 12•11
**Sidelight** – 12•10
**Slave cylinder (clutch)** – 6•6
**Spare parts** – REF•3
**Speakers** – 12•28
**Speed control actuator cruise control
  system** – 12•26
**Speed sensor** – 4A•13, 4A•14
**Speedometer**
  cable – 12•19
  drive pinion – 7•4
  drive pinion oil seal – 7•5
**Sprinsg** – 10•16, REF•12
**Starting system** – 5•4, 5•5
**Start-up after overhaul** – 2B•17
**Steering** – 1•14, 1•17, REF•11, REF•12
  angles – 10•23
  column – 10•19, REF•10

**Note:** *References throughout this index are in the form* "**Chapter number**" • "**Page number**". *So, for example, 2C•15 refers to page 15 of Chapter 2C.*

column flexible coupling – 10•21
fluid cooler – 10•22
gear – 10•21
gear rubber gaiters – 10•22
lock – 12•5
pump – 10•22
wheel – 10•18, REF•10
wheel switches (cruise control system) – 12•25
**Stop lever** – 4A•5
**Stop solenoid** – 4A•8
**Stop-light** – 12•13
switch – 9•18
**Striker** – 11•15
**Strut**
suspension – 10•6, 10•7, 10•11, 10•13
tailgate support – 11•19
**Sump** – 2A•21
**Sun visor** – 11•25
**Sunroof** – 11•22
switch – 12•7
*Suspension and steering* – 1•14, 1•17, 10•1 *et seq*, REF•11, REF•12
fault finding – REF•20
**Switches** – 12•5
air conditioning system – 3•12
brake pedal (cruise control system) – 12•26
clutch pedal (cruise control system – 12•26
cooling system – 3•4
heater fan – 12•14
low coolant level – 3•5
main light – 12•14
oil pressure warning light – 2A•23
power steering pressure – 4A•13, 4A•14
radiator fan – 3•5
reversing light – 7•5
service indicator reset – 12•22
steering wheel cruise control system – 12•25
stop-light – 9•18

**T**

**Tailgate** – 11•18, 11•19
lock – 11•21
washer system – 12•26
wiper motor – 12•21

**Tappets** – 2A•15
*Technical terms* – REF•23 *et seq*
**Temperature gauge sender** – 3•4
**Temperature sensor** – 3•5, 4A•11
**Tensioner (timing belt and injection pump drivebelt)** – 2A•14
**Thermostat** – 3•3
**Throttle lever position sensor** – 4A•13
**Tie-bar** – 10•14, 10•18
**Timer module** – 12•3
**Timing belt** – 2A•10
covers – 2A•10
tensioner and toothed pulleys – 2A•13
*Tools and working facilities* – REF•5, REF•8 et seq
**Top Dead Centre (TDC) for No 1 piston location** – 2A•5
**Towing** – 0•10
**Track rod end** – 10•23
**Traction control system**
switch – 12•8
throttle actuator – 9•17
*Transmission* – 7•1 *et seq*
oil – 0•17, 1•13
oil seals – 7•4
**Trim mouldings** – 11•22
**Trim panels** – 11•8, 11•12, 11•15, 11•25
**Trip computer module** – 12•22
**Turbocharger** – 1•13
boost advance solenoid – 4A•11, 4A•13
**Tyres** – REF•13
condition and pressure – 0•14
pressures – 0•17
specialists – REF•3

**U**

**Underbody** – 1•15
**Underbonnet check points** – 0•11
fluid leaks and hose condition – 1•11
**Underframe** – 11•2
**Upholstery** – 11•3
**Upper arm** – 10•17

**V**

**Vacuum hoses** – 1•12, 9•15

**Vacuum pump** – 9•20, 9•21
**Vacuum servo unit** – 9•14, 9•15
**Valve clearances** – 1•19, 2A•4, 2A•17
**Valves** – 2B•9
**Vehicle identification** – REF•4, REF•11
**Vehicle speed sensor** – 4A•13, 4A•14
**Vehicle support** – REF•6
**Ventilation system** – 3•2, 3•7
pollen filter – 1•17
**Voltage regulator** – 5•4

**W**

**Warning lights** – 12•14
**Washer fluid** – 0•16
level switch – 12•23
**Washer nozzles** – 12•27
**Washer reservoir and pump** – 12•26
**Water pump** – 3•7
*Weekly checks* – 0•11 *et seq*
**Weights** – REF•1
**Wheels** – REF•13
alignment – 10•23
bearings – 10•5, REF•12
changing – 0•9
**Wheel arch liner** – 11•29
**Wheel cylinder** – 9•7
**Wheel sensor (ABS)** – 9•17
**Windows** – 11•21
glass – 11•11
switch – 12•6, 12•7
**Windscreen** – 11•21, REF•10
washer nozzle – 12•27
washer system – 12•26
wiper motor – 12•20
wiper switch – 12•5
**Wiper arms** – 12•20
**Wiper blades** – 0•16
**Wiper motor**
tailgate – 12•21
windscreen – 12•20
*Wiring diagrams* – 12•32 *et seq*
wiring – 1•12
**Working facilities** – REF•9

# Haynes Manuals – The Complete UK Car List

| Title | Book No. |
|---|---|
| **ALFA ROMEO** Alfasud/Sprint (74 - 88) up to F * | 0292 |
| Alfa Romeo Alfetta (73 - 87) up to E * | 0531 |
| **AUDI** 80, 90 & Coupe Petrol (79 - Nov 88) up to F | 0605 |
| Audi 80, 90 & Coupe Petrol (Oct 86 - 90) D to H | 1491 |
| Audi 100 & 200 Petrol (Oct 82 - 90) up to H | 0907 |
| Audi 100 & A6 Petrol & Diesel (May 91 - May 97) H to P | 3504 |
| Audi A3 Petrol & Diesel (96 - May 03) P to 03 | 4253 |
| Audi A4 Petrol & Diesel (95 - 00) M to X | 3575 |
| Audi A4 Petrol & Diesel (01 - 04) X to 54 | 4609 |
| **AUSTIN** A35 & A40 (56 - 67) up to F * | 0118 |
| Austin/MG/Rover Maestro 1.3 & 1.6 Petrol (83 - 95) up to M | 0922 |
| Austin/MG Metro (80 - May 90) up to G | 0718 |
| Austin/Rover Montego 1.3 & 1.6 Petrol (84 - 94) A to L | 1066 |
| Austin/MG/Rover Montego 2.0 Petrol (84 - 95) A to M | 1067 |
| Mini (59 - 69) up to H * | 0527 |
| Mini (69 - 01) up to X | 0646 |
| Austin/Rover 2.0 litre Diesel Engine (86 - 93) C to L | 1857 |
| Austin Healey 100/6 & 3000 (56 - 68) up to G * | 0049 |
| **BEDFORD** CF Petrol (69 - 87) up to E | 0163 |
| Bedford/Vauxhall Rascal & Suzuki Supercarry (86 - Oct 94) C to M | 3015 |
| **BMW** 316, 320 & 320i (4-cyl) (75 - Feb 83) up to Y * | 0276 |
| BMW 320, 320i, 323i & 325i (6-cyl) (Oct 77 - Sept 87) up to E | 0815 |
| BMW 3- & 5-Series Petrol (81 - 91) up to J | 1948 |
| BMW 3-Series Petrol (Apr 91 - 99) H to V | 3210 |
| BMW 3-Series Petrol (Sept 98 - 03) S to 53 | 4067 |
| BMW 520i & 525e (Oct 81 - June 88) up to E | 1560 |
| BMW 525, 528 & 528i (73 - Sept 81) up to X * | 0632 |
| BMW 5-Series 6-cyl Petrol (April 96 - Aug 03) N to 03 | 4151 |
| BMW 1500, 1502, 1600, 1602, 2000 & 2002 (59 - 77) up to S * | 0240 |
| **CHRYSLER** PT Cruiser Petrol (00 - 03) W to 53 | 4058 |
| **CITROËN** 2CV, Ami & Dyane (67 - 90) up to H | 0196 |
| Citroën AX Petrol & Diesel (87 - 97) D to P | 3014 |
| Citroën Berlingo & Peugeot Partner Petrol & Diesel (96 - 05) P to 55 | 4281 |
| Citroën BX Petrol (83 - 94) A to L | 0908 |
| Citroën C15 Van Petrol & Diesel (89 - Oct 98) F to S | 3509 |
| Citroën C3 Petrol & Diesel (02 - 05) 51 to 05 | 4197 |
| Citroën CX Petrol (75 - 88) up to F | 0528 |
| Citroën Saxo Petrol & Diesel (96 - 04) N to 54 | 3506 |
| Citroën Visa Petrol (79 - 88) up to F | 0620 |
| Citroën Xantia Petrol & Diesel (93 - 01) K to Y | 3082 |
| Citroën XM Petrol & Diesel (89 - 00) G to X | 3451 |
| Citroën Xsara Petrol & Diesel (97 - Sept 00) R to W | 3751 |
| Citroën Xsara Picasso Petrol & Diesel (00 - 02) W to 52 | 3944 |
| Citroën ZX Diesel (91 - 98) J to S | 1922 |
| Citroën ZX Petrol (91 - 98) H to S | 1881 |
| Citroën 1.7 & 1.9 litre Diesel Engine (84 - 96) A to N | 1379 |
| **FIAT** 126 (73 - 87) up to E * | 0305 |
| Fiat 500 (57 - 73) up to M * | 0090 |
| Fiat Bravo & Brava Petrol (95 - 00) N to W | 3572 |
| Fiat Cinquecento (93 - 98) K to R | 3501 |
| Fiat Panda (81 - 95) up to M | 0793 |
| Fiat Punto Petrol & Diesel (94 - Oct 99) L to V | 3251 |
| Fiat Punto Petrol (Oct 99 - July 03) V to 03 | 4066 |
| Fiat Regata Petrol (84 - 88) A to F | 1167 |
| Fiat Tipo Petrol (88 - 91) E to J | 1625 |
| Fiat Uno Petrol (83 - 95) up to M | 0923 |
| Fiat X1/9 (74 - 89) up to G * | 0273 |
| **FORD** Anglia (59 - 68) up to G * | 0001 |
| Ford Capri II (& III) 1.6 & 2.0 (74 - 87) up to E * | 0283 |
| Ford Capri II (& III) 2.8 & 3.0 V6 (74 - 87) up to E | 1309 |

| Title | Book No. |
|---|---|
| Ford Cortina Mk I & Corsair 1500 ('62 - '66) up to D* | 0214 |
| Ford Cortina Mk III 1300 & 1600 (70 - 76) up to P * | 0070 |
| Ford Escort Mk I 1100 & 1300 (68 - 74) up to N * | 0171 |
| Ford Escort Mk I Mexico, RS 1600 & RS 2000 (70 - 74) up to N * | 0139 |
| Ford Escort Mk II Mexico, RS 1800 & RS 2000 (75 - 80) up to W * | 0735 |
| Ford Escort (75 - Aug 80) up to V * | 0280 |
| Ford Escort Petrol (Sept 80 - Sept 90) up to H | 0686 |
| Ford Escort & Orion Petrol (Sept 90 - 00) H to X | 1737 |
| Ford Escort & Orion Diesel (Sept 90 - 00) H to X | 4081 |
| Ford Fiesta (76 - Aug 83) up to Y | 0334 |
| Ford Fiesta Petrol (Aug 83 - Feb 89) A to F | 1030 |
| Ford Fiesta Petrol (Feb 89 - Oct 95) F to N | 1595 |
| Ford Fiesta Petrol & Diesel (Oct 95 - Mar 02) N to 02 | 3397 |
| Ford Fiesta Petrol & Diesel (Apr 02 - 05) 02 to 54 | 4170 |
| Ford Focus Petrol & Diesel (98 - 01) S to Y | 3759 |
| Ford Focus Petrol & Diesel (Oct 01 - 05) 51 to 05 | 4167 |
| Ford Galaxy Petrol & Diesel (95 - Aug 00) M to W | 3984 |
| Ford Granada Petrol (Sept 77 - Feb 85) up to B * | 0481 |
| Ford Granada & Scorpio Petrol (Mar 85 - 94) B to M | 1245 |
| Ford Ka (96 - 02) P to 52 | 3570 |
| Ford Mondeo Petrol (93 - Sept 00) K to X | 1923 |
| Ford Mondeo Petrol & Diesel (Oct 00 - Jul 03) X to 03 | 3990 |
| Ford Mondeo Petrol & Diesel (July 03 - 07) 03 to 56 | 4619 |
| Ford Mondeo Diesel (93 - 96) L to N | 3465 |
| Ford Orion Petrol (83 - Sept 90) up to H | 1009 |
| Ford Sierra 4-cyl Petrol (82 - 93) up to K | 0903 |
| Ford Sierra V6 Petrol (82 - 91) up to J | 0904 |
| Ford Transit Petrol (Mk 2) (78 - Jan 86) up to C | 0719 |
| Ford Transit Petrol (Mk 3) (Feb 86 - 89) C to G | 1468 |
| Ford Transit Diesel (Feb 86 - 99) C to T | 3019 |
| Ford 1.6 & 1.8 litre Diesel Engine (84 - 96) A to N | 1172 |
| Ford 2.1, 2.3 & 2.5 litre Diesel Engine (77 - 90) up to H | 1606 |
| **FREIGHT ROVER** Sherpa Petrol (74 - 87) up to E | 0463 |
| **HILLMAN** Avenger (70 - 82) up to Y | 0037 |
| Hillman Imp (63 - 76) up to R * | 0022 |
| **HONDA** Civic (Feb 84 - Oct 87) A to E | 1226 |
| Honda Civic (Nov 91 - 96) J to N | 3199 |
| Honda Civic Petrol (Mar 95 - 00) M to X | 4050 |
| Honda Civic Petrol & Diesel (01 - 05) X to 55 | 4611 |
| Honda Jazz (01 - Feb 08) 51 - 57 | 4735 |
| **HYUNDAI** Pony (85 - 94) C to M | 3398 |
| **JAGUAR** E Type (61 - 72) up to L * | 0140 |
| Jaguar MkI & II, 240 & 340 (55 - 69) up to H * | 0098 |
| Jaguar XJ6, XJ & Sovereign; Daimler Sovereign (68 - Oct 86) up to D | 0242 |
| Jaguar XJ6 & Sovereign (Oct 86 - Sept 94) D to M | 3261 |
| Jaguar XJ12, XJS & Sovereign; Daimler Double Six (72 - 88) up to F | 0478 |
| **JEEP** Cherokee Petrol (93 - 96) K to N | 1943 |
| **LADA** 1200, 1300, 1500 & 1600 (74 - 91) up to J | 0413 |
| Lada Samara (87 - 91) D to J | 1610 |
| **LAND ROVER** 90, 110 & Defender Diesel (83 - 07) up to 56 | 3017 |
| Land Rover Discovery Petrol & Diesel (89 - 98) G to S | 3016 |
| Land Rover Discovery Diesel (Nov 98 - Jul 04) S to 04 | 4606 |
| Land Rover Freelander Petrol & Diesel (97 - Sept 03) R to 53 | 3929 |
| Land Rover Freelander Petrol & Diesel (Oct 03 - Oct 06) 53 to 56 | 4623 |
| Land Rover Series IIA & III Diesel (58 - 85) up to C | 0529 |
| Land Rover Series II, IIA & III 4-cyl Petrol (58 - 85) up to C | 0314 |

| Title | Book No. |
|---|---|
| **MAZDA** 323 (Mar 81 - Oct 89) up to G | 1608 |
| Mazda 323 (Oct 89 - 98) G to R | 3455 |
| Mazda 626 (May 83 - Sept 87) up to E | 0929 |
| Mazda B1600, B1800 & B2000 Pick-up Petrol (72 - 88) up to F | 0267 |
| Mazda RX-7 (79 - 85) up to C * | 0460 |
| **MERCEDES-BENZ** 190, 190E & 190D Petrol & Diesel (83 - 93) A to L | 3450 |
| Mercedes-Benz 200D, 240D, 240TD, 300D & 300TD 123 Series Diesel (Oct 76 - 85) | 1114 |
| Mercedes-Benz 250 & 280 (68 - 72) up to L * | 0346 |
| Mercedes-Benz 250 & 280 123 Series Petrol (Oct 76 - 84) up to B * | 0677 |
| Mercedes-Benz 124 Series Petrol & Diesel (85 - Aug 93) C to K | 3253 |
| Mercedes-Benz C-Class Petrol & Diesel (93 - Aug 00) L to W | 3511 |
| **MG**A (55 - 62) * | 0475 |
| MGB (62 - 80) up to W | 0111 |
| MG Midget & Austin-Healey Sprite (58 - 80) up to W * | 0265 |
| **MINI** Petrol (July 01 - 05) Y to 05 | 4273 |
| **MITSUBISHI** Shogun & L200 Pick-Ups Petrol (83 - 94) up to M | 1944 |
| **MORRIS** Ital 1.3 (80 - 84) up to B | 0705 |
| Morris Minor 1000 (56 - 71) up to K | 0024 |
| **NISSAN** Almera Petrol (95 - Feb 00) N to V | 4053 |
| Nissan Almera & Tino Petrol (Feb 00 - 07) V to 56 | 4612 |
| Nissan Bluebird (May 84 - Mar 86) A to C | 1223 |
| Nissan Bluebird Petrol (Mar 86 - 90) C to H | 1473 |
| Nissan Cherry (Sept 82 - 86) up to D | 1031 |
| Nissan Micra (83 - Jan 93) up to K | 0931 |
| Nissan Micra (93 - 02) K to 52 | 3254 |
| Nissan Primera Petrol (90 - Aug 99) H to T | 1851 |
| Nissan Stanza (82 - 86) up to D | 0824 |
| Nissan Sunny Petrol (May 82 - Oct 86) up to D | 0895 |
| Nissan Sunny Petrol (Oct 86 - Mar 91) D to H | 1378 |
| Nissan Sunny Petrol (Apr 91 - 95) H to N | 3219 |
| **OPEL** Ascona & Manta (B Series) (Sept 75 - 88) up to F * | 0316 |
| Opel Ascona Petrol (81 - 88) | 3215 |
| Opel Astra Petrol (Oct 91 - Feb 98) | 3156 |
| Opel Corsa Petrol (83 - Mar 93) | 3160 |
| Opel Corsa Petrol (Mar 93 - 97) | 3159 |
| Opel Kadett Petrol (Nov 79 - Oct 84) up to B | 0634 |
| Opel Kadett Petrol (Oct 84 - Oct 91) | 3196 |
| Opel Omega & Senator Petrol (Nov 86 - 94) | 3157 |
| Opel Rekord Petrol (Feb 78 - Oct 86) up to D | 0543 |
| Opel Vectra Petrol (Oct 88 - Oct 95) | 3158 |
| **PEUGEOT** 106 Petrol & Diesel (91 - 04) J to 53 | 1882 |
| Peugeot 205 Petrol (83 - 97) A to P | 0932 |
| Peugeot 206 Petrol & Diesel (98 - 01) S to X | 3757 |
| Peugeot 206 Petrol & Diesel (02 - 06) 51 to 06 | 4613 |
| Peugeot 306 Petrol & Diesel (93 - 02) K to 02 | 3073 |
| Peugeot 307 Petrol & Diesel (01 - 04) Y to 54 | 4147 |
| Peugeot 309 Petrol (86 - 93) C to K | 1266 |
| Peugeot 405 Petrol (88 - 97) E to P | 1559 |
| Peugeot 405 Diesel (88 - 97) E to P | 3198 |
| Peugeot 406 Petrol & Diesel (96 - Mar 99) N to T | 3394 |
| Peugeot 406 Petrol & Diesel (Mar 99 - 02) T to 52 | 3982 |
| Peugeot 505 Petrol (79 - 89) up to G | 0762 |
| Peugeot 1.7/1.8 & 1.9 litre Diesel Engine (82 - 96) up to N | 0950 |
| Peugeot 2.0, 2.1, 2.3 & 2.5 litre Diesel Engines (74 - 90) up to H | 1607 |
| **PORSCHE** 911 (65 - 85) up to C | 0264 |

* Classic reprint

| Title | Book No. |
|---|---|
| Porsche 924 & 924 Turbo (76 - 85) up to C | 0397 |
| **PROTON** (89 - 97) F to P | 3255 |
| **RANGE ROVER** V8 Petrol (70 - Oct 92) up to K | 0606 |
| **RELIANT** Robin & Kitten (73 - 83) up to A * | 0436 |
| **RENAULT** 4 (61 - 86) up to D * | 0072 |
| Renault 5 Petrol (Feb 85 - 96) B to N | 1219 |
| Renault 9 & 11 Petrol (82 - 89) up to F | 0822 |
| Renault 18 Petrol (79 - 86) up to D | 0598 |
| Renault 19 Petrol (89 - 96) F to N | 1646 |
| Renault 19 Diesel (89 - 96) F to N | 1946 |
| Renault 21 Petrol (86 - 94) C to M | 1397 |
| Renault 25 Petrol & Diesel (84 - 92) B to K | 1228 |
| Renault Clio Petrol (91 - May 98) H to R | 1853 |
| Renault Clio Diesel (91 - June 96) H to N | 3031 |
| Renault Clio Petrol & Diesel (May 98 - May 01) R to Y | 3906 |
| Renault Clio Petrol & Diesel (June '01 - '05) Y to 55 * | 4168 |
| Renault Espace Petrol & Diesel (85 - 96) C to N | 3197 |
| Renault Laguna Petrol & Diesel (94 - 00) L to W | 3252 |
| Renault Laguna Petrol & Diesel (Feb 01 - Feb 05) X to 54 | 4283 |
| Renault Mégane & Scénic Petrol & Diesel (96 - 99) N to T | 3395 |
| Renault Mégane & Scénic Petrol & Diesel (Apr 99 - 02) T to 52 | 3916 |
| Renault Megane Petrol & Diesel (Oct 02 - 05) 52 to 55 | 4284 |
| Renault Scenic Petrol & Diesel (Sept 03 - 06) 53 to 06 | 4297 |
| **ROVER** 213 & 216 (84 - 89) A to G | 1116 |
| Rover 214 & 414 Petrol (89 - 96) G to N | 1689 |
| Rover 216 & 416 Petrol (89 - 96) G to N | 1830 |
| Rover 211, 214, 216, 218 & 220 Petrol & Diesel (Dec 95 - 99) N to V | 3399 |
| Rover 25 & MG ZR Petrol & Diesel (Oct 99 - 04) V to 54 | 4145 |
| Rover 414, 416 & 420 Petrol & Diesel (May 95 - 98) M to R | 3453 |
| Rover 45 / MG ZS Petrol & Diesel (99 - 05) V to 55 | 4384 |
| Rover 618, 620 & 623 Petrol (93 - 97) K to P | 3257 |
| Rover 75 / MG ZT Petrol & Diesel (99 - 06) S to 06 | 4292 |
| Rover 820, 825 & 827 Petrol (86 - 95) D to N | 1380 |
| Rover 3500 (76 - 87) up to E * | 0365 |
| Rover Metro, 111 & 114 Petrol (May 90 - 98) G to S | 1711 |
| **SAAB** 95 & 96 (66 - 76) up to R * | 0198 |
| Saab 90, 99 & 900 (79 - Oct 93) up to L | 0765 |
| Saab 900 (Oct 93 - 98) L to R | 3512 |
| Saab 9000 (4-cyl) (85 - 98) C to S | 1686 |
| Saab 9-3 Petrol & Diesel (98 - Aug 02) R to 02 | 4614 |
| Saab 9-5 4-cyl Petrol (97 - 04) R to 54 | 4156 |
| **SEAT** Ibiza & Cordoba Petrol & Diesel (Oct 93 - Oct 99) L to V | 3571 |
| Seat Ibiza & Malaga Petrol (85 - 92) B to K | 1609 |
| **SKODA** Estelle (77 - 89) up to G | 0604 |
| Skoda Fabia Petrol & Diesel (00 - 06) W to 06 | 4376 |
| Skoda Favorit (89 - 96) F to N | 1801 |
| Skoda Felicia Petrol & Diesel (95 - 01) M to X | 3505 |
| Skoda Octavia Petrol & Diesel (98 - Apr 04) R to 04 | 4285 |
| **SUBARU** 1600 & 1800 (Nov 79 - 90) up to H * | 0995 |
| **SUNBEAM** Alpine, Rapier & H120 (67 - 74) up to N * | 0051 |
| **SUZUKI** SJ Series, Samurai & Vitara (4-cyl) Petrol (82 - 97) up to P | 1942 |
| Suzuki Supercarry & Bedford/Vauxhall Rascal (86 - Oct 94) C to M | 3015 |
| **TALBOT** Alpine, Solara, Minx & Rapier (75 - 86) up to D | 0337 |

| Title | Book No. |
|---|---|
| Talbot Horizon Petrol (78 - 86) up to D | 0473 |
| Talbot Samba (82 - 86) up to D | 0823 |
| **TOYOTA** Avensis Petrol (98 - Jan 03) R to 52 | 4264 |
| Toyota Carina E Petrol (May 92 - 97) J to P | 3256 |
| Toyota Corolla (80 - 85) up to C | 0683 |
| Toyota Corolla (Sept 83 - Sept 87) A to E | 1024 |
| Toyota Corolla (Sept 87 - Aug 92) E to K | 1683 |
| Toyota Corolla Petrol (Aug 92 - 97) K to P | 3259 |
| Toyota Corolla Petrol (July 97 - Feb 02) P to 51 | 4286 |
| Toyota Hi-Ace & Hi-Lux Petrol (69 - Oct 83) up to A | 0304 |
| Toyota Yaris Petrol (99 - 05) T to 05 | 4265 |
| **TRIUMPH** GT6 & Vitesse (62 - 74 ) up to N * | 0112 |
| Triumph Herald (59 - 71) up to K * | 0010 |
| Triumph Spitfire (62 - 81) up to X * | 0113 |
| Triumph Stag (70 - 78) up to T * | 0441 |
| Triumph TR2, TR3, TR3A, TR4 & TR4A (52 - 67) up to F * | 0028 |
| Triumph TR5 & 6 (67 - 75) up to P * | 0031 |
| Triumph TR7 (75 - 82) up to Y * | 0322 |
| **VAUXHALL** Astra Petrol (80 - Oct 84) up to B | 0635 |
| Vauxhall Astra & Belmont Petrol (Oct 84 - Oct 91) B to J | 1136 |
| Vauxhall Astra Petrol (Oct 91 - Feb 98) J to R | 1832 |
| Vauxhall/Opel Astra & Zafira Petrol (Feb 98 - Apr 04) R to 04 | 3758 |
| Vauxhall/Opel Astra & Zafira Diesel (Feb 98 - Apr 04) R to 04 | 3797 |
| Vauxhall/Opel Astra Petrol (04 - 07) 04 - 07 | 4732 |
| Vauxhall/Opel Astra Diesel (04 - 07) 04 - 07 | 4733 |
| Vauxhall/Opel Calibra (90 - 98) G to S | 3502 |
| Vauxhall Carlton Petrol (Oct 78 - Oct 86) up to D | 0480 |
| Vauxhall Carlton & Senator Petrol (Nov 86 - 94) D to L | 1469 |
| Vauxhall Cavalier Petrol (81 - Oct 88) up to F | 0812 |
| Vauxhall Cavalier Petrol (Oct 88 - 95) F to N | 1570 |
| Vauxhall Chevette (75 - 84) up to B | 0285 |
| Vauxhall/Opel Corsa Diesel (Mar 93 - Oct 00) K to X | 4087 |
| Vauxhall Corsa Petrol (Mar 93 - 97) K to R | 1985 |
| Vauxhall/Opel Corsa Petrol (Apr 97 - Oct 00) P to X | 3921 |
| Vauxhall/Opel Corsa Petrol & Diesel (Oct 00 - Sept 03) X to 53 | 4079 |
| Vauxhall/Opel Corsa Petrol & Diesel (Oct 03 - Aug 06) 53 to 06 | 4617 |
| Vauxhall/Opel Frontera Petrol & Diesel (91 - Sept 98) J to S | 3454 |
| Vauxhall Nova Petrol (83 - 93) up to K | 0909 |
| Vauxhall/Opel Omega Petrol (94 - 99) L to T | 3510 |
| Vauxhall/Opel Vectra Petrol & Diesel (95 - Feb 99) N to S | 3396 |
| Vauxhall/Opel Vectra Petrol & Diesel (Mar 99 - May 02) T to 02 | 3930 |
| Vauxhall/Opel Vectra Petrol & Diesel (June 02 - Sept 05) 02 to 55 | 4618 |
| Vauxhall/Opel 1.5, 1.6 & 1.7 litre Diesel Engine (82 - 96) up to N | 1222 |
| **VW** 411 & 412 (68 - 75) up to P * | 0091 |
| VW Beetle 1200 (54 - 77) up to S | 0036 |
| VW Beetle 1300 & 1500 (65 - 75) up to P | 0039 |
| VW 1302 & 1302S (70 - 72) up to L * | 0110 |
| VW Beetle 1303, 1303S & GT (72 - 75) up to P | 0159 |
| VW Beetle Petrol & Diesel (Apr 99 - 01) T to 51 | 3798 |
| VW Golf & Jetta Mk 1 Petrol 1.1 & 1.3 (74 - 84) up to A | 0716 |
| VW Golf, Jetta & Scirocco Mk 1 Petrol 1.5, 1.6 & 1.8 (74 - 84) up to A | 0726 |

| Title | Book No. |
|---|---|
| VW Golf & Jetta Mk 1 Diesel (78 - 84) up to A | 0451 |
| VW Golf & Jetta Mk 2 Petrol (Mar 84 - Feb 92) A to J | 1081 |
| VW Golf & Vento Petrol & Diesel (Feb 92 - Mar 98) J to R | 3097 |
| VW Golf & Bora Petrol & Diesel (April 98 - 00) R to X | 3727 |
| VW Golf & Bora 4-cyl Petrol & Diesel (01 - 03) X to 53 | 4169 |
| VW Golf & Jetta Petrol & Diesel (04 - 07) 53 to 07 | 4610 |
| VW LT Petrol Vans & Light Trucks (76 - 87) up to E | 0637 |
| VW Passat & Santana Petrol (Sept 81 - May 88) up to E | 0814 |
| VW Passat 4-cyl Petrol & Diesel (May 88 - 96) E to P | 3498 |
| VW Passat 4-cyl Petrol & Diesel (Dec 96 - Nov 00) P to X | 3917 |
| VW Passat Petrol & Diesel (Dec 00 - May 05) X to 05 | 4279 |
| VW Polo & Derby (76 - Jan 82) up to X | 0335 |
| VW Polo (82 - Oct 90) up to H | 0813 |
| VW Polo Petrol (Nov 90 - Aug 94) H to L | 3245 |
| VW Polo Hatchback Petrol & Diesel (94 - 99) M to S | 3500 |
| VW Polo Hatchback Petrol (00 - Jan 02) V to 51 | 4150 |
| VW Polo Petrol & Diesel (02 - May 05) 51 to 05 | 4608 |
| VW Scirocco (82 - 90) up to H * | 1224 |
| VW Transporter 1600 (68 - 79) up to V | 0082 |
| VW Transporter 1700, 1800 & 2000 (72 - 79) up to V * | 0226 |
| VW Transporter (air-cooled) Petrol (79 - 82) up to Y * | 0638 |
| VW Transporter (water-cooled) Petrol (82 - 90) up to H | 3452 |
| VW Type 3 (63 - 73) up to M * | 0084 |
| **VOLVO** 120 & 130 Series (& P1800) (61 - 73) up to M * | 0203 |
| Volvo 142, 144 & 145 (66 - 74) up to N * | 0129 |
| Volvo 240 Series Petrol (74 - 93) up to K | 0270 |
| Volvo 262, 264 & 260/265 (75 - 85) up to C * | 0400 |
| Volvo 340, 343, 345 & 360 (76 - 91) up to J | 0715 |
| Volvo 440, 460 & 480 Petrol (87 - 97) D to P | 1691 |
| Volvo 740 & 760 Petrol (82 - 91) up to J | 1258 |
| Volvo 850 Petrol (92 - 96) J to P | 3260 |
| Volvo 940 petrol (90 - 98) H to R | 3249 |
| Volvo S40 & V40 Petrol (96 - Mar 04) N to 04 | 3569 |
| Volvo S40 & V50 Petrol & Diesel (Mar 04 - Jun 07) 04 to 07 | 4731 |
| Volvo S70, V70 & C70 Petrol (96 - 99) P to V | 3573 |
| Volvo V70 / S80 Petrol & Diesel (98 - 05) S to 55 | 4263 |

**AUTOMOTIVE TECHBOOKS**

| Title | Book No. |
|---|---|
| Automotive Electrical and Electronic Systems Manual | 3049 |
| Automotive Gearbox Overhaul Manual | 3473 |
| Automotive Service Summaries Manual | 3475 |
| Automotive Timing Belts Manual – Austin/Rover | 3549 |
| Automotive Timing Belts Manual – Ford | 3474 |
| Automotive Timing Belts Manual – Peugeot/Citroën | 3568 |
| Automotive Timing Belts Manual – Vauxhall/Opel | 3577 |

**DIY MANUAL SERIES**

| Title | Book No. |
|---|---|
| The Haynes Air Conditioning Manual | 4192 |
| The Haynes Car Electrical Systems Manual | 4251 |
| The Haynes Manual on Bodywork | 4198 |
| The Haynes Manual on Brakes | 4178 |
| The Haynes Manual on Carburettors | 4177 |
| The Haynes Manual on Diesel Engines | 4174 |
| The Haynes Manual on Engine Management | 4199 |
| The Haynes Manual on Fault Codes | 4175 |
| The Haynes Manual on Practical Electrical Systems | 4267 |
| The Haynes Manual on Small Engines | 4250 |
| The Haynes Manual on Welding | 4176 |

* Classic reprint

# Preserving Our Motoring Heritage

< The Model J Duesenberg Derham Tourster. Only eight of these magnificent cars were ever built – this is the only example to be found outside the United States of America

Almost every car you've ever loved, loathed or desired is gathered under one roof at the Haynes Motor Museum. Over 300 immaculately presented cars and motorbikes represent every aspect of our motoring heritage, from elegant reminders of bygone days, such as the superb Model J Duesenberg to curiosities like the bug-eyed BMW Isetta. There are also many old friends and flames. Perhaps you remember the 1959 Ford Popular that you did your courting in? The magnificent 'Red Collection' is a spectacle of classic sports cars including AC, Alfa Romeo, Austin Healey, Ferrari, Lamborghini, Maserati, MG, Riley, Porsche and Triumph.

## A Perfect Day Out

Each and every vehicle at the Haynes Motor Museum has played its part in the history and culture of Motoring. Today, they make a wonderful spectacle and a great day out for all the family. Bring the kids, bring Mum and Dad, but above all bring your camera to capture those golden memories for ever. You will also find an impressive array of motoring memorabilia, a comfortable 70 seat video cinema and one of the most extensive transport book shops in Britain. The Pit Stop Cafe serves everything from a cup of tea to wholesome, home-made meals or, if you prefer, you can enjoy the large picnic area nestled in the beautiful rural surroundings of Somerset.

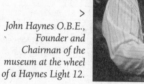

> John Haynes O.B.E., Founder and Chairman of the museum at the wheel of a Haynes Light 12.

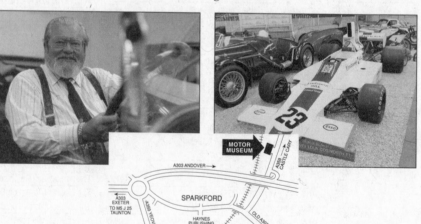

< Graham Hill's Lola Cosworth Formula 1 car next to a 1934 Riley Sports.

The Museum is situated on the A359 Yeovil to Frome road at Sparkford, just off the A303 in Somerset. It is about 40 miles south of Bristol, and 25 minutes drive from the M5 intersection at Taunton.
Open 9.30am - 5.30pm (10.00am - 4.00pm Winter) 7 days a week, *except Christmas Day, Boxing Day and New Years Day*
Special rates available for schools, coach parties and outings  Charitable Trust No. 292048